A-Level

Mathematics

for AQA Core 4

The Complete Course for AQA C4

Contents

About this book

In this book you'll find...

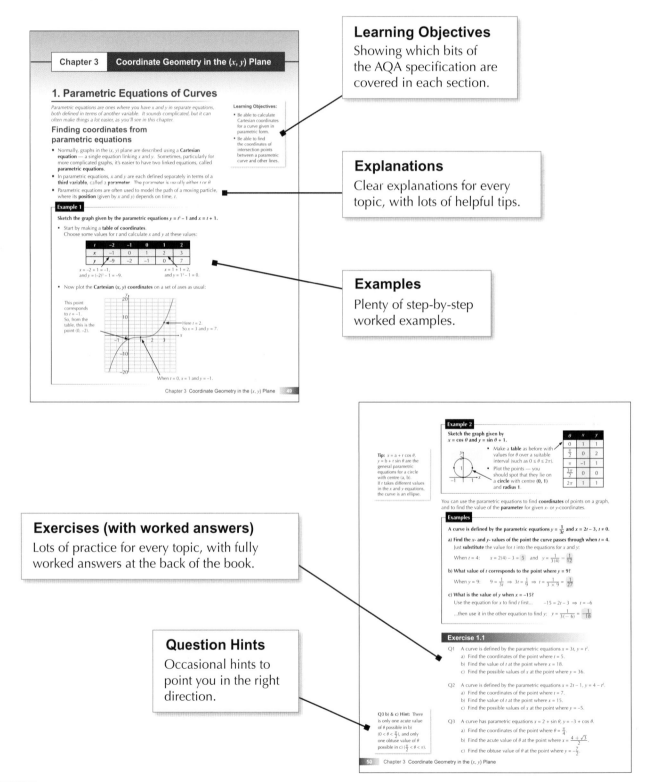

Learning Objectives

Showing which bits of the AQA specification are covered in each section.

Explanations

Clear explanations for every topic, with lots of helpful tips.

Examples

Plenty of step-by-step worked examples.

Exercises (with worked answers)

Lots of practice for every topic, with fully worked answers at the back of the book.

Question Hints

Occasional hints to point you in the right direction.

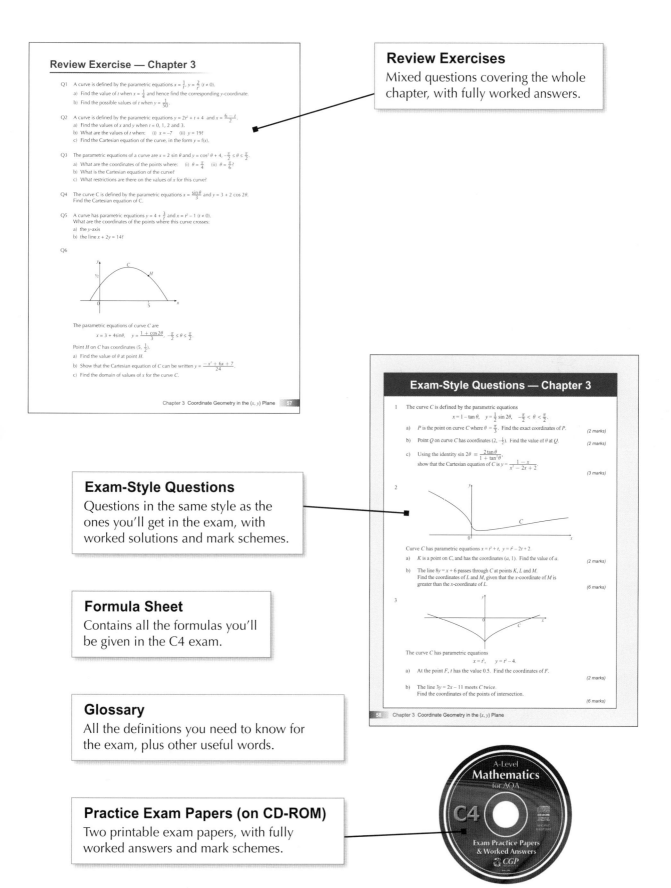

Review Exercise — Chapter 3

Q1 A curve is defined by the parametric equations $x = \frac{1}{t}$, $y = \frac{2}{t^2}$ $(t \neq 0)$.
a) Find the value of t when $x = \frac{1}{4}$ and hence find the corresponding y-coordinate.
b) Find the possible values of t when $y = \frac{1}{50}$.

Q2 A curve is defined by the parametric equations $y = 2t^2 + t + 4$ and $x = \frac{6 - t}{2}$.
a) Find the values of x and y when $t = 0$, 1, 2 and 3.
b) What are the values of t when: (i) $x = -7$ (ii) $y = 19$?
c) Find the Cartesian equation of the curve, in the form $y = f(x)$.

Q3 The parametric equations of a curve are $x = 2 \sin \theta$ and $y = \cos^2 \theta + 4$, $-\frac{\pi}{2} \leq \theta \leq \frac{\pi}{2}$.
a) What are the coordinates of the points where: (i) $\theta = \frac{\pi}{4}$ (ii) $\theta = \frac{\pi}{6}$?
b) What is the Cartesian equation of the curve?
c) What restrictions are there on the values of x for this curve?

Q4 The curve C is defined by the parametric equations $x = \frac{\sin \theta}{3}$ and $y = 3 + 2 \cos 2\theta$.
Find the Cartesian equation of C.

Q5 A curve has parametric equations $y = 4 + \frac{3}{t}$ and $x = t^2 - 1$ $(t \neq 0)$.
What are the coordinates of the points where this curve crosses:
a) the y-axis
b) the line $x + 2y = 14$?

Q6

The parametric equations of curve C are
$$x = 3 + 4\sin\theta, \quad y = \frac{1 + \cos 2\theta}{3}, \quad -\frac{\pi}{2} \leq \theta \leq \frac{\pi}{2}.$$
Point H on C has coordinates $(5, \frac{1}{2})$.
a) Find the value of θ at point H.
b) Show that the Cartesian equation of C can be written $y = \frac{-x^2 + 6x + 7}{24}$.
c) Find the domain of values of x for the curve C.

Review Exercises
Mixed questions covering the whole chapter, with fully worked answers.

Exam-Style Questions — Chapter 3

1 The curve C is defined by the parametric equations
$$x = 1 - \tan \theta, \quad y = \frac{1}{2} \sin 2\theta, \quad -\frac{\pi}{2} < \theta < \frac{\pi}{2}.$$
a) P is the point on curve C where $\theta = \frac{\pi}{3}$. Find the exact coordinates of P. *(2 marks)*
b) Point Q on curve C has coordinates $(2, -\frac{1}{2})$. Find the value of θ at Q. *(2 marks)*
c) Using the identity $\sin 2\theta \equiv \frac{2 \tan \theta}{1 + \tan^2 \theta}$,
show that the Cartesian equation of C is $y = \frac{1 - x}{x^2 - 2x + 2}$. *(3 marks)*

2

Curve C has parametric equations $x = t^3 + t$, $y = t^2 - 2t + 2$.
a) K is a point on C, and has the coordinates $(a, 1)$. Find the value of a. *(2 marks)*
b) The line $8y = x + 6$ passes through C at points K, L and M.
Find the coordinates of L and M, given that the x-coordinate of M is greater than the x-coordinate of L. *(6 marks)*

3

The curve C has parametric equations
$$x = t^3, \quad y = t^2 - 4.$$
a) At the point F, t has the value 0.5. Find the coordinates of F. *(2 marks)*
b) The line $3y = 2x - 11$ meets C twice.
Find the coordinates of the points of intersection. *(6 marks)*

Exam-Style Questions
Questions in the same style as the ones you'll get in the exam, with worked solutions and mark schemes.

Formula Sheet
Contains all the formulas you'll be given in the C4 exam.

Glossary
All the definitions you need to know for the exam, plus other useful words.

Practice Exam Papers (on CD-ROM)
Two printable exam papers, with fully worked answers and mark schemes.

A-Level
Mathematics
for AQA

C4

Exam Practice Papers
& Worked Answers
CGP

Published by CGP

Editors:
Paul Jordin, Sharon Keeley-Holden, Kirstie McHale, David Ryan, Caley Simpson, Charlotte Whiteley,
Dawn Wright.

Contributors:
Jane Chow, Claire Creasor, Anna Gainey, Dave Harding, Phil Harvey, Frances Knight, Rosemary Rogers,
Manpreet Sambhi.

ISBN: 978 1 84762 805 3

With thanks to Simon Little for the proofreading.

www.cgpbooks.co.uk

Printed by Elanders Ltd, Newcastle upon Tyne.
Clipart from Corel®

1. Simplifying Expressions

Simplifying expressions in C4 involves a lot of algebraic fractions. You'll have to factorise, cancel, multiply, divide, add and subtract them. You'll find that this will come in handy in other parts of maths, so it's a pretty important skill.

Simplifying algebraic fractions

Algebraic fractions are a lot like normal fractions — and you can treat them in the same way, whether you're adding, subtracting, multiplying or dividing them. All fractions are much easier to deal with when they're in their **simplest form**, so the first thing to do with algebraic fractions is to simplify them as much as possible.

- Look for **common factors** in the numerator and denominator — **factorise** top and bottom and see if there's anything you can **cancel**.

- If there's a **fraction** in the numerator or denominator (e.g. $\frac{1}{x}$), **multiply** the whole thing (i.e. top and bottom) by the same factor to get rid of it (for $\frac{1}{x}$, you'd multiply through by x).

Learning Objectives:

- Be able to simplify rational expressions (i.e. algebraic fractions with linear or quadratic denominators) by factorising and cancelling.

- Be able to simplify rational expressions by adding and subtracting algebraic fractions.

- Be able to simplify rational expressions by multiplying and dividing algebraic fractions.

Examples

Simplify the following:

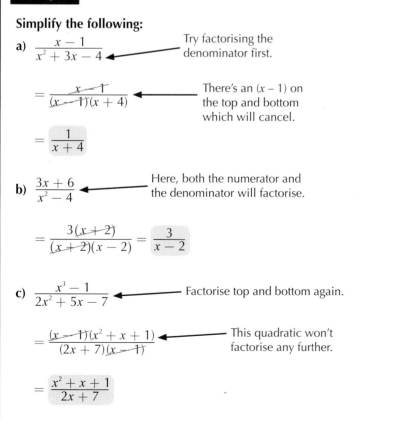

a) $\dfrac{x-1}{x^2+3x-4}$ ← Try factorising the denominator first.

$= \dfrac{x-1}{(x-1)(x+4)}$ ← There's an $(x-1)$ on the top and bottom which will cancel.

$= \dfrac{1}{x+4}$

b) $\dfrac{3x+6}{x^2-4}$ ← Here, both the numerator and the denominator will factorise.

$= \dfrac{3(x+2)}{(x+2)(x-2)} = \dfrac{3}{x-2}$

c) $\dfrac{x^3-1}{2x^2+5x-7}$ ← Factorise top and bottom again.

$= \dfrac{(x-1)(x^2+x+1)}{(2x+7)(x-1)}$ ← This quadratic won't factorise any further.

$= \dfrac{x^2+x+1}{2x+7}$

Tip: Watch out for the difference of two squares — see C1.

Tip: You should have come across methods for factorising cubics in C1.

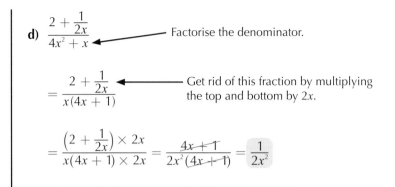

Tip: Take your time with messy expressions and work things out in separate steps.

d) $\dfrac{2 + \dfrac{1}{2x}}{4x^2 + x}$ ← Factorise the denominator.

$= \dfrac{2 + \dfrac{1}{2x}}{x(4x + 1)}$ ← Get rid of this fraction by multiplying the top and bottom by $2x$.

$= \dfrac{\left(2 + \dfrac{1}{2x}\right) \times 2x}{x(4x + 1) \times 2x} = \dfrac{4x + 1}{2x^2(4x + 1)} = \dfrac{1}{2x^2}$

Exercise 1.1

Simplify the following:

Q1 $\dfrac{4}{2x + 10}$

Q2 $\dfrac{5x}{x^2 + 2x}$

Q3 $\dfrac{6x^2 - 3x}{3x^2}$

Q4 $\dfrac{4x^3}{x^3 + 3x^2}$

Q5 $\dfrac{3x + 6}{x^2 + 3x + 2}$

Q6 $\dfrac{x^2 + 3x}{x^2 + x - 6}$

Q7 $\dfrac{2x - 6}{x^2 - 9}$

Q8 $\dfrac{5x^2 - 20x}{2x^2 - 5x - 12}$

Q9 $\dfrac{3x^2 - 7x - 6}{2x^2 - x - 15}$

Q10 $\dfrac{x^3 - 4x^2 - 19x - 14}{x^2 - 6x - 7}$

Q11 $\dfrac{x^3 - 2x^2}{x^3 - 4x}$

Q12 $\dfrac{1 + \dfrac{1}{x}}{x + 1}$

Q14 Hint: You need to multiply the top and bottom by the same term to get rid of the fractions. Don't just multiply the top by $2x$ and the bottom by x.

Q13 $\dfrac{3 + \dfrac{1}{x}}{2 + \dfrac{1}{x}}$

Q14 $\dfrac{1 + \dfrac{1}{2x}}{2 + \dfrac{1}{x}}$

Q15 $\dfrac{\dfrac{1}{3x} - 1}{3x^2 - x}$

Q16 $\dfrac{2 + \dfrac{1}{x}}{6x^2 + 3x}$

Q17 Hint: Once you've multiplied through by $x + 2$ this is not as bad as it looks.

Q17 $\dfrac{\dfrac{3x}{x + 2}}{\dfrac{x}{x + 2} + \dfrac{1}{x + 2}}$

Q18 $\dfrac{2 + \dfrac{1}{x + 1}}{3 + \dfrac{1}{x + 1}}$

Q20 Hint: Multiplying each term by x^2 will get rid of all the fractions.

Q19 $\dfrac{1 - \dfrac{2}{x + 3}}{x + 2}$

Q20 $\dfrac{4 - \dfrac{1}{x^2}}{2 - \dfrac{1}{x} - \dfrac{1}{x^2}}$

Adding and subtracting algebraic fractions

You'll have come across adding and subtracting fractions before in C1,
so here's a little reminder of how to do it:

1. Find the common denominator

- Take all the individual 'bits' from the
  bottom lines and **multiply** them together.
- Only use each bit **once** unless something
  on the bottom line is raised to a **power**.

Tip: The common denominator should be the lowest common multiple (LCM) of all the denominators.

2. Put each fraction over the common denominator

- Multiply both top and bottom of each fraction by the same term —
  whatever term will turn the denominator into the **common denominator**.

3. Combine into one fraction

- Once everything's over the common denominator
  you can just **add** (or **subtract**) the **numerators**.

Examples

a) **Simplify:** $\dfrac{2}{x-1} - \dfrac{3}{3x+2}$

- Multiply the denominators to get the **common denominator**:
$$(x-1)(3x+2)$$

- Multiply the top and bottom lines of each fraction by whatever term
  changes the denominator into the common denominator:

$$\frac{2 \times (3x+2)}{(x-1) \times (3x+2)} - \frac{3 \times (x-1)}{(3x+2) \times (x-1)}$$

Tip: Always check if there's any more factorising and cancelling that can be done at the end. Your final answer needs to be fully simplified to get all the marks in an exam question.

- All the denominators are the same
  — so you can just subtract the numerators:

$$\frac{2(3x+2) - 3(x-1)}{(3x+2)(x-1)} = \frac{6x+4-3x+3}{(3x+2)(x-1)} = \frac{3x+7}{(3x+2)(x-1)}$$

b) **Simplify:** $\dfrac{2y}{x(x+3)} + \dfrac{1}{y^2(x+3)} - \dfrac{x}{y}$

The individual 'bits' here are x, $(x+3)$ and y, but you need to use y^2 because there's a y^2 in the second fraction's denominator.

- The common denominator is: $xy^2(x+3)$

Tip: In theory there's nothing wrong here with having a common denominator of all the denominators multiplied together (i.e. $xy^3(x+3)^2$). You'd still get the same final answer by cancelling down. Being a bit clever about it saves you a lot of effort though, so always try to use the simplest common denominator possible (the LCM).

- Multiply the top and bottom lines of each fraction by whatever term
  changes the denominator into the common denominator:

$$\frac{2y \times y^2}{x(x+3) \times y^2} + \frac{1 \times x}{y^2(x+3) \times x} - \frac{x \times xy(x+3)}{y \times xy(x+3)}$$

- All the denominators are the same
  — so you can just add the numerators:

$$= \frac{2y^3 + x - x^2y(x+3)}{xy^2(x+3)} = \frac{2y^3 + x - x^3y - 3x^2y}{xy^2(x+3)}$$

Simplify the following:

Q2 Hint: Both denominators are a multiple of x. So the common denominator will just be another multiple of x.

Q1 $\quad \dfrac{2x}{3} + \dfrac{x}{5}$

Q2 $\quad \dfrac{2}{3x} - \dfrac{1}{5x}$

Q3 $\quad \dfrac{3}{x^2} + \dfrac{2}{x}$

Q4 $\quad \dfrac{x+1}{3} + \dfrac{x+2}{4}$

Q5 $\quad \dfrac{2x}{3} + \dfrac{x-1}{7x}$

Q6 $\quad \dfrac{3x}{4} - \dfrac{2x-1}{5x}$

Q7 $\quad \dfrac{2}{x-1} + \dfrac{3}{x}$

Q8 $\quad \dfrac{3}{x+1} + \dfrac{2}{x+2}$

Q9 $\quad \dfrac{4}{x-3} - \dfrac{1}{x+4}$

Q10 $\quad \dfrac{6}{x+2} + \dfrac{6}{x-2}$

Q11 $\quad \dfrac{3}{x-2} - \dfrac{5}{2x+3}$

Q12 $\quad \dfrac{3}{x+2} + \dfrac{x}{x+1}$

Q13 $\quad \dfrac{5x}{(x+1)^2} - \dfrac{3}{x+1}$

Q14 $\quad \dfrac{5}{x(x+3)} + \dfrac{3}{x+2}$

Q15 Hint: Factorise the first denominator before you do anything else.

Q15 $\quad \dfrac{x}{x^2-4} - \dfrac{1}{x+2}$

Q16 $\quad \dfrac{3}{x+1} + \dfrac{6}{2x^2+x-1}$

Q17 $\quad \dfrac{2}{x} + \dfrac{3}{x+1} + \dfrac{4}{x+2}$

Q18 $\quad \dfrac{3}{x+4} - \dfrac{2}{x+1} + \dfrac{1}{x-2}$

Q19 Hint: To turn the 2 into a fraction just use '1' as the denominator.

Q19 $\quad 2 - \dfrac{3}{x+1} + \dfrac{4}{(x+1)^2}$

Q20 $\quad \dfrac{2x^2-x-3}{x^2-1} + \dfrac{1}{x(x-1)}$

Multiplying and dividing algebraic fractions

Multiplying algebraic fractions

You **multiply** algebraic fractions in exactly the same way that you multiply normal fractions — multiply the numerators together, then multiply the denominators. Try to **cancel** any **common factors** before multiplying.

Examples

Simplify the following:

a) $\dfrac{x^3}{2y} \times \dfrac{8y^2}{3}$

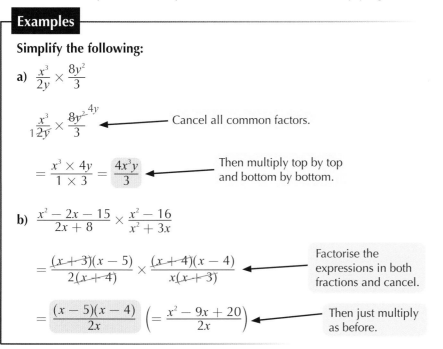

$$\dfrac{x^3}{{}_1\cancel{2y}} \times \dfrac{\cancel{8y^2}^{4y}}{3}$$ ← Cancel all common factors.

$$= \dfrac{x^3 \times 4y}{1 \times 3} = \dfrac{4x^3y}{3}$$ ← Then multiply top by top and bottom by bottom.

Tip: Check whether you can cancel down any further at the end, just in case you missed something before.

b) $\dfrac{x^2 - 2x - 15}{2x + 8} \times \dfrac{x^2 - 16}{x^2 + 3x}$

$$= \dfrac{(x+3)(x-5)}{2(x+4)} \times \dfrac{(x+4)(x-4)}{x(x+3)}$$ ← Factorise the expressions in both fractions and cancel.

$$= \dfrac{(x-5)(x-4)}{2x} \left(= \dfrac{x^2 - 9x + 20}{2x} \right)$$ ← Then just multiply as before.

Tip: In cases like these, it's a lot easier to do all the factorising and cancelling before you multiply.

Dividing algebraic fractions

To **divide** by an algebraic fraction, you just **multiply** by its reciprocal. The reciprocal is 1 ÷ the original thing — for fractions you just turn the fraction upside down.

Examples

Simplify the following:

a) $\dfrac{8}{5x} \div \dfrac{12}{x^3}$ ← Turn the second fraction upside down.

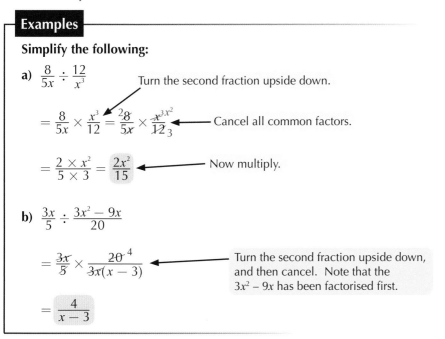

$$= \dfrac{8}{5x} \times \dfrac{x^3}{12} = \dfrac{\cancel{8}^2}{5x} \times \dfrac{\cancel{x^3}^{x^2}}{\cancel{12}_3}$$ ← Cancel all common factors.

$$= \dfrac{2 \times x^2}{5 \times 3} = \dfrac{2x^2}{15}$$ ← Now multiply.

b) $\dfrac{3x}{5} \div \dfrac{3x^2 - 9x}{20}$

$$= \dfrac{3x}{\cancel{5}} \times \dfrac{\cancel{20}^4}{3x(x-3)}$$ ← Turn the second fraction upside down, and then cancel. Note that the $3x^2 - 9x$ has been factorised first.

$$= \dfrac{4}{x-3}$$

Simplify the following:

Q1 Hint: Remember — cancelling **before** you multiply will make things a whole lot simpler.

Q1 a) $\dfrac{2x}{3} \times \dfrac{5x}{4}$ b) $\dfrac{6x^3}{7} \times \dfrac{2}{x^2}$

   c) $\dfrac{8x^2}{3y^2} \times \dfrac{x^3}{4y}$ d) $\dfrac{8x^4}{3y} \times \dfrac{6y^2}{5x}$

Q2 a) $\dfrac{x}{3} \div \dfrac{3}{x}$ b) $\dfrac{4x^3}{3} \div \dfrac{x}{2}$

   c) $\dfrac{3}{2x} \div \dfrac{6}{x^3}$ d) $\dfrac{2x^3}{3y} \div \dfrac{4x}{y^2}$

Q3 $\dfrac{x+2}{4} \times \dfrac{x}{3x+6}$

Q4 $\dfrac{4x}{5} \div \dfrac{4x^2+8x}{15}$

Q5 Hint: Always be on the look out for hidden 'difference of two squares' expressions.

Q5 $\dfrac{2x^2-2}{x} \times \dfrac{5x}{3x-3}$

Q6 $\dfrac{2x^2+8x}{x^2-2x} \times \dfrac{x-1}{x+4}$

Q7 $\dfrac{x^2-4}{9} \div \dfrac{x-2}{3}$

Q8 $\dfrac{2}{x^2+4x} \div \dfrac{1}{x+4}$

Q9 $\dfrac{x^2+4x+3}{x^2+5x+6} \times \dfrac{x^2+2x}{x+1}$

Q10 $\dfrac{x^2+5x+6}{x^2-2x-3} \times \dfrac{3x+3}{x^2+2x}$

Q11 $\dfrac{x^2-4}{6x-3} \times \dfrac{2x^2+5x-3}{x^2+2x}$

Q12 $\dfrac{x^2+7x+6}{4x-4} \div \dfrac{x^2+8x+12}{x^2-x}$

Q13 $\dfrac{x^2+4x+4}{x^2-4x+3} \times \dfrac{x^2-2x-3}{2x^2-2x} \times \dfrac{4x-4}{x^2+2x}$

Q14 Hint: Turn the fraction you're dividing by upside down and multiply.

Q14 $\dfrac{x}{6x+12} \div \dfrac{x^2-x}{x+2} \times \dfrac{3x-3}{x+1}$

Q15 $\dfrac{x^2+5x}{2x^2+7x+3} \times \dfrac{2x+1}{x^3-x^2} \div \dfrac{x+5}{x^2+x-6}$

2. Algebraic Division

Algebraic division (dividing one expression by another) is just another way of simplifying an algebraic fraction.

Algebraic division

Important terms

There are a few words that come up a lot in algebraic division, so make sure you know what they all mean.

> - **Degree** — the highest power of x in the polynomial.
>   For example, the degree of $4x^5 + 6x^2 - 3x - 1$ is 5.
> - **Divisor** — this is the thing you're dividing by.
>   For example, if you divide $x^2 + 4x - 3$ by $x + 2$, the divisor is $x + 2$.
> - **Quotient** — the bit that you get when you divide by the divisor
>   (not including the **remainder** — see below).

Method 1 — using the formula

There's a handy **formula** you can use to do algebraic division:

> A polynomial f(x) can be written in the form:
> $$f(x) \equiv q(x)d(x) + r(x)$$
> where: q(x) is the quotient,
>   d(x) is the divisor,
>   and r(x) is the remainder.

This comes from the **Remainder Theorem** that you met in C1. You'll be given f(x) and d(x) in the question, and it's down to you to work out q(x) and r(x).

> **Example**
>
> Divide $4x^5 - 7x^2 + 3x - 9$ by $x^2 - 5x + 8$.
>
> This bit is f(x). ↗   ← This bit is d(x), the divisor.
> It has a degree of 5.   It has a degree of 2.

Here's a step-by-step guide to using the formula:

> - First, you have to work out the **degrees** of the **quotient** and **remainder**, which depend on the degrees of the polynomial and the divisor. The degree of the quotient is **deg f(x) – deg d(x)**, and the degree of the remainder has to be **less** than the degree of the divisor.
> - Write out the division using the formula, but replace q(x) and r(x) with **general polynomials**. A general polynomial of degree 2 is Ax^2 + Bx + C, and a general polynomial of degree 1 is Ax + B, where A, B, C, etc. are constants to be found.
> - The next step is to work out the values of the **constants** (A, B, etc.). You do this by substituting in values for x to make bits disappear, and by **equating coefficients**.
> - It's best to start with the **constant term** and work **backwards** from there.
> - Finally, write out the division again, replacing A, B, C, etc. with the values you've found.

Learning Objectives:

- Be able to simplify algebraic fractions with linear or quadratic denominators by using algebraic division.

Tip: A **polynomial** is an algebraic expression made up of the sum of constant terms and variables raised to positive integer powers. For example $x^3 - 2x + \frac{1}{2}$ is a polynomial, but $x^{-3} - 2x^{\frac{3}{2}}$ is not as it has a negative power and a fractional power of x.

Tip: Remember from C1 — the **Remainder Theorem** says that for a polynomial f(x), when you divide f(x) by ($ax - b$), the remainder is f($\frac{b}{a}$). The **Factor Theorem** says that if f(a) = 0, then ($x - a$) is a factor of f(x).

Tip: The degree of the divisor will always be less than or equal to the degree of the polynomial.

Tip: Equating coefficients means comparing the coefficients of each power of x on the left hand side and the right hand side of the identity.

When you're using this method, you might have to use **simultaneous equations** to work out some of the coefficients. (Have a look back at your C1 notes for a reminder of how to do this if you need to.) The method looks a bit intense, but follow through these examples to see how it works.

Example 1

Divide $x^4 - 3x^3 - 3x^2 + 10x + 5$ by $x^2 - 5x + 6$.

- First, work out the **degrees** of the **quotient** and **remainder**:
  f(x) has degree 4 and d(x) has degree 2, which means that the quotient q(x) has degree $4 - 2 = 2$. The remainder r(x) has degree 1 or 0 (it must be less than the degree of d(x)) — so assume it's 1.

- Write out the division in the form **f(x) $\equiv$ q(x)d(x) + r(x)**, replacing q(x) and r(x) with general polynomials of degree 2 and 1:
  $x^4 - 3x^3 - 3x^2 + 10x + 5 \equiv (Ax^2 + Bx + C)(x^2 - 5x + 6) + Dx + E$

- d(x) factorises to give $(x - 2)(x - 3)$:
  $x^4 - 3x^3 - 3x^2 + 10x + 5 \equiv (Ax^2 + Bx + C)(x - 2)(x - 3) + Dx + E$

- Substitute $x = 2$ and $x = 3$ into the identity to make the q(x)d(x) bit disappear. This gives the following equations:
  when $x = 2$, $5 = 2D + E$
  when $x = 3$, $8 = 3D + E$

- Solve these simultaneously to get $D = 3$ and $E = -1$.
  So now the identity looks like this:
  $x^4 - 3x^3 - 3x^2 + 10x + 5 \equiv (Ax^2 + Bx + C)(x^2 - 5x + 6) + 3x - 1$

- Now substitute $x = 0$ into the identity:
  when $x = 0$, $5 = 6C - 1$

- Solving this gives $C = 1$. So now the identity looks like this:
  $x^4 - 3x^3 - 3x^2 + 10x + 5 \equiv (Ax^2 + Bx + 1)(x^2 - 5x + 6) + 3x - 1$

- Finally, **equate the coefficients** of x^4 and x^3.
  On the LHS the coefficient of x^4 is 1, and the coefficient of x^3 is -3. Expanding the brackets on the RHS lets you see that the coefficient of x^4 is A, and the coefficient of x^3 is $B - 5A$. Equating these gives $1 = A$ and $-3 = -5A + B$, so $B = 2$. So the identity looks like this:

  $$x^4 - 3x^3 - 3x^2 + 10x + 5 \equiv (x^2 + 2x + 1)(x^2 - 5x + 6) + 3x - 1$$

Example 2

Divide $x^3 + 5x^2 - 18x - 10$ by $x - 3$.

- f(x) has degree 3 and d(x) has degree 1, which means that q(x) has degree $3 - 1 = 2$. The remainder has degree 0 (it must be less than 1).

- Write out the division in the form f(x) $\equiv$ q(x)d(x) + r(x):
  $x^3 + 5x^2 - 18x - 10 \equiv (Ax^2 + Bx + C)(x - 3) + D$

- Putting $x = 3$ into the identity gives $D = 8$, so:
  $x^3 + 5x^2 - 18x - 10 \equiv (Ax^2 + Bx + C)(x - 3) + 8$

- Now, setting $x = 0$ gives the equation $-10 = -3C + 8$, so $C = 6$.
  $x^3 + 5x^2 - 18x - 10 \equiv (Ax^2 + Bx + 6)(x - 3) + 8$

- Equating the coefficients of x^3 and x^2 gives $A = 1$ and $-3A + B = 5$, so $B = 8$. So:

  $$x^3 + 5x^2 - 18x - 10 \equiv (x^2 + 8x + 6)(x - 3) + 8$$

Tip: If you're not sure what the degree is, assume it's the highest it could be (in this case 1). If it turns out to be lower it just means that some coefficients will be 0.

Tip: Factorising the divisor helps you to work out the values of x you need to put in to make certain terms disappear. When you've put it in brackets, pick values of x that will make one of the brackets zero.

Tip: After you've done a few of these you'll get used to spotting what the coefficients are going to be in terms of A and B, so you won't have to expand the brackets fully each time.

Tip: If the remainder has a degree of 0 it just means that it's a constant.

Simply stating the identity at the end doesn't properly answer the question. If you've been asked to divide one thing by another, then you need to state the **quotient** and the **remainder** which you've worked out using the formula.

So for Example 1 on the previous page:

$(x^4 - 3x^3 - 3x^2 + 10x + 5) \div (x^2 - 5x + 6) = x^2 + 2x + 1$ **remainder $3x - 1$**.

For Example 2: $(x^3 + 5x^2 - 18x - 10) \div (x - 3) = x^2 + 8x + 6$ **remainder 8**.

Method 2 — algebraic long division

You can also use **long division** to divide two algebraic expressions (using the same method you'd use for numbers).

Example

Divide $(2x^3 - 7x^2 - 16x + 11)$ by $(x - 5)$.

- Start by dividing the first term in the polynomial by the first term of the divisor: $2x^3 \div x = 2x^2$. Write this answer above the polynomial:

$$\begin{array}{r} 2x^2 \\ x - 5 \overline{\smash{)}2x^3 - 7x^2 - 16x + 11} \end{array}$$

> **Tip:** Note that we only divide each term by the 'x' term, not the '$x - 5$'. The –5 bit is dealt with in the steps in between.

- Multiply the divisor $(x - 5)$ by this answer $(2x^2)$ to get $2x^3 - 10x^2$:

$$\begin{array}{r} 2x^2 \\ x - 5 \overline{\smash{)}2x^3 - 7x^2 - 16x + 11} \\ 2x^3 - 10x^2 \end{array}$$

- Subtract this from the main expression to get $3x^2$. Bring down the $-16x$ term just to make things clearer for the next subtraction.

$$\begin{array}{r} 2x^2 \\ x - 5 \overline{\smash{)}2x^3 - 7x^2 - 16x + 11} \\ -\ 2x^3 - 10x^2 \\ \hline 3x^2 - 16x \end{array}$$

- Now divide the first term of the remaining polynomial ($3x^2$) by the first term of the divisor (x) to get $3x$ (the second term in the answer).

$$\begin{array}{r} 2x^2 + 3x \\ x - 5 \overline{\smash{)}2x^3 - 7x^2 - 16x + 11} \\ -\ 2x^3 - 10x^2 \\ \hline 3x^2 - 16x \end{array}$$

- Multiply $(x - 5)$ by $3x$ to get $3x^2 - 15x$, then subtract again and bring down the $+11$ term.

$$\begin{array}{r} 2x^2 + 3x \\ x - 5 \overline{\smash{)}2x^3 - 7x^2 - 16x + 11} \\ -\ 2x^3 - 10x^2 \\ \hline 3x^2 - 16x \\ -\ 3x^2 - 15x \\ \hline -x + 11 \end{array}$$

- Divide $-x$ by x to get -1 (the third term in the answer).
  Then multiply $(x - 5)$ by -1 to get $-x + 5$.

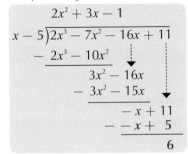

$$2x^2 + 3x - 1$$
$$x - 5\overline{)2x^3 - 7x^2 - 16x + 11}$$
$$-\underline{2x^3 - 10x^2}$$
$$3x^2 - 16x$$
$$-\underline{3x^2 - 15x}$$
$$-x + 11$$
$$-\underline{-x + 5}$$
$$6$$

- After subtracting, this term (6) has a degree that's **less** than the degree of the divisor, $(x - 5)$, so it can't be divided. This is the **remainder**.

Tip: You can multiply the quotient by $(x - 5)$, and then add on the remainder, 6, to check you've got it right.

- So $(2x^3 - 7x^2 - 16x + 11) \div (x - 5) = \boxed{2x^2 + 3x - 1 \text{ remainder } 6.}$

This could also be written as:
$$\frac{2x^3 - 7x^2 - 16x + 11}{x - 5} = 2x^2 + 3x - 1 + \frac{6}{x - 5}.$$

You can use the long division method when the divisor has a degree bigger than 1 (e.g. a quadratic), as long as the expression you're dividing has an even higher degree. The example below shows the working out all in one go.

Example

Divide $(2x^4 - x^2 - 6x + 5)$ by $(2x^2 + 4x + 5)$.

- First make sure you write out the expressions with all terms included — put a coefficient of 0 for the 'missing' x^3 term here.

Tip: If the original polynomial doesn't have an x term, for example, just put $0x$ where the x term should be.

- $2x^4 \div 2x^2 = x^2$. $\longrightarrow$ $x^2 - 2x + 1$

- Multiply $2x^2 + 4x + 5$ by x^2 to get $2x^4 + 4x^3 + 5x^2$.

$$2x^2 + 4x + 5\overline{)2x^4 + 0x^3 - x^2 - 6x + 5}$$
$$-2x^4 + 4x^3 + 5x^2$$

- Subtract this and bring down the $-6x$ term. $\longrightarrow$ $-4x^3 - 6x^2 - 6x$

- $-4x^3 \div 2x^2 = -2x$ (the second term in the answer). $-\ -4x^3 - 8x^2 - 10x$

- Multiply $2x^2 + 4x + 5$ by $-2x$ to get $-4x^3 - 8x^2 - 10x$. $2x^2 + 4x + 5$

- Subtract this and bring down the $+5$ term. $-2x^2 + 4x + 5$

- $2x^2 \div 2x^2 = +1$ (the third term in the answer). 0

Tip: Remember from the Factor Theorem, a remainder of zero means it divides exactly.

- Multiply $2x^2 + 4x + 5$ by 1 to get $2x^2 + 4x + 5$. Subtracting this gives a remainder of 0.

- So $(2x^4 - x^2 - 6x + 5) \div (2x^2 + 4x + 5) = \boxed{x^2 - 2x + 1.}$

Q1 Use the formula $f(x) \equiv q(x)d(x) + r(x)$ to divide the following expressions. In each case state the quotient and remainder.

Q1 Hint: If you're told which method to use make sure you show all your working clearly to prove that you know how to use the method.

a) $(x^3 - 14x^2 + 6x + 11) \div (x + 1)$

b) $(2x^3 + 5x^2 - 8x - 17) \div (x - 2)$

c) $(2x^3 + 4x^2 - 5x + 2) \div (x^2 - 2x + 1)$

Q2 Write $6x^4 + 11x^3 + 9x^2 + 15x - 2$ in the form:
$(Ax^2 + Bx + C)(2x^2 + x + 3) + Dx + E$.

Using your answer, state the result when
$6x^4 + 11x^3 + 9x^2 + 15x - 2$ is divided by $2x^2 + x + 3$.

Q2 Hint: This is just another way of asking you to use the formula.

Q3 Use long division to divide the following expressions. In each case state the quotient and remainder.

a) $(x^3 - 14x^2 + 6x + 11) \div (x + 1)$

b) $(x^3 + 10x^2 + 15x - 13) \div (x + 3)$

c) $(2x^3 + 5x^2 - 8x - 17) \div (x - 2)$

d) $(3x^3 - 78x + 9) \div (x + 5)$

e) $(x^4 - 1) \div (x - 1)$

f) $(8x^3 - 6x^2 + x + 10) \div (2x - 3)$

g) $(2x^3 + 4x^2 - 5x + 2) \div (x^2 - 2x + 1)$

h) $(6x^4 + 11x^3 + 9x^2 + 15x - 2) \div (2x^2 + x + 3)$

In the following questions you can choose which method to use.

Q4 Divide $10x^3 + 7x^2 - 5x + 21$ by $2x + 1$, stating the quotient and remainder.

Q5 Divide $3x^3 - 8x^2 + 15x - 12$ by $x^2 + x - 2$, stating the quotient and remainder.

Q6 Divide $6x^4 - 7x^2 - 3$ by $2x^2 - 3$, stating the quotient and remainder.

3. Partial Fractions

Learning Objectives:

- Be able to write algebraic fractions as partial fractions, including fractions with repeated linear factors, e.g. $(ax + b)(cx + d)^2$.

Sometimes an algebraic fraction with a complicated denominator can be split into a sum of simpler fractions. In this section you'll see a couple of methods you can use to do this, depending on what type of denominator you have.

Expressing in partial fractions

- You can split a fraction with **more than one linear factor** in the denominator into **partial fractions**.
- This means writing it as a **sum** of two or more **simpler fractions**.
- The **denominators** of these simpler fractions will be **factors** of the denominator of the original fraction.

Tip: If you're asked to write an algebraic fraction as partial fractions, start by writing the partial fractions out with A, B and C as numerators as shown here. You might have to factorise the denominator first, like in the last example.

Examples

- $\dfrac{7x - 7}{(2x + 1)(x - 3)}$ can be written as

  partial fractions of the form $\dfrac{A}{(2x + 1)} + \dfrac{B}{(x - 3)}$.

- $\dfrac{9x^2 + x + 16}{(x + 2)(2x - 1)(x - 3)}$ can be written as

  partial fractions of the form $\dfrac{A}{(x + 2)} + \dfrac{B}{(2x - 1)} + \dfrac{C}{(x - 3)}$.

- $\dfrac{21x - 2}{9x^2 - 4}$ can be written as partial fractions of the form $\dfrac{A}{(3x - 2)} + \dfrac{B}{(3x + 2)}$.

The tricky bit is **working out** what A, B and C are. Follow this method:

Tip: The $\equiv$ symbol means it's an identity.

- **Write out** the expression as an identity, e.g.
  $$\frac{7x - 7}{(2x + 1)(x - 3)} \equiv \frac{A}{(2x + 1)} + \frac{B}{(x - 3)}$$
- **Add** the partial fractions together, i.e. write them over a **common denominator**.
- **Cancel** the denominators from both sides (they'll be the same).
- This will give you an **identity** for A and B, for example:
  $$7x - 7 \equiv A(x - 3) + B(2x + 1)$$
- Use the **Substitution** method or the Equating Coefficients method:

Substitution	**Equating Coefficients**
Substitute a number for x to leave you with just one constant on the right hand side.	Equate the constant terms, coefficients of x and coefficients of x^2, then solve the equations simultaneously.

Example 1

Express $\dfrac{9x^2 + x + 16}{(x + 2)(2x - 1)(x - 3)}$ **in partial fractions.**

- Write it out as an **identity**:

$$\frac{9x^2 + x + 16}{(x + 2)(2x - 1)(x - 3)} \equiv \frac{A}{(x + 2)} + \frac{B}{(2x - 1)} + \frac{C}{(x - 3)}$$

- **Add** the partial fractions —
this means writing them over a **common denominator**:

$$\frac{A}{(x + 2)} + \frac{B}{(2x - 1)} + \frac{C}{(x - 3)} \equiv$$
$$\frac{A(2x - 1)(x - 3) + B(x + 2)(x - 3) + C(2x - 1)(x + 2)}{(x + 2)(2x - 1)(x - 3)}$$

- **Cancel** the denominators from both sides of the original identity,
so the numerators are **equal**:

$$9x^2 + x + 16 \equiv A(2x - 1)(x - 3) + B(x + 2)(x - 3) + C(2x - 1)(x + 2)$$

> **Tip:** The adding step can be a bit fiddly, so you should always check that each term will cancel to produce the original fraction. Another method is to multiply both sides of the original identity by the left hand denominator to get the identity you want.

Substitution Method

Substitute values of x which make one of the expressions in brackets equal zero to get rid of all but one of A, B and C.

- Substituting $x = 3$ gets rid of A and B:

$$(9 \times 3^2) + 3 + 16 = 0 + 0 + C((2 \times 3) - 1)(3 + 2)$$
$$100 = 25C \qquad \Rightarrow C = 4$$

- Substituting $x = -2$ gets rid of B and C:

$$(9 \times (-2)^2) + (-2) + 16 = A((2 \times -2) - 1)(-2 - 3) + 0 + 0$$
$$50 = 25A \qquad \Rightarrow A = 2$$

- Substituting $x = 0.5$ gets rid of A and C:

$$(9 \times (0.5^2)) + 0.5 + 16 = 0 + B(0.5 + 2)(0.5 - 3) + 0$$
$$18.75 = -6.25B \qquad \Rightarrow B = -3$$

> **Tip:** For some questions one method will be easier than the other — if one seems too tricky try the other. Sometimes you might want to use a combination of both methods.

Equating Coefficients Method

- Compare coefficients in the numerators:
$$9x^2 + x + 16 \equiv$$
$$A(2x - 1)(x - 3) + B(x + 2)(x - 3) + C(2x - 1)(x + 2)$$

Equating x^2 coefficients: $\qquad 9 = 2A + B + 2C$
Equating x coefficients: $\qquad 1 = -7A - B + 3C$
Equating constant terms: $\qquad 16 = 3A - 6B - 2C$

> You'll need to multiply out the brackets on the RHS for this, e.g.
> $A(2x - 1)(x - 3)$
> $= 2Ax^2 - 7Ax + 3A$

- Solving these equations simultaneously gives:
$A = 2$, $B = -3$ and $C = 4$ (the same as the substitution method).

> **Tip:** Generally it's easier to use the substitution method first. In this example, it's actually quite tricky to solve the simultaneous equations that you get by equating coefficients, so you're better off using substitution.

- Finally, **replace** A, B and C in the original identity:

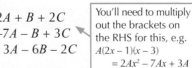

$$\frac{9x^2 + x + 16}{(x + 2)(2x - 1)(x - 3)} \equiv \frac{2}{(x + 2)} - \frac{3}{(2x - 1)} + \frac{4}{(x - 3)}$$

> **Tip:** Don't forget to write out your solution like this once you've done all the working.

Example 2

Express $\dfrac{3-x}{x^2+x}$ **in partial fractions.**

- First you need to **factorise** the denominator: $\dfrac{3-x}{x^2+x} \equiv \dfrac{3-x}{x(x+1)}$.

- Now write as an **identity** with partial fractions: $\dfrac{3-x}{x(x+1)} \equiv \dfrac{A}{x} + \dfrac{B}{x+1}$.

- **Add** the partial fractions and **cancel** the denominators from both sides:
$$\dfrac{3-x}{x(x+1)} \equiv \dfrac{A(x+1)+Bx}{x(x+1)} \quad \Rightarrow \quad 3-x \equiv A(x+1)+Bx$$

- In this example it's easier to **equate** coefficients because A is the only letter that appears in the constant term on the right hand side.

- **Compare coefficients** in $3-x \equiv A(x+1)+Bx$:

  Equating constant terms: $\quad 3 = A$
  Equating x coefficients: $\quad -1 = A + B \Rightarrow -1 = 3 + B \Rightarrow \boldsymbol{B = -4}$

- **Replace** A and B in the identity: $\dfrac{3-x}{x^2+x} \equiv \dfrac{3}{x} - \dfrac{4}{(x+1)}$

Tip: In this example equating coefficients is a good bet because you get one of the constants without any work.

Exercise 3.1

Q1 & 2 Hint: Use the substitution method for Q1, and equate coefficients for Q2.

Q1 Express $\dfrac{3x+3}{(x-1)(x-4)}$ in the form $\dfrac{A}{x-1} + \dfrac{B}{x-4}$.

Q2 Express $\dfrac{5x-1}{x(2x+1)}$ in the form $\dfrac{A}{x} + \dfrac{B}{2x+1}$.

Q3 Find the values of the constants A and B in the identity $\dfrac{3x-2}{x^2+x-12} \equiv \dfrac{A}{x+4} + \dfrac{B}{x-3}$.

Q4 Hint: Look out for the difference of two squares.

Q4 Write $\dfrac{2}{x^2-16}$ in partial fractions.

Q5 Factorise x^2-x-6 and hence express $\dfrac{5}{x^2-x-6}$ in partial fractions.

Q6 Write $\dfrac{11x}{2x^2+5x-12}$ in partial fractions.

Q7 a) Factorise x^3-9x fully.

     b) Hence write $\dfrac{x^2-3x+2}{x^3-9x}$ in partial fractions.

Q8 Write $\dfrac{4x^2-14}{x^3-36x}$ in the form $\dfrac{A}{x} + \dfrac{B}{x+6} + \dfrac{C}{x-6}$.

Q9 a) Hint: Have a look back at page 7 for a reminder of the Factor Theorem.

Q9 a) Use the Factor Theorem to fully factorise x^3-7x-6.

     b) Hence write $\dfrac{5x^2-7x-4}{x^3-7x-6}$ in partial fractions.

Q10 Express $\dfrac{6x^2-x+5}{(x+4)(x-1)(x+1)}$ in partial fractions.

Q11 Express $\dfrac{3x^2-6x+3}{x^3-6x^2+3x+10}$ in partial fractions.

14   Chapter 1 Algebra and Functions

Repeated factors

If the denominator of an algebraic fraction has **repeated linear factors** the partial fractions will take a slightly **different form**, as shown in the examples below.

> The **power** of the repeated factor tells you **how many** times that factor should appear in the partial fractions.
>
> - $\dfrac{3x^2 - 7x + 5}{(x+1)^2(x-4)}$ is written as $\dfrac{A}{(x+1)} + \dfrac{B}{(x+1)^2} + \dfrac{C}{(x-4)}$.
>
>   A factor that's **squared** in the original denominator will appear in the denominator of **two** of your partial fractions — once squared and once just as it is.
>
> - $\dfrac{7x^2 + 31x - 14}{x^2(2x+7)}$ is written as $\dfrac{A}{x} + \dfrac{B}{x^2} + \dfrac{C}{(2x+7)}$.
>
> - $\dfrac{x^2 + 4x + 6}{(x+3)^3}$ is written as $\dfrac{A}{(x+3)} + \dfrac{B}{(x+3)^2} + \dfrac{C}{(x+3)^3}$.
>
>   A factor that's **cubed** will appear **three** times — once cubed, once squared and once just as it is.

Tip: Make sure you don't miss repeated factors like x^2 and x^3.

Example 1

Express $\dfrac{2x^2 + 9x - 9}{x^2(x-3)}$ in partial fractions.

x is a **repeated factor** so the answer will be of the form $\dfrac{A}{x} + \dfrac{B}{x^2} + \dfrac{C}{(x-3)}$.

- Write it out as an **identity**: $\dfrac{2x^2 + 9x - 9}{x^2(x-3)} \equiv \dfrac{A}{x} + \dfrac{B}{x^2} + \dfrac{C}{(x-3)}$.

- **Add** the partial fractions:

$$\frac{2x^2 + 9x - 9}{x^2(x-3)} \equiv \frac{Ax(x-3) + B(x-3) + Cx^2}{x^2(x-3)}$$

- **Cancel** the denominators from both sides, so the numerators are **equal**:

$$2x^2 + 9x - 9 \equiv Ax(x-3) + B(x-3) + Cx^2.$$

- **Substituting** $x = 3$ gets rid of A and B:

$$(2 \times 3^2) + (9 \times 3) - 9 = 0 + 0 + C(3^2)$$
$$36 = 9C \qquad \Rightarrow C = 4$$

- **Substituting** $x = 0$ gets rid of A and C:

$$(2 \times 0^2) + (9 \times 0) - 9 = 0 + B(0 - 3) + 0$$
$$-9 = -3B \qquad \Rightarrow B = 3$$

Tip: You don't need to multiply through by every denominator to add these fractions together. Have a look back at page 3 if you're not sure about this.

- There's no value of x you can substitute to get rid of B and C and just leave A, so **equate coefficients** of x^2:

> Coefficients of x^2 are: $\quad 2 = A + C$
> You know $C = 4$, so: $\quad 2 = A + 4 \qquad \Rightarrow A = -2$

- **Replace** A, B and C in the identity: $\quad \dfrac{2x^2 + 9x - 9}{x^2(x-3)} \equiv \dfrac{-2}{x} + \dfrac{3}{x^2} + \dfrac{4}{(x-3)}$

Tip: You could equate coefficients of x here instead, but you can't equate constant terms because A only appears as a coefficient of x or x^2 in the identity.

Example 2

Express $\dfrac{x^2 + 17x + 16}{(x + 2)^2(3x - 1)}$ in partial fractions.

- Write the **identity**: $\dfrac{x^2 + 17x + 16}{(x + 2)^2(3x - 1)} \equiv \dfrac{A}{(x + 2)} + \dfrac{B}{(x + 2)^2} + \dfrac{C}{(3x - 1)}$

Tip: Remember, you won't need to multiply through by all of the denominators.
E.g. for the second fraction you just need to multiply the top and bottom by $(3x - 1)$.

- **Add** the partial fractions:

$$\dfrac{A}{(x + 2)} + \dfrac{B}{(x + 2)^2} + \dfrac{C}{(3x - 1)} \equiv$$
$$\dfrac{A(x + 2)(3x - 1) + B(3x - 1) + C(x + 2)^2}{(x + 2)^2(3x - 1)}$$

- **Cancel** the denominators from both sides:

$$x^2 + 17x + 16 \equiv A(x + 2)(3x - 1) + B(3x - 1) + C(x + 2)^2.$$

- **Substituting** $x = -2$ gets rid of A and C:

$$(-2)^2 + (17 \times -2) + 16 = 0 + B((3 \times -2) - 1) + 0$$
$$-14 = -7B \qquad \Rightarrow B = 2$$

- **Substituting** $x = \frac{1}{3}$ gets rid of A and B:

$$\left(\tfrac{1}{3}\right)^2 + \left(17 \times \tfrac{1}{3}\right) + 16 = 0 + 0 + C\left(\tfrac{1}{3} + 2\right)^2$$
$$\dfrac{196}{9} = \dfrac{49}{9}C \qquad \Rightarrow C = 4$$

Tip: Another method you can use when there's no value of x which will get rid of B and C is to substitute in any simple value of x, e.g. $x = 1$, and the values that you have calculated for B and C to work out A.

- There's no value of x you can substitute to get rid of B and C to just leave A, so try **equating coefficients** instead:

  Equate coefficients of x^2: $\qquad 1 = 3A + C$
  You know $C = 4$, so: $\qquad\qquad -3 = 3A \qquad \Rightarrow A = -1$

- **Replace** A, B and C in the original identity:

$$\dfrac{x^2 + 17x + 16}{(x + 2)^2(3x - 1)} \equiv -\dfrac{1}{(x + 2)} + \dfrac{2}{(x + 2)^2} + \dfrac{4}{(3x - 1)}$$

Exercise 3.2

Q1 Express $\dfrac{3x}{(x + 5)^2}$ in the form $\dfrac{A}{(x + 5)} + \dfrac{B}{(x + 5)^2}$.

Q2 Write $\dfrac{x^2 - 5x + 2}{x^2(x + 1)}$ in the form $\dfrac{A}{x} + \dfrac{B}{x^2} + \dfrac{C}{(x + 1)}$.

Q3 Express $\dfrac{x^2 + 5x - 1}{(x - 2)^3}$ in the form $\dfrac{A}{(x - 2)} + \dfrac{B}{(x - 2)^2} + \dfrac{C}{(x - 2)^3}$.

Q4 Write the following in partial fractions.

a) $\dfrac{2x - 7}{(x - 3)^2}$ b) $\dfrac{x + 4}{(x + 2)^2}$ c) $\dfrac{2x^2 - 9x + 5}{(x - 4)^2(x + 2)}$ d) $\dfrac{3x^2 - 7x - 25}{x(x - 5)^2}$

Q5 Hint: Factorising the denominator should leave you with a repeated factor.

Q5 Express $\dfrac{5x^2 - 10x - 5}{x^3 - 10x^2 + 25x}$ in partial fractions.

Improper fractions as partial fractions

- The **numerator** of an **improper** algebraic fraction has a degree **equal to or greater than** the degree of the **denominator**.
- The **degree** of a polynomial is the highest power of x.

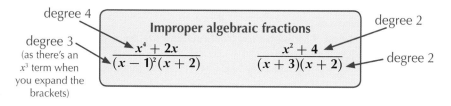

degree 4

degree 3 (as there's an x^3 term when you expand the brackets)

Improper algebraic fractions

$$\frac{x^4 + 2x}{(x-1)^2(x+2)} \qquad \frac{x^2 + 4}{(x+3)(x+2)}$$

degree 2

degree 2

- Before you can express an **improper fraction** as partial fractions, you first need to **divide** the numerator by the denominator to give $q(x) + \frac{r(x)}{d(x)}$ (where $\frac{r(x)}{d(x)}$ is a **proper fraction**).

Tip: You've seen methods of algebraic division on pages 7-9 — have a look back to remind yourself of them if you need to. Remember $q(x)$ = quotient, $d(x)$ = divisor and $r(x)$ = remainder.

Example

a) Use division to get the improper fraction $\dfrac{x^4 - 3x^3 - 3x^2 + 10x + 5}{(x-3)(x-2)}$ in the form $q(x) + \dfrac{r(x)}{d(x)}$.

- You're working out $(x^4 - 3x^3 - 3x^2 + 10x + 5) \div (x-3)(x-2)$:

- To use **long division** you'll need to multiply out $(x-3)(x-2)$:
$$(x-3)(x-2) = x^2 - 5x + 6$$

- Now **divide** $(x^4 - 3x^3 - 3x^2 + 10x + 5)$ by $(x^2 - 5x + 6)$:

Tip: You can use whichever algebraic division method you like — it doesn't have to be long division.

$$
\begin{array}{r}
x^2 + 2x + 1 \\
x^2 - 5x + 6 \overline{) \, x^4 - 3x^3 - 3x^2 + 10x + 5} \\
-(x^4 - 5x^3 + 6x^2) \\
\hline
2x^3 - 9x^2 + 10x + 5 \\
-(2x^3 - 10x^2 + 12x) \\
\hline
x^2 - 2x + 5 \\
-(x^2 - 5x + 6) \\
\hline
3x - 1
\end{array}
$$

- So: $\dfrac{x^4 - 3x^3 - 3x^2 + 10x + 5}{(x-3)(x-2)} \equiv (x^2 + 2x + 1) + \dfrac{3x - 1}{(x-3)(x-2)}$

Tip: You could check your answer by multiplying both sides by $(x-3)(x-2)$, and then multiplying out the brackets on the RHS.

b) Hence express $\dfrac{x^4 - 3x^3 - 3x^2 + 10x + 5}{(x-3)(x-2)}$ as partial fractions.

Express the **proper fraction** as **partial fractions** by the usual method:

- Write out the **identity**: $\dfrac{3x - 1}{(x-3)(x-2)} \equiv \dfrac{A}{(x-3)} + \dfrac{B}{(x-2)}$.

- **Add** the partial fractions and **cancel** the denominators from both sides:

$$\frac{3x-1}{(x-3)(x-2)} \equiv \frac{A(x-2) + B(x-3)}{(x-3)(x-2)} \Rightarrow 3x - 1 \equiv A(x-2) + B(x-3)$$

- **Substituting** $x = 2$ gets rid of A:

$$(3 \times 2) - 1 = 0 + B(2 - 3)$$
$$5 = -B \qquad\qquad \Rightarrow \mathbf{\mathit{B} = -5}$$

- **Substituting** $x = 3$ gets rid of B:

$$(3 \times 3) - 1 = A(3 - 2) + 0$$
$$8 = A \qquad\qquad \Rightarrow \mathbf{\mathit{A} = 8}$$

- **Replacing** A and B in the partial fractions identity gives that:

$$\frac{3x - 1}{(x - 3)(x - 2)} \equiv \frac{8}{(x - 3)} - \frac{5}{(x - 2)}$$

Tip: Don't forget to put the partial fractions you've worked out back into your expression for the improper fraction.

- **Go back** to the expression you worked out for $(x^4 - 3x^3 - 3x^2 + 10x + 5) \div (x - 3)(x - 2)$:

$$\frac{x^4 - 3x^3 - 3x^2 + 10x + 5}{(x - 3)(x - 2)} \equiv x^2 + 2x + 1 + \frac{3x - 1}{(x - 3)(x - 2)}$$

- **Replace** the **proper fraction** with the **partial fractions**:

$$\frac{x^4 - 3x^3 - 3x^2 + 10x + 5}{(x - 3)(x - 2)} \equiv x^2 + 2x + 1 + \frac{8}{(x - 3)} - \frac{5}{(x - 2)}$$

Exercise 3.3

Q1 a) Use algebraic division to express $\dfrac{2x^2 - 4x + 6}{(x - 3)(x + 1)}$ in the form $q(x) + \dfrac{r(x)}{d(x)}$.

Q1 b) Hint: It's $\dfrac{r(x)}{d(x)}$ that you want to express in partial fractions.

    b) Hence express $\dfrac{2x^2 - 4x + 6}{(x - 3)(x + 1)}$ using partial fractions.

Q2 Express the improper fraction $\dfrac{3x^3 + 4x^2 + 2x - 5}{(x + 2)(x + 3)}$ in partial fractions.

Q3 Show that the fraction $\dfrac{2x^2 + 4x + 7}{(x - 1)(x + 2)}$ can be expressed in the form $A + \dfrac{B}{(x - 1)} + \dfrac{C}{(x + 2)}$, and find the constants A, B and C.

Q4 Use algebraic division to show that:

$$\frac{3x^2 - 5x + 2}{(x - 3)^2} \equiv A + \frac{B}{(x - 3)} + \frac{C}{(x - 3)^2}$$

and find the values of A, B and C.

Q5 Show that the improper fraction $\dfrac{x^3 - 3x^2 - 3x + 9}{x^2 + 3x - 4}$ can be expressed in the form $Ax + B + \dfrac{C}{(x + 4)} + \dfrac{D}{(x - 1)}$.

Find the values of the constants A, B, C and D.

Q6 Hint: Remember x^2 is a repeated factor.

Q6 Express $\dfrac{x^3 + 4x^2 - 3x + 8}{x^2(x - 2)}$ in partial fractions.

4. Exponential Growth and Decay

You've seen exponential functions in C3 — they're functions where the rate of increase / decrease of the function is proportional to the function itself.

Learning Objectives:

- Be able to use exponential functions to model real-life problems and make predictions about growth and decay.

Modelling growth and decay

Modelling growth and decay means using a formula to **predict** how something will increase or decrease. This formula is called a **model**.

In an exam you'll often be given a background **story** to an exponential equation. There's nothing here you haven't seen before, you just need to know how to deal with all the **wordy** bits.

But first, here's a quick recap of **exponential functions**:

- The main feature of exponential growth/decay is that the **rate of increase/decrease** of the function is **proportional** to the function itself.
- There is a value of 'a' for which the gradient of $y = a^x$ is **exactly the same** as a^x. This value is the irrational number known as **e**, and $y = e^x$ is known as **'the' exponential function**. $y = e^x > 0$ for all values of x.
- **ln** x (or 'natural log') is the **inverse function** of e^x. So $\ln e^x = x = e^{\ln x}$. $\ln x$ does not exist for $x \leq 0$.

Tip: Have a look back at your C3 notes for more on exponentials.

Example 1

The exponential growth of a colony of bacteria can be modelled by the equation $B = 60e^{0.03t}$, where B is the number of bacteria and t is the time in hours from the point at which the colony is first monitored ($t \geq 0$). Use the model to:

a) **Work out the initial population of bacteria.**

The initial population of bacteria is given by the formula when $t = 0$.

$B = 60e^{0.03t} = 60e^{(0.03 \times 0)} = 60e^0 = 60 \times 1 = \boxed{60}$

Tip: Don't forget — $e^0 = 1$.

b) **Predict the number of bacteria after 4 hours.**

- Substitute $t = 4$ into the equation to find B after 4 hours.
- Round down because you want to know the number of whole bacteria.

$B = 60 \times e^{(0.03 \times 4)}$
$= 60 \times 1.1274...$
$= 67.6498...$
So $B = 67$ bacteria.

c) **Predict the time taken for the colony to grow to 1000.**

- You need to find the time, t, when the population is 1000.
- Substitute in the value of B.
- Take 'ln' of both sides as $\ln x$ is the inverse of e^x.

$B = 1000$
$1000 = 60e^{0.03t}$
$e^{0.03t} = 1000 \div 60 = 16.6666...$
$\ln e^{0.03t} = \ln(16.6666...)$
$0.03t = 2.8134...$
$t = 2.8134... \div 0.03$
$= 93.8$ hours to 3 s.f.

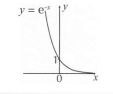

$y = e^{-x}$

Example 2

The concentration (C) of a drug in the bloodstream, t hours after taking an initial dose, decreases exponentially according to $C = Ae^{-kt}$, where A and k are constants. If the initial concentration is 0.72, and this halves after 5 hours, find the values of A and k and sketch a graph of C against t.

0.72 is the initial concentration — so start by putting this information into the equation and solving for A.

When $t = 0$, $C = 0.72$ $\Rightarrow$ So $0.72 = A \times e^0$ $\Rightarrow$ $0.72 = A \times 1$ $\Rightarrow$ $\boxed{A = 0.72}$

After 5 hours the initial concentration has halved — so you can put in the value of C at $t = 5$, and then solve for k.

When $t = 5$, $C = 0.72 \div 2 = 0.36$

$$0.36 = 0.72 \times e^{-5k}$$

$$0.36 = \frac{0.72}{e^{5k}}$$

$$e^{5k} = \frac{0.72}{0.36} = 2$$

$\ln e^{5k} = \ln 2$ $\longleftarrow$ Apply $\ln$ to solve for k.

$$5k = \ln 2$$

$$k = \ln 2 \div 5$$

$$\boxed{k = 0.139 \text{ to 3 s.f.}}$$ So the equation is $\boxed{C = 0.72e^{-0.139t}}$.

OK — the last thing left to do is to sketch the graph.
Now whenever you're asked to draw a sketch of an exponential or logarithmic function, the key is to find any intercepts and asymptotes.

When $t = 0$, $C = 0.72$.
This is the **intercept.**

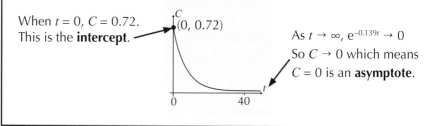

(0, 0.72)

As $t \to \infty$, $e^{-0.139t} \to 0$
So $C \to 0$ which means $C = 0$ is an **asymptote.**

Exercise 4.1

Give your answers correct to 3 significant figures.

Q1 A radioactive substance has a half-life of 10 years. Its decay is modelled by the equation $M = M_0 e^{-kt}$, where M is the mass in grams after t years and M_0 and k are constants.
a) After how many years will the substance be reduced to a quarter of its original mass?
b) What was the original mass if the mass after 5 years is 200 grams?
c) Find the mass remaining after 15 years.

Q2 The value of a painting, V, is increasing according to the model $V = Ak^t$, where t is the time in years and A and k are constants. Its initial value is £300, and after 3 years it is worth £500. Find the values of A and k, and work out how many whole years it will take for the value of the painting to triple.

Q3 An oven is turned on at 12:00. After t minutes its temperature, $T\,^\circ C$, is given by the formula:

$$T = 225 - 207e^{-\frac{t}{8}}$$

a) What was the initial temperature of the oven?

b) What temperature would the oven approach if it was left on indefinitely?

c) What was the temperature after 5 minutes?

d) At what time does the oven reach a temperature of 190 °C?

e) Sketch the graph of T against t.

Q4 A woman is prescribed a medicine, and the concentration of the medicine in her bloodstream is monitored. Initially the concentration in her bloodstream is 3 mg per litre of blood (mg/l). After t hours, the concentration of the drug is N mg/l, where $N = Ae^{-t}$.

a) What is the concentration after 30 minutes?

b) How long does it take for the level to reduce to 0.1 mg/l?

c) Sketch the graph of N against t.

Q5 A forest fire spreads in such a way that the burnt area (H hectares) after t hours is given by the relation $H = 20\,e^{bt}$. Assume that the fire burns unchecked.

a) If $e^b = 1.8$, find b.

b) Find the area burnt after 3 hours.

c) How long would it take to burn an area of 500 hectares?

d) What constant factor is the burnt area multiplied by every hour? What percentage does the burnt area increase by each hour?

Q6 A bowl of soup is cooling so that its temperature, $\theta\,^\circ C$ after t seconds, can be predicted from the formula $\theta = 65\,e^{-ct} + 18$.

a) What was the initial temperature of the heated soup?

b) After the first minute, the soup has cooled by 8 °C.
   Find the value of c.

c) Find the temperature of the soup after a total of 3 minutes.

d) How long will it take for the soup to cool down to 40 °C?

e) Sketch the graph of θ against t.

Q7 The formula $p = \dfrac{1}{(1 + Re^{-qt})}$ models the spread of information through a population, where p is the proportion of the population aware of some information after t hours.

At 8:00, 5% of the population of Illyria have heard about the death of the King. By 10:00, 30% know of it.

> **Q7 Hint:** Don't forget to convert the percentages into proportions (decimals or fractions).

a) Find the constants R and q.

b) What proportion of the population of Illyria will the model predict to have heard the news by 14:00?

c) At what time will the model predict that 70% of the population know about the King's death?

Review Exercise — Chapter 1

Q1 Simplify the following:

a) $\dfrac{\dfrac{x}{x-5}}{\dfrac{2x}{x-5}+\dfrac{3}{x-5}}$

b) $\dfrac{5-\dfrac{2}{2x+3}}{7+\dfrac{1}{2x+3}}$

c) $\dfrac{\dfrac{4}{2x+7}+6}{x+2}$

Q2 Simplify the following:

a) $\dfrac{4x^2-25}{6x-15}$

b) $\dfrac{2x+3}{x-2}\times\dfrac{4x-8}{2x^2-3x-9}$

c) $\dfrac{x^2-3x}{x+1}\div\dfrac{x}{2}$

Q3 Write the following as a single fraction:

a) $\dfrac{x}{2x+1}+\dfrac{3}{x^2}+\dfrac{1}{x}$

b) $\dfrac{2}{x^2-1}-\dfrac{3x}{x-1}+\dfrac{x}{x+1}$

Q4 Use the formula $f(x)\equiv q(x)d(x)+r(x)$ to divide the following expressions. In each case state the quotient and remainder.

a) $(x^3+8x^2-3x+13)\div(x+2)$

b) $(3x^3-4x^2-12x+9)\div(x-3)$

Q5 Use algebraic long division to divide:

a) x^3+2x^2-x+19 by $x+4$

b) $2x^3+8x^2+7x+8$ by $x+3$.

Q6 Write $\dfrac{2x}{(x-5)(x+5)}$ as partial fractions in the form $\dfrac{A}{(x-5)}+\dfrac{B}{(x+5)}$.

Q7 Find the values of the constants A and B in the identity $\dfrac{2-x}{(3x+2)(x+1)}\equiv\dfrac{A}{(3x+2)}+\dfrac{B}{(x+1)}$.

Q8 Find the values of the constants A, B and C in the identity $\dfrac{x^2-3x-8}{x^3+3x^2+2x}\equiv\dfrac{A}{x}+\dfrac{B}{(x+1)}+\dfrac{C}{(x+2)}$.

Q9 Express the following as partial fractions.

a) $\dfrac{2x+2}{(x+3)^2}$

b) $\dfrac{6x^2+17x+5}{x(x+2)^2}$

c) $\dfrac{-18x+14}{(2x-1)^2(x+2)}$

d) $\dfrac{8x^2-x-5}{x^3-x^2}$

Q10 Show that $\dfrac{5x^2-10x+42}{(5x-1)(x+2)}\equiv A+\dfrac{B}{(5x-1)}+\dfrac{C}{(x+2)}$,

and find the values of the constants A, B and C.

Q11 Express the improper fraction $\dfrac{4x^3+12x^2-x-5}{(x+1)(2x-1)}$ in partial fractions.

Q12 Express the following improper fractions as partial fractions:

a) $\dfrac{2x^2 + 18x + 26}{(x+2)(x+4)}$

b) $\dfrac{3x^2 + 9x + 2}{x(x+1)}$

c) $\dfrac{3x^3 - 2x^2 - 2x - 3}{(x+1)(x-2)}$

d) $\dfrac{24x^2 - 70x + 53}{(2x-3)^2}$

Q13 A scientist uses software to produce a series of curves using test data. He expects all of the curves to have equations of the form $y = pe^{qt}$.

a) If the first curve passes through the points (3, 20) and (0, 5), find p and q.

b) Another curve passes through (9, 20) and (6, 5). Find its equation.

Q14 The value of a motorbike (£V) varies with age (in t years from new) according to $V = 7500k^{-0.2t}$.

a) How much did it originally cost?

b) After 5 years, its value is £3,000. What is the value of k?

c) What is its value after 10 years (to the nearest £)?

d) After how many years will the motorbike's value have fallen below £500?

Q15 A nature reserve has a population of 20 leopards in 2010. The number of leopards in the nature reserve can be modelled by the formula $L = L_0 e^{\frac{t}{12}}$ where L is the number of leopards in the population, L_0 is the initial population size and t is the time in years.

a) How many leopards does the model predict the nature reserve will have after 10 years?

b) The reserve has enough space for 60 leopards.
How long will it be until the reserve runs out of space?

When a number of leopards are released into the wild, the wild population can be modelled by the formula $W = W_0 e^{-\frac{t}{3}}$ where W is the population, t is the time in years and W_0 is the initial population.

c) If the zoo releases a population of 15 leopards into the wild, predict how many will be in this population after 5 years in the wild.

Q16 The spread of a zombie apocalypse through a population can be modelled by the exponential formula:

$$Z = 10 + 20e^t$$

where Z is the number of zombies and t is the time in weeks.

a) How many zombies were there initially?

b) Predict how many people will have become zombies after 2 weeks if it spreads according to the model.

c) How many weeks will it be before there are 60 million zombies?

d) Sketch a graph of Z against t, labelling any key points.

1   Given that $\dfrac{5+9x}{(1+3x)^2} \equiv \dfrac{A}{(1+3x)^2} + \dfrac{B}{(1+3x)}$,

where A and B are integers, find the values of A and B.

(3 marks)

2   Write $\dfrac{2x^2 - 9x - 35}{x^2 - 49}$ as a fraction in its simplest form.

(3 marks)

3   Simplify the following:

a) $\dfrac{x^2 - x - 20}{2x + 4} \cdot \dfrac{x^2 - 16}{x + 2}$

(3 marks)

b) $\dfrac{x^2 - x - 20}{2x + 4} - \dfrac{x^2 - 16}{x + 2}$

(3 marks)

4   Write $x^3 + 15x^2 + 43x - 30$ in the form $(Ax^2 + Bx + C)(x + 6) + D$, where A, B, C and D are constants to be found.

(3 marks)

5   Show that $\dfrac{18x^2 - 15x - 62}{(3x + 4)(x - 2)} \equiv A + \dfrac{B}{(3x + 4)} + \dfrac{C}{(x - 2)}$,

and find the values of the integers A, B and C.

(4 marks)

6   $f(x) = \dfrac{5x^2 + 3x + 6}{(3 - x)(2x - 1)^2}$

Given that f(x) can be expressed in the form $f(x) = \dfrac{A}{(3 - x)} + \dfrac{B}{(2x - 1)^2} + \dfrac{C}{(2x - 1)}$,

find the values of A, B and C.

(4 marks)

7   Given that $\dfrac{-2x^3 - 4x^2 + 18x + 6}{x^2 + 2x - 3}$ can be expressed in the form:

$$Ax + B + \dfrac{C}{(x + 3)} + \dfrac{D}{(x - 1)}$$

find the values of A, C and D, and show that $B = 0$.

(5 marks)

8   A breed of mink is introduced to a new habitat.
     The number of mink, M, after t years in the habitat, is modelled by:

$$M = 74e^{0.6t} \qquad (t \geq 0)$$

   a)   State the number of mink that were introduced to the new habitat originally.
                                                                                   (1 mark)

   b)   Predict the number of mink after 3 years in the habitat.
                                                                                   (2 marks)

   c)   Predict the number of complete years it would take for the
        population of mink to exceed 10 000.
                                                                                   (2 marks)

   d)   Sketch a graph to show how the mink population varies with time
        in the new habitat.
                                                                                   (2 marks)

9   a)   Fully factorise $2x^3 - 19x^2 + 32x + 21$.
                                                                                   (2 marks)

   b)   Hence express $\dfrac{x^2 - 9x - 21}{2x^3 - 19x^2 + 32x + 21}$ in partial fractions.
                                                                                   (4 marks)

10   Express $\dfrac{6x - 1}{x^2 + 4x + 4}$ in partial fractions.
                                                                                   (4 marks)

11   $\dfrac{18x^3 - 57x^2 + 38}{(x - 3)(3x + 2)} \equiv Ax + B + \dfrac{C}{(x - 3)} + \dfrac{D}{(3x + 2)}$

     Find the values of the constants A, B, C and D.
                                                                                   (5 marks)

12   A radioactive substance decays exponentially so that its activity, A, can be modelled by
$$A = Be^{-kt}$$
     where t is the time in days, and $t \geq 0$. Some experimental data is shown below.

t	0	5	10
A	50	42	

   a)   State the value of B.
                                                                                   (1 mark)

   b)   Find the value of k, to 3 significant figures.
                                                                                   (2 marks)

   c)   Find the missing value from the table, to the nearest whole number.
                                                                                   (2 marks)

   d)   The half-life of a substance is the time it takes for the activity to halve.
        Find the half-life of this substance, in days.
        Give your answer to the nearest day.
                                                                                   (3 marks)

1. The Addition Formulas

Learning Objective:

- Know, and be able to use, the formulas for sin ($A \pm B$), cos ($A \pm B$) and tan ($A \pm B$).

There are some trig formulas you need for C4 — they can be used for finding exact values, solving, simplifying and proving identities.

Finding exact values

The identities shown below are known as the **addition formulas**. You can use the addition formulas to find the **sin**, **cos** or **tan** of the **sum** or **difference** of two angles, and to 'expand the brackets' in expressions such as sin ($x + 60°$) or cos ($n - \frac{\pi}{2}$).

Tip: These formulas are given on the formula sheet in the exam.

$$\sin (A \pm B) \equiv \sin A \cos B \pm \cos A \sin B$$

$$\cos (A \pm B) \equiv \cos A \cos B \mp \sin A \sin B$$

$$\tan (A \pm B) \equiv \frac{\tan A \pm \tan B}{1 \mp \tan A \tan B}$$

Tip: Watch out for the $\pm$ and $\mp$ signs in the formulas — especially for cos and tan. If you use the sign on the top on the left-hand side of the identity, you have to use the sign on the top on the right-hand side.

Examples

a) **Find the exact value of sin 18° cos 12° + cos 18° sin 12°.**

Using the **sin** addition formula:

$\sin A \cos B + \cos A \sin B \equiv \sin (A + B).$ ← *A is 18° and B is 12°.*

$\sin 18° \cos 12° + \cos 18° \sin 12° = \sin (18° + 12°) = \sin 30° = \dfrac{1}{2}$

b) **Write $\dfrac{\tan 5x - \tan 2x}{1 + \tan 5x \tan 2x}$ as a single trigonometric ratio.**

Tip: Note that it's tan A – tan B (rather than +) on the top line, which means it's the tan ($A - B$) formula.

Use the **tan** addition formula, with $A = 5x$ and $B = 2x$:

$$\frac{\tan 5x - \tan 2x}{1 + \tan 5x \tan 2x} = \tan (5x - 2x) = \boxed{\tan 3x}$$

c) **Find cos($x + y$) if sin $x = \dfrac{4}{5}$ and sin $y = \dfrac{15}{17}$. Both x and y are acute. Give an exact answer.**

- In order to use the **cos** addition formula, first find **cos x** and **cos y**.
- Draw triangles and use **SOH CAH TOA** and Pythagoras to work out cos x and cos y...

Tip: You could also use the identity $\cos^2 \theta + \sin^2 \theta \equiv 1$ from C2 to work out cos x and cos y here.

$$\cos x = \frac{\text{adj}}{\text{hyp}} = \frac{3}{5} \longrightarrow \qquad \longleftarrow \cos y = \frac{\text{adj}}{\text{hyp}} = \frac{8}{17}$$

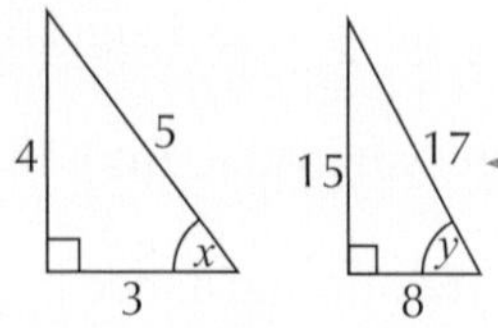

- $\cos (x + y) = \cos x \cos y - \sin x \sin y$

$$= \left(\frac{3}{5} \times \frac{8}{17}\right) - \left(\frac{4}{5} \times \frac{15}{17}\right) = \boxed{-\frac{36}{85}}$$

You should know the value of sin, cos and tan for **common angles**, in degrees and radians, from C2 and C3. You can use this knowledge, along with the addition formulas, to find the **exact value** of sin, cos or tan for **other** angles.

Find a **pair** of common angles which **add or subtract** to give the angle you're after. Then plug them into the addition formula, and work it through.

Tip: In C3, you drew triangles and used SOH CAH TOA to work out the sin, cos and tan of common angles:

	0°	30°	45°	60°	90°
	0	$\frac{\pi}{6}$	$\frac{\pi}{4}$	$\frac{\pi}{3}$	$\frac{\pi}{2}$
sin	0	$\frac{1}{2}$	$\frac{1}{\sqrt{2}}$	$\frac{\sqrt{3}}{2}$	1
cos	1	$\frac{\sqrt{3}}{2}$	$\frac{1}{\sqrt{2}}$	$\frac{1}{2}$	0
tan	0	$\frac{1}{\sqrt{3}}$	1	$\sqrt{3}$	—

Example

Using the addition formula for tangent, show that tan 15° = 2 − $\sqrt{3}$.

- Pick two angles that **add or subtract** to give **15°**, and put them into the **tan** addition formula. It's easiest to use **tan 60°** and **tan 45°** here, since neither of them are fractions:

$$\tan(A - B) \equiv \frac{\tan A - \tan B}{1 + \tan A \tan B}$$

$$\tan 15° = \tan (60° - 45°) = \frac{\tan 60° - \tan 45°}{1 + \tan 60° \tan 45°}$$

- **Substitute** the values for tan 60° (= $\sqrt{3}$) and tan 45° (= 1) into the equation.

$$= \frac{\sqrt{3} - 1}{1 + (\sqrt{3} \times 1)} = \frac{\sqrt{3} - 1}{\sqrt{3} + 1}$$

- Now **rationalise the denominator** of the fraction to get rid of the $\sqrt{3}$.

$$= \frac{\sqrt{3} - 1}{\sqrt{3} + 1} \times \frac{\sqrt{3} - 1}{\sqrt{3} - 1} = \frac{3 - 2\sqrt{3} + 1}{3 - \sqrt{3} + \sqrt{3} - 1}$$

Tip: If you can't remember how to rationalise the denominator have a look at your C1 notes.

- Now **simplify** the expression...

$$= \frac{4 - 2\sqrt{3}}{2} = 2 - \sqrt{3}$$

...and there's the **right-hand side**.

Exercise 1.1

Q1 Use the addition formulas to find the exact values of the following:

a) cos 72° cos 12° + sin 72° sin 12°

b) cos 13° cos 17° − sin 13° sin 17°

c) $\dfrac{\tan 12° + \tan 18°}{1 - \tan 12° \tan 18°}$

d) $\dfrac{\tan 500° - \tan 140°}{1 + \tan 500° \tan 140°}$

e) sin 35° cos 10° + cos 35° sin 10°

f) sin 69° cos 9° − cos 69° sin 9°

Q1-2 Hint: You've been asked for exact values, which is a big clue that they'll have something to do with the common angles you should know.

Q2 Use the addition formulas to find the exact values of the following:

a) $\sin \frac{2\pi}{3} \cos \frac{\pi}{2} - \cos \frac{2\pi}{3} \sin \frac{\pi}{2}$

b) $\cos 4\pi \cos 3\pi + \sin 4\pi \sin 3\pi$

c) $\dfrac{\tan \frac{5\pi}{12} + \tan \frac{5\pi}{4}}{1 - \tan \frac{5\pi}{12} \tan \frac{5\pi}{4}}$

Q3 Write the following expressions as a single trigonometric ratio:

a) $\sin 5x \cos 2x - \cos 5x \sin 2x$

b) $\cos 4x \cos 6x - \sin 4x \sin 6x$

c) $\dfrac{\tan 7x + \tan 3x}{1 - \tan 7x \tan 3x}$

d) $5 \sin 2x \cos 3x + 5 \cos 2x \sin 3x$

e) $8 \cos 7x \cos 5x + 8 \sin 7x \sin 5x$

Q4 Hint: You'll need to work out cos x and sin y before you can answer parts a)-d). You can use the triangle method or the identity $\cos^2 \theta + \sin^2 \theta \equiv 1$ to work them out.

Remember from C3 that $\mathrm{cosec}\, \theta = \frac{1}{\sin \theta}$ and $\sec \theta = \frac{1}{\cos \theta}$.

Q4 $\sin x = \frac{3}{4}$ and $\cos y = \frac{3}{\sqrt{10}}$, where x and y are both acute angles.

Calculate the exact value of:

a) $\sin (x + y)$ b) $\cos (x - y)$ c) $\mathrm{cosec}\, (x + y)$ d) $\sec (x - y)$

Q5 Using the addition formula for cos, show that $\cos \frac{\pi}{12} = \frac{\sqrt{6} + \sqrt{2}}{4}$.

Q6 Using the addition formula for sin, show that $\sin 75° = \frac{\sqrt{6} + \sqrt{2}}{4}$.

Q7 Using the addition formula for tan, show that $\tan 75° = \frac{\sqrt{3} + 1}{\sqrt{3} - 1}$.

Simplifying, solving equations and proving identities

You might be asked to use the addition formulas to **prove an identity**. All you need to do is put the numbers and variables from the left-hand side into the addition formulas and simplify until you get the expression you're after.

Example 1

Prove that $\cos(a + 60°) + \sin(a + 30°) \equiv \cos a$.

- Put the numbers from the question into the addition formulas:

$\cos(a + 60°) + \sin(a + 30°)$
$\equiv (\cos a \cos 60° - \sin a \sin 60°) + (\sin a \cos 30° + \cos a \sin 30°)$

Tip: Be careful with the + and − signs here.

- Now substitute in any sin and cos values that you know...

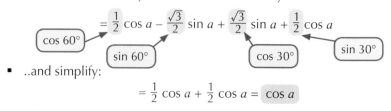

- ...and simplify:

$= \frac{1}{2} \cos a + \frac{1}{2} \cos a = \boxed{\cos a}$

Example 2

Use the sine and cosine addition formulas to prove that
$$\tan(A + B) \equiv \frac{\tan A + \tan B}{1 - \tan A \tan B}.$$

$$\tan(A + B) \equiv \frac{\sin(A + B)}{\cos(A + B)}$$

> Start with the identity $\tan\theta \equiv \frac{\sin\theta}{\cos\theta}$.

$$\equiv \frac{\sin A \cos B + \cos A \sin B}{\cos A \cos B - \sin A \sin B}$$

> Replace $\sin(A + B)$ and $\cos(A + B)$ with the addition formulas for each.

$$\equiv \frac{\dfrac{\sin A \cos B}{\cos A \cos B} + \dfrac{\cos A \sin B}{\cos A \cos B}}{\dfrac{\cos A \cos B}{\cos A \cos B} - \dfrac{\sin A \sin B}{\cos A \cos B}}$$

> Divide each part of the fraction by $\cos A \cos B$ and cancel where possible.

$$\equiv \frac{\dfrac{\sin A}{\cos A} + \dfrac{\sin B}{\cos B}}{1 - \left(\dfrac{\sin A}{\cos A}\right)\left(\dfrac{\sin B}{\cos B}\right)}$$

> Finally, replace each $\frac{\sin}{\cos}$ with tan.

$$\equiv \frac{\tan A + \tan B}{1 - \tan A \tan B}$$

Tip: You know that the first term on the denominator needs to be '1' — so divide through by whatever this term is and you'll get the 1 in the right place.

You can also use the addition formulas to **solve** complicated trig equations.

Example 3

Solve $\sin\left(x + \frac{\pi}{2}\right) = \sin x$ in the interval $0 \leq x \leq 2\pi$.

- First replace $\sin\left(x + \frac{\pi}{2}\right)$ using the **sin** addition formula:

$$\sin x \cos\frac{\pi}{2} + \cos x \sin\frac{\pi}{2} = \sin x$$

$$\Rightarrow 0 + \cos x = \sin x$$

> $\cos\frac{\pi}{2} = 0$ and $\sin\frac{\pi}{2} = 1$.

- **Divide** through by **cos** x:

$$\frac{\cos x}{\cos x} = \frac{\sin x}{\cos x}$$

- Replace $\frac{\sin x}{\cos x}$ with **tan** x:

$$1 = \tan x$$

$$\Rightarrow \tan x = 1$$

- Solve for $0 \leq x \leq 2\pi$:

$$x = \frac{\pi}{4} \text{ and } \frac{5\pi}{4}$$

Tip: Remember — to solve a trig equation you need to get it all in terms of sin, cos or tan. You can use any of the identities you've learnt so far to do this.

Q1 Hint: Look at the proof of tan $(A + B)$ on the previous page.

Q1 Use the sine and cosine addition formulas to prove that

$$\tan(A - B) \equiv \frac{\tan A - \tan B}{1 + \tan A \tan B}.$$

Q2 Prove the following identities:

a) $\dfrac{\cos(A - B) - \cos(A + B)}{\cos A \sin B} \equiv 2 \tan A$

b) $\dfrac{1}{2}[\cos(A - B) - \cos(A + B)] \equiv \sin A \sin B$

c) $\sin(x + 90°) \equiv \cos x$

Q3 Hint: Remember, you usually need to write an expression in terms of one type of trig function in order to solve an equation.

Q3 Solve $4 \sin\left(x - \dfrac{\pi}{3}\right) = \cos x$ in the interval $-\pi \le x \le \pi$. Give your answers in radians to 2 decimal places.

Q4 a) Show that $\tan\left(-\dfrac{\pi}{12}\right) = \sqrt{3} - 2$.

b) Use your answer to a) to solve the equation $\cos x = \cos\left(x + \dfrac{\pi}{6}\right)$ in the interval $0 \le x \le \pi$. Give your answer in terms of π.

Q5 Show that $2 \sin(x + 30°) \equiv \sqrt{3} \sin x + \cos x$.

Q6 Write an expression for $\tan\left(\dfrac{\pi}{3} - x\right)$ in terms of $\tan x$ only.

Q7 $\tan A = \dfrac{3}{8}$ and $\tan(A + B) = \dfrac{1}{4}$. Find the exact value of $\tan B$.

Q8 a) Given that $\sin(x + y) = 4 \cos(x - y)$, write an expression for $\tan x$ in terms of $\tan y$.

b) Use your answer to a) to solve $\sin\left(x + \dfrac{\pi}{4}\right) = 4 \cos\left(x - \dfrac{\pi}{4}\right)$ in the interval $0 \le x \le 2\pi$.

Q9 Solve the following equations in the given interval. Give your answers to 2 decimal places.

a) $\sqrt{2} \sin(\theta + 45°) = 3 \cos\theta, \quad 0° \le \theta \le 360°$

b) $2 \cos\left(\theta - \dfrac{2\pi}{3}\right) - 5 \sin\theta = 0, \quad 0 \le \theta \le 2\pi$

c) $\sin(\theta - 30°) - \cos(\theta + 60°) = 0, \quad 0° \le \theta \le 360°$

2. The Double Angle Formulas

The double angle formulas are really just special versions of the addition formulas — using (A + A) instead of (A + B).

Deriving the double angle formulas

Double angle formulas are just a slightly different kind of **identity** — a special case of the addition formulas. They're called "double angle" formulas because they take an expression with a $2x$ term (a double angle) inside a trig function, and change it into an expression with only single x's inside the trig functions.

You need to know the double angle formulas for sin, cos and tan. Their derivations are given below.

Learning Objective:

- Know, and be able to use, the double angle formulas for sin $2A$, cos $2A$ and tan $2A$.

$$\sin 2A \equiv 2\sin A \cos A$$

- Start with the **sin addition formula** (see p.26), but replace 'B' with 'A':

$$\sin (A + A) \equiv \sin A \cos A + \cos A \sin A$$

- Sin $(A + A)$ can be written as sin $2A$, and so:

$$\sin 2A \equiv \sin A \cos A + \cos A \sin A \equiv 2\sin A \cos A$$

Tip: These formulas are **not** on the formula sheet but they can be derived from the addition formulas. It helps to know them off by heart — that way you can spot them if they sneak into a question (e.g. $\sin x \cos x$ is just $\frac{1}{2}\sin 2x$).

$$\cos 2A \equiv \cos^2 A - \sin^2 A$$

- Start with the **cos addition formula**, but again replace 'B' with 'A':

$$\cos (A + A) \equiv \cos A \cos A - \sin A \sin A$$

$$\Rightarrow \cos 2A \equiv \cos^2 A - \sin^2 A$$

- You can then use $\cos^2 A + \sin^2 A \equiv 1$ to get:

$$\cos 2A \equiv \cos^2 A - (1 - \cos^2 A) \quad \text{and} \quad \cos 2A \equiv (1 - \sin^2 A) - \sin^2 A$$

$$\cos 2A \equiv 2\cos^2 A - 1 \qquad \cos 2A \equiv 1 - 2\sin^2 A$$

Tip: The double angle formula for cos has three different forms which are all very useful — but you can work out the second two from the general one as shown.

$$\tan 2A \equiv \frac{2\tan A}{1 - \tan^2 A}$$

- Start with the **tan addition formula**, and again replace 'B' with 'A':

$$\tan(A + A) \equiv \frac{\tan A + \tan A}{1 - \tan A \tan A}$$

- Simplifying this gives:

$$\tan 2A \equiv \frac{2\tan A}{1 - \tan^2 A}.$$

Using the double angle formulas

Like the addition formulas in the previous section, the double angle formulas are useful when you need to find an **exact value**.

Tip: In the exam, they won't usually tell you which identity to use, so work on being able to spot the clues. If you're asked for an 'exact value' you should be thinking of your common angles. 15° is half of a common angle, so this should get you thinking about double angle formulas.

Example

a) Use a double angle formula to work out the exact value of sin 15° cos 15°.

- This looks the most like the **sin** double angle formula, $\sin 2A \equiv 2 \sin A \cos A$, but it needs to be **rearranged** slightly:

$$\sin 2A \equiv 2 \sin A \cos A \Rightarrow \sin A \cos A \equiv \frac{1}{2} \sin 2A$$

- Now put in the **numbers** from the question:

$$\sin 15° \cos 15° = \frac{1}{2} \sin 30° = \frac{1}{2} \times \frac{1}{2} = \frac{1}{4}$$

b) $\sin x = \frac{2}{3}$, where x is acute. Find the exact value of $\cos 2x$ and $\sin 2x$.

- For **cos 2x**, use the **cos** double angle formula in terms of **sin**:

$$\cos 2A \equiv 1 - 2 \sin^2 A$$

$$\Rightarrow \cos 2x = 1 - 2\left(\frac{2}{3}\right)^2 = \frac{1}{9}$$

- For **sin 2x**, use the **sin** double angle formula.

$$\sin 2A \equiv 2 \sin A \cos A$$

- To use this, first work out **cos x** from sin x using the triangle method:

$$\cos x = \frac{\text{adj}}{\text{hyp}} = \frac{\sqrt{5}}{3}$$

- Now put the values into the sin double angle formula as usual:

$$\sin 2x = 2 \sin x \cos x = 2 \times \frac{2}{3} \times \frac{\sqrt{5}}{3} = \frac{4\sqrt{5}}{9}$$

The double angle formulas are also handy for **simplifying expressions** in order to solve equations.

Example

Write $1 - 2 \sin^2 \left(\frac{3x}{2}\right)$ as a single trigonometric ratio.

- Look for an identity that is similar to this expression, containing a 'sin²'. The **cos** double angle formula (in terms of **sin**) looks best:

$$\cos 2A \equiv 1 - 2\sin^2 A$$

- Comparing the expression with the right-hand side of the identity, we need to use $A = \frac{3x}{2}$, and so $2A = 3x$.

- Putting this into the identity gives:

$$1 - 2\sin^2 \frac{3x}{2} \equiv \cos 3x$$

Exercise 2.1

Q1 Use the double angle formulas to write down the exact values of:

a) $4 \sin \frac{\pi}{12} \cos \frac{\pi}{12}$

b) $\cos \frac{2\pi}{3}$

c) $\frac{\sin 120°}{2}$

d) $\frac{\tan 15°}{2 - 2\tan^2 15°}$

e) $2 \sin^2 15° - 1$

Q1 Hint: For some of these there are other ways to find the answer, but if you've been asked to use a certain method then show your working using that method.

Q2 An acute angle x has $\sin x = \frac{1}{6}$. Find the exact values of:

a) $\cos 2x$ b) $\sin 2x$ c) $\tan 2x$

Q3 Angle x has $\sin x = -\frac{1}{4}$, and $\pi \leq x \leq \frac{3\pi}{2}$. Find the exact values of:

a) $\cos 2x$ b) $\sin 2x$ c) $\tan 2x$

Q3 Hint: Angle x lies in the 3rd quadrant of the CAST diagram, so sin x and cos x are negative but tan x is positive. (You covered CAST diagrams back in C2 — if you're not sure about them, have a look at your C2 notes.)

Q4 Write the following expressions as a single trigonometric ratio:

a) $\frac{\sin 3\theta \cos 3\theta}{3}$

b) $\sin^2 \left(\frac{2y}{3}\right) - \cos^2 \left(\frac{2y}{3}\right)$

c) $\frac{1 - \tan^2\left(\frac{x}{2}\right)}{2\tan\left(\frac{x}{2}\right)}$

Solving equations and proving identities

If an equation has a mixture of sin x and sin $2x$ terms in it, there's not much that you can do with it in that state. But you can use one of the double angle formulas to simplify it, and then solve it.

Example

Solve the equation cos $2x$ – 5 cos x = 2 in the interval $0 \leq x \leq 2\pi$.

- First use the **cos double angle formula** to get rid of cos $2x$:

$$\cos 2A \equiv 2\cos^2 A - 1$$

$$\Rightarrow 2\cos^2 x - 1 - 5\cos x = 2$$

Tip: Use this version of the formula so that you don't end up with a mix of sin and cos terms.

- **Simplify** so you have zero on one side...

$$2\cos^2 x - 5\cos x - 3 = 0$$

Tip: Let $y - \cos x$ and write as a quadratic in y if it helps.

- ...then **factorise** and **solve** the **quadratic** that you've made:

$$(2\cos x + 1)(\cos x - 3) = 0$$

$$\Rightarrow (2\cos x + 1) = 0 \text{ or } (\cos x - 3) = 0$$

- The second bracket gives you...

$$\cos x = 3$$

...which has **no solutions** since $-1 \leq \cos x \leq 1$.

- So all that's left is to solve the first bracket to find x:

$$2\cos x + 1 = 0$$

$$\cos x = -\frac{1}{2}$$

You know that cos $x = \frac{1}{2}$ for $x = \frac{\pi}{3}$ so using the symmetry of the graph below you get:

Tip: You can also use the CAST diagram.

$$x = \frac{2\pi}{3} \text{ or } x = \frac{4\pi}{3}$$

- Remember — you can sketch the **graph** of cos x to find all values of x in the given interval:

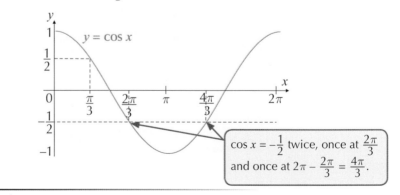

cos $x = -\frac{1}{2}$ twice, once at $\frac{2\pi}{3}$ and once at $2\pi - \frac{2\pi}{3} = \frac{4\pi}{3}$.

The examples below show how the double angle formulas can be used to **prove** other identities.

Example 1

Prove that $2\cot\frac{x}{2}(1 - \cos^2\frac{x}{2}) \equiv \sin x.$

- Use the identity $\sin^2\theta \equiv 1 - \cos^2\theta$ to replace the $1 - \cos^2\frac{x}{2}$ on the left-hand side, so you have:

$$\text{Left-hand side: } 2\cot\frac{x}{2}\sin^2\frac{x}{2}$$

Tip: Remember from C3 that cot is $\frac{1}{\tan}$, and tan is $\frac{\sin}{\cos}$, so cot is $\frac{\cos}{\sin}$.

- Now write $\cot\theta$ as $\frac{\cos\theta}{\sin\theta}$:

$$\frac{2\cos\frac{x}{2}\sin^2\frac{x}{2}}{\sin\frac{x}{2}} \equiv 2\cos\frac{x}{2}\sin\frac{x}{2}$$

- Now use the **sin double angle formula**, using $A = \frac{x}{2}$, to write...

$$2\cos\frac{x}{2}\sin\frac{x}{2} \equiv \boxed{\sin x}$$

...which gives you the right-hand side.

In this next example, you have to use both the addition formulas (p.26) and the double angle formulas.

Example 2

Show that $\cos 3\theta \equiv 4\cos^3\theta - 3\cos\theta$.

- First, write $\cos 3\theta$ as $\cos(2\theta + \theta)$.

- Now use the **cos addition formula**:

$$\cos 3\theta \equiv \cos(2\theta + \theta) \equiv \cos 2\theta\cos\theta - \sin 2\theta\sin\theta.$$

Tip: Clever tricks like splitting up the angle so you can use the addition formulas can really help if you're stuck on a trig identity question.

- Now use the **cos** and **sin double angle formulas** to get rid of the 2θ:

$$\cos 2\theta\cos\theta - \sin 2\theta\sin\theta \equiv (2\cos^2\theta - 1)\cos\theta - (2\sin\theta\cos\theta)\sin\theta$$

cos double angle formula   sin double angle formula

- **Tidy this up** by expanding the brackets and using $\sin^2\theta \equiv 1 - \cos^2\theta$:

$$\equiv 2\cos^3\theta - \cos\theta - 2\sin^2\theta\cos\theta$$

$$\equiv 2\cos^3\theta - \cos\theta - 2(1 - \cos^2\theta)\cos\theta$$

$$\equiv 2\cos^3\theta - \cos\theta - 2\cos\theta + 2\cos^3\theta$$

$$\equiv \boxed{4\cos^3\theta - 3\cos\theta}$$

Tip: You can use a similar method to show that $\sin 3\theta = 3\sin\theta - 4\sin^3\theta$.

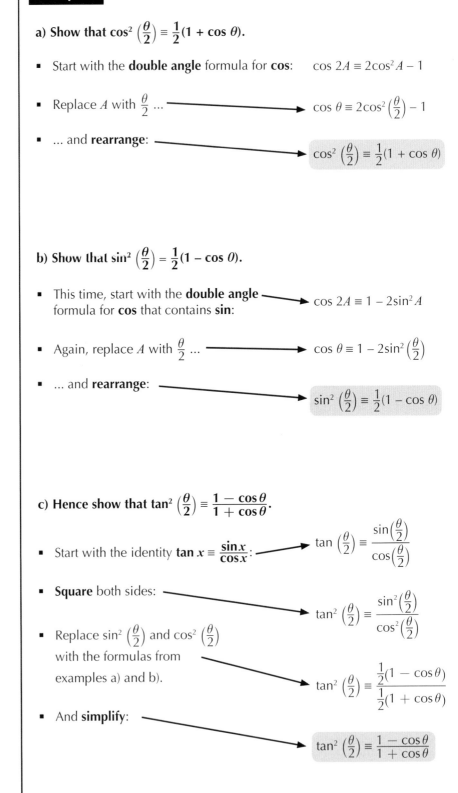

Example 3

a) Show that $\cos^2\left(\dfrac{\theta}{2}\right) \equiv \dfrac{1}{2}(1 + \cos\theta)$.

- Start with the **double angle** formula for **cos**: $\quad \cos 2A \equiv 2\cos^2 A - 1$

- Replace A with $\dfrac{\theta}{2}$ ... $\longrightarrow$ $\cos\theta \equiv 2\cos^2\left(\dfrac{\theta}{2}\right) - 1$

- ... and **rearrange**: $\longrightarrow$ $\cos^2\left(\dfrac{\theta}{2}\right) \equiv \dfrac{1}{2}(1 + \cos\theta)$

b) Show that $\sin^2\left(\dfrac{\theta}{2}\right) \equiv \dfrac{1}{2}(1 - \cos\theta)$.

- This time, start with the **double angle** formula for **cos** that contains **sin**: $\longrightarrow$ $\cos 2A \equiv 1 - 2\sin^2 A$

- Again, replace A with $\dfrac{\theta}{2}$ ... $\longrightarrow$ $\cos\theta \equiv 1 - 2\sin^2\left(\dfrac{\theta}{2}\right)$

- ... and **rearrange**: $\longrightarrow$ $\sin^2\left(\dfrac{\theta}{2}\right) \equiv \dfrac{1}{2}(1 - \cos\theta)$

c) Hence show that $\tan^2\left(\dfrac{\theta}{2}\right) \equiv \dfrac{1 - \cos\theta}{1 + \cos\theta}$.

Tip: That 'hence' in the question tells you to use your results for sin and cos. Any time you have to use sin and cos to prove something for tan you should be thinking of the identity $\tan\theta \equiv \sin\theta / \cos\theta$.

- Start with the identity $\tan x \equiv \dfrac{\sin x}{\cos x}$: $\longrightarrow$ $\tan\left(\dfrac{\theta}{2}\right) \equiv \dfrac{\sin\left(\dfrac{\theta}{2}\right)}{\cos\left(\dfrac{\theta}{2}\right)}$

- **Square** both sides: $\longrightarrow$ $\tan^2\left(\dfrac{\theta}{2}\right) \equiv \dfrac{\sin^2\left(\dfrac{\theta}{2}\right)}{\cos^2\left(\dfrac{\theta}{2}\right)}$

- Replace $\sin^2\left(\dfrac{\theta}{2}\right)$ and $\cos^2\left(\dfrac{\theta}{2}\right)$ with the formulas from examples a) and b). $\longrightarrow$ $\tan^2\left(\dfrac{\theta}{2}\right) \equiv \dfrac{\frac{1}{2}(1 - \cos\theta)}{\frac{1}{2}(1 + \cos\theta)}$

- And **simplify**: $\longrightarrow$ $\tan^2\left(\dfrac{\theta}{2}\right) \equiv \dfrac{1 - \cos\theta}{1 + \cos\theta}$

Tip: These three formulas are known as the **half angle formulas**. You don't need to know them for the exam though.

Q1 Solve the equations below in the interval $0 \le x \le 360°$.
Give your answers in degrees to 1 decimal place.

    a) $4 \cos 2x = 14 \sin x$

    b) $5 \cos 2x + 9 \cos x = -7$

    c) $4 \cot 2x + \cot x = 5$

    d) $\tan x - 5 \sin 2x = 0$

> **Q1 d) Hint:** There should be 7 solutions in the given interval, but two of them are easy to miss...

Q2 Solve the equations below in the interval $0 \le x \le 2\pi$.
Give your answers in radians to 3 significant figures.

    a) $4 \cos 2x - 10 \cos x + 1 = 0$

    b) $\dfrac{\cos 2x - 3}{2 \sin^2 x - 1} = 3$

Q3 Solve the equations below in the interval $0 \le x \le 2\pi$.
Give your answers in radians in terms of π.

    a) $\cos 2x + 7 \cos x = -4$

    b) $\sin x + \cos \frac{x}{2} = 0$

> **Q3 b) Hint:** Try writing $\sin x$ as $\sin 2\left(\frac{x}{2}\right)$ and using the sin double angle formula.

Q4 Use the double angle formulas to prove each of the identities below.

    a) $\sin 2x \sec^2 x \equiv 2 \tan x$

    b) $\dfrac{2}{1 + \cos 2x} \equiv \sec^2 x$

    c) $\cot x - 2 \cot 2x \equiv \tan x$

    d) $\tan 2x + \cot 2x \equiv 2 \operatorname{cosec} 4x$

> **Q4 d) Hint:** Write the left-hand side in terms of sin and cos first.

Q5 a) Show that $\dfrac{1 + \cos 2x}{\sin 2x} \equiv \cot x$.

    b) Use your answer to a) to solve $\dfrac{1 + \cos 4\theta}{\sin 4\theta} = 7$
in the interval $0 \le \theta \le 360°$.
Give your answers in degrees to 1 decimal place.

Q6 a) Show that $\operatorname{cosec} x - \cot \frac{x}{2} \equiv -\cot x$.

    b) Use your answer to a) to solve $\operatorname{cosec} y = \cot \frac{y}{2} - 2$
in the interval $-\pi \le y \le \pi$.
Give your answers in radians to 3 significant figures.

> **Q6 a) Hint:** Write $\operatorname{cosec} x$ as $\dfrac{1}{\sin x}$ and then use $\sin x = \sin 2\left(\frac{x}{2}\right)$.

3. The R Addition Formulas

Learning Objective:

- Know, and be able to use, expressions for $a \cos \theta + b \sin \theta$ in the equivalent forms of: $R \cos (\theta \pm \alpha)$ or $R \sin (\theta \pm \alpha)$.

The R addition formulas are used to help solve equations which contain a mix of cos and sin terms.

Expressions of the form $a \cos \theta + b \sin \theta$

If you're solving an equation that contains both $\sin \theta$ and $\cos \theta$ terms, e.g. $3 \sin \theta + 4 \cos \theta = 1$, you need to rewrite it so that it only contains one trig function. The formulas that you use to do that are known as the **R formulas**:

One set for **sine**:

$$a \sin \theta \pm b \cos \theta \equiv R \sin (\theta \pm \alpha)$$

And one set for **cosine**:

$$a \cos \theta \pm b \sin \theta \equiv R \cos (\theta \mp \alpha)$$

where a, b and R are **positive**, and α is **acute**.

You need to be careful with the + and − signs in the cosine formula. If you have $a \cos \theta + b \sin \theta$ then use $R \cos (\theta - \alpha)$.

Using the R formulas

- You'll start with an identity like $2 \sin x + 5 \cos x \equiv R \sin (x + \alpha)$, where R and α need to be found.

- First, **expand** the right hand side using the **addition formulas** (see p.26): $2 \sin x + 5 \cos x \equiv R \sin x \cos \alpha + R \cos x \sin \alpha$.

- **Equate the coefficients** of $\sin x$ and $\cos x$.
  You'll get two equations: **(1)** $R \cos \alpha = 2$ and **(2)** $R \sin \alpha = 5$.

- To find α, **divide** equation **(2)** by equation **(1)**,
  (because $\dfrac{R \sin \alpha}{R \cos \alpha} = \tan \alpha$) then take **tan⁻¹** of the result.

- To find R, **square** equations **(1)** and **(2)** and **add** them together, then take the **square root** of the answer. This works because:
  $(R \sin \alpha)^2 + (R \cos \alpha)^2 \equiv R^2 (\sin^2 \alpha + \cos^2 \alpha) \equiv R^2$
  (using the identity $\sin^2 \alpha + \cos^2 \alpha \equiv 1$).

Tip: This method looks a bit scary, but follow through the example below and it should make more sense.

Example 1

Express $4 \cos x + 5 \sin x$ in the form $R \cos (x \pm \alpha)$.

- First you need to get the **sign** right in the formula. For this use:

$$4 \cos x + 5 \sin x \equiv R \cos (x - \alpha)$$

- Now **expand** the right hand side using the **cos addition formula**:

$$4 \cos x + 5 \sin x \equiv R \cos x \cos \alpha + R \sin x \sin \alpha.$$

Tip: The addition formula used here is:
$\cos (A - B) = \cos A \cos B + \sin A \sin B$.

- **Equating the coefficients** of $\cos x$ gives:

$$(1) \ R \cos \alpha = 4$$

and equating the coefficients of $\sin x$ gives:

$$(2) \ R \sin \alpha = 5$$

- Dividing **(2)** by **(1)** gives:

$$\tan \alpha = \frac{5}{4} \Rightarrow \boxed{\alpha = 51.3° \text{ (to 1 d.p.)}}$$

Tip: Equating coefficients is a useful technique when you are working with identities like this — you know that the two sides are identical for all x, so the coefficients of $\sin x$ and $\cos x$ will be the same on each side.

- Squaring **(1)** and **(2)** gives:

$$\textbf{(1)}^2 : \ R^2 \cos^2 \alpha = 16$$
$$\textbf{(2)}^2 : \ R^2 \sin^2 \alpha = 25$$

$$\textbf{(1)}^2 + \textbf{(2)}^2 : \ R^2 \cos^2 \alpha + R^2 \sin^2 \alpha = 16 + 25$$
$$\Rightarrow R^2 (\cos^2 \alpha + \sin^2 \alpha) = 41$$
$$\Rightarrow R^2 = 41$$
$$\Rightarrow \boxed{R = \sqrt{41}}$$

- Finally, put the values for α and R back into the identity to give:

$$\boxed{4 \cos x + 5 \sin x \equiv \sqrt{41} \cos (x - 51.3°)}$$

Tip: Remember that R is always positive (so take the positive root) and α is always acute (so take the angle in the first quadrant of the CAST diagram when solving).

Example 2

a) Show that $5 \sin x - 5\sqrt{3} \cos x \equiv 10 \sin (x - \frac{\pi}{3})$.

As before, pick a formula and find values for R and α — then you can show that they are the **same** as in the right-hand side of the given identity.

- $5 \sin x - 5\sqrt{3} \cos x \equiv R \sin (x - \alpha)$ ← Expand using the **sin addition formula**.

- $5 \sin x - 5\sqrt{3} \cos x \equiv R \sin x \cos \alpha - R \cos x \sin \alpha$.

- **(1)** $R \cos \alpha = 5$ and **(2)** $R \sin \alpha = 5\sqrt{3}$ ← (by **equating coefficients**)

- $\dfrac{R \sin \alpha}{R \cos \alpha} = \tan \alpha = \dfrac{5\sqrt{3}}{5} = \sqrt{3} \Rightarrow \alpha = \dfrac{\pi}{3}$ ← **(2)** ÷ **(1)**

- $R^2 \cos^2 \alpha + R^2 \sin^2 \alpha = 5^2 + (5\sqrt{3})^2$ (by **squaring** and **adding (1)** and **(2)**)
  $\Rightarrow R^2 = 100 \Rightarrow \boxed{R = 10}$

Tip: $\sin (A - B) =$ $\sin A \cos B - \cos A \sin B$.

- So, putting the values for α and R back into the identity gives...

$$5 \sin x - 5\sqrt{3} \cos x \equiv 10 \sin (x - \tfrac{\pi}{3})$$

...which is the **right-hand side** of the identity you're trying to prove.

b) Hence sketch the graph of $y = 5 \sin x - 5\sqrt{3} \cos x$ in the interval $-\pi \le x \le \pi$.

Writing $y = 5 \sin x - 5\sqrt{3} \cos x$ as $y = \textbf{10 sin} \left(x - \frac{\pi}{3}\right)$ makes it a lot easier to sketch the graph — just **transform** the graph of $y = \sin x$ as appropriate:

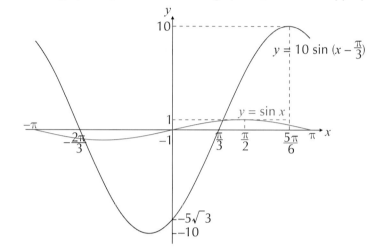

Tip: This transformation is just a translation of the graph of $y = \sin x$ horizontally right by $\frac{\pi}{3}$ followed by a stretch vertically by a scale factor of 10.

You can transform the **maximum** and **minimum** points of the graph in the same way. E.g. the maximum on $y = \sin x$ at $\left(\frac{\pi}{2}, 1\right)$, gets translated right by $\frac{\pi}{3}$ (so add $\frac{\pi}{3}$ to the x-coordinate) and stretched vertically by 10 (so multiply the y-coordinate by 10), to become $\left(\frac{5\pi}{6}, 10\right)$.

Exercise 3.1

Q1 Express $3 \sin x - 2 \cos x$ in the form $R \sin (x - \alpha)$.
Give R in surd form and α in degrees to 1 decimal place.

Q2 Express $6 \cos x - 5 \sin x$ in the form $R \cos (x + \alpha)$.
Give R in surd form and α in degrees to 1 decimal place.

Q3 Express $\sin x + \sqrt{7} \cos x$ in the form $R \sin (x + \alpha)$.
Give R in the form $m\sqrt{2}$ and α in radians to 3 significant figures.

Q4 Show that $\sqrt{2} \sin x - \cos x \equiv \sqrt{3} \sin (x - \alpha)$, where $\tan \alpha = \frac{1}{\sqrt{2}}$.

Q5 Hint: Treat the $2x$ just the same as an x.

Q5 Show that $3 \cos 2x + 5 \sin 2x \equiv \sqrt{34} \cos (2x - \alpha)$, where $\tan \alpha = \frac{5}{3}$.

Q6 a) Express $\sqrt{3} \sin x + \cos x$ in the form $R \sin (x + \alpha)$.
Give R and α as exact answers and α in radians in terms of π.

Q6 c) Hint: Write down their coordinates on the graph of $y = \sin x$ first, then apply the transformations to them.

b) Hence sketch the graph of $y = \sqrt{3} \sin x + \cos x$ in the interval $-\pi \le x \le \pi$.

c) State the coordinates of any maximum and minimum points and intersections with the axes of the graph in b).

Applying the R addition formulas

To solve equations of the form $a \sin \theta + b \cos \theta = c$, it's best to work things out in different stages — first writing out the equation in the form of one of the R formulas, then solving it. The example below shows how.

Tip: In exam questions they'll usually ask the question in stages anyway. You might be asked for something else too, like the maximum and minimum values of the function.

Example

a) **Solve $2 \sin x - 3 \cos x = 1$ in the interval $0 \le x \le 360°$.**

- Before you can **solve** this equation you need to get $2 \sin x - 3 \cos x$ in the form $R \sin (x - \alpha)$:

$$2 \sin x - 3 \cos x \equiv R \sin (x - \alpha)$$
$$2 \sin x - 3 \cos x \equiv R \sin x \cos \alpha - R \cos x \sin \alpha$$

- Equating coefficients gives the equations:

$$\textbf{(1) } R \cos \alpha = 2 \quad \text{and} \quad \textbf{(2) } R \sin \alpha = 3$$

- Solving for α:

$$\frac{R \sin \alpha}{R \cos \alpha} = \tan \alpha = \frac{3}{2}$$
$$\Rightarrow \alpha = \tan^{-1} 1.5 = 56.31° \text{ (to 2 d.p.)}$$

- Solving for R:

$$R^2 \cos^2 \alpha + R^2 \sin^2 \alpha = 2^2 + 3^2$$
$$\Rightarrow R^2 = 13 \Rightarrow R = \sqrt{13}$$

- So $\boxed{2 \sin x - 3 \cos x = \sqrt{13} \sin (x - 56.31°)}$

- Now **solve the equation**. If $2 \sin x - 3 \cos x = 1$, then:

$$\sqrt{13} \sin (x - 56.31°) = 1$$
$$\Rightarrow \sin (x - 56.31°) = \frac{1}{\sqrt{13}}$$

- Since, $0 \le x \le 360°$, you should be looking for solutions in the interval **$-56.31° \le (x - 56.31°) \le 303.69°$** (just take 56.31 away from the original interval).

- Solve the equation:

$$x - 56.31° = \sin^{-1}\left(\frac{1}{\sqrt{13}}\right) = 16.10°,$$
$$\text{or } 180 - 16.10 = 163.90°.$$

There are no solutions in the range $-56.31° \le (x - 56.31°) \le 0$ since $\sin x$ is negative in the range $-90° \le x \le 0$.

Tip: The other positive solution for sin is in the second quadrant of the CAST diagram, at $180° - 16.10°$ (the angle in the first quadrant).

- So $x = 16.10 + 56.31 = \boxed{72.4°}$ or $x = 163.90 + 56.31 = \boxed{220.2°}$.

b) **What are the maximum and minimum values of $2 \sin x - 3 \cos x$?**

The maximum and minimum values of the **sin** (and cos) function are ± 1, so the maximum and minimum values of $R \sin (x - \alpha)$ are $\pm R$.

As $2 \sin x - 3 \cos x = \sqrt{13} \sin (x - 56.31°)$, $R = \sqrt{13}$,

so the maximum and minimum values are $\boxed{\pm \sqrt{13}}$.

Tip: This is similar to being asked for the coordinates of the maximum and minimum points on the graph, so you can use a graph to help if you prefer.

Q1 a) Express $5 \cos \theta - 12 \sin \theta$ in the form $R \cos (\theta + \alpha)$, where $R > 0$ and α is an acute angle (in degrees, to 1 decimal place).

b) Hence solve $5 \cos \theta - 12 \sin \theta = 4$ in the interval $0 \leq \theta \leq 360°$.

c) State the maximum and minimum values of $5 \cos \theta - 12 \sin \theta$.

Q2 a) Express $2 \sin 2\theta + 3 \cos 2\theta$ in the form $R \sin (2\theta + \alpha)$, where $R > 0$ (given in surd form) and $0 < \alpha < \frac{\pi}{2}$ (to 3 significant figures).

b) Hence solve $2 \sin 2\theta + 3 \cos 2\theta = 1$ in the interval $0 \leq \theta \leq 2\pi$.

Q2 b) Hint: Take care with the interval here to make sure you get all the correct solutions for θ.

Q3 a) Express $3 \sin \theta - 2\sqrt{5} \cos \theta$ in the form $R \sin (\theta - \alpha)$. Give R in surd form and α in degrees to 1 decimal place.

b) Hence solve $3 \sin \theta - 2\sqrt{5} \cos \theta = 5$ in the interval $0 \leq \theta \leq 360°$.

c) Find the maximum value of $f(x) = 3 \sin x - 2\sqrt{5} \cos x$ and the smallest positive value of x at which it occurs.

Q4 $f(x) = 3 \sin x + \cos x$.

a) Express $f(x)$ in the form $R \sin (x + \alpha)$ where $R > 0$ (given in surd form) and $0 < \alpha < 90°$ (to 1 d.p.).

b) Hence solve the equation $f(x) = 2$ in the interval $0 \leq x \leq 360°$.

c) State the maximum and minimum values of $f(x)$.

Q5 a) Express $4 \sin x + \cos x$ in the form $R \sin (x + \alpha)$, where $R > 0$ (given in surd form) and $0 < \alpha < \frac{\pi}{2}$ (to 3 significant figures).

b) Hence find the greatest value of $(4 \sin x + \cos x)^4$.

c) Solve the equation $4 \sin x + \cos x = 1$ for values of x in the interval $0 \leq x \leq \pi$.

Q6 $f(x) = 8 \cos x + 15 \sin x$.

a) Write $f(x)$ in the form $R\cos(x - \alpha)$, where $R > 0$ and $0 < \alpha < \frac{\pi}{2}$.

b) Solve the equation $f(x) = 5$ in the interval $0 \leq x \leq 2\pi$.

$g(x) = (8 \cos x + 15 \sin x)^2$

Q6 c) Hint: Think about what happens to the negative values when you square a function.

c) Find the minimum value of $g(x)$ and the smallest positive value of x at which it occurs.

Q7 The function g is given by $g(x) = 2 \cos x + \sin x$, $x \in \mathbb{R}$. $g(x)$ can be written as $R \cos (x - \alpha)$, where $R > 0$ and $0 < \alpha < 90°$.

a) Show that $R = \sqrt{5}$, and find the value of α (to 3 s.f.).

b) Hence state the range of $g(x)$.

Q7 b) Hint: This is just another way of asking for the maximum and minimum values of the function.

Q8 Express $3 \sin \theta - \frac{3}{2}\cos \theta$ in the form $R \sin (\theta - \alpha)$, where $R > 0$ and $0 < \alpha < \frac{\pi}{2}$, and hence solve the equation $3 \sin \theta - \frac{3}{2} \cos \theta = 3$ for values of θ in the interval $0 \leq \theta \leq 2\pi$.

Q9 Solve the equation $4 \sin 2\theta + 3 \cos 2\theta = 2$ for values of θ in the interval $0 \leq \theta \leq \pi$.

4. The Factor Formulas

Here come the last lot of trig formulas for this chapter. These ones are given to you in the exam so you don't need to learn them off by heart.

Proving and using the factor formulas

The trig identities shown below are called the **factor formulas**. They follow from the **addition formulas**, as shown in the proof below. They'll come in handy for some **integrations** — it's a bit tricky to integrate 2 cos 3θ cos θ, but integrating cos 4θ + cos 2θ is much easier.

Learning Objective:

▪ Know, and be able to use, the factor formulas for: sin A ± sin B, and cos A ± cos B.

Tip: You should know how to integrate sin, cos and tan from C3.

$$\sin A + \sin B \equiv 2 \sin\left(\frac{A+B}{2}\right)\cos\left(\frac{A-B}{2}\right)$$

$$\sin A - \sin B \equiv 2 \cos\left(\frac{A+B}{2}\right)\sin\left(\frac{A-B}{2}\right)$$

$$\cos A + \cos B \equiv 2 \cos\left(\frac{A+B}{2}\right)\cos\left(\frac{A-B}{2}\right)$$

$$\cos A - \cos B \equiv -2 \sin\left(\frac{A+B}{2}\right)\sin\left(\frac{A-B}{2}\right)$$

Example

Use the addition formulas to show that
$$\cos A + \cos B \equiv 2 \cos\left(\frac{A+B}{2}\right)\cos\left(\frac{A-B}{2}\right).$$

Tip: You can derive the other formulas using the same method.

▪ Start with the **cos addition formulas**:

$$\cos(x + y) \equiv \cos x \cos y - \sin x \sin y$$
$$\text{and}$$
$$\cos(x - y) \equiv \cos x \cos y + \sin x \sin y.$$

▪ **Add them together** to get:
$$\cos(x + y) + \cos(x - y)$$
$$\equiv \cos x \cos y - \sin x \sin y + \cos x \cos y + \sin x \sin y$$
$$\equiv 2\cos x \cos y.$$

▪ Now **substitute** in $A = x + y$ and $B = x - y$.

Subtracting these gives $A - B = x + y - (x - y) = 2y$, so $y = \dfrac{A-B}{2}$.

Adding gives $A + B = x + y + (x - y) = 2x$, so $x = \dfrac{A+B}{2}$.

▪ So $\cos A + \cos B = 2\cos\left(\dfrac{A+B}{2}\right)\cos\left(\dfrac{A-B}{2}\right)$.

Like the other trig identities in this chapter, the factor formulas come in useful when you need to find exact values without a calculator.

Example

Use a factor formula to write down the exact value of cos 105° + cos 15°.

- Use one of the **cos factor formulas**:

$$\cos A + \cos B = 2 \cos\left(\frac{A+B}{2}\right)\cos\left(\frac{A-B}{2}\right),$$

where A = 105° and B = 15°.

- Plug in the **numbers** to get:

$$\cos 105° + \cos 15° = 2 \cos\left(\frac{105° + 15°}{2}\right)\cos\left(\frac{105° - 15°}{2}\right)$$

$$\Rightarrow \cos 105° + \cos 15° = 2 \cos 60° \cos 45°$$

$$\Rightarrow \cos 105° + \cos 15° = 2 \times \left(\frac{1}{2}\right) \times \left(\frac{1}{\sqrt{2}}\right) = \boxed{\frac{1}{\sqrt{2}}}$$

Tip: Always be on the lookout for those common angles when you're asked for an exact value.

Exercise 4.1

Q1-3 Hint: The proofs are all similar to the one for cos A + cos B on the previous page.

Q1 Show that $\sin A + \sin B \equiv 2 \sin\left(\frac{A+B}{2}\right)\cos\left(\frac{A-B}{2}\right)$.

Q2 Show that $\sin A - \sin B \equiv 2 \cos\left(\frac{A+B}{2}\right)\sin\left(\frac{A-B}{2}\right)$.

Q3 Show that $\cos A - \cos B \equiv -2 \sin\left(\frac{A+B}{2}\right)\sin\left(\frac{A-B}{2}\right)$.

Q4 Use the factor formulas to show that $\sin 75° - \sin 15° = \frac{\sqrt{2}}{2}$.

Q5 Use the factor formulas to find the exact value of cos 165° − cos 75°.

Q6 a) Hint: Simplify the numerator first — find values of A and B such that $\frac{A+B}{2} = 140°$ and $\frac{A-B}{2} = 50°$.

Q6 Use the factor formulas to find the exact values of the following:

a) $\dfrac{\cos 140° \cos 50°}{\cos 190°}$

b) 2 sin 15° cos 75°

Q6 b) Hint: Switch round the cos and sin so that B is the smaller number.

Q7 Use the factor formulas to show that $4 \sin 52.5° \cos 7.5° = \sqrt{3} + \sqrt{2}$.

Q8 Use the factor formulas to show that $\dfrac{\cos\frac{\pi}{12} - \cos\frac{5\pi}{12}}{\sin\frac{5\pi}{12} + \sin\frac{\pi}{12}} = \dfrac{\sqrt{3}}{3}$.

Solving equations and proving other identities

The examples below show some of the ways the factor formulas can be used to simplify expressions and solve equations.

Examples

a) Express $4 \cos \theta \cos \frac{\theta}{5}$ as the sum of two cosines.

- Start with the **factor formula** for the **sum** of two **cosines**:

$$\cos A + \cos B \equiv 2 \cos \left(\frac{A + B}{2}\right) \cos \left(\frac{A - B}{2}\right)$$

$$\Rightarrow 2 \cos A + 2 \cos B \equiv 4 \cos \left(\frac{A + B}{2}\right) \cos \left(\frac{A - B}{2}\right)$$

- Comparing the expression with the **right-hand side** of the identity gives:

$$\textbf{(1)} \quad \theta = \left(\frac{A + B}{2}\right) \quad \text{and} \quad \textbf{(2)} \quad \frac{\theta}{5} = \left(\frac{A - B}{2}\right)$$

Tip: Note that $\left(\frac{A - B}{2}\right)$ corresponds to the smaller angle.

- Rearranging **(1)** gives: $A = 2\theta - B$

- Substituting in **(2)** gives: $\frac{\theta}{5} = \left(\frac{2\theta - B - B}{2}\right) = \theta - B \Rightarrow B = \frac{4\theta}{5}$

- Substituting this back into **(1)** to find A gives: $A = 2\theta - \frac{4\theta}{5} = \frac{6\theta}{5}$

- So $4 \cos \theta \cos \frac{\theta}{5} \equiv \boxed{2 \cos \frac{6\theta}{5} + 2 \cos \frac{4\theta}{5}}$.

b) Express $\sin 2\theta - \sin \frac{\theta}{3}$ as the product of sines and cosines.

- Start with the **factor formula** for the **difference** of two **sines**:

$$\sin A - \sin B \equiv 2 \cos \left(\frac{A + B}{2}\right) \sin \left(\frac{A - B}{2}\right)$$

- Comparing the expression with the **left-hand side** of the identity gives:

$$A = 2\theta \quad \text{and} \quad B = \frac{\theta}{3}$$

$$\frac{A + B}{2} = \frac{2\theta + \frac{\theta}{3}}{2} = \frac{7\theta}{6} \quad \text{and} \quad \frac{A - B}{2} = \frac{2\theta - \frac{\theta}{3}}{2} = \frac{5\theta}{6}$$

Tip: It's always a good idea to use the smaller angle as B so that $(A - B)$ is not negative. This might mean you have to swap things around.

- Putting this into the identity gives: $\boxed{\sin 2\theta - \sin \frac{\theta}{3} \equiv 2 \cos \frac{7\theta}{6} \sin \frac{5\theta}{6}}$

c) Use your answer to part b) to solve $\sin 2\theta - \sin \frac{\theta}{3} = 0$, for $0 \leq \theta \leq 360°$.

- This is the same as solving: $2 \cos \frac{7\theta}{6} \sin \frac{5\theta}{6} = 0$.

- Either... $\cos \frac{7\theta}{6} = 0 \Rightarrow \frac{7\theta}{6} = 90°, 270° \Rightarrow \boxed{\theta = 77.1°, 231.4° \text{ (1 d.p.)}}$

- ...or... $\sin \frac{5\theta}{6} = 0 \Rightarrow \frac{5\theta}{6} = 0°, 180°, 360° \Rightarrow \boxed{\theta = 0°, 216°}$

Tip: $\frac{5\theta}{6} = 360°$ gives a solution of $\theta = 432°$, but this is outside the given range.

Chapter 2 Trigonometry   45

You can also use the factor formulas to prove other identities.

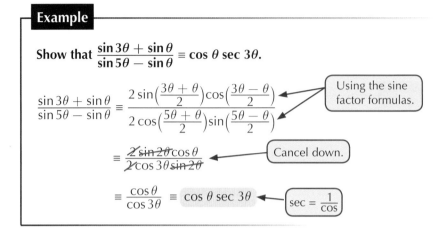

Example

Show that $\dfrac{\sin 3\theta + \sin \theta}{\sin 5\theta - \sin \theta} \equiv \cos \theta \sec 3\theta.$

$\dfrac{\sin 3\theta + \sin \theta}{\sin 5\theta - \sin \theta} \equiv \dfrac{2 \sin\left(\frac{3\theta + \theta}{2}\right)\cos\left(\frac{3\theta - \theta}{2}\right)}{2 \cos\left(\frac{5\theta + \theta}{2}\right)\sin\left(\frac{5\theta - \theta}{2}\right)}$ — Using the sine factor formulas.

$\equiv \dfrac{2\sin 2\theta \cos \theta}{2\cos 3\theta \sin 2\theta}$ — Cancel down.

$\equiv \dfrac{\cos \theta}{\cos 3\theta} \equiv \cos \theta \sec 3\theta$ — $\sec = \dfrac{1}{\cos}$

Exercise 4.2

Q1 Express the following as the sum or difference of two sines:

    a) $2 \sin 6\theta \cos 3\theta$ b) $2 \sin 8\theta \cos 4\theta$

    c) $2 \sin 3\theta \cos \theta$ d) $2 \cos 5\theta \sin 2\theta$

    e) $2 \cos 7\theta \sin 3\theta$ f) $2 \cos 12\theta \sin \frac{5}{2}\theta$

Q2 Express the following as the sum or difference of two cosines:

    a) $2 \cos 13\theta \cos 5\theta$ b) $2 \cos \frac{7}{2}\theta \cos \frac{1}{2}\theta$

    c) $2 \cos 17\theta \cos 2\theta$ d) $4 \cos 10\theta \cos 6\theta$

    e) $-2 \sin 13\theta \sin 9\theta$ f) $-2 \sin 15\theta \sin \frac{1}{2}\theta$

Q3 a) Express $\cos 5x - \cos 4x$ as the product of two sines.

    b) Use your answer to a) to solve $\dfrac{\cos 5x}{\cos 4x} = 1$ for $0 \le x \le 360°$.

Q4 a) Express $\cos 2x + \cos 3x$ as the product of two cosines.

    b) Use your answer to a) to solve $\cos 2x + \cos 3x = 0$ for $0 \le x \le 2\pi$.

Q5 Solve $\sin (x + 15°) \cos (x - 15°) = 0.5$ in the interval $0 \le x \le 180°$.

Q6 Hint: Use the factor formula on cos 6x + cos 4x, then factorise.

Q6 Solve $\cos 6x + \cos 4x + \cos x = 0$ in the interval $0 \le x \le \pi$.

Q7 Prove the following identities:

    a) $\dfrac{\sin 9x + \sin x}{\sin 8x + \sin 2x} \equiv \dfrac{\cos 4x}{\cos 3x}$

    b) $\dfrac{\sin 5x - \sin x}{\cos 5x + \cos x} \equiv \tan 2x$

    c) $\dfrac{\sin x + \sin y}{\cos x + \cos y} \equiv \tan\left(\dfrac{x + y}{2}\right)$

Review Exercise — Chapter 2

Q1 State the three different versions of the double angle formula for cos.

Q2 Using the addition formula for cos, find the exact value of $\cos \frac{\pi}{12}$.

Q3 Find $\sin (A + B)$, given that $\sin A = \frac{4}{5}$ and $\sin B = \frac{7}{25}$
and that both A and B are acute angles.
You might find these triangles useful:

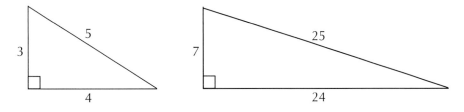

Q4 Use the double angle formula to solve the equation: $\sin 2\theta = -\sqrt{3} \sin \theta$, $0 \le \theta \le 360°$.

Q5 Solve the equations below in the interval $0 \le x \le 2\pi$.
Give your answers in radians to 3 significant figures.

> **Q5 Hint:** x is the 'double angle' here.

a) $4 \sin x = \sin \frac{x}{2}$
b) $\tan \frac{x}{2} \tan x = 2$

Q6 Solve the equations below in the interval $0 \le x \le 2\pi$.
Give your answers in radians in terms of π.

a) $2 \tan 2x = \tan x$
b) $\sin 6x - \cos 3x = 0$

> **Q6 b) Hint:** There are 12 solutions for this one.

Q7 Which two R formulas could you use to write $a \cos \theta + b \sin \theta$ $(a, b > 0)$
in terms of just sin or just cos?

Q8 Write $5 \sin \theta - 6 \cos \theta$ in the form $R \sin (\theta - \alpha)$, where $R > 0$ and $0 \le \alpha \le 90°$.

Q9 Show that $\frac{\cos \theta}{\sin \theta} + \frac{\sin \theta}{\cos \theta} \equiv 2 \csc 2\theta$.

1   a)   Write $9 \sin \theta + 12 \cos \theta$ in the form $R \sin (\theta + \alpha)$,
        where $R > 0$ and $0 \leq \alpha \leq \frac{\pi}{2}$.

        (3 marks)

    b)   Using the result from part a), solve $9 \sin \theta + 12 \cos \theta = 3$,
        giving all solutions for θ in the range $0 \leq \theta \leq 2\pi$.

        (5 marks)

2   Using the double angle and addition identities for sin and cos,
    find an expression for $\sin 3x$ in terms of $\sin x$ only.

    (4 marks)

3   **Figure 1** shows an isosceles triangle ABC with $AB = AC = 2\sqrt{2}$ cm and $\angle BAC = 2\theta$.
    The mid-points of AB and AC are D and E respectively. A rectangle $DEFG$ is drawn
    inscribed in the triangle, with F and G on BC. The perimeter of rectangle $DEFG$ is P cm.

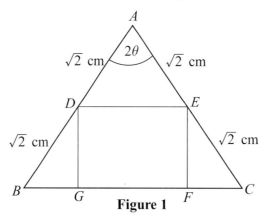

Figure 1

    a)   Using the cosine rule, $DE^2 = 4 - 4 \cos 2\theta$.
        Use a trigonometric identity to show that $DE = 2\sqrt{2} \sin \theta$.

        (2 marks)

    b)   Show that $P = 4\sqrt{2} \sin \theta + 2\sqrt{2} \cos \theta$.

        (2 marks)

    c)   Express P in the form $R \sin (\theta + \alpha)$ where $R > 0$ and $0 < \alpha < \frac{\pi}{2}$.

        (3 marks)

4   a)   Write $5 \cos \theta + 12 \sin \theta$ in the form $R \cos (\theta - \alpha)$,
        where $R > 0$ and $0 \leq \alpha \leq 90°$.

        (4 marks)

    b)   Hence solve $5 \cos \theta + 12 \sin \theta = 2$ for $0 \leq \theta \leq 360°$,
        giving your answers to 2 decimal places.

        (5 marks)

    c)   Use your results from part a) above to find the minimum value of
        $(5 \cos \theta + 12 \sin \theta)^3$.

        (2 marks)

1. Parametric Equations of Curves

Parametric equations are ones where you have x and y in separate equations, both defined in terms of another variable. It sounds complicated, but it can often make things a lot easier, as you'll see in this chapter.

Learning Objectives:

- Be able to calculate Cartesian coordinates for a curve given in parametric form.
- Be able to find the coordinates of intersection points between a parametric curve and other lines.

Finding coordinates from parametric equations

- Normally, graphs in the (x, y) plane are described using a **Cartesian equation** — a single equation linking x and y. Sometimes, particularly for more complicated graphs, it's easier to have two linked equations, called **parametric equations**.

- In parametric equations, x and y are each defined separately in terms of a **third variable**, called a **parameter**. The parameter is usually either t or θ.

- Parametric equations are often used to model the path of a moving particle, where its **position** (given by x and y) depends on time, t.

Example 1

Sketch the graph given by the parametric equations $y = t^3 - 1$ and $x = t + 1$.

- Start by making a **table of coordinates**.
  Choose some values for t and calculate x and y at these values:

t	-2	-1	0	1	2
x	-1	0	1	2	3
y	-9	-2	-1	0	7

$x = -2 + 1 = -1$,
and $y = (-2)^3 - 1 = -9$.

$x = 1 + 1 = 2$,
and $y = 1^3 - 1 = 0$.

- Now plot the **Cartesian (x, y) coordinates** on a set of axes as usual:

This point corresponds to $t = -1$. So, from the table, this is the point $(0, -2)$.

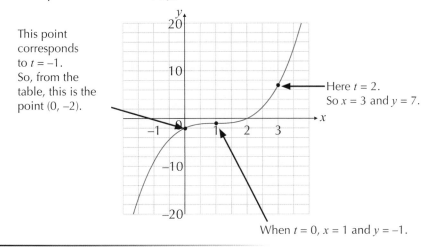

Here $t = 2$. So $x = 3$ and $y = 7$.

When $t = 0$, $x = 1$ and $y = -1$.

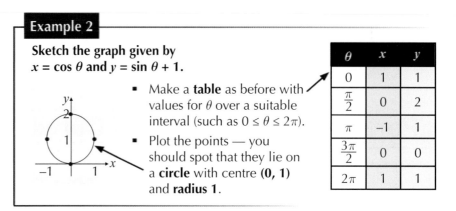

Example 2

Sketch the graph given by
$x = \cos\theta$ and $y = \sin\theta + 1$.

- Make a **table** as before with values for θ over a suitable interval (such as $0 \le \theta \le 2\pi$).
- Plot the points — you should spot that they lie on a **circle** with centre **(0, 1)** and **radius 1**.

θ	x	y
0	1	1
$\dfrac{\pi}{2}$	0	2
π	−1	1
$\dfrac{3\pi}{2}$	0	0
2π	1	1

Tip: $x = a + r\cos\theta$, $y = b + r\sin\theta$ are the general parametric equations for a circle with centre (a, b).
If r takes different values in the x and y equations, the curve is an ellipse.

You can use the parametric equations to find **coordinates** of points on a graph, and to find the value of the **parameter** for given x- or y-coordinates.

Examples

A curve is defined by the parametric equations $y = \dfrac{1}{3t}$ and $x = 2t - 3$, $t \ne 0$.

a) **Find the x- and y- values of the point the curve passes through when $t = 4$.**

Just **substitute** the value for t into the equations for x and y:

When $t = 4$: $\quad x = 2(4) - 3 = \boxed{5}$ and $y = \dfrac{1}{3(4)} = \boxed{\dfrac{1}{12}}$

b) **What value of t corresponds to the point where $y = 9$?**

When $y = 9$: $\quad 9 = \dfrac{1}{3t} \Rightarrow 3t = \dfrac{1}{9} \Rightarrow t = \dfrac{1}{3 \times 9} = \boxed{\dfrac{1}{27}}$

c) **What is the value of y when $x = -15$?**

Use the equation for x to find t first... $\quad -15 = 2t - 3 \Rightarrow t = -6$

...then use it in the other equation to find y: $\quad y = \dfrac{1}{3(-6)} = \boxed{-\dfrac{1}{18}}$

Exercise 1.1

Q1 A curve is defined by the parametric equations $x = 3t$, $y = t^2$.
   a) Find the coordinates of the point where $t = 5$.
   b) Find the value of t at the point where $x = 18$.
   c) Find the possible values of x at the point where $y = 36$.

Q2 A curve is defined by the parametric equations $x = 2t - 1$, $y = 4 - t^2$.
   a) Find the coordinates of the point where $t = 7$.
   b) Find the value of t at the point where $x = 15$.
   c) Find the possible values of x at the point where $y = -5$.

Q3 b) & c) Hint: There is only one acute value of θ possible in b) $(0 < \theta < \frac{\pi}{2})$, and only one obtuse value of θ possible in c) $(\frac{\pi}{2} < \theta < \pi)$.

Q3 A curve has parametric equations $x = 2 + \sin\theta$, $y = -3 + \cos\theta$.
   a) Find the coordinates of the point where $\theta = \dfrac{\pi}{4}$.
   b) Find the acute value of θ at the point where $x = \dfrac{4 + \sqrt{3}}{2}$.
   c) Find the obtuse value of θ at the point where $y = -\dfrac{7}{2}$.

Q4 A curve is defined by the parametric equations $x = 5 \cos 2t$, $y = 3 \sin t$.

a) Find the acute value(s) of t at the point where $x = \dfrac{5\sqrt{3}}{2}$.

b) Find two possible values of t at the point where $y = -\dfrac{3\sqrt{3}}{2}$.

Q5 Complete the table below, and hence sketch the curve represented by the parametric equations $x = 5t$, $y = \dfrac{2}{t}$.

t	−5	−4	−3	−2	−1	0	1	2	3	4	5
x											
y											

Q6 Complete the table below and hence sketch the curve represented by the parametric equations $x = t^2$, $y = t + 1$.

t	−5	−4	−3	−2	−1	0	1	2	3	4	5
x											
y											

Q7 Sketch the curve represented by the parametric equations $x = 1 + \sin \theta$, $y = 2 + \cos \theta$ for the values $0 \le \theta \le 2\pi$.
Use the table below to help you, and give your answers to 2 d.p.

Q7 Hint: Make sure your calculator's set to radians.

θ	0	$\dfrac{\pi}{4}$	$\dfrac{\pi}{3}$	$\dfrac{\pi}{2}$	$\dfrac{2\pi}{3}$	$\dfrac{3\pi}{4}$	π	$\dfrac{4\pi}{3}$	$\dfrac{3\pi}{2}$	$\dfrac{5\pi}{3}$	2π
x											
y											

Q8 Sketch the curve represented by the parametric equations $x = 3 \sin t$, $y = 5 \cos t$ for the values $0 \le t \le 2\pi$.
Use the table below to help you, giving your answers to 2 d.p.

t	0	$\dfrac{\pi}{4}$	$\dfrac{\pi}{2}$	$\dfrac{3\pi}{4}$	π	$\dfrac{5\pi}{4}$	$\dfrac{3\pi}{2}$	$\dfrac{7\pi}{4}$	2π
x									
y									

Q9 Sketch the curve $x = t - 1$, $y = 16 - t^2$ for the values $-5 \le t \le 5$.
Use a table of values if you need to.

Finding intersections

A lot of parametric equations questions involve identifying points on the curve defined by the equations. You'll often be given the parametric equations of a curve, and asked to find the coordinates of the **points of intersection** of this curve with another line (which could be the x- or y-axis).

Use the information in the question to **solve for** t at the intersection point(s). Then **substitute the value(s) of** t into the parametric equations to work out the **x and y values** (i.e. the **coordinates**) at the intersection point(s).

The example on the next page shows how to tackle a question like this.

The curve shown has the
parametric equations
$y = t^3 - t$ and $x = 4t^2 - 1$.

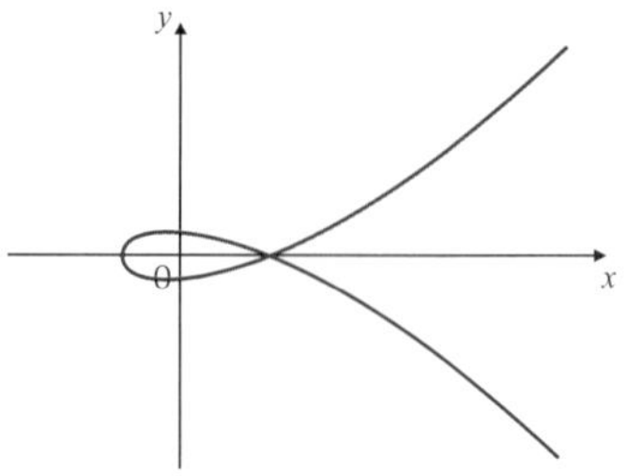

Find the coordinates of the points
where the graph crosses:
a) the x-axis,   b) the y-axis,
and c) the line $8y = 3x + 3$.

a) On the x-axis, $y = 0$.

- Use the parametric equation for y to find the values of t where the graph
  crosses the x-axis. This involves factorising and solving the cubic:
  $$0 = t^3 - t \Rightarrow t(t^2 - 1) = 0 \Rightarrow t(t + 1)(t - 1) = 0$$
  $$\Rightarrow t = 0, t = -1, t = 1$$

- Now use those values of t to find the x-coordinates:

  When $t = 0$: $x = 4(0)^2 - 1 = -1$
  When $t = -1$: $x = 4(-1)^2 - 1 = 3$
  When $t = 1$: $x = 4(1)^2 - 1 = 3$

Tip: $t = -1$ and $t = 1$
give the same coordinates
— that's where the curve
crosses over itself.

- So the graph crosses the x-axis at the points $(-1, 0)$ and $(3, 0)$.

b) On the y-axis, $x = 0$.

So: $0 = 4t^2 - 1 \Rightarrow t^2 = \frac{1}{4} \Rightarrow t = \pm\frac{1}{2}$

When $t = \frac{1}{2}$: $y = \left(\frac{1}{2}\right)^3 - \frac{1}{2} = -\frac{3}{8}$

When $t = -\frac{1}{2}$ $y = \left(-\frac{1}{2}\right)^3 - \left(-\frac{1}{2}\right) = \frac{3}{8}$

So the graph crosses the y-axis at the points $\left(0, -\frac{3}{8}\right)$ and $\left(0, \frac{3}{8}\right)$.

Tip: The sketch shows
there are two points
where the graph crosses
each axis.

c) Part c) is just a little trickier.

- First, **substitute** the **parametric equations** into $8y = 3x + 3$:
  $$8y = 3x + 3 \Rightarrow 8(t^3 - t) = 3(4t^2 - 1) + 3$$

- **Rearrange** and **factorise** to find the values of t you need:
  $$8t^3 - 8t = 12t^2 \Rightarrow 8t^3 - 12t^2 - 8t = 0 \Rightarrow t(2t + 1)(t - 2) = 0$$
  $$\Rightarrow t = 0, t = -\frac{1}{2}, t = 2$$

- Go back to the parametric equations to find the x- and y-coordinates:

  When $t = 0$: $x = -1, y = 0$
  When $t = -\frac{1}{2}$: $x = 4\left(\frac{1}{4}\right) - 1 = 0, y = \left(-\frac{1}{2}\right)^3 + \frac{1}{2} = \frac{3}{8}$
  When $t = 2$: $x = 4(4) - 1 = 15, y = 2^3 - 2 = 6$

Tip: You can check
the answers by sticking
these values back into
$8y = 3x + 3$.

- So the graph crosses the line $8y = 3x + 3$ at the following points:

$$(-1, 0), \left(0, \frac{3}{8}\right), (15, 6)$$

Q1   The curve with parametric equations $x = 3 + t$, $y = -2 + t$ meets the x-axis at the point A and the y-axis at the point B. Find the coordinates of A and B.

Q1 Hint: A lies on the x-axis and B lies on the y-axis, so in each case you know one of the coordinates.

Q2   The curve C has parametric equations $x = 2t^2 - 50$, $y = 3t^3 - 24$.

a) Find the value of t where the curve meets the x-axis.

b) Find the values of t where the curve meets the y-axis.

Q3   The curve with parametric equations $x = 64 - t^3$, $y = \dfrac{1}{t}$ meets the y-axis at the point P. Find the coordinates of the point P.

Q4   Find the coordinates of the point of intersection, P, of the line $y = x - 3$ and the curve with parametric equations $x = 2t + 1$, $y = 4t$.

Q4 Hint: Replace the x and y in the Cartesian equation with the parametric equations.

Q5   Find the coordinates of the point(s) of intersection of the curve $y = x^2 + 32$ and the curve with parametric equations $x = 2t$, $y = 6t^2$.

Q6   Find the points of intersection of the circle $x^2 + y^2 = 32$ and the curve with parametric equations $x = t^2$, $y = 2t$.

Q7   The curve with parametric equations $x = a(t - 2)$, $y = 2at^2 + 3$ (where $a \neq 0$), meets the y-axis at the point $(0, 4)$.

a) Find the value of the constant a.

b) Hence determine whether the curve meets the x-axis.

Q8   A curve has parametric equations $x = \dfrac{2}{t}$, $y = t^2 - 9$.

a) Find the point(s) at which the curve crosses the x-axis.

b) Does the curve meet the y-axis? Explain your answer.

c) Find the coordinates of the point(s) at which this curve meets the curve $y = \dfrac{10}{x} - 3$.

Q9   A curve has parametric equations $x = 3 \sin t$, $y = 5 \cos t$ and is defined for the domain $-2\pi \leq t \leq 2\pi$.

a) Determine the coordinates at which this curve meets the x- and y-axes.

b) Find the points where the curve meets the line $y = \left(\dfrac{5\sqrt{3}}{9} \right) x$.

2. Parametric and Cartesian Equations

As well as finding Cartesian coordinates for a curve given in parametric form, you might have to work out its Cartesian equation too.

Converting parametric equations to Cartesian equations

Some parametric equations can be **converted** into **Cartesian equations**. There are two main ways to do this:

> - **Rearrange** one of the equations to make the **parameter** the subject, then **substitute** the result into the **other** equation.

> - If your equations involve **trig functions**, use **trig identities** to **eliminate** the parameter.

Tip: You'll have come across loads of trig identities in both C2 and C3, as well as in Chapter 2 of this book. Look back if you need to refresh your memory.

You can use the first method to combine the parametric equations used in the examples on pages 49-50, as shown below.

Examples

Give the Cartesian equations, in the form $y = f(x)$, of the curves represented by the following pairs of parametric equations:

a) $y = t^3 - 1$ and $x = t + 1$,

b) $y = \dfrac{1}{3t}$ and $x = 2t - 3$, $t \neq 0$.

a) You want the answer in the form $y = f(x)$, so leave y alone for now, and **rearrange** the equation for x to **make t the subject**:

$$x = t + 1 \implies t = x - 1$$

Tip: Just replace every 't' in the equation for y with '$x - 1$'.

Now you can **eliminate** t from the equation for y:

$$y = t^3 - 1$$
$$\implies y = (x - 1)^3 - 1 = (x - 1)(x^2 - 2x + 1) - 1$$
$$\implies y = x^3 - 2x^2 + x - x^2 + 2x - 1 - 1$$
$$\implies y = x^3 - 3x^2 + 3x - 2$$

Tip: You could use the binomial theorem or Pascal's triangle to find the coefficients in the expansion of $(x - 1)^3$.

So the Cartesian equation is $\boxed{y = x^3 - 3x^2 + 3x - 2.}$

b) Use the same method as above:

$$x = 2t - 3 \implies t = \frac{x + 3}{2}$$

$$\text{So } y = \frac{1}{3t} \implies y = \frac{1}{3\left(\frac{x + 3}{2}\right)}$$

$$\implies y = \frac{1}{\left(\frac{3(x + 3)}{2}\right)} \quad \implies \quad \boxed{y = \frac{2}{3x + 9}}$$

Trigonometric functions

Things get a little trickier when the likes of sin and cos decide to put in an appearance. For trig functions you need to use **trig identities**.

Example 1

A curve has parametric equations $x = 1 + \sin \theta$, $y = 1 - \cos 2\theta$.
Give the Cartesian equation of the curve in the form $y = f(x)$.

- If you try to make θ the subject of these equations, things will just get messy. The trick is to find a way to get both x and y in terms of the **same trig function**. You can get $\sin \theta$ into the equation for y using the identity $\cos 2\theta \equiv 1 - 2 \sin^2 \theta$ (see page 31):

$$y = 1 - \cos 2\theta = 1 - (1 - 2 \sin^2 \theta) = 2 \sin^2 \theta$$

- **Rearranging** the equation for x gives: $\sin \theta = x - 1$

- **Replace** '$\sin \theta$' in the equation for y with '$x - 1$' to get y in terms of x:

$$y = 2 \sin^2 \theta \implies y = 2(x - 1)^2 = 2x^2 - 4x + 2$$

- So the **Cartesian equation** is $y = 2x^2 - 4x + 2$.

> **Tip:** If one of the parametric equations includes $\cos 2\theta$ or $\sin 2\theta$, that's probably the one you need to substitute — so make sure you know the **double angle formulas** from page 31.

Example 2

A curve is defined parametrically by $x = 4 \sec \theta$, $y = 4 \tan \theta$.
Give the equation of the curve in the form $y^2 = f(x)$, and hence determine whether the curve intersects the line $y + 3x = 4$.

- Start by **rearranging** each equation to make the **trig function** the subject:

$$x = 4 \sec \theta \implies \sec \theta = \frac{x}{4} \quad \text{and} \quad y = 4 \tan \theta \implies \tan \theta = \frac{y}{4}$$

- Find an **identity** that contains both **sec θ** and **tan θ**:

$$\sec^2 \theta \equiv 1 + \tan^2 \theta$$

- **Substitute** the trig functions with the x and y terms:

$$\left(\frac{x}{4}\right)^2 = 1 + \left(\frac{y}{4}\right)^2$$

- **Rearrange** to get an equation in the right form:

$$x^2 = 16 + y^2 \implies y^2 = x^2 - 16$$

- To see whether the curve intersects $y + 3x = 4$, **rearrange** to $y = 4 - 3x$ and **replace** in the equation of the curve:

$$(4 - 3x)^2 = x^2 - 16$$
$$\implies 16 - 24x + 9x^2 = x^2 - 16$$
$$\implies 8x^2 - 24x + 32 = 0$$
$$\implies x^2 - 3x + 4 = 0$$

- There are **no real roots** to this equation ($b^2 - 4ac < 0$), so the line and the curve **do not intersect**.

> **Tip:** Note that you're asked for the equation in the form $y^2 = f(x)$ not $y = f(x)$.

> **Tip:** The last bit comes from the **quadratic formula**. For a quadratic $ax^2 + bx + c = 0$, there are only real solutions when $b^2 - 4ac \geq 0$, because of the $\sqrt{b^2 - 4ac}$ bit in the formula.

Q1 For each of the following parametrically-defined curves, find the Cartesian equation of the curve in an appropriate form.

a) $x = t + 3, y = t^2$

b) $x = 3t, y = \dfrac{6}{t}$

c) $x = 2t^3, y = t^2$

d) $x = t + 7, y = 12 - 2t$

e) $x = t + 4, y = t^2 - 9$

f) $x = \sin \theta, y = \cos \theta$

g) $x = 1 + \sin \theta, y = 2 + \cos \theta$

h) $x = \sin \theta, y = \cos 2\theta$

i) $x = \cos \theta, y = \cos 2\theta$

j) $x = \cos \theta - 5, y = \cos 2\theta$

Q2 By eliminating the parameter θ, express the curve defined by the parametric equations $x = \tan \theta, y = \sec \theta$ in the form $y^2 = f(x)$.

Q3 Write the curve $x = 2 \cot \theta, y = 3 \csc \theta$ in the form $y^2 = f(x)$.

Q4 A circle is defined by the parametric equations $x = 5 + \sin \theta$, $y = -3 + \cos \theta$.

a) Find the coordinates of the centre of the circle, and the radius of the circle.

b) Write the equation of the curve in Cartesian form.

Q5 A curve has parametric equations $x = \dfrac{1 + 2t}{t}, y = \dfrac{3 + t}{t^2}$.

a) Express t in terms of x.

b) Hence show that the Cartesian equation of the curve is:
$y = (3x - 5)(x - 2)$.

c) Sketch the curve.

Q6 Express $x = \dfrac{2 - 3t}{1 + t}, y = \dfrac{5 - t}{4t + 1}$ in Cartesian form.

Q7 Find the Cartesian equation of the curve defined by the parametric equations $x = 5 \sin^2 \theta, y = \cos \theta$. Express your answer in the form $y^2 = f(x)$.

Q8 b) Hint: Find the x- and y-intercepts first — it will give you an idea of the graph's shape.

Q8 a) Express $x = a \sin \theta, y = b \cos \theta$ in Cartesian form.

b) Use your answer to a) to sketch the curve.

c) What type of curve has the form $x = a \sin \theta, y = b \cos \theta$?

Q9 A curve has parametric equations $x = 3t^2, y = 2t - 1$.

a) Show that the Cartesian equation of the curve is $x = \dfrac{3}{4}(y + 1)^2$.

b) Hence find the point(s) of intersection of this curve with the line $y = 4x - 3$.

Q10 Hint: You might need to look back at your notes on transformations of curves from C3 — it's much easier to sketch if you can transform a standard curve shape.

Q10 Find the Cartesian equation of the curve $x = 7t + 2, y = \dfrac{5}{t}$ in the form $y = f(x)$ and hence sketch the curve, labelling any asymptotes and points of intersection with the axes clearly.

Review Exercise — Chapter 3

Q1   A curve is defined by the parametric equations $x = \frac{1}{t}$, $y = \frac{2}{t^2}$ ($t \neq 0$).

   a) Find the value of t when $x = \frac{1}{4}$ and hence find the corresponding y-coordinate.

   b) Find the possible values of t when $y = \frac{1}{50}$.

Q2   A curve is defined by the parametric equations $y = 2t^2 + t + 4$ and $x = \frac{6-t}{2}$.

   a) Find the values of x and y when $t = 0, 1, 2$ and 3.

   b) What are the values of t when: (i) $x = -7$ (ii) $y = 19$?

   c) Find the Cartesian equation of the curve, in the form $y = f(x)$.

Q3   The parametric equations of a curve are $x = 2 \sin \theta$ and $y = \cos^2 \theta + 4$, $-\frac{\pi}{2} \leq \theta \leq \frac{\pi}{2}$.

   a) What are the coordinates of the points where: (i) $\theta = \frac{\pi}{4}$ (ii) $\theta = \frac{\pi}{6}$?

   b) What is the Cartesian equation of the curve?

   c) What restrictions are there on the values of x for this curve?

Q4   The curve C is defined by the parametric equations $x = \frac{\sin \theta}{3}$ and $y = 3 + 2 \cos 2\theta$.
   Find the Cartesian equation of C.

Q5   A curve has parametric equations $y = 4 + \frac{3}{t}$ and $x = t^2 - 1$ ($t \neq 0$).
   What are the coordinates of the points where this curve crosses:

   a) the y-axis

   b) the line $x + 2y = 14$?

Q6

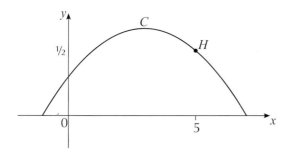

The parametric equations of curve C are

$$x = 3 + 4\sin\theta, \quad y = \frac{1 + \cos 2\theta}{3}, \quad -\frac{\pi}{2} \leq \theta \leq \frac{\pi}{2}.$$

Point H on C has coordinates $(5, \frac{1}{2})$.

   a) Find the value of θ at point H.

   b) Show that the Cartesian equation of C can be written $y = \frac{-x^2 + 6x + 7}{24}$.

   c) Find the domain of values of x for the curve C.

1   The curve C is defined by the parametric equations

$$x = 1 - \tan\theta, \quad y = \frac{1}{2}\sin 2\theta, \quad -\frac{\pi}{2} < \theta < \frac{\pi}{2}.$$

a) P is the point on curve C where $\theta = \frac{\pi}{3}$. Find the exact coordinates of P.

(2 marks)

b)   Point Q on curve C has coordinates $(2, -\frac{1}{2})$. Find the value of θ at Q.

(2 marks)

c)   Using the identity $\sin 2\theta \equiv \dfrac{2\tan\theta}{1 + \tan^2\theta}$,

show that the Cartesian equation of C is $y = \dfrac{1 - x}{x^2 - 2x + 2}$.

(3 marks)

2

Curve C has parametric equations $x = t^3 + t, \ y = t^2 - 2t + 2$.

a) K is a point on C, and has the coordinates $(a, 1)$. Find the value of a.

(2 marks)

b)   The line $8y = x + 6$ passes through C at points K, L and M.
Find the coordinates of L and M, given that the x-coordinate of M is
greater than the x-coordinate of L.

(6 marks)

3

The curve C has parametric equations

$$x = t^3, \quad y = t^2 - 4.$$

a)   At the point F, t has the value 0.5. Find the coordinates of F.

(2 marks)

b)   The line $3y = 2x - 11$ meets C twice.
Find the coordinates of the points of intersection.

(6 marks)

Chapter 4

1. The Binomial Expansion

You might well recognise binomial expansions from C2. This chapter should refresh your memory on the formula and take it a step further — including what to do if you have to raise an expression to a fractional or negative power.

Expansions where n is a positive integer

The **binomial expansion** is a way to raise a given expression to any power.

For simpler cases it's basically a fancy way of multiplying out brackets.
You can also use it to approximate more complicated expressions.

This is the **general formula** for binomial expansions:

$$(1 + x)^n = 1 + nx + \frac{n(n - 1)}{1 \times 2}x^2 + ... + \frac{n(n - 1)...(n - r + 1)}{1 \times 2 \times ... \times r}x^r + ...$$

From the general formula, it looks like the expansion always goes on forever.
But if *n* **is a positive integer**, the binomial expansion is **finite**.

Learning Objectives:

- Be able to expand $(p + qx)^n$ for any rational n using the general formula for binomial expansions.

- Be able to state the validity of the expansion — i.e. the values of x for which the expansion is valid.

Example 1

Give the binomial expansion of $(1 + x)^5$.

Use the **general formula** and plug in *n* = 5:

$n = 5$ $n(n - 1)$

$$(1 + x)^5 = 1 + 5x + \frac{5(5 - 1)}{1 \times 2}x^2 + \frac{5(5 - 1)(5 - 2)}{1 \times 2 \times 3}x^3$$

$$+ \frac{5(5 - 1)(5 - 2)(5 - 3)}{1 \times 2 \times 3 \times 4}x^4 + \frac{5(5 - 1)(5 - 2)(5 - 3)(5 - 4)}{1 \times 2 \times 3 \times 4 \times 5}x^5$$

$$+ \frac{5(5 - 1)(5 - 2)(5 - 3)(5 - 4)(5 - 5)}{1 \times 2 \times 3 \times 4 \times 5 \times 6}x^6 + ...$$

$$= 1 + 5x + \frac{5 \times 4}{1 \times 2}x^2 + \frac{5 \times 4 \times 3}{1 \times 2 \times 3}x^3 + \frac{5 \times 4 \times 3 \times 2}{1 \times 2 \times 3 \times 4}x^4$$

$$+ \frac{5 \times 4 \times 3 \times 2 \times 1}{1 \times 2 \times 3 \times 4 \times 5}x^5 + \frac{5 \times 4 \times 3 \times 2 \times 1 \times 0}{1 \times 2 \times 3 \times 4 \times 5 \times 6}x^6 + ...$$

> You can stop here — all the terms after this one are **zero**.

$$= 1 + 5x + \frac{20}{2}x^2 + \frac{60}{6}x^3 + \frac{120}{24}x^4 + \frac{120}{120}x^5 + \frac{0}{720}x^6 + ...$$

$$= 1 + 5x + 10x^2 + 10x^3 + 5x^4 + x^5$$

Tip: It may seem a bit dull to write all the steps out in this way for simple expansions, but it's important for more complex ones to make sure you don't miss anything out.

Tip: The expansion is finite because at some point you introduce an $(n - n)$ (i.e. zero) term in the numerator which then appears in every coefficient from that point on, making them all zero.

The formula still works if the coefficient of x **isn't 1**, i.e. $(1 + ax)^n$ — just **replace** each 'x' in the formula with **(ax)**. The 'a' should be raised to the **same power** as the 'x' in each term, and included in the coefficient when you simplify at the end. This next example shows you how it's done.

Example 2

Give the binomial expansion of $(1 - 3x)^4$.

Use the **formula** with **$n = 4$**, but replace every x with **$-3x$**. Think of this as $(1 + (-3x))^4$ — put the **minus** into the formula as well as the $3x$.

$n = 4 \qquad n(n-1)$

$$(1 - 3x)^4 = 1 + 4(-3x) + \frac{4 \times 3}{1 \times 2}(-3x)^2 + \frac{4 \times 3 \times 2}{1 \times 2 \times 3}(-3x)^3$$

$$+ \frac{4 \times 3 \times 2 \times 1}{1 \times 2 \times 3 \times 4}(-3x)^4 + \frac{4 \times 3 \times 2 \times 1 \times 0}{1 \times 2 \times 3 \times 4 \times 5}(-3x)^5 + \dots$$

Don't forget to square the -3 as well. $\qquad$ Stop here.

$$= 1 + 4(-3x) + \frac{12}{2}(9x^2) + \frac{4}{1}(-27x^3) + (81x^4) + \frac{0}{5}(-243x^5) + \dots$$

$$= 1 - 12x + 54x^2 - 108x^3 + 81x^4$$

Tip: Make life easier for yourself by cancelling down the fractions before you multiply.

Validity

Some binomial expansions are **only valid for certain values of x**. When you find a binomial expansion, you usually have to state which values of x the expansion is valid for.

Tip: So far you've only dealt with expansions of $(p + qx)^n$ where p is 1, but there are more complicated examples to come on page 65.

> If n is a **positive integer**, the binomial expansion of $(p + qx)^n$ is valid for **all values of x**.

There's more on the validity of other expansions on page 62.

Exercise 1.1

Use the binomial expansion formula to expand each of the following functions in ascending powers of x.

Q1 Expand fully: $(1 + x)^3$

Q2 Expand $(1 + x)^7$ up to and including the term in x^3.

Q3 Expand fully: $(1 - x)^4$

Q3 Hint: Watch out for that minus sign — replace 'x' in the formula with $(-x)$.

Q4 Give the first 3 terms of $(1 + 3x)^6$.

Q5 Give the first 4 terms of $(1 + 2x)^8$.

Q6 Expand $(1 - 5x)^5$ up to and including the term in x^2.

Q7 Expand fully: $(1 - 4x)^3$

Q8 Expand $(1 + 6x)^6$ up to and including the term in x^3.

Expansions where n is negative or a fraction

n is negative

If n is **negative**, the expansion gets more complicated. You can still use the **formula** in the same way, but it will produce an **infinite** number of terms (see the example below). You can just write down the **first few terms** in the series, but this will only be an **approximation** to the whole expansion.

This type of expansion can be 'hidden' as a fraction — remember:

$$\frac{1}{(1+x)^n} = (1+x)^{-n}$$

Tip: The question will usually tell you how many terms to give.

Example

Find the binomial expansion of $\dfrac{1}{(1+x)^2}$ up to and including the term in x^3.

- First, **rewrite** the expression: $\dfrac{1}{(1+x)^2} = (1+x)^{-2}$.

- Now you can use the **general formula**. This time $n = -2$:

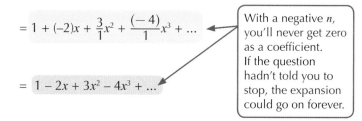

$$n = -2 \qquad n(n-1)$$

$$(1+x)^{-2} = 1 + (-2)x + \frac{(-2)\times(-2-1)}{1\times 2}x^2$$
$$+ \frac{(-2)\times(-2-1)\times(-2-2)}{1\times 2\times 3}x^3 + \dots$$

$$= 1 + (-2)x + \frac{(-2)\times(-3)}{1\times 2}x^2 + \frac{(-2)\times(-3)\times(-4)}{1\times 2\times 3}x^3 + \dots$$

$$= 1 + (-2)x + \frac{3}{1}x^2 + \frac{(-4)}{1}x^3 + \dots$$

$$= 1 - 2x + 3x^2 - 4x^3 + \dots$$

With a negative n, you'll never get zero as a coefficient. If the question hadn't told you to stop, the expansion could go on forever.

Tip: Again, you can cancel down before you multiply — but be careful with those minus signs.

- We've left out all the terms after $-4x^3$, so the cubic expression you've ended up with is an **approximation** to the original expression.
- You could also write the answer like this:

$$\frac{1}{(1+x)^2} \approx 1 - 2x + 3x^2 - 4x^3$$

---

n is a fraction

The binomial expansion formula doesn't just work for integer values of n. If n is a **fraction**, you'll have to take care multiplying out the fractions in the coefficients, but otherwise the formula is **exactly the same**.

Remember that **roots** are fractional powers:

$$\sqrt[n]{1+x} = (1+x)^{\frac{1}{n}}$$

Example

Find the binomial expansion of $\sqrt[3]{1 + 2x}$, up to and including the term in x^3.

- First rewrite the expression as a fractional power: $\sqrt[3]{1 + 2x} = (1 + 2x)^{\frac{1}{3}}$

- This time $n = \frac{1}{3}$, and you also need to replace x with $2x$:

$n = \frac{1}{3}$ $n(n-1)$

$$(1 + 2x)^{\frac{1}{3}} = 1 + \frac{1}{3}(2x) + \frac{\frac{1}{3} \times \left(\frac{1}{3} - 1\right)}{1 \times 2}(2x)^2$$

$$+ \frac{\frac{1}{3} \times \left(\frac{1}{3} - 1\right) \times \left(\frac{1}{3} - 2\right)}{1 \times 2 \times 3}(2x)^3 + \dots$$

$$= 1 + \frac{2}{3}x + \frac{\frac{1}{3} \times \left(-\frac{2}{3}\right)}{1 \times 2}(4x^2) + \frac{\frac{1}{3} \times \left(-\frac{2}{3}\right) \times \left(-\frac{5}{3}\right)}{1 \times 2 \times 3}(8x^3) + \dots$$

$$= 1 + \frac{2}{3}x + \frac{\left(-\frac{2}{9}\right)}{2}(4x^2) + \frac{\left(\frac{10}{27}\right)}{6}(8x^3) + \dots$$

$$= 1 + \frac{2}{3}x + \left(-\frac{1}{9}\right)(4x^2) + \left(\frac{5}{81}\right)(8x^3) + \dots$$

$$= 1 + \frac{2}{3}x - \frac{4}{9}x^2 + \frac{40}{81}x^3 - \dots$$

Tip: Cancelling down is much trickier with this type of expansion — it's often safer to multiply everything out fully.

Validity when n is negative or a fraction

Binomial expansions where n is negative or a fraction are **not valid** for **all** values of x. The **rule** to work out the validity of an expansion is as follows:

> If n is a negative integer or a fraction,
> the binomial expansion of $(p + qx)^n$ is **valid** when $\left|\frac{qx}{p}\right| < 1$,
> i.e. when $|x| < \left|\frac{p}{q}\right|$.

Tip: You might already know the rules
$|ab| = |a||b|$
and $\left|\frac{a}{b}\right| = \frac{|a|}{|b|}$.

If you don't, then get to know them — they're handy for rearranging these limits.

This just means that the **absolute value** (or **modulus**) of x (i.e. ignoring any negative signs) must be **smaller** than the absolute value of $\frac{p}{q}$ for the expansion to be valid.

Tip: When n is negative or a fraction, binomial expansions are infinite — so the few terms you write down are only an approximation. This approximation is only valid if the sequence converges — this only happens if x is small enough (i.e. if $|x| < \left|\frac{p}{q}\right|$).

Examples

State the validity of the expansions given in the previous two examples.

a) For the expansion $(1 + x)^{-2} = 1 - 2x + 3x^2 - 4x^3 + \dots$, $p = 1$ and $q = 1$.

So the expansion is valid if $\left|\frac{1x}{1}\right| < 1$, i.e. if $|x| < 1$.

b) For $(1 + 2x)^{\frac{1}{3}} = 1 + \frac{2}{3}x - \frac{4}{9}x^2 + \frac{40}{81}x^3 - \dots$, $p = 1$ and $q = 2$.

So the expansion is valid if $|2x| < 1 \Rightarrow 2|x| < 1 \Rightarrow |x| < \frac{1}{2}$.

Combinations of expansions

- You can use the binomial expansion formula for more complicated combinations of expansions — e.g. where different brackets raised to different powers are **multiplied together**.
- Start by dealing with the different expansions **separately**, then **multiply** the expressions together at the end.
- For situations where one bracket is being **divided** by another, change the **sign** of the **power** and **multiply** instead (e.g. $\dfrac{(1 + x)}{(1 + 2x)^3} = (1 + x)(1 + 2x)^{-3}$).
- For the **combined** expansion to be **valid**, x must be in the valid range for **both** expansions, i.e. where they overlap. In practice this just means sticking to the **narrowest** of the valid ranges for each separate expansion.

Tip: You'll usually be asked to give the expansion to a specified number of terms, so the multiplication shouldn't get too complicated as you can ignore terms in higher powers of x.

Example

Write down the first three terms in the expansion of $\dfrac{(1 + 2x)^3}{(1 - x)^2}$.

State the range of x for which the expansion is valid.

- First re-write the expression as a product of two expansions:
$$\frac{(1 + 2x)^3}{(1 - x)^2} = (1 + 2x)^3 (1 - x)^{-2}$$

- Expand each of these separately using the formula:

$$(1 + 2x)^3 = 1 + 3(2x) + \frac{3 \times 2}{1 \times 2}(2x)^2 + \frac{3 \times 2 \times 1}{1 \times 2 \times 3}(2x)^3$$
$$= 1 + 6x + 3(4x^2) + 8x^3 = 1 + 6x + 12x^2 + 8x^3$$

$$(1 - x)^{-2} = 1 + (-2)(-x) + \frac{(-2) \times (-3)}{1 \times 2}(-x)^2 + \frac{(-2) \times (-3) \times (-4)}{1 \times 2 \times 3}(-x)^3 + \ldots$$
$$= 1 + 2x + 3x^2 + 4x^3 + \ldots$$

Tip: You actually only need to go up to the term in x^2 in each expansion (as you're only asked for the first three terms), but make sure you don't cut your expansion too short — it's better to expand too many terms than too few.

- **Multiply** the two expansions together. Since you're only asked for the **first three terms**, ignore any terms with **higher powers** of x than x^2.

$$(1 + 2x)^3(1 - x)^{-2} = (1 + 6x + 12x^2 + 8x^3)(1 + 2x + 3x^2 + 4x^3 + \ldots)$$
$$= 1(1 + 2x + 3x^2) + 6x(1 + 2x) + 12x^2(1) + \ldots$$
$$= 1 + 2x + 3x^2 + 6x + 12x^2 + 12x^2 + \ldots$$
$$= \boxed{1 + 8x + 27x^2 + \ldots}$$

Tip: Notice that you can cut down on the amount of working at this stage by leaving out of the brackets any terms that, when multiplied out, would give you an x^3 term or higher.

- Now find the **validity** of each expansion:

$(1 + 2x)^3$ is valid for all values of x, since n is a positive integer.

$(1 - x)^{-2}$ is valid if $|-x| < 1 \Rightarrow |x| < 1$.

So the combined expression $\dfrac{(1 + 2x)^3}{(1 - x)^2}$ is only valid if $\boxed{|x| < 1}$,

since this is the narrower range of the two separate expansions.

Q1 Use the binomial formula to find the first four terms in the expansion of $(1 + x)^{-4}$.

Q2 a) Find the binomial expansion of $(1 - 6x)^{-3}$, up to and including the term in x^3.

b) For what values of x is this expansion valid?

Q3 Use the binomial formula to find the first three terms in the expansion of:

a) $(1 + 4x)^{\frac{1}{3}}$

b) $(1 + 4x)^{-\frac{1}{2}}$

c) For each of the expansions above, state the range of x for which the expansion is valid.

Q4 Find the binomial expansion of the following functions, up to and including the term in x^3.

a) $\dfrac{1}{(1 - 4x)^2}$ for $|x| < \dfrac{1}{4}$

b) $\sqrt{1 + 6x}$ for $|x| < \dfrac{1}{6}$

c) $\dfrac{1}{\sqrt{1 - 3x}}$ for $|x| < \dfrac{1}{3}$

d) $\sqrt[3]{1 + \dfrac{x}{2}}$ for $|x| < 2$

Q5 a) Find the coefficient of the x^3 term in the expansion of $\dfrac{1}{(1 + 7x)^4}$.

b) For what range of x is this expansion valid?

Q5-6 Hint: You don't need to bother doing the full expansion — just work out the coefficient of the term you need.

Q6 a) What is the coefficient of x^5 in the expansion of $\sqrt[4]{1 - 4x}$?

b) For what values of x is the binomial expansion of $\sqrt[4]{1 - 4x}$ valid?

Q7 a) Write down the first three terms of the expansion of $(1 - 5x)^{\frac{1}{6}}$.

b) Hence find the binomial expansion of $(1 + 4x)^4 (1 - 5x)^{\frac{1}{6}}$, up to and including the term in x^2.

c) State the validity of the expansion in b).

Q8 a) Find the first three terms of the binomial expansion of $\dfrac{(1 + 3x)^4}{(1 + x)^3}$.

b) State the range of x for which the expansion is valid.

Expanding $(p + qx)^n$

- You've seen over the last few pages that the general binomial expansion of $(1 + x)^n$ works for **any n**, and that you can replace the x with other x-terms.

- However, the 1 at the start **has to be a 1** before you can expand.

- If it's **not a 1**, you'll need to **factorise first** before you can use the formula.

- This means you have to rewrite the expression as follows:

$$(p + qx)^n = p^n\left(1 + \frac{qx}{p}\right)^n$$

Tip: This rearrangement uses the power law $(ab)^k = a^k b^k$ — note that the p outside the brackets is still raised to the power n.

Example 1

Give the binomial expansion of $(3 - x)^4$ and state its validity.

- To use the general formula, you need the constant term in the brackets to be 1. You can take the 3 outside the brackets by factorising:

$$3 - x = 3\left(1 - \frac{1}{3}x\right)$$

$$\Rightarrow (3 - x)^4 = \left[3\left(1 - \frac{1}{3}x\right)\right]^4$$

The aim here is to get an expression in the form $c(1 + dx)^n$, where c and d are constants.

$$= 3^4\left(1 - \frac{1}{3}x\right)^4$$

$$= 81\left(1 - \frac{1}{3}x\right)^4$$

Tip: Don't forget to raise the 3 to the power 4.

- Now use the general formula, with $n = 4$, and $-\frac{1}{3}x$ instead of x:

$$\left(1 - \frac{1}{3}x\right)^4 = 1 + 4\left(-\frac{1}{3}x\right) + \frac{4 \times 3}{1 \times 2}\left(-\frac{1}{3}x\right)^2 + \frac{4 \times 3 \times 2}{1 \times 2 \times 3}\left(-\frac{1}{3}x\right)^3$$
$$+ \frac{4 \times 3 \times 2 \times 1}{1 \times 2 \times 3 \times 4}\left(-\frac{1}{3}x\right)^4$$

$$= 1 - \frac{4}{3}x + 6\left(\frac{1}{9}x^2\right) + 4\left(-\frac{1}{27}x^3\right) + \frac{1}{81}x^4$$

$$= 1 - \frac{4x}{3} + \frac{2x^2}{3} - \frac{4x^3}{27} + \frac{x^4}{81}$$

- Finally, put this back into the original expression:

$$(3 - x)^4 = 81\left(1 - \frac{1}{3}x\right)^4$$

$$= 81\left(1 - \frac{4x}{3} + \frac{2x^2}{3} - \frac{4x^3}{27} + \frac{x^4}{81}\right)$$

$$= 81 - 108x + 54x^2 - 12x^3 + x^4$$

Tip: For this example, you could just pop $a = 3$ and $b = -x$ into the formula for $(a + b)^n$, which will be given to you in the exam. This formula only works when n is a positive integer though, so you'll need to use the method shown here if the power is negative or a fraction.

- The expansion is valid for **all values of x**.

  This is because n is a positive integer — so the expansion is finite.

Example 2

Give the first 3 terms in the binomial expansion of $(3x + 4)^{\frac{3}{2}}$.

- Again, you need to **factorise** before using the formula, taking care to choose the **right factor**...

$$3x + 4 = 4 + 3x = 4\left(1 + \frac{3}{4}x\right)$$

> Make sure you've got the bracket written in the form $(p + qx)^n$ before you factorise.

$$\Rightarrow (3x + 4)^{\frac{3}{2}} = \left[4\left(1 + \frac{3}{4}x\right)\right]^{\frac{3}{2}}$$

$$= 4^{\frac{3}{2}}\left(1 + \frac{3}{4}x\right)^{\frac{3}{2}}$$

$$= 8\left(1 + \frac{3}{4}x\right)^{\frac{3}{2}}$$

Tip: It's tempting to take the 3 outside the brackets because of the order the numbers are written in, but don't be fooled.

- Use the **general formula** with $n = \frac{3}{2}$, and $\frac{3}{4}x$ instead of x:

$$\left(1 + \frac{3}{4}x\right)^{\frac{3}{2}} = 1 + \frac{3}{2}\left(\frac{3}{4}x\right) + \frac{\frac{3}{2} \times \left(\frac{3}{2} - 1\right)}{1 \times 2}\left(\frac{3}{4}x\right)^2 + \ldots$$

$$= 1 + \frac{9}{8}x + \frac{\frac{3}{2} \times \frac{1}{2}}{2}\left(\frac{9}{16}x^2\right) + \ldots$$

$$= 1 + \frac{9x}{8} + \frac{27x^2}{128} + \ldots$$

- Put this back into the **original expression**:

$$(3x + 4)^{\frac{3}{2}} = 8\left(1 + \frac{3}{4}x\right)^{\frac{3}{2}} = 8\left(1 + \frac{9x}{8} + \frac{27x^2}{128} + \ldots\right)$$

$$= 8 + 9x + \frac{27x^2}{16} + \ldots$$

Tip: This expansion is only valid for $\left|\frac{qx}{p}\right| < 1$, i.e. $\left|\frac{3x}{4}\right| < 1 \Rightarrow |x| < \frac{4}{3}$.

Example 3

Expand $\dfrac{1 + 2x}{(2 - x)^2}$ up to the term in x^3.

State the range of x for which the expansion is valid.

- First you need to **rearrange** and **separate** the different expansions:

$$\frac{1 + 2x}{(2 - x)^2} = (1 + 2x)(2 - x)^{-2}$$
$$p = 2 \quad q = -1$$

- The first bracket doesn't need expanding, so deal with the second bracket as usual, **factorising** first...

$$2 - x = 2\left(1 - \frac{1}{2}x\right) \quad \Rightarrow \quad (2 - x)^{-2} = 2^{-2}\left(1 - \frac{1}{2}x\right)^{-2} = \frac{1}{4}\left(1 - \frac{1}{2}x\right)^{-2}$$

Tip: For expressions where both brackets need expanding, just take your time and set everything out in steps, only combining the expansions at the end.

- ... then using the **formula** with $n = -2$, and $-\frac{1}{2}x$ instead of x:

$$\left(1 - \frac{1}{2}x\right)^{-2} = 1 + (-2)\left(-\frac{1}{2}x\right) + \frac{-2 \times -3}{1 \times 2}\left(-\frac{1}{2}x\right)^2$$

$$+ \frac{-2 \times -3 \times -4}{1 \times 2 \times 3}\left(-\frac{1}{2}x\right)^3 + \ldots$$

$$= 1 + x + \frac{3x^2}{4} + \frac{x^3}{2} + \ldots$$

- So this means that:

$$(2 - x)^{-2} = \frac{1}{4}\left(1 - \frac{1}{2}x\right)^{-2} = \frac{1}{4}\left(1 + x + \frac{3x^2}{4} + \frac{x^3}{2} + \ldots\right)$$

$$= \frac{1}{4} + \frac{x}{4} + \frac{3x^2}{16} + \frac{x^3}{8} + \ldots$$

- Putting all this into the **original expression** gives:

$$\frac{1 + 2x}{(2 - x)^2} = (1 + 2x)(2 - x)^{-2} = (1 + 2x)\left(\frac{1}{4} + \frac{x}{4} + \frac{3x^2}{16} + \frac{x^3}{8} + \ldots\right)$$

$$= \frac{1}{4} + \frac{x}{4} + \frac{3x^2}{16} + \frac{x^3}{8} + 2x\left(\frac{1}{4} + \frac{x}{4} + \frac{3x^2}{16}\right) + \ldots$$

$$= \frac{1}{4} + \frac{x}{4} + \frac{3x^2}{16} + \frac{x^3}{8} + \frac{x}{2} + \frac{x^2}{2} + \frac{3x^3}{8} + \ldots$$

$$= \frac{1}{4} + \frac{3x}{4} + \frac{11x^2}{16} + \frac{x^3}{2} + \ldots$$

- The **validity** of the whole expansion will depend on the validity of the expansion of $(2 - x)^{-2}$.

    This is valid only if $\left|\frac{-x}{2}\right| < 1 \Rightarrow |x| < 2$

Tip: Remember — if both expansions have a limited validity, choose the one with the narrower valid range of x for the combined expansion.

Exercise 1.3

Q1 Find the binomial expansion of the following functions, up to and including the term in x^3:

a) $(2 + 4x)^3$ b) $(3 + 4x)^5$

c) $(4 + x)^{\frac{1}{2}}$ d) $(8 + 2x)^{-\frac{1}{3}}$

Q2 If the x^2 coefficient of the binomial expansion of $(a + 5x)^5$ is 2000, what is the value of a?

Q2 Hint: Work out the x^2 term of the expansion in terms of a.

Q3 a) Find the binomial expansion of $(2 - 5x)^7$ up to and including the term in x^2.

     b) Hence, or otherwise, find the binomial expansion of $(1 + 6x)^3(2 - 5x)^7$, up to and including the term in x^2.

Q4 a) Find the binomial expansion of $\left(1 + \frac{6}{5}x\right)^{-\frac{1}{2}}$, up to and including the term in x^3, stating the range of x for which it is valid.

     b) Hence, or otherwise, express $\sqrt{\dfrac{20}{5 + 6x}}$ in the form $a + bx + cx^2 + dx^3 + \ldots$

Q4 b) Hint: Rewrite the expression in the form $z\left(1 + \frac{6}{5}x\right)^{-\frac{1}{2}}$, where z is a number or another expression.

Q5 $f(x) = \dfrac{1}{\sqrt{5 - 2x}}$

     a) Find the binomial expansion of $f(x)$ in ascending powers of x, up to and including the term in x^2.

     b) Hence show that $\dfrac{3 + x}{\sqrt{5 - 2x}} \approx \dfrac{3}{\sqrt{5}} + \dfrac{8x}{5\sqrt{5}} + \dfrac{19x^2}{50\sqrt{5}}$.

Q6 a) Find the binomial expansion of $(9 + 4x)^{-\frac{1}{2}}$, up to and including the term in x^2.

     b) Hence, or otherwise, find the binomial expansion of $\dfrac{(1 + 6x)^4}{\sqrt{9 + 4x}}$, up to and including the term in x^2.

2. Using the Binomial Expansion as an Approximation

Learning Objective:

- Be able to substitute values into a binomial expansion in order to find approximations.

One of the reasons that binomial expansions are so useful is that they can be used to estimate nasty-looking roots, powers and fractions. All you need to work out is the right value of x to use.

Approximating with binomial expansions

- When you've done an expansion, you can use it to work out the **value** of the original expression for **given values of** x, by **substituting** those values into the **expansion**.

- For most expansions this will only be an **approximate** answer, because you'll have had to limit the expansion to the first few terms.

- Often you'll have to do some **rearranging** of the expression so that you know what value of x to substitute.

Tip: You also need to check the validity of the expansion — the approximation will only work for values of x in the valid range.

- For example, $\sqrt[3]{1.3}$ can be written as $(1 + 0.3)^{\frac{1}{3}}$, which can be approximated by expanding $(1 + x)^{\frac{1}{3}}$ and substituting $x = 0.3$ into the expansion.

Example 1

The binomial expansion of $(1 + 3x)^{-1}$ up to the term in x^3 is:

$(1 + 3x)^{-1} \approx 1 - 3x + 9x^2 - 27x^3$. The expansion is valid for $|x| < \frac{1}{3}$.

Use this expansion to approximate $\frac{100}{103}$. Give your answer to 4 d.p.

- For this type of question, you need to find the **right value of** x to make the expression you're expanding equal to the thing you're looking for.

- This means a bit of clever **rearranging**:

$$\frac{100}{103} = \frac{1}{1.03} = \frac{1}{1 + 0.03} = (1 + 0.03)^{-1}$$

- This is the same as an expansion of $(1 + 3x)^{-1}$ with $3x = 0.03 \Rightarrow x = 0.01$.

- Check that this value is in the **valid range**:

$$0.01 < \frac{1}{3}, \text{ so the expansion is valid for this value of } x.$$

- **Substituting** this value for x into the expansion gives:

$$(1 + 3(0.01))^{-1} \approx 1 - 3(0.01) + 9(0.01^2) - 27(0.01^3)$$

$$= 1 - 0.03 + 0.0009 - 0.000027$$

$$= 1.0009 - 0.030027$$

$$= 0.970873$$

$$(1 + 3(0.01))^{-1} \approx 0.9709 \text{ to 4 d.p.}$$

> This is the expansion given in the question, with $x = 0.01$.

> $\frac{100}{103} = 0.97087...$ so this is a pretty good approximation.

Tip: You need to use a "$\approx$" when you give the answer — it's an approximation because you're only using the first few terms of the expansion.

In some cases you might have to **rearrange the expansion** first to get it into a
form that fits with the given expression.

Example 2

The binomial expansion of $(1 - 5x)^{\frac{1}{2}}$ up to the term in x^2 is
$(1 - 5x)^{\frac{1}{2}} \approx 1 - \frac{5x}{2} - \frac{25x^2}{8}$. The expansion is valid for $|x| < \frac{1}{5}$.

a) Use $x = \frac{1}{50}$ in this expansion to find an approximate value for $\sqrt{10}$.

- First, substitute $x = \frac{1}{50}$ into **both sides** of the given expansion:

$$\sqrt{\left(1 - 5\left(\frac{1}{50}\right)\right)} \approx 1 - \frac{5}{2}\left(\frac{1}{50}\right) - \frac{25}{8}\left(\frac{1}{50}\right)^2$$

$$\sqrt{\left(1 - \frac{1}{10}\right)} \approx 1 - \frac{1}{20} - \frac{1}{800}$$

$$\boxed{\sqrt{\frac{9}{10}} \approx \frac{759}{800}}$$

- Now **simplify the square root**...

$$\sqrt{\frac{9}{10}} = \frac{\sqrt{9}}{\sqrt{10}} = \frac{3}{\sqrt{10}} \approx \frac{759}{800}$$

- ...and **rearrange** to find an estimate for $\sqrt{10}$:

$$\frac{3}{\sqrt{10}} \approx \frac{759}{800}$$

$$3 \times 800 \approx 759\sqrt{10}$$

$$\sqrt{10} \approx \frac{3 \times 800}{759}$$

$$\boxed{\sqrt{10} \approx \frac{800}{253}}$$

Tip: If you're not
quite sure how the
expansion's going to
fit, the best thing to do
is put the numbers in
and see what comes
out. It's much clearer
at this stage in the
example where your
$\sqrt{10}$ is coming from, but
you'd be forgiven for not
making the link at the
start of the question.

b) **Find the percentage error in your approximation, to 2 s.f.**

Work out the percentage error by finding the difference between your
estimate and a calculated 'real' value, and give this as a percentage of
the real value:

$$\left|\frac{\text{real value} - \text{estimate}}{\text{real value}}\right| \times 100$$

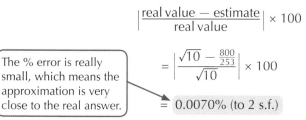

$$= \left|\frac{\sqrt{10} - \frac{800}{253}}{\sqrt{10}}\right| \times 100$$

$$= 0.0070\% \text{ (to 2 s.f.)}$$

The % error is really
small, which means the
approximation is very
close to the real answer.

Tip: The modulus sign
means you always
get a positive answer,
whether the estimate is
bigger or smaller than
the real value. You're
only interested in the
difference between them.

Q1 a) Find the binomial expansion of $(1 + 6x)^{-1}$, up to and including the term in x^2.

b) What is the validity of the expansion in part a)?

Q1 c) Hint: Always check that the value you've decided to use for x is within the valid range for the expansion.

c) Use an appropriate substitution to find an approximation for $\dfrac{100}{106}$.

d) What is the percentage error of this approximation? Give your answer correct to 1 significant figure.

Q2 a) Use the binomial theorem to expand $(1 + 3x)^{\frac{1}{4}}$ in ascending powers of x, up to and including the term in x^3.

b) For what values of x is this expansion valid?

c) Use this expansion to find an approximate value of $\sqrt[4]{1.9}$ correct to 4 decimal places.

d) Find the percentage error of this approximation, correct to 3 significant figures.

Q3 a) Find the first four terms in the binomial expansion of $(1 - 2x)^{-\frac{1}{2}}$.

b) For what range of x is this expansion valid?

Q3 c) Hint: Put the value for x into both sides of the expansion, and rearrange the left-hand side until you get $\sqrt{5}$.

c) Use $x = \dfrac{1}{10}$ in this expansion to find an approximate value of $\sqrt{5}$.

d) Find the percentage error of this approximation, correct to 2 significant figures.

Q4 a) Expand $(2 - 5x)^6$ up to and including the x^2 term.

b) By substituting an appropriate value of x into the expansion in a), find an approximate value for 1.95^6.

c) What is the percentage error of this approximation? Give your answer to 2 significant figures.

Q5 a) Find the first four terms in the binomial expansion of $\sqrt{3 - 4x}$.

b) For what values of x is this expansion valid?

c) Use $x = \dfrac{9}{20}$ in this expansion to estimate the value of $\dfrac{2}{\sqrt{10}}$. Leave your answer as a fraction.

d) Find the percentage error of this approximation, correct to 3 significant figures.

3. Binomial Expansion and Partial Fractions

You'll need to deal with some tricky expressions in C4 — but you can use partial fractions to make things simpler. You met these back in Chapter 1.

Learning Objective:

- Be able to split rational functions into partial fractions, then find the binomial expansion of the function.

Finding binomial expansions using partial fractions

You can find the binomial expansion of more complicated functions by:

- splitting them into **partial fractions** first,
- expanding **each fraction** using the formula (usually with $n = -1$),
- then **adding** the expansions together.

Example

The function $f(x) = \dfrac{x - 1}{(3 + x)(1 - 5x)}$ **can be expressed**

as partial fractions in the form: $\dfrac{A}{(3 + x)} + \dfrac{B}{(1 - 5x)}$.

a) Find the values of A and B, and hence express $f(x)$ as partial fractions.

- Start by writing out the problem as an **identity**:

$$\frac{x - 1}{(3 + x)(1 - 5x)} \equiv \frac{A}{(3 + x)} + \frac{B}{(1 - 5x)}$$

> Add the fractions together and cancel the denominators on either side of the identity.

$$\Rightarrow \frac{x - 1}{(3 + x)(1 - 5x)} \equiv \frac{A(1 - 5x) + B(3 + x)}{(3 + x)(1 - 5x)}$$

$$\Rightarrow \qquad x - 1 \equiv A(1 - 5x) + B(3 + x)$$

- You can then work out the values of A and B by putting in values of x that make each bracket in turn equal to zero.
  (This is known as the '**substitution**' method.)

Let $x = -3$, then: $\qquad -3 - 1 = A(1 - (-15))$

$$\Rightarrow -4 = 16A$$

$$\Rightarrow \boxed{A = -\frac{1}{4}}$$

Let $x = \frac{1}{5}$, then: $\qquad \frac{1}{5} - 1 = B\left(3 + \frac{1}{5}\right)$

$$\Rightarrow -\frac{4}{5} = \frac{16}{5}B$$

$$\Rightarrow \boxed{B = -\frac{1}{4}}$$

- So $f(x)$ can also be written as: $\quad -\dfrac{1}{4(3 + x)} - \dfrac{1}{4(1 - 5x)}$

Tip: Look back at pages 12-13 for a recap on this method.

Tip: You could also **equate the coefficients** of x and the constant terms to find A and B.

Tip: Remember to put A and B back into the expression to give $f(x)$ as partial fractions.

b) Use your answer to part a) to find the binomial expansion of f(x), up to and including the term in x^2.

- Start by **rewriting** the **partial fractions** from a) in $(p + qx)^n$ form:

$$f(x) = -\frac{1}{4}(3 + x)^{-1} - \frac{1}{4}(1 - 5x)^{-1}$$

Tip: There are a lot of different stages to this type of question — which means a lot of places that you could make a mistake, especially with all these negatives and fractions flying around. Set your working out clearly and don't skip stages.

- Now do the two binomial expansions **separately**:

$$(3 + x)^{-1} = \left(3\left(1 + \frac{1}{3}x\right)\right)^{-1}$$
$$= \frac{1}{3}\left(1 + \frac{1}{3}x\right)^{-1}$$
$$= \frac{1}{3}\left(1 + (-1)\left(\frac{1}{3}x\right) + \frac{(-1)(-2)}{2}\left(\frac{1}{3}x\right)^2 + \ldots\right)$$
$$= \frac{1}{3}\left(1 - \frac{1}{3}x + \frac{1}{9}x^2 - \ldots\right)$$
$$= \frac{1}{3} - \frac{1}{9}x + \frac{1}{27}x^2 - \ldots$$

$$(1 - 5x)^{-1} = 1 + (-1)(-5x) + \frac{(-1)(-2)}{2}(-5x)^2 + \ldots$$
$$= 1 + 5x + 25x^2 + \ldots$$

- Finally, put everything together by adding the expansions in the rearranged form of f(x):

$$f(x) = -\frac{1}{4}(3 + x)^{-1} - \frac{1}{4}(1 - 5x)^{-1}$$

$$\approx -\frac{1}{4}\left(\frac{1}{3} - \frac{1}{9}x + \frac{1}{27}x^2\right) - \frac{1}{4}(1 + 5x + 25x^2)$$

$$= -\frac{1}{12} + \frac{x}{36} - \frac{x^2}{108} - \frac{1}{4} - \frac{5x}{4} - \frac{25x^2}{4}$$

$$= \boxed{-\frac{1}{3} - \frac{11x}{9} - \frac{169x^2}{27}}$$

c) Find the range of values of x for which your answer to part b) is valid.

- The two expansions from b) are valid for **different values of x**.

- The **combined** expansion of f(x) is valid where these **two ranges overlap**, i.e. over the **narrower** of the two ranges.

  (This is the same as when you combine expansions by multiplying them together, as shown on page 63.)

  The expansion of $(3 + x)^{-1}$ is valid when $\left|\frac{x}{3}\right| < 1 \Rightarrow |x| < 3$.

  The expansion of $(1 - 5x)^{-1}$ is valid when $|-5x| < 1 \Rightarrow |x| < \frac{1}{5}$.

- The expansion of f(x) is valid for values of x in both ranges, so the expansion of f(x) is valid for $\boxed{|x| < \frac{1}{5}}$.

Tip: Remember, the expansion of $(p + qx)^n$ is valid when $\left|\frac{qx}{p}\right| < 1$.

Q1 a) $\dfrac{5 - 12x}{(1 + 6x)(4 + 3x)} \equiv \dfrac{A}{(1 + 6x)} + \dfrac{B}{(4 + 3x)}$. Find A and B.

b) (i) Find the binomial expansion of $(1 + 6x)^{-1}$, up to and including the term in x^2.

(ii) Find the binomial expansion of $(4 + 3x)^{-1}$, up to and including the term in x^2.

c) Hence find the binomial expansion of $\dfrac{5 - 12x}{(1 + 6x)(4 + 3x)}$, up to and including the term in x^2.

d) For what values of x is this expansion valid?

Q2 $f(x) = \dfrac{60x^2 + 5x + 7}{(4 - 3x)(1 + 4x)^2}$

a) Show that $f(x)$ can be expressed as:
$$\dfrac{3}{(4 - 3x)} - \dfrac{1}{(1 + 4x)} + \dfrac{2}{(1 + 4x)^2}.$$

b) Give the binomial expansion of $f(x)$ in ascending powers of x, up to and including the term in x^2.

c) Find the percentage error when you use this expansion to estimate $f(0.01)$, giving your answer to 2 significant figures.

Q3 a) Factorise fully $6x^3 + 11x^2 + 4x$.

b) Hence express $\dfrac{22x^2 + 40x + 12}{6x^3 + 11x^2 + 4x}$ as partial fractions.

c) Find the binomial expansion of $\dfrac{22x^2 + 40x + 12}{6x^3 + 11x^2 + 4x}$, up to and including the term in x^2.

d) For what values of x is this expansion valid?

> **Q3 c) Hint:** You'll end up with a term in x^{-1}, which you wouldn't usually get with a binomial expansion — this comes from the partial fractions and you can just leave it as it is.

Q4 $f(x) = \dfrac{12x^2 - 27x - 33}{(3x + 1)(2x - 5)}$

a) Express $f(x)$ in the form $A + \dfrac{B}{(3x + 1)} + \dfrac{C}{(2x - 5)}$, where A, B and C are all integers to be found.

b) Hence, or otherwise, use the binomial theorem to expand $f(x)$ in ascending powers of x, up to and including the term in x^2.

> **Q4 Hint:** This is a top heavy fraction, so you can multiply out the denominator and divide top by bottom to find the constants. This should give you 'A', then split the **remainder** into partial fractions. See page 17 for more on this.

Review Exercise — Chapter 4

Q1 Give the binomial expansion of:

a) $(1 + 2x)^3$

b) $(1 - x)^5$

c) $(1 - 4x)^4$

Q2 For what values of n does the binomial expansion of $(1 + x)^n$ result in a finite expression?

Q3 a) If the x^2 coefficient of the binomial expansion of $(1 + ax)^7$ is 189, and a is a positive integer, what is the value of a?

b) If the x^4 coefficient of the binomial expansion of $(1 - ax)^6$ is 240, and a is positive, what is the value of a?

Q4 If the full binomial expansion of $(c + dx)^n$ is an infinite series, what values of x is the expansion valid for?

Q5 Find the binomial expansion of each of the following, up to and including the term in x^3:

a) $\dfrac{1}{(1 + x)^5}$

b) $\dfrac{1}{(1 - 3x)^3}$

c) $\sqrt{1 - 5x}$

Q6 For which values of x are the expansions from question 5 valid?

Q7 a) Give the binomial expansions of the following, up to and including the term in x^2. State which values of x each expansion is valid for.

(i) $\dfrac{1}{(3 + 2x)^2}$

(ii) $\sqrt[3]{8 - x}$

b) Use your answers to a) to give the binomial expansion of $\dfrac{\sqrt[3]{8 - x}}{(3 + 2x)^2}$, up to and including the term in x^2. State the range of x that this expansion is valid for.

c) (i) Use the expansion in a)(ii) to find an approximate value of $\sqrt[3]{7}$, leaving your answer as a fraction.

(ii) Find the percentage error of this approximation, correct to 2 significant figures.

Q8 a) Show that $\dfrac{5 - 10x}{(1 + 2x)(2 - x)}$ can be expressed as: $\dfrac{4}{(1 + 2x)} - \dfrac{3}{(2 - x)}$.

b) Give the binomial expansion of the expression in a), up to and including the term in x^2.

c) Find the percentage error when you use $x = 0.1$ in this expansion to estimate $\dfrac{4}{1.2 \times 1.9}$, giving your answer to 2 significant figures.

1 $$f(x) = \frac{1}{\sqrt{(9-4x)}}, \text{ for } |x| < \frac{9}{4}.$$

a) Find the binomial expansion of $f(x)$, up to and including the term in x^3.

(5 marks)

b) Hence find the first three terms in the expansion of:

$$\frac{2-x}{\sqrt{(9-4x)}}$$

(4 marks)

2 $$f(x) = \frac{36x^2 + 3x - 10}{(4+3x)(1-3x)^2}$$

a) Given that $f(x)$ can be expressed in the form

$$f(x) = \frac{A}{(4+3x)} + \frac{B}{(1-3x)} + \frac{C}{(1-3x)^2}$$

find the values of A, B and C.

(4 marks)

b) Find the binomial expansion of $f(x)$, up to and including the term in x^2.

(6 marks)

c) Find the range of values of x for which the binomial expansion of $f(x)$ is valid.

(2 marks)

3 a) Find the binomial expansion of:

$$(16 + 3x)^{\frac{1}{4}}, \text{ for } |x| < \frac{16}{3},$$

up to and including the term in x^2.

(5 marks)

b) (i) Estimate $\sqrt[4]{12.4}$ by substituting a suitable value of x into your expansion from part (a). Give your answer to 6 decimal places.

(2 marks)

(ii) What is the percentage error in this estimate? Give your answer to 3 s.f.

(2 marks)

4 a) Find the binomial expansion of $\left(1 - \frac{4}{3}x\right)^{-\frac{1}{2}}$,

up to and including the term in x^3.

(4 marks)

b) Hence find the values of integer constants a, b and c, such that

$$\sqrt{\frac{27}{(3 - 4x)}} \approx a + bx + cx^2,$$

and state the range of values of x for which this approximation is valid.

(3 marks)

5 a) (i) Show that:

$$\sqrt{\frac{1 + 2x}{1 - 3x}} \approx 1 + \frac{5}{2}x + \frac{35}{8}x^2$$

(5 marks)

(ii) For what values of x is your expansion valid?

(2 marks)

b) Using the above expansion with $x = \frac{2}{15}$,

show that $\sqrt{19} \approx \frac{127}{30}$.

(2 marks)

6 a) Find the values of A and B such that

$$\frac{13x - 17}{(5 - 3x)(2x - 1)} \equiv \frac{A}{(5 - 3x)} + \frac{B}{(2x - 1)}.$$

(3 marks)

b) (i) Find the binomial expansion of $(2x - 1)^{-1}$,
up to and including the term in x^2.

(2 marks)

(ii) Show that:

$$\frac{1}{(5 - 3x)} \approx \frac{1}{5} + \frac{3}{25}x + \frac{9}{125}x^2,$$

for $|x| < \frac{5}{3}$.

(5 marks)

c) Using your answers to parts (a) and (b), find the first three terms
of the binomial expansion of $\frac{13x - 17}{(5 - 3x)(2x - 1)}$.

(2 marks)

1. Differentiation with Parametric Equations

You met parametric equations in Chapter 3 — they're equations where x and y are defined separately in terms of a third variable. Differentiating them is simpler than you might expect — but you need to remember how to differentiate things like trig functions, exponentials and logs.

Differentiating parametric equations

- A curve can be defined by **two parametric equations**, often with the parameter t: $y = f(t)$ and $x = g(t)$.

- To find the gradient, $\dfrac{dy}{dx}$, you could convert the equations into **Cartesian** form (see pages 54-55), but this isn't always possible or convenient.

- The **chain rule** you met in C3 can be used to differentiate parametric equations without needing to convert to Cartesian form. It looks like this:

$$\frac{dy}{dx} = \frac{dy}{dt} \div \frac{dx}{dt}$$

- So to find $\dfrac{dy}{dx}$ from parametric equations, **differentiate** each equation with respect to the parameter t, then put them into the formula.

> **Learning Objectives:**
> - Be able to differentiate functions defined parametrically.
> - Be able to find the equations of tangents and normals to curves given parametrically.

> **Tip:** In C3 you'll have seen it given as '$\times \dfrac{dt}{dx}$' instead of '$\div \dfrac{dx}{dt}$', but it means the same thing.

Example

The curve C is defined by the parametric equations
$y = t^3 - 3t + 4$ and $x = t^2 - 1$.

a) Find $\dfrac{dy}{dx}$ in terms of t.

- Start by **differentiating** the two parametric equations **with respect to t**:

$$y = t^3 - 3t + 4 \quad \Rightarrow \quad \frac{dy}{dt} = 3t^2 - 3 = 3(t^2 - 1)$$

$$x = t^2 - 1 \quad \Rightarrow \quad \frac{dx}{dt} = 2t$$

- Now use the **chain rule** to combine them:

$$\frac{dy}{dx} = \frac{dy}{dt} \div \frac{dx}{dt} = \frac{3(t^2 - 1)}{2t}$$

b) Find the gradient of C when $t = -2$.

- Use the answer to a) to find the gradient for a specific value of t. So, when $t = -2$:

$$\frac{dy}{dx} = \frac{3((-2)^2 - 1)}{2(-2)} = \frac{3(3)}{-4} = -\frac{9}{4}$$

c) Find the coordinates of the stationary points.

- The stationary points occur when $\frac{dy}{dx} = 0$,

  so solve to find the values of t at the stationary points:

$$\frac{dy}{dx} = \frac{3(t^2 - 1)}{2t} = 0$$

$$\Rightarrow 3(t^2 - 1) = 0 \Rightarrow t^2 = 1 \Rightarrow t = \pm 1$$

Tip: Remember — Cartesian coordinates are just the (x, y) coordinates.

- Now put these values for t into the original parametric equations to find the Cartesian coordinates of the stationary points:

When $t = 1$ $x = (1)^2 - 1 = 0$

$y = (1)^3 - 3(1) + 4 = 2$

So there's a stationary point at $(0, 2)$ ...

When $t = -1$ $x = (-1)^2 - 1 = 0$

$y = (-1)^3 - 3(-1) + 4 = 6$

...and there's another one at $(0, 6)$.

Exercise 1.1

Q1 For each curve C, defined by the parametric equations given below, find $\frac{dy}{dx}$ in terms of t.
  a) $x = t^2,\ y = t^3 - t$.
  b) $x = t^3 + t,\ y = 2t^2 + 1$
  c) $x = t^4,\ y = t^3 - t^2$
  d) $x = \cos t,\ y = 4t - t^2$

Q2-6 Hint: You need to remember how to differentiate trig functions, e^x and $\ln x$ — you did them in C3.

Q2 The curve C is defined by the parametric equations $x = t^2$, $y = e^{2t}$.
  a) Find $\frac{dy}{dx}$ in terms of t.   b) Find the gradient of C when $t = 1$.

Q3 The curve C is defined by the parametric equations
  $x = e^{3t}$, $y = 4t^3 - 2t^2$.
  a) Find $\frac{dy}{dx}$ in terms of t.   b) Find the gradient of C when $t = 0$.

Q4-5 Hint: You'll need to use the product rule to find dy/dt and dx/dt. Look back at your C3 notes if you need to.

Q4 The curve C is defined by the parametric equations $x = t^3$, $y = t^2 \cos t$.
  a) Find $\frac{dy}{dx}$ in terms of t.   b) Find the gradient of C when $t = \pi$.

Q5 The curve C is defined by the parametric equations
  $x = t^2 \sin t$, $y = t^3 \sin t + \cos t$.
  a) Find $\frac{dy}{dx}$ in terms of t.   b) Find the gradient of C when $t = \pi$.

Q6 The curve C is defined by the parametric equations
  $x = \ln t$, $y = 3t^2 - t^3$.
  a) Find $\frac{dy}{dx}$ in terms of t.   b) Evaluate $\frac{dy}{dx}$ when $t = -1$.
  c) Find the exact coordinates of the stationary point of the curve C.

Finding tangents and normals

Once you've found the gradient of a parametric curve at a particular point, you can use this to find the **equation** of the **tangent** or **normal** to the curve at that point. You'll have seen this before, but here's a recap of the method:

- The gradient of the **tangent** is the **same** as the gradient of the curve at that point.

- The gradient of the **normal** at that point is $\dfrac{-1}{\text{gradient of tangent}}$.

- Put the values for the gradient, m, and the (x, y) coordinates of the point into $y = mx + c$ to find the equation of the line.

Tip: You could also use $y - y_1 = m(x - x_1)$ to get the equation.

Example

The curve C is defined by the following parametric equations:
$x = \sin t,\ y = 2t \cos t.$

a) Find the gradient of the curve, and the (x, y) coordinates, when $t = \pi$.

$$\frac{dx}{dt} = \cos t$$

$$\frac{dy}{dt} = 2\cos t - 2t \sin t$$

$$\longrightarrow \qquad \frac{dy}{dx} = \frac{2\cos t - 2t \sin t}{\cos t} = \boxed{2 - 2t \tan t}$$

When $t = \pi$, $\dfrac{dy}{dx} = 2 - 2\pi(0) = 2$

When $t = \pi$, $x = 0$, and $y = -2\pi$, so the coordinates are $(0, -2\pi)$.

b) Hence find the equation of the tangent to C when $t = \pi$.

- The gradient of the tangent at $t = \pi$ is the same as $\dfrac{dy}{dx}$ at that point, i.e. 2.

- So substitute m = 2, $x = 0$ and $y = -2\pi$ into $y = mx + c$, to find c:

$$y = mx + c$$
$$-2\pi = 2(0) + c \implies c = -2\pi$$

- Putting c back into the equation gives:

$$\boxed{y = 2x - 2\pi \ \text{ or } \ y = 2(x - \pi)}$$

c) Find the equation of the normal to C when $t = \pi$.

- The gradient of the normal at $t = \pi$ is $-\dfrac{1}{2}$.

- So substitute m = $-\dfrac{1}{2}$, $x = 0$ and $y = -2\pi$ into $y = mx + c$, to find c:

$$y = mx + c$$
$$-2\pi = -\frac{1}{2}(0) + c \implies c = -2\pi$$

- Putting c back into the equation gives:

$$\boxed{y = -\frac{1}{2}x - 2\pi \ \text{ or } \ x + 2y + 4\pi = 0}$$

Q1   A curve is defined by the parametric equations $x = t^2$, $y = t^3 - 6t$. Find the equation of the tangent to the curve at $t = 3$, giving your answer in the form $ax + by + c = 0$.

Q2   A curve C is defined parametrically by $x = t^3 - 2t^2$, $y = t^3 - t^2 + 5t$. Find the equation of the tangent at the point $t = -1$.

Q3   A curve C is defined by the parametric equations $x = \sin 2t$, $y = t \cos t + 2 \sin t$. Find the equation of the normal to the curve at $t = \pi$.

Q4 Hint: Use the product rule to differentiate $t \ln t$.

Q4   The parametric representation of a curve is given by $x = t \ln t$, $y = t^3 - t^2 + 3$. Find the equation of the tangent to the curve at $t = 1$.

Q5   The path of a particle is given parametrically by $x = \theta \sin 2\theta$, $y = \theta^2 + \theta \cos \theta$. Find the equation of the normal to the particle's path at $\theta = \dfrac{\pi}{2}$.

Q6   The motion of a particle is described by the parametric equations $x = t^2 - t$, $y = 3t - t^3$.

  a) Find the equation of the tangent to the path of the particle when $t = 2$, giving your answer in a suitable form.

  b) Find the Cartesian coordinates of the point at which the normal to the path at $t = 2$ cuts the x-axis.

Q7   A particle moves along a path given by the parametric equations $x = \sin 2\theta + 2 \cos \theta$, $y = \theta \sin \theta$.

  a) Find the gradient $\dfrac{dy}{dx}$ of the particle's path in terms of θ.

  b) Evaluate $\dfrac{dy}{dx}$ at $\theta = \dfrac{\pi}{2}$ and hence obtain equations of the tangent and normal to the path at this point.

Q8   A particle moves along a path given parametrically by $x = s^3 \ln s$, $y = s^3 - s^2 \ln s$.

  a) Give the value(s) of s at which the path cuts the y-axis.

  b) Hence show that the equation of a tangent to the curve when $x = 0$ is $y = 2x + 1$.

Q9 Hint: Use the quotient rule to find $\dfrac{dy}{d\theta}$.

Q9   A curve is given parametrically by $x = \theta^2 \sin \theta$, $y = \dfrac{\cos \theta}{\theta^3}$.

  a) Show that the gradient of the curve when $\theta = \pi$ is $-\dfrac{3}{\pi^6}$.

  b) Hence find the equation of the normal to the curve at this point.

2. Implicit Differentiation

For equations that you can't write in the form $y = f(x)$, you need to use implicit differentiation. It works for equations that contain a mixture of x and y terms, such as xy^2.

Learning Objectives:

- Be able to differentiate functions defined implicitly.
- Be able to find the equations of tangents and normals to curves given implicitly.

Implicit differentiation

An '**implicit relation**' is the mathematical name for any equation in x and y that's written in the form $\mathbf{f(x, y) = g(x, y)}$ instead of $y = f(x)$. For example, $y^2 = xy + x + 2$ is implicit.

Some implicit relations are either awkward or impossible to rewrite in the form $y = f(x)$. This can happen, for example, if the equation contains a number of different powers of y, or terms where x is multiplied by y.

This can make implicit relations tricky to differentiate — the solution is **implicit differentiation**:

Tip: $f(x, y)$ and $g(x, y)$ don't actually both have to include x and y — one of them could even be a constant.

To find $\dfrac{dy}{dx}$ for an implicit relation between x and y:

- **Step 1:** Differentiate terms in x **only** (and **constant** terms) with respect to x, as normal.

- **Step 2:** Use the **chain rule** to differentiate terms in y **only**:
$$\frac{d}{dx}f(y) = \frac{d}{dy}f(y)\frac{dy}{dx}$$ In practice, this means 'differentiate with respect to y, and stick a $\frac{dy}{dx}$ on the end'.

- **Step 3:** Use the **product rule** to differentiate terms in **both x and y**:
$$\frac{d}{dx}u(x)v(y) = u(x)\frac{d}{dx}v(y) + v(y)\frac{d}{dx}u(x)$$

- **Step 4:** **Rearrange** the resulting equation in x, y and $\dfrac{dy}{dx}$ to make $\dfrac{dy}{dx}$ the subject.

Tip: $\frac{d}{dx}f(y)$ just means 'the derivative of $f(y)$ with respect to x'.

Tip: This version of the product rule is slightly different from the one you'll have seen in C3 — it's got $v(y)$ instead of $v(x)$.

Example 1

a) Use implicit differentiation to find $\dfrac{dy}{dx}$ for $y^3 + y^2 = e^x + x^3$.

We need to differentiate each term of the equation with respect to x. Start by sticking '$\frac{d}{dx}$' in front of each term:

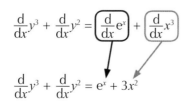

$$\frac{d}{dx}y^3 + \frac{d}{dx}y^2 = \boxed{\frac{d}{dx}e^x} + \boxed{\frac{d}{dx}x^3}$$

Step 1: Differentiate the terms in x only.

$$\frac{d}{dx}y^3 + \frac{d}{dx}y^2 = e^x + 3x^2$$

Tip: Just differentiate with respect to y, but don't forget to put a $\frac{dy}{dx}$ after each term.

Step 2: Use the **chain rule** for the terms in y only.

$$3y^2\frac{dy}{dx} + 2y\frac{dy}{dx} = e^x + 3x^2$$

Step 3: There are no terms in both x and y to deal with, so...

Step 4: Rearrange to make $\frac{dy}{dx}$ the subject: $\quad (3y^2 + 2y)\frac{dy}{dx} = e^x + 3x^2$

$$\Rightarrow \frac{dy}{dx} = \frac{e^x + 3x^2}{3y^2 + 2y}$$

Example 2

a) Use implicit differentiation to find $\frac{dy}{dx}$ for $2x^2y + y^3 = 6x^2 - 15$.

- Again, start by sticking '$\frac{d}{dx}$' in front of each term:

$$\frac{d}{dx}2x^2y + \frac{d}{dx}y^3 = \frac{d}{dx}6x^2 - \frac{d}{dx}15$$

Tip: Once you're happy with this method you might not need to write all the steps out separately, but you can do if you find it easier.

- First, deal with the **terms in x** and **constant** terms — in this case that's the two terms on the right-hand side:

$$\frac{d}{dx}2x^2y + \frac{d}{dx}y^3 = 12x + 0$$

- Now use the **chain rule** on the term in y.

$$\frac{d}{dx}2x^2y + 3y^2\frac{dy}{dx} = 12x + 0$$

- Use the **product rule** on the term in x and y, where $u(x) = 2x^2$ and $v(y) = y$:

$$2x^2\frac{d}{dx}(y) + y\frac{d}{dx}(2x^2) + 3y^2\frac{dy}{dx} = 12x + 0$$

$$\Rightarrow 2x^2\frac{dy}{dx} + y4x + 3y^2\frac{dy}{dx} = 12x + 0$$

Tip: Take your time using the product rule as it's easy to forget terms if you're not careful. Always start by identifying $u(x)$ and $v(y)$, and do it in steps if you need to.

This $\frac{dy}{dx}$ term comes from using the chain rule:
$$\frac{d}{dx}(y) = \frac{d}{dy}(y)\frac{dy}{dx} = 1\frac{dy}{dx} = \frac{dy}{dx}$$

- Finally, **rearrange** to make $\frac{dy}{dx}$ the subject:

$$\frac{dy}{dx}(2x^2 + 3y^2) = 12x - 4xy \Rightarrow \frac{dy}{dx} = \frac{12x - 4xy}{2x^2 + 3y^2}$$

b) Find the gradient of the curve $2x^2y + y^3 = 6x^2 - 15$ at the point (2, 1).

Just substitute the values for x and y into $\frac{dy}{dx}$:

$$\frac{dy}{dx} = \frac{12(2) - 4(2)(1)}{2(2)^2 + 3(1)^2} = \frac{16}{11}$$

Q1 Use implicit differentiation to find $\frac{dy}{dx}$ for each of these curves:

a) $y + y^3 = x^2 + 4$

b) $x^2 + y^2 = 2x + 2y$

c) $3x^3 - 4y = y^2 + x$

d) $5x - y^2 = x^5 - 6y$

e) $\cos x + \sin y = x^2 + y^3$

f) $x^3y^2 + \cos x = 4xy$

g) $e^x + e^y = x^3 - y$

h) $3xy^2 + 2x^2y = x^3 + 4x$

Q2 Find the gradient, $\frac{dy}{dx}$, for each of these curves given below:

a) $x^3 + 2xy = y^4$

b) $x^2y + y^2 = x^3$

c) $y^3x + y = \sin x$

d) $y \cos x + x \sin y = xy$

e) $e^x + e^y = xy$

f) $\ln x + x^2 = y^3 + y$

g) $e^{2x} + e^{3y} = 3x^2y^2$

h) $x \ln x + y \ln x = x^5 + y^3$

Q3 a) Show that the curve C, defined implicitly by $e^x + 2 \ln y = y^3$, passes through $(0, 1)$.

b) Find the gradient of the curve at this point.

> **Q3 a) Hint:** Evaluate the left-hand and right-hand sides of the equation separately to show they're the same.

Q4 A curve is defined implicitly by $x^3 + y^2 - 2xy = 0$

a) Find $\frac{dy}{dx}$ for this curve.

b) Show that $y = -2 \pm 2\sqrt{3}$ when $x = -2$.

c) Evaluate the gradient at $(-2, -2 + 2\sqrt{3})$, leaving your answer in surd form.

Q5 The curve $x^3 - xy = 2y^2$ passes through the points $(1, -1)$ and $(1, a)$.

a) Find the value of a.

b) Evaluate the gradient of the curve at each of these points.

Q6 A curve is defined implicitly by $x^2y + y^2x = xy + 4$.

a) At which two values of y does the line $x = 1$ cut the curve?

b) By finding $\frac{dy}{dx}$, evaluate the gradient at each of these points.

Applications of implicit differentiation

Most implicit differentiation questions aren't really that different from any other differentiation question. Once you've got an expression for the gradient, you'll have to use it to do the sort of things you'd normally expect, like finding stationary points of curves and equations of tangents and normals.

Example 1

Curve A has the equation $x^2 + 2xy - y^2 = 10x + 4y - 21$.

a) Show that when $\dfrac{dy}{dx} = 0$, $y = 5 - x$.

For starters, we're going to need to find $\dfrac{dy}{dx}$ by implicit differentiation:

$$\frac{d}{dx}x^2 + \frac{d}{dx}2xy - \frac{d}{dx}y^2 = \frac{d}{dx}10x + \frac{d}{dx}4y - \frac{d}{dx}21$$

$$\Rightarrow \quad 2x + \frac{d}{dx}2xy - \frac{d}{dx}y^2 = 10 + \frac{d}{dx}4y - 0$$

> Differentiate x^2, $10x$ and 21 with respect to x.

$$\Rightarrow \quad 2x + \frac{d}{dx}2xy - 2y\frac{dy}{dx} = 10 + 4\frac{dy}{dx}$$

> Use the chain rule to differentiate y^2 and $4y$.

$$\Rightarrow \quad 2x + 2x\frac{dy}{dx} + y\frac{d}{dx}2x - 2y\frac{dy}{dx} = 10 + 4\frac{dy}{dx}$$

$$\Rightarrow \quad 2x + 2x\frac{dy}{dx} + 2y - 2y\frac{dy}{dx} = 10 + 4\frac{dy}{dx}$$

> Use the product rule to differentiate $2xy$.

$$\Rightarrow \quad 2x\frac{dy}{dx} - 2y\frac{dy}{dx} - 4\frac{dy}{dx} = 10 - 2x - 2y$$

$$\Rightarrow \quad (2x - 2y - 4)\frac{dy}{dx} = 10 - 2x - 2y$$

$$\Rightarrow \quad \frac{dy}{dx} = \frac{10 - 2x - 2y}{2x - 2y - 4} = \boxed{\frac{5 - x - y}{x - y - 2}}$$

So when $\dfrac{dy}{dx} = 0$:

$$\frac{5 - x - y}{x - y - 2} = 0 \Rightarrow 5 - x - y = 0 \Rightarrow \boxed{y = 5 - x}$$

b) Find the coordinates of the stationary points of A.

Use the answer to part a) to find the points where $\dfrac{dy}{dx} = 0$.

When $\dfrac{dy}{dx} = 0$, $y = 5 - x$. So at the stationary points:

$$x^2 + 2xy - y^2 = 10x + 4y - 21$$

$$\Rightarrow \quad x^2 + 2x(5 - x) - (5 - x)^2 = 10x + 4(5 - x) - 21$$

$$\Rightarrow \quad x^2 + 10x - 2x^2 - 25 + 10x - x^2 = 10x + 20 - 4x - 21$$

$$\Rightarrow \quad -2x^2 + 14x - 24 = 0$$

$$\Rightarrow \quad x^2 - 7x + 12 = 0$$

$$\Rightarrow \quad (x - 3)(x - 4) = 0$$

$$\Rightarrow \quad x = 3 \text{ or } x = 4$$

> Put each value of x into $y = 5 - x$ to find the corresponding y-coordinate.

$x = 3 \Rightarrow y = 5 - 3 = 2 \qquad x = 4 \Rightarrow y = 5 - 4 = 1$

So the stationary points of A are $(3, 2)$ and $(4, 1)$.

Tip: Here you're just putting $y = 5 - x$ into the original equation to find the values of x at the stationary points.

Example 2

A curve defined implicitly by $\sin x - y \cos x = y^2$
passes through two points (π, a) and (π, b), where $a < b$.

a) Find the values of a and b.

▪ Put $x = \pi$ into the equation and solve for y:

$$\sin \pi - y \cos \pi = y^2$$
$$\Rightarrow 0 + y = y^2$$
$$\Rightarrow y^2 - y = 0$$
$$\Rightarrow y(y - 1) = 0$$
$$\Rightarrow y = 0 \text{ and } y = 1$$

▪ So $a = 0$ and $b = 1$.

b) Find the equations of the tangents to the curve at each of these points.

▪ First find $\dfrac{dy}{dx}$ using implicit differentiation as usual:

$$\cos x + y \sin x - \cos x \frac{dy}{dx} = 2y \frac{dy}{dx}$$

$$\Rightarrow \frac{dy}{dx} = \frac{\cos x + y \sin x}{2y + \cos x}$$

▪ Now put in $x = \pi$ and $y = 0$ to find the gradient at $(\pi, 0)$.

$$\frac{dy}{dx} = \frac{\cos \pi + 0 \sin \pi}{2(0) + \cos \pi} = 1$$

▪ So the gradient of the tangent at $(\pi, 0)$ is 1.
Putting these values into $y = mx + c$ gives:

$$0 = \pi + c \Rightarrow c = -\pi$$

So the equation of the tangent at $(\pi, 0)$ is $y = x - \pi.$

▪ Do the same to find the equation of the tangent at $(\pi, 1)$.

$$\frac{dy}{dx} = \frac{\cos \pi + \sin \pi}{2(1) + \cos \pi} = -1$$

$$1 = -\pi + c \Rightarrow c = 1 + \pi$$

So the equation of the tangent at $(\pi, 1)$ is $y = 1 + \pi - x.$

Tip: It's good to know some standard trig results off by heart. $\cos \pi = -1$ and $\sin \pi = 0$.

c) Show that the tangents intersect at the point $\left(\dfrac{1 + 2\pi}{2}, \dfrac{1}{2}\right)$.

▪ The two tangents intersect when:

$$x - \pi = 1 + \pi - x$$
$$\Rightarrow 2x = 1 + 2\pi$$
$$\Rightarrow x = \frac{1 + 2\pi}{2}$$

▪ Putting this value of x into one of the equations gives:

$$y = \left(\frac{1 + 2\pi}{2}\right) - \pi = \frac{1}{2} + \pi - \pi = \frac{1}{2}$$

▪ So they intersect at $\left(\dfrac{1 + 2\pi}{2}, \dfrac{1}{2}\right).$

Q1 A curve is defined implicitly by $x^2 + 2x + 3y - y^2 = 0$.

   a) Find the coordinates of the stationary points (to 2 decimal places).

   b) Show that the curve intersects the y-axis when $y = 0$ and $y = 3$. Hence find the equation of the tangent at each of these points.

Q2 A curve is defined implicitly by $x^3 + x^2 + y = y^2$.

   a) Find the coordinates of the stationary points (to 2 decimal places).

   b) Show that the curve intersects the line $x = 2$ when $y = 4$ and $y = -3$. Hence find the equation of the tangent at each of these points.

Q2 Hint: You should find 4 stationary points.

Q3 A curve is defined implicitly by $x^2y + y^3 = x + 7$.

   a) Calculate the x-coordinates of the points on the curve where $y = 1$ and hence find the equations of the normals at these points.

   b) Find the coordinates of the point where the normals intersect.

Q4 $e^x + y^2 - xy = 5 - 3y$ is a curve passing through two points $(0, a)$ and $(0, b)$, where $a < b$.

   a) Find the values of a and b and show that one of these points is a stationary point of the curve.

   b) Find the equations of the tangent and normal to the curve at the other point.

Q5 The curve C is defined by $\ln x + y^2 = x^2y + 6$.

   a) Show that C passes through $(1, 3)$ and $(1, -2)$.

   b) Find the equations of the normals to the curve at each of these points and explain why these normals cannot intersect.

Q6 Hint: Work out the values of a and b first.

Q6 A curve is defined implicitly by $e^y + x^2 = y^3 + 4x$. Find the equations of the tangents that touch the curve at $(a, 0)$ and $(b, 0)$. Leave your answer in surd form.

Q7 Show that any point on the curve $y \ln x + x^2 = y^2 - y + 1$ which satisfies $y + 2x^2 = 0$ is a stationary point.

Q8 A curve is defined by $e^{2y} + e^x - e^4 = 2xy + 1$.

   a) Find the equation of the tangent to the curve when $y = 0$.

   b) Find the equation of the normal to the curve when $y = 0$.

   c) Show that these two lines intersect when $x = \dfrac{4e^8 - 144}{e^8 + 36}$.

Q8 Hint: Remember — $\dfrac{1}{e^x}$ is the same as e^{-x}.

Q9 $y^2x + 2xy - 3x^3 = x^2 + 2$ passes through two points where $x = 2$. Find the equations of the tangents to the curve at these points, and hence show that they intersect at $\left(-\dfrac{14}{25}, -1\right)$.

Q10 Hint: You won't need your calculator for the trig here but you will need to remember your common angles.

Q10 The curve C is defined implicitly by $\cos y \cos x + \cos y \sin x = \dfrac{1}{2}$.

   a) Find y when $x = \dfrac{\pi}{2}$ and when $x = \pi$, $0 \leq y \leq \pi$.

   b) Find the equations of the tangents at these points.

3. Integration Using Partial Fractions

By rewriting algebraic expressions as partial fractions, you can turn difficult-looking integrations into ones you're more familiar with.

Use of partial fractions

You can integrate algebraic fractions where the denominator can be written as a product of **linear factors** by splitting them up into **partial fractions**. Each fraction can then be **integrated separately** using methods from C3.

Learning Objective:

- Be able to integrate rational expressions in which the denominator can be written as a product of linear factors, by splitting them into partial fractions.

Example 1

Find $\int \dfrac{12x + 6}{4x^2 - 9}\,dx$ where $x > 2$.

- The first step is to write the function as **partial fractions** as follows:

  - **Factorise** the denominator:
  $$\frac{12x + 6}{4x^2 - 9} \equiv \frac{12x + 6}{(2x + 3)(2x - 3)}$$

  - Write as an **identity** with partial fractions:
  $$\frac{12x + 6}{4x^2 - 9} \equiv \frac{12x + 6}{(2x + 3)(2x - 3)} \equiv \frac{A}{2x + 3} + \frac{B}{2x - 3}$$

  - **Add** the partial fractions and **cancel** the denominators:
  $$\frac{12x + 6}{(2x + 3)(2x - 3)} \equiv \frac{A(2x - 3) + B(2x + 3)}{(2x + 3)(2x - 3)}$$
  $$12x + 6 \equiv A(2x - 3) + B(2x + 3)$$

  - Use the **substitution method** to find A and B:

  Substituting $x = \frac{3}{2}$ into the identity gives
  $$18 + 6 = 0A + 6B \Rightarrow 24 = 6B \Rightarrow B = 4$$

  Substituting $x = -\frac{3}{2}$ into the identity gives
  $$-18 + 6 = -6A + 0B \Rightarrow -12 = -6A \Rightarrow A = 2$$

  - Replace A and B in the **original identity**:
  $$\frac{12x + 6}{4x^2 - 9} \equiv \frac{2}{2x + 3} + \frac{4}{2x - 3}$$

- So $\int \dfrac{12x + 6}{4x^2 - 9}\,dx = \int \dfrac{2}{2x + 3} + \dfrac{4}{2x - 3}\,dx.$

- Integrate each term **separately**.
  $$= 2 \times \frac{1}{2}\ln|2x + 3| + 4 \times \frac{1}{2}\ln|2x - 3| + C$$
  $$= \ln|2x + 3| + 2\ln|2x - 3| + C$$

- $x > 2$ so $2x + 3 > 7$ and $2x - 3 > 1$ so remove the modulus signs:
  $$= \ln(2x + 3) + 2\ln(2x - 3) + C$$
  $$= \ln(2x + 3)(2x - 3)^2 + C$$

Tip: Writing expressions as partial fractions is covered in Chapter 1 — but it's recapped here to remind you what they're all about.

Tip: You could also use the 'equating coefficients' method to find A and B.

Tip: Remember —
$$\int \frac{1}{ax + b}\,dx$$
$$= \frac{1}{a}\ln|ax + b| + C$$

Tip: It's a good idea to tidy up your answers using the log laws.

Example 2

Find the exact value of $\int_3^4 \dfrac{2}{x(x-2)} \, dx$, **writing it as a single logarithm.**

- Start by writing $\dfrac{2}{x(x-2)}$ as **partial fractions**.

  - Write as an **identity** with partial fractions:
  $$\frac{2}{x(x-2)} \equiv \frac{A}{x} + \frac{B}{x-2}$$

  - **Add** the partial fractions and **cancel** the denominators:
  $$\frac{2}{x(x-2)} \equiv \frac{A(x-2) + Bx}{x(x-2)}$$
  $$\Rightarrow 2 \equiv A(x-2) + Bx$$

  - Use the **equating coefficients method** to find A and B:

    Equating constant terms: $2 = -2A \Rightarrow \boldsymbol{A = -1}$
    Equating x coefficients: $0 = A + B \Rightarrow 0 = 1 + B \Rightarrow \boldsymbol{B = 1}$

  - Replace A and B in the **original identity**:
  $$\frac{2}{x(x-2)} \equiv \frac{-1}{x} + \frac{1}{x-2} \equiv \frac{1}{x-2} - \frac{1}{x}$$

Tip: When the constant term only contains one of the unknowns, it'll often be easier to compare coefficients than to substitute.

- So $\int_3^4 \dfrac{2}{x(x-2)} \, dx = \int_3^4 \dfrac{1}{(x-2)} - \dfrac{1}{x} \, dx$

- Integrate each term separately.
$$= [\ln|x-2| - \ln|x|]_3^4$$

Tip: The question asks for the answer as a single logarithm so make sure you fully simplify your answer.

$\boxed{\log a - \log b = \log\left(\frac{a}{b}\right)}$

$$= \left[\ln\left|\frac{x-2}{x}\right|\right]_3^4 = \left[\ln\left|\frac{4-2}{4}\right|\right] - \left[\ln\left|\frac{3-2}{3}\right|\right]$$

$$= \ln\left(\tfrac{1}{2}\right) - \ln\left(\tfrac{1}{3}\right) = \ln\left(\tfrac{3}{2}\right)$$

Example 3

Find $\int \dfrac{x^2 + 17x + 16}{(x+2)^2(3x-1)} \, dx$.

- First, write it as partial fractions.

  - It has a repeated factor so the $(x+2)$ needs to feature in two of the denominators, squared and on its own:
  $$\frac{x^2 + 17x + 16}{(x+2)^2(3x-1)} \equiv \frac{A}{(x+2)^2} + \frac{B}{(x+2)} + \frac{C}{(3x-1)}$$
  $$x^2 + 17x + 16 \equiv A(3x-1) + B(x+2)(3x-1) + C(x+2)^2$$

  - Use the substitution method (and equate coefficients to get B):

    Substituting $x = \tfrac{1}{3}$ gives: $\dfrac{196}{9} = 0A + 0B + \dfrac{49}{9}C \Rightarrow C = 4$

    Substituting $x = -2$ gives: $-14 = -7A + 0B + 0C \Rightarrow A = 2$

    Equate coefficients of x^2 to get B: $1 = 3B + C = 3B + 4$ so $B = -1$

- So you have:

$$\int \frac{x^2 + 17x + 16}{(x + 2)^2(3x - 1)}\, dx = \int \frac{2}{(x + 2)^2} - \frac{1}{(x + 2)} + \frac{4}{(3x - 1)}\, dx$$

$$\int 2(x + 2)^{-2}\, dx$$

$$= -\frac{2}{x + 2} - \ln|x + 2| + \frac{4}{3}\ln|3x - 1| + C$$

- Use the log laws $\log a^b = b \log a$ and $\log a - \log b = \log\left(\frac{a}{b}\right)$ to simplify:

$$= \ln\left|\frac{(3x - 1)^{\frac{4}{3}}}{x + 2}\right| - \frac{2}{x + 2} + C$$

Exercise 3.1

Q1 Integrate the following functions by writing them as partial fractions:

a) $\displaystyle\int \frac{24(x - 1)}{9 - 4x^2}\, dx$

b) $\displaystyle\int \frac{-4x^2 - 21x + 82}{(5x + 2)(x - 3)(x - 4)}\, dx$

c) $\displaystyle\int \frac{7x + 4}{(x + 2)^2(x - 3)}\, dx$

Q2 Find $\displaystyle\int_0^1 \frac{x}{(x - 2)(x - 3)}\, dx$ by expressing as partial fractions.

Give your answer as a single logarithm.

Q3 a) Express $\displaystyle\frac{6}{2x^2 - 5x + 2}$ in partial fractions.

b) Hence find $\displaystyle\int \frac{6}{2x^2 - 5x + 2}\, dx$ where $x > 2$.

c) Evaluate $\displaystyle\int_3^5 \frac{6}{2x^2 - 5x + 2}\, dx$, expressing your answer as a single logarithm.

Q4 Express $\displaystyle\frac{3y + 5}{y(y + 10)}$ as the sum of partial fractions and hence evaluate $\displaystyle\int_1^2 \frac{3y + 5}{y(y + 10)}\, dy$.

Q5 Given that $f(x) = 3x^2 + 17x - 32$ and $g(x) = (x - 4)(x - 1)(x + 3)$, find $\displaystyle\int_b^a \frac{f(x)}{g(x)}\, dx$, where $x > 4$, by expressing $\frac{f(x)}{g(x)}$ as partial fractions.

Q6 Show that $\displaystyle\int_0^{\frac{2}{3}} \frac{-(t + 3)}{(3t + 2)(t + 1)}\, dt = 2\ln\frac{5}{3} - \frac{7}{3}\ln 2$.

Q7 $\displaystyle\frac{18x^2 + 3x - 8}{(2x + 1)(3x - 1)} \equiv A + \frac{B}{(2x + 1)} + \frac{C}{(3x - 1)}$

a) Find the values of the constants A, B and C.

b) Hence show that the exact value of

$$\int_2^5 \frac{18x^2 + 3x - 8}{(2x + 1)(3x - 1)}\, dx = p + \ln q,$$

giving the values of the constants p and q.

Q7 Hint: This is an improper fraction (the degree of the numerator is the same as the degree of the denominator) — this is why it has a whole number, A, as well as the fractions. Have a look at p.17-18 if you need a reminder of how to deal with these.

4. Using Trigonometric Identities in Integration

You can sometimes use the trig identities you learnt in Chapter 2 to manipulate difficult-looking trig integrations to give functions you know how to integrate.

Integrating using the double angle formulas

If you're given a tricky **trig function** to integrate, you might be able to simplify it using one of the **double angle formulas**. They're especially useful for things like **cos² x**, **sin² x** and **sin x cos x**. Here are the double angle formulas from Chapter 2:

$$\sin 2x \equiv 2\sin x \cos x \qquad \cos 2x \equiv \cos^2 x - \sin^2 x$$

$$\tan 2x \equiv \frac{2\tan x}{1 - \tan^2 x}$$

You'll also have come across two other ways of writing the double angle formula for cos, which come from using the identity $\sin^2 x + \cos^2 x \equiv 1$:

$$\cos 2x \equiv 2\cos^2 x - 1 \qquad \cos 2x \equiv 1 - 2\sin^2 x$$

Tip: Remember:
$$\int \sin x = -\cos x + C$$
$$\int \cos x = \sin x + C$$
$$\int \tan x = \ln|\sec x| + C$$
$$\qquad\quad = -\ln|\cos x| + C$$

Once you've rearranged the original function using one of the **double angle formulas**, the function you're left with should be easier to integrate using the rules you've seen in C3.

Examples

Find the following:

a) $\int \sin^2 x \, dx$

- Rearranging the **cos** double angle formula: $\cos 2x \equiv 1 - 2\sin^2 x$ gives $\sin^2 x \equiv \frac{1}{2}(1 - \cos 2x)$.

Tip: Use one of the cos double angle formulas when you've got a $\cos^2 x$ or a $\sin^2 x$ to integrate.

- So rewrite the integration:
$$\int \sin^2 x \, dx = \int \tfrac{1}{2}(1 - \cos 2x)dx = \tfrac{1}{2}\int (1 - \cos 2x)dx$$
$$= \tfrac{1}{2}\left(x - \tfrac{1}{2}\sin 2x\right) + C = \tfrac{1}{2}x - \tfrac{1}{4}\sin 2x + C$$

b) $\int \cos^2 5x \, dx$

- Rearranging the **cos** double angle formula: $\cos 2x \equiv 2\cos^2 x - 1$

  gives $\cos^2 x \equiv \frac{1}{2}(\cos 2x + 1)$.

  > Don't forget to double the x coefficient and to divide by 10 when you integrate.

- So rewrite the integration:

$$\int \cos^2 5x \, dx = \int \frac{1}{2}(\cos 10x + 1)dx = \frac{1}{2}\int (\cos 10x + 1)dx$$

$$= \frac{1}{2}\left(\frac{1}{10}\sin 10x + x\right) + C = \boxed{\frac{1}{20}\sin 10x + \frac{1}{2}x + C}$$

Examples

Find the following integrals:

a) $\int \sin x \cos x \, dx$

- Rearranging the **sin** double angle formula: $\sin 2x \equiv 2\sin x \cos x$

  gives $\sin x \cos x \equiv \frac{1}{2}\sin 2x$.

- So rewrite the integration:

$$\int \sin x \cos x \, dx = \int \frac{1}{2}\sin 2x \, dx = \frac{1}{2}\left(-\frac{1}{2}\cos 2x\right) + C = \boxed{-\frac{1}{4}\cos 2x + C}$$

Tip: If you need to integrate a function of the form sin x cos x, use the double angle formula for sin.

b) $\int_0^{\frac{\pi}{4}} \sin 2x \cos 2x \, dx$

- Rearranging the **sin** double angle formula
  with x replaced with $2x$: $\sin 4x \equiv 2\sin 2x \cos 2x$

  gives $\sin 2x \cos 2x \equiv \frac{1}{2}\sin 4x$.

- So rewrite the integration:

$$\int_0^{\frac{\pi}{4}} \sin 2x \cos 2x \, dx = \int_0^{\frac{\pi}{4}} \frac{1}{2}\sin 4x \, dx = \left[\frac{1}{2}\left(-\frac{1}{4}\cos 4x\right)\right]_0^{\frac{\pi}{4}} = -\frac{1}{8}\left[\cos 4x\right]_0^{\frac{\pi}{4}}$$

$$= -\frac{1}{8}\left(\left[\cos\frac{4\pi}{4}\right] - [\cos 0]\right) = \frac{1}{8}(\cos 0 - \cos\pi)$$

$$= \frac{1}{8}(1 - (-1)) = \frac{2}{8} = \boxed{\frac{1}{4}}$$

Tip: Don't forget to 'double the angle' when using these formulas.

Example

Find $\int \dfrac{4\tan\frac{x}{2}}{1 - \tan^2\frac{x}{2}} \, dx$.

- Rearrange, then use the double angle formula for **tan**:

$$\frac{4\tan\frac{x}{2}}{1 - \tan^2\frac{x}{2}} = 2\left(\frac{2\tan\frac{x}{2}}{1 - \tan^2\frac{x}{2}}\right) = 2\left(\tan\left(2 \times \frac{x}{2}\right)\right) = 2\tan x$$

- Rewrite the integration:

$$\int \frac{4\tan\frac{x}{2}}{1 - \tan^2\frac{x}{2}} \, dx = \int 2\tan x \, dx = \boxed{-2\ln|\cos x| + C}$$

Q1 Find the following indefinite integrals:

a) $\int \cos^2 x \, dx$

b) $\int 6 \sin x \cos x \, dx$

c) $\int \sin^2 6x \, dx$

d) $\int \dfrac{2 \tan 2x}{1 - \tan^2 2x} \, dx$

e) $\int 2 \sin 4x \cos 4x \, dx$

f) $\int 2 \cos^2 4x \, dx$

g) $\int \cos x \sin x \, dx$

h) $\int \sin 3x \cos 3x \, dx$

i) $\int \dfrac{6 \tan 3x}{1 - \tan^2 3x} \, dx$

j) $\int 5 \sin 2x \cos 2x \, dx$

k) $\int (\sin x + \cos x)^2 \, dx$

l) $\int 4 \sin x \cos x \cos 2x \, dx$

m) $\int (\cos x + \sin x)(\cos x - \sin x) \, dx$

n) $\int \sin^2 x \cot x \, dx$

Q1 l) Hint: Use the sin double angle formula twice.

Q2 Evaluate the following definite integrals:

a) $\int_0^{\frac{\pi}{4}} \sin^2 x \, dx$

b) $\int_0^{\pi} \cos^2 2x \, dx$

c) $\int_0^{\pi} \sin \frac{x}{2} \cos \frac{x}{2} \, dx$

d) $\int_{\frac{\pi}{4}}^{\frac{\pi}{2}} \sin^2 2x \, dx$

e) $\int_0^{\frac{\pi}{4}} \cos 2x \sin 2x \, dx$

f) $\int_{\frac{\pi}{4}}^{\frac{\pi}{2}} \sin^2 x - \cos^2 x \, dx$

Integrating using other trigonometric identities

- There are a couple of other **identities** you can use to simplify trig functions (you met these in C3):

$$\sec^2 x \equiv 1 + \tan^2 x \qquad \qquad \text{cosec}^2 x \equiv 1 + \cot^2 x$$

Tip: If you use one of these identities to get rid of a $\cot^2 x$ or a $\tan^2 x$, don't forget the stray 1s flying around — they'll just integrate to x.

- These identities are really useful if you have to integrate **$\tan^2 x$** or **$\cot^2 x$**, as you already know how to integrate $\sec^2 x$ and $\text{cosec}^2 x$ (see your C3 notes).

$$\int \sec^2 x \, dx = \tan x + C \qquad \int \text{cosec}^2 x \, dx = -\cot x + C$$

Examples

Find the following integrals:

a) $\int \tan^2 x - 1 \, dx$

- Rewrite the function in terms of $\sec^2 x$:

$$\boxed{\sec^2 x \equiv 1 + \tan^2 x}$$

$$\tan^2 x - 1 = (\sec^2 x - 1) - 1 = \sec^2 x - 2$$

- Now integrate:

$$\int \tan^2 x - 1 \, dx = \int \sec^2 x - 2 \, dx = \tan x - 2x + C$$

b) $\int \cot^2 3x \, dx$

- Get the function in terms of $\text{cosec}^2 x$:

$$\boxed{\text{cosec}^2 x \equiv 1 + \cot^2 x}$$

$$\cot^2 3x = \text{cosec}^2 3x - 1$$

- Remember to divide by 3, the coefficient of x, when you integrate:

$$\int \cot^2 3x \, dx = \int \text{cosec}^2 3x - 1 \, dx = -\frac{1}{3}\cot 3x - x + C$$

c) $\int \cos^3 x \, dx$

- You don't know how to integrate $\cos^3 x$ but you can split it into $\cos^2 x$ and $\cos x$ and use identities.

$$\cos^3 x = \cos^2 x \cos x = (1 - \sin^2 x)\cos x$$
$$= \cos x - \cos x \sin^2 x$$
$$= \cos x - \cos x(\sin x)^2$$

$$\boxed{\sin^2 x + \cos^2 x \equiv 1}$$

- Now write out the integral:

$$\int \cos^3 x \, dx = \int \cos x - \cos x(\sin x)^2 \, dx$$
$$= \int \cos x \, dx - \int \cos x(\sin x)^2 \, dx$$

- The second integral is a product of a function (to a power) and its derivative so use the formula from C3 with $f(x) = \sin x$, $f'(x) = \cos x$, $n = 2$ and $n + 1 = 3$:

$$\int 3 \cos x \sin^2 x \, dx = \sin^3 x + c$$
$$\text{So } \int \cos x \sin^2 x \, dx = \frac{1}{3}\sin^3 x + c$$

> **Tip:** In case you've forgotten, the formula from C3 for integrating a function raised to a power and multiplied by its derivative is:
> $$\int (n + 1)f'(x)[f(x)]^n \, dx$$
> $$= [f(x)]^{n+1} + C$$

- So the whole integral is:

$$\int \cos^3 x \, dx = \int \cos x \, dx - \int \cos x(\sin x)^2 \, dx$$
$$= \sin x - \frac{1}{3}\sin^3 x + C$$

Evaluate $\int_0^{\frac{\pi}{3}} 6 \sin 3x \cos 3x + \tan^2 \frac{1}{2}x + 1 \, dx$.

- Using the **sin** double angle formula:
$$6 \sin 3x \cos 3x \equiv 3 \sin 6x$$

and using the identity for **tan² x**:
$$\tan^2 \frac{1}{2}x + 1 \equiv \sec^2 \frac{1}{2}x$$

- Now integrate:
$$\int_0^{\frac{\pi}{3}} 6 \sin 3x \cos 3x + \tan^2 \frac{1}{2}x + 1 \, dx$$

$$= \int_0^{\frac{\pi}{3}} 3 \sin 6x + \sec^2 \frac{1}{2}x \, dx = \left[-\frac{3}{6} \cos 6x + 2 \tan \frac{1}{2}x \right]_0^{\frac{\pi}{3}}$$

$$= \left[-\frac{1}{2} \cos 6\left(\frac{\pi}{3}\right) + 2 \tan \frac{1}{2}\left(\frac{\pi}{3}\right) \right] - \left[-\frac{1}{2} \cos 6(0) + 2 \tan \frac{1}{2}(0) \right]$$

$$= \left[-\frac{1}{2} \cos(2\pi) + 2 \tan\left(\frac{\pi}{6}\right) \right] - \left[-\frac{1}{2} \cos(0) + 2 \tan(0) \right] \quad \text{Put in the limits.}$$

$$= \left[-\frac{1}{2}(1) + 2\left(\frac{1}{\sqrt{3}}\right) \right] - \left[-\frac{1}{2}(1) + 2(0) \right]$$

$$= -\frac{1}{2} + \frac{2}{\sqrt{3}} + \frac{1}{2}$$

$$= \frac{2}{\sqrt{3}} = \frac{2\sqrt{3}}{3} \quad \longleftarrow \quad \text{Rationalise the denominator.}$$

Exercise 4.2

Q1   Find the following integrals:

a) $\int \cot^2 x - 4 \, dx$

b) $\int \tan^2 x \, dx$

c) $\int 3 \cot^2 x \, dx$

d) $\int \tan^2 4x \, dx$

Q2   Find the exact value of $\int_0^{\frac{\pi}{4}} \tan^2 x + \cos^2 x - \sin^2 x \, dx$.

Q3 Hint: Factorise.

Q3   Integrate the following functions with respect to x.

a) $\tan^3 x + \tan^5 x$ b) $\cot^5 x + \cot^3 x$ c) $\sin^3 x$

Q4   Find $\int 4 + \cot^2 3x \, dx$

Q5   a) Use the identity $\sin A + \sin B \equiv 2 \sin\left(\frac{A+B}{2}\right) \cos\left(\frac{A-B}{2}\right)$
to show that $2 \sin 4x \cos x = \sin 5x + \sin 3x$.

b) Hence find $\int 2 \sin 4x \cos x \, dx$

Q6-7 Hint: Remember,
if f(x) = sec x,
f'(x) = sec x tan x
and if f(x) = cosec x,
f'(x) = –cosec x cot x.
These are both in the
formula booklet.

Q6   Find $\int (\sec x + \tan x)^2 \, dx$

Q7   Find $\int (\cot x + \text{cosec} \, x)^2 \, dx$

5. Differential Equations

Differential equations involve differentiation as well as integration. The differentiation comes in because they always include a derivative term, usually to describe a rate of change, and integration is used to solve them.

Learning Objectives:

- Be able to formulate a differential equation for a given situation.
- Be able to find general and particular solutions to differential equations.
- Be able to formulate and solve differential equations that model real-life situations, and interpret the results in context.

Differential equations

- A **differential equation** is an equation that includes a **derivative term** such as $\frac{dy}{dx}$ (or $\frac{dP}{dt}, \frac{ds}{dt}, \frac{dV}{dr}$ etc, depending on the variables), as well as **other variables** (like x and y).

- Before you even think about **solving** them, you have to be able to **set up** ('**formulate**') differential equations.

- Differential equations tend to involve a **rate of change** (giving a derivative term) and a **proportion relation**, where the rate of change will be directly or inversely proportional to some function of the variables.

- It'll help to think about what the derivative **actually means**.
  $\frac{dy}{dx}$ is defined as 'the **rate of change** of y with respect to x',
  in other words, it tells you how y changes as x changes.

Tip: One of the variables in a differential equation will often be time, t, — so the question will be about how something changes over time.

Example 1

The number of bacteria in a petri dish, b, is increasing over time, t, at a rate directly proportional to the number of bacteria.
Formulate a differential equation that shows this information.

- The question tells you that you need to write a differential equation, so you know there'll be a **derivative term**. Work out what that is first.

- You're told that the number of bacteria (b) increases as time (t) increases — so that's the rate of change of b with respect to t, or $\frac{db}{dt}$.

- The rate of change, $\frac{db}{dt}$, is proportional to b, so $\frac{db}{dt} \propto b$.

- We're looking for an equation, not a proportion relation, so rewrite it:

  So $\frac{db}{dt} = kb$ for some constant k, $k > 0$.

Tip: Remember — if $a \propto b$, then $a = kb$ for some constant k.

Example 2

The volume of interdimensional space jelly, V, in a container is decreasing over time, t, at a rate inversely proportional to the square of its volume. Show this as a differential equation.

- This time the question tells you how V decreases as t increases — the derivative term is the rate of change of V with respect to t, or $\frac{dV}{dt}$.

- $\frac{dV}{dt}$ is **inversely proportional** to the **square** of V, so $\frac{dV}{dt} \propto \frac{1}{V^2}$.

- The equation needs a minus sign, because V is **decreasing** as t increases.

  $\frac{dV}{dt} = -\frac{k}{V^2}$ for some constant k, $k > 0$.

Tip: 'x is inversely proportional to y' means x is directly proportional to $\frac{1}{y}$.

Example 3

The rate of cooling of a hot liquid is proportional to the difference between the temperature of the liquid and the temperature of the room. Formulate a differential equation to represent this situation.

- Let L = temperature of the liquid, R = room temperature and t = time.

- The derivative term is the rate of change of L with respect to t, or $\dfrac{\mathrm{d}L}{\mathrm{d}t}$.

- The rate of change is proportional to the difference between L and R, so $\dfrac{\mathrm{d}L}{\mathrm{d}t} \propto (L - R)$.

- $\dfrac{\mathrm{d}L}{\mathrm{d}t}$ is the rate of cooling — so the temperature is **decreasing** and you need a minus sign in the equation again.

$$\frac{\mathrm{d}L}{\mathrm{d}t} = -k(L - R) \text{ for some constant } k, \ k > 0.$$

Tip: If the variables aren't given in the question, you'll have to come up with them for yourself.

Exercise 5.1

Q1 The number of fleas (N) on a cat is increasing over time, t, at a rate directly proportional to the number of fleas. Show this as a differential equation.

Q2 The value of x is increasing over time, t, at a rate inversely proportional to the square of x. Formulate a differential equation to show this.

Q3 The rate of depreciation of the amount (£A) a car is worth is directly proportional to the square root of A. Show this as a differential equation.

Q4 The rate of decrease of y with respect to time, t, is directly proportional to the difference between y and λ where λ is a constant. Formulate a differential equation to show this.

Q5 Hint: The overall rate of change of V is the difference between the rate at which water is flowing in and the rate at which it's flowing out.

Q5 The volume of water which is being poured into a container is directly proportional to the volume of water (V) in the container. The container has a hole in it from which water flows out at a rate of 20 cm³s⁻¹. Show this as a differential equation.

Solving differential equations

- **Solving** a differential equation means using it to find an **equation** in terms of the two variables, **without** a derivative term. To do this, you need to use **integration**.

- The only differential equations containing x and y terms that you'll be able to solve in C4 are ones with **separable variables** — where x and y can be separated into functions $f(x)$ and $g(y)$.

Tip: Remember — your equation might not be in terms of x and y.

Here's the method:

- **Step 1:** Write the differential equation in the form $\dfrac{dy}{dx} = f(x)g(y)$.

- **Step 2:** **Rearrange** the equation into the form: $\dfrac{1}{g(y)}dy = f(x)dx$.

  To do this, get all the terms containing y on the **left-hand side**, and all the terms containing x on the **right-hand side** and split up the $\dfrac{dy}{dx}$.

Tip: Although $\dfrac{dy}{dx}$ isn't really a fraction, you can treat it as if it is here.

- **Step 3:** Now **integrate both sides**: $\displaystyle\int \dfrac{1}{g(y)}dy = \int f(x)dx$.

  Don't forget the **constant of integration** (you only need one — not one on each side). It might be useful to write the constant as **ln k** rather than **C**.

- **Step 4:** **Rearrange** your answer to get it in a **nice form** — you might be asked to find it in the form $y = h(x)$.

- **Step 5:** If you're asked for a **general solution**, leave C (or k) in your answer. If they want a **particular solution**, they'll give you x and y values for a certain point. All you do is put these values into your equation and use them to **find C** (or k).

Tip: Sometimes there'll already be another k in the differential equation (e.g. if you've formulated the equation yourself). Obviously, in that case you can't use ln k as the constant of integration, so pick another letter — you might see examples that use ln A instead.

Example 1

Find the general solution of the differential equation $\dfrac{ds}{dt} = -6t^2$.

- **Step 1** is already done — $f(t) = -6t^2$, $g(s) = 1$.

- **Step 2** — rearrange the equation: $\qquad ds = -6t^2\,dt$

- **Step 3** — integrate both sides: $\qquad \displaystyle\int 1\,ds = \int -6t^2\,dt$

  $\Rightarrow \qquad \boxed{s = -2t^3 + C}$

Steps 4 and 5 aren't needed here — the equation doesn't need rearranging, and you're only looking for the general solution, so you're done.

Tip: There's no 's' term in this differential equation. When this is the case, you can just integrate 'normally' without separating the variables.

$$s = \int \dfrac{ds}{dt}\,dt$$

Example 2

Find the particular solution of $\dfrac{dy}{dx} = 2y(1 + x)^2$ when $x = -1$ and $y = 4$.

- Identify f(x) and g(y): $f(x) = 2(1 + x)^2$ and $g(y) = y$.

- Separate the variables: $\dfrac{1}{y}\,dy = 2(1 + x)^2\,dx$

- And integrate: $\int \dfrac{1}{y}\,dy = \int 2(1 + x)^2\,dx$

                                   $\Rightarrow$ $\ln|y| = \dfrac{2}{3}(1 + x)^3 + C$

- Now to find the particular solution, work out the value of C for the given values of x and y:

                                  $\ln 4 = \dfrac{2}{3}(1 + (-1))^3 + C$

                               $\Rightarrow$ $\ln 4 = C$

                             so $\boxed{\ln|y| = \dfrac{2}{3}(1 + x)^3 + \ln 4}$

Example 3

Find the general solution of $(x - 2)(2x + 3)\dfrac{dy}{dx} = xy + 5y$, where $x > 2$. Give your answer in the form $y = f(x)$.

- First, separate the variables: $\dfrac{dy}{dx} = \dfrac{x + 5}{(x - 2)(2x + 3)} \times y$

                                   $\dfrac{1}{y}\,dy = \dfrac{x + 5}{(x - 2)(2x + 3)}\,dx$

- To make the right-hand side easier to integrate, write it as partial fractions (see Chapter 1):

                       $\dfrac{x + 5}{(x - 2)(2x + 3)} \equiv \dfrac{A}{x - 2} + \dfrac{B}{2x + 3}$

          $\Rightarrow$ $x + 5 \equiv A(2x + 3) + B(x - 2)$

- Solving for A and B gives $A = 1$, $B = -1$, so $\dfrac{1}{y}\,dy = \dfrac{1}{x - 2} - \dfrac{1}{2x + 3}\,dx$

- Now you can integrate: $\int \dfrac{1}{y}\,dy = \int \dfrac{1}{x - 2} - \dfrac{1}{2x + 3}\,dx$

                   $\Rightarrow$ $\ln|y| = \ln|x - 2| - \dfrac{1}{2}\ln|2x + 3| + \ln k$

                   $\Rightarrow$ $\ln|y| = \ln\left| \dfrac{k(x - 2)}{\sqrt{2x + 3}} \right|$

  You know $x > 2$ so $x - 2$ is positive and the modulus can be removed. $\Rightarrow$ $\boxed{y = \dfrac{k(x - 2)}{\sqrt{2x + 3}}}$

Tip: Since all the other terms are ln(something), it makes sense to use ln k as the constant of integration here, then you can use the log laws to simplify.

Example 4

Find the particular solution to the differential equation $\dfrac{db}{dt} = 4\sqrt{b}$,
given that when $t = 12$, $b = 900$.

Give your answer in the form $b = f(t)$.

- Rearranging $\dfrac{db}{dt} = 4\sqrt{b}$ gives: $\qquad\qquad \dfrac{1}{\sqrt{b}}\, db = 4\, dt$

- Integrate both sides: $\qquad\qquad\qquad \displaystyle\int b^{-\frac{1}{2}}\, db = \int 4\, dt$

$$\Rightarrow \qquad 2b^{\frac{1}{2}} = 4t + C$$

- In this case, it's easier to find C for the given values of b and t before you rearrange the equation:

$$2\sqrt{b} = 4t + C \quad\Rightarrow\quad 2\sqrt{900} = 4(12) + C$$
$$\Rightarrow\quad 60 = 48 + C$$
$$\Rightarrow\quad C = 12$$

> **Tip:** Rearranging the equation first, then finding C would give you a quadratic in C to solve, so it's easier to leave the rearrangement till last here.

- Now rearrange to get the form $b = f(t)$:

$$2\sqrt{b} = 4t + 12 \quad\Rightarrow\quad \sqrt{b} = 2t + 6$$
$$\Rightarrow\quad \boxed{b = 4t^2 + 24t + 36}$$

Exercise 5.2

Q1 Find the general solutions of the following differential equations where $x \geq 0$. Give your answers in the form $y = f(x)$.

a) $\dfrac{dy}{dx} = 8x^3$

b) $\dfrac{dy}{dx} = 5y$

c) $\dfrac{dy}{dx} = 6x^2 y$

d) $\dfrac{dy}{dx} = \dfrac{y}{x}$

e) $\dfrac{dy}{dx} = (y + 1)\cos x$

f) $\dfrac{dy}{dx} = \dfrac{(3x - 6)y}{(x - 4)(2x - 5)}$

> **Q1 f) Hint:** You'll need to do some work before you can integrate with respect to x.

Q2 Find the particular solutions of the following differential equations at the given conditions:

a) $\dfrac{dy}{dx} = -\dfrac{x}{y}$ $\qquad\qquad x = 0,\ y = 2$

b) $\dfrac{dx}{dt} = \dfrac{2}{\sqrt{x}}$ $\qquad\qquad t = 5,\ x = 9$

c) $\dfrac{dV}{dt} = 3(V - 1)$ $\qquad\quad t = 0,\ V = 5$

d) $\dfrac{dy}{dx} = \dfrac{\tan y}{x}$ $\qquad\qquad x = 2,\ y = \dfrac{\pi}{2}$

e) $\dfrac{dx}{dt} = 10x(x + 1)$ $\qquad t = 0,\ x = 1$

Q3 The rate of increase of the variable V at time t satisfies the differential equation $\frac{dV}{dt} = a - bV$, where a and b are positive constants.

a) Show that $V = \frac{a}{b} - Ae^{-bt}$, where A is a positive constant.

b) Given that $V = \frac{a}{4b}$ when $t = 0$, find A in terms of a and b.

c) Find the value V approaches as t gets very large.

Q4 a) Solve the differential equation $\frac{dx}{dt} = (x + 2)(2x + 3)\tan t$, where $x \neq -2, -\frac{3}{2}$, given that $x = 0$ when $t = 0$.

b) Find x when $t = \frac{\pi}{3}$.

Applying differential equations to real-life problems

- Some questions involve taking **real-life problems** and using differential equations to **model** them.

- **Population** questions come up quite often — the population might be **increasing** or **decreasing**, and you have to find and solve differential equations to show it. In cases like this, one variable will usually be t, **time**.

- You might be given a **starting condition** — e.g. the **initial population**. The important thing to remember is that:

> the starting condition occurs when $t = 0$

Tip: This might seem pretty obvious, but it's really important.

- Once you've solved the differential equation you can use it to **answer questions** about the model. For example, if the equation is for population you might be asked to find the **population** after a certain number of years, or the **number of years** it takes to reach a certain population. Don't forget to relate the answer back to the situation given in the question.

Questions like the ones below can be a bit **overwhelming**, but follow things through **step by step** and they shouldn't be too bad.

Example 1

The population of rabbits in a park is decreasing as winter approaches. The rate of decrease is directly proportional to the current number of rabbits (P).

a) Explain why this situation can be modelled by the differential equation $\frac{dP}{dt} = -kP$, where t is the time in days and k is a positive constant.

- The model states that the rate of decrease in the rabbit population (i.e. $\frac{dP}{dt}$) is **proportional** to P. This means $\frac{dP}{dt} \propto P$.

- By introducing a **constant** of proportionality, the model becomes:
$$\frac{dP}{dt} = -kP$$

- The minus sign shows that the population is decreasing.

---

b) **If the initial population is P_0, solve your differential equation to find P in terms of P_0, k and t.**

- First, solve the differential equation to find the general solution:

$$\frac{dP}{dt} = -kP \implies \frac{1}{P}\,dP = -k\,dt$$

$$\implies \int \frac{1}{P}\,dP = \int -k\,dt$$

$$\implies \ln P = -kt + C$$

Tip: You don't need modulus signs when you integrate to get $\ln P$ here. $P \geq 0$ as you can't have a negative population.

- At $t = 0$, $P = P_0$. Putting these values into the equation gives:

$$\ln P_0 = -k(0) + C \implies \ln P_0 = C$$

- So the equation becomes:

$$\ln P = -kt + \ln P_0 \implies P = e^{(-kt + \ln P_0)} = e^{-kt}e^{\ln P_0}$$

$$\implies P = P_0 e^{-kt}$$

Tip: Look back at your C3 notes and p.19-20 of this book for more on dealing with equations containing e or ln.

c) **Given that $k = 0.1$, find the time at which the population of rabbits will have halved, to the nearest day.**

- When the population of rabbits has halved, $P = \frac{1}{2}P_0$. You've been told that $k = 0.1$, so substitute these values into the equation above and solve for t:

$$\frac{1}{2}P_0 = P_0 e^{-0.1t} \implies \frac{1}{2} = e^{-0.1t}$$

$$\implies \ln\frac{1}{2} = -0.1t$$

$$\implies -0.6931 = -0.1t$$

$$\implies t = 6.931$$

- So to the nearest day, $t = 7$.
  This means that it will take 7 days for the population to halve.

Tip: Make sure you always link the numbers back to the situation.

Example 2

Water is leaking from the bottom of a water tank shaped like a vertical cylinder, so that at time t seconds the depth, D, of water in the tank is decreasing at a rate proportional to $\frac{1}{D^2}$.

a) **Explain why the depth of water satisfies the differential equation $\frac{dD}{dt} = -\frac{k}{D^2}$ for some constant $k > 0$.**

The question tells you that the rate at which D decreases (i.e. $\frac{dD}{dt}$) is inversely proportional to D^2. This can be written as:

$$\frac{dD}{dt} \propto \frac{1}{D^2} \implies \frac{dD}{dt} = -\frac{k}{D^2}, \text{ for some } k > 0 .$$

The minus sign indicates that the depth of the water is decreasing.

b) **Given that D is decreasing at a rate of 2 cm s^{-1} when $D = 40$ cm, find k.**

Use the differential equation for D: $\frac{dD}{dt} = -\frac{k}{D^2}$

So $\frac{dD}{dt} = -2$ when $D = 40 \implies -\frac{k}{40^2} = -2$

$$\implies k = 2 \times 40^2 = 3200$$

c) **Given that $D = 60$ cm at $t = 0$ s, find the particular solution to the differential equation for D, and hence calculate how long it takes for the tank to empty.**

- Solve the differential equation, using the value of k from part b), to find the general solution:

$$\frac{dD}{dt} = -\frac{3200}{D^2} \Rightarrow D^2\, dD = -3200\, dt$$

$$\Rightarrow \int D^2\, dD = \int -3200\, dt$$

$$\Rightarrow \frac{1}{3}D^3 = -3200t + C$$

- When $t = 0$, $D = 60$. Putting these values into the equation gives:

$$\frac{1}{3}60^3 = -3200(0) + C \Rightarrow C = 72\,000$$

So $\frac{1}{3}D^3 = 72\,000 - 3200t$

- The tank is empty when $D = 0 \Rightarrow 72\,000 = 3200t$

$$\Rightarrow \boxed{t = 22.5 \text{ s}}$$

d) **Given that the radius of the cylinder is 20 cm, calculate the rate at which the volume of water in the tank is decreasing when $t = 10$ s.**

- The volume of water in the tank is $V = \pi r^2 h = \pi(20)^2 D = 400\pi D$.

$$\Rightarrow \frac{dV}{dD} = 400\pi$$

- So using the chain rule:

$$\frac{dV}{dt} = \frac{dV}{dD} \times \frac{dD}{dt} = 400\pi \times -\frac{3200}{D^2} = -\frac{1280000\pi}{D^2}$$

- When $t = 10$, $\frac{1}{3}D^3 = 72000 - 3200(10) = 40000$

$$\Rightarrow D = \sqrt[3]{3 \times 40000} = 49.324 \text{ cm}$$

So $\frac{dV}{dt} = \frac{-1280000\pi}{49.324^2} = -1652.87 \text{cm}^3\text{s}^{-1}$

- So the volume is decreasing at a rate of $\boxed{1650 \text{ cm}^3\text{s}^{-1} \text{ (3 s.f.)}}$

Exercise 5.3

Q1 A virus spreads so that t hours after infection, the rate of increase of the number of germs (N) in the body of an infected person is directly proportional to the number of germs in the body.

a) Given that this can be represented by the differential equation $\frac{dN}{dt} = kN$, show that the general solution of this equation is $N = Ae^{kt}$, where A and k are positive constants.

b) Given that a person catching the virus will initially be infected with 200 germs and that this will double to 400 germs in 8 hours, find the number of infected germs a person has after 24 hours.

Q2 The rate of depreciation of the value (V) of a car at time t after it is first purchased is directly proportional to V.

a) If the initial value of the car is V_0, show that $V = V_0 e^{-kt}$, where k is a positive constant.

b) If the car drops to one half of its initial value in the first year after purchase, how long (to the nearest month) will it take to be worth 5% of its initial value?

Q3 It is thought that the rate of increase of the number of field mice (N) in a given area is directly proportional to N.

a) Formulate a differential equation for N.

b) Given that in 4 weeks the number of mice in a particular field has risen from 20 to 30, find the length of time, to the nearest week, before the field is over-run with 1000 mice.

A biologist believes that the rate of increase of the number field mice is actually directly proportional to the square root of N when natural factors such as predators and disease are taken into account.

c) Repeat parts a) and b) using this new model.

Q4 A cube has side length x. At time t seconds, the side length is increasing at a rate of $\dfrac{1}{x^2(t+1)} \text{cm s}^{-1}$.

a) Show that the volume (V) is increasing at a rate which satisfies the differential equation $\dfrac{dV}{dt} = \dfrac{3}{t+1}$.

b) Given that the volume of the cube is initially 15 cm³, find the length of time, to 3 s.f., for it to reach a volume of 19 cm³.

Q5 A sinister cult has developed a new recruitment strategy. The rate of increase of the number of cult members (y) in a town can be represented by the differential equation $\dfrac{dy}{dt} = k(p - y)$, where p is the population of the town and t is the time in days since the new strategy was introduced in the town.

a) Find the general solution of this equation.

b) The cult tests its strategy in the town of Mathchester. Given that the population of Mathchester is 30 000, the cult initially has 10 000 members in the town, and it takes 5 days for the membership to reach 12 000, how long, to the nearest day, will it take to reach 25 000?

c) Draw a graph to show this.

d) The Supreme Leader wants 28 000 cult members in Mathchester within 92 days of introducing the new recruitment strategy. According to the model, will he achieve this?

Q5 c) Hint: You just need to sketch the graph of the equation you found in part b).

Review Exercise — Chapter 5

Q1 A curve is defined by the parametric equations $x = t^2$, $y = 3t^3 - 4t$.

a) Find $\dfrac{dy}{dx}$ for this curve.

b) Find the coordinates of the stationary points of the curve.

Q2 A curve C defined by $x = t^3 - t^2$, $y = t^3 + 3t^2 - 9t$ has turning points at (a, b) and (c, d).

a) Find the coordinates (a, b) and (c, d).

b) Find the values of t at the points where C cuts the x-axis and hence show that C passes through the origin. Leave your answers in surd form if necessary.

c) Find the equation of the tangent to C when $t = 2$.

Q3 A curve is given parametrically by $x = 3se^s$, $y = e^{2s} + se^{2s}$

a) Find the equations of the tangents to the curve at $s = 0$ and $s = 2$.

b) Hence find the coordinates of the point of intersection of these tangents, leaving your answer in terms of e.

Q4 The trajectory of a particle is given by the parametric equations $x = t^3 + t^2$, $y = \dfrac{1}{2}t^2 - 6t$.

a) Find the gradient $\dfrac{dy}{dx}$ of the trajectory in terms of t.

b) Hence find the turning point of the trajectory.

c) Find the equations of the tangents to the trajectory when $y = 0$.

Q5 Use implicit differentiation to find $\dfrac{dy}{dx}$ for each of the following equations:

a) $4x^2 - 2y^2 = 7x^2y$ b) $3x^4 - 2xy^2 = y$ c) $\cos x \sin y = xy$

Q6 Using your answers to Q5 above, find:

a) the gradient of the tangent to the graph of $4x^2 - 2y^2 = 7x^2y$ at $(1, -4)$,

b) the gradient of the normal to the graph of $3x^4 - 2xy^2 = y$ at $(1, 1)$.

Q7 A curve is defined implicitly by $x \cos x + y \sin x = y^3$.

a) Find the gradient $\dfrac{dy}{dx}$ of the curve.

b) Show that at the stationary points of the curve, $y = x \tan x - 1$.

c) Show that there are three points on the curve with coordinates $\left(\dfrac{\pi}{2}, a\right)$.

d) Find the equations of the tangents at each of these points and hence show that two of these tangents will never intersect.

Q8 The curve $x \ln x + x^2y = y^2x - 6x$ passes through two points $(1, a)$ and $(1, b)$, where $a > b$.

a) Find a and b.

b) Use implicit differentiation to find the gradient of the curve at each of these points and hence the equations of the normals passing through the points.

c) Find the coordinates of the point where the normals intersect.

Q9 Given that $\dfrac{3x + 10}{(2x + 3)(x - 4)} \equiv \dfrac{A}{2x + 3} + \dfrac{B}{x - 4}$, find $\displaystyle\int \dfrac{3x + 10}{(2x + 3)(x - 4)}\,dx$.

Q10 Given that $f(x) = \dfrac{-2x^2 + 12x + 31}{(x - 3)^2(2x + 1)} \equiv \dfrac{A}{(x - 3)^2} + \dfrac{B}{(x - 3)} + \dfrac{C}{(2x + 1)}$, find $\displaystyle\int_4^9 f(x)\,dx$.

Q11 Use an appropriate trig identity to find $\displaystyle\int \dfrac{2\tan 3x}{1 - \tan^2 3x}\,dx$.

Q12 Find $\displaystyle\int \cos^2 4x + \cot^2 4x\,dx$.

Q13 Formulate differential equations to represent the following:

a) The rate of increase of x as y increases is directly proportional to the square of x.

b) The volume (V) of water in a container is decreasing with time (t) at a rate inversely proportional to the square root of V.

c) The speed, s, of a moving object is decreasing with time at a rate directly proportional to the difference between s and the object's initial speed, s_0.

Q14 Find the general solution to the differential equation $\dfrac{dy}{dx} = \dfrac{1}{y}\cos x$.
Give your answer in the form $y^2 = f(x)$.

Q15 Find the particular solution of the differential equation $\dfrac{dx}{dt} = kte^t$,
given that $x = 0$ when $t = 1$ and $x = -3$ when $t = 0$.

Q16 a) Find the general solution of the equation $\dfrac{dx}{d\theta} = \cos^2 x \cot\theta$.

b) Given that $x = \dfrac{\pi}{4}$ when $\theta = \dfrac{\pi}{2}$, find a particular solution.

c) Hence find the value of x when $\theta = \dfrac{\pi}{6}$, for $0 < x < \dfrac{\pi}{2}$.

Q17 The population of squirrels is increasing suspiciously quickly.
The rate of increase is directly proportional to the current number of squirrels, S.

a) Formulate a differential equation to model the rate of increase in terms of S,
t (time in weeks) and k, a positive constant.

b) The squirrels need a population of 150 to successfully take over the forest. If, initially,
$S = 30$ and $\dfrac{dS}{dt} = 6$, how long (to the nearest week) will it take before they can overthrow
the evil hedgehogs?

Q18 The rate of decrease of temperature ($T\,°C$) of a cup of tea with time (t minutes) satisfies the
differential equation $\dfrac{dT}{dt} = -k(T - 21)$, where k is a positive constant.

a) Given that the initial temperature of the tea is 90 °C, and it cools
to 80 °C in 5 minutes, find a particular solution for T.

b) Use this solution to find: (i)   the temperature of the tea after 15 minutes,

(ii)   the time it takes to drop to 40 °C.

c) Sketch the graph of T against t.

1   The curve C is defined by the parametric equations
$$x = 3\theta - \cos 3\theta, \quad y = 2 \sin \theta, \quad -\pi \leq \theta \leq \pi.$$

a)   Find an expression for $\dfrac{dy}{dx}$.

(3 marks)

b)   (i)   Show that the gradient of C at the point $(\pi + 1, \sqrt{3})$ is $\dfrac{1}{3}$.

(3 marks)

     (ii)   Find the equation of the normal to C when $\theta = \dfrac{\pi}{6}$.

(4 marks)

2    $f(x) = \dfrac{11x^2 + 42x + 36}{3x^3 + 16x^2 + 28x + 16}$

a)   Express $f(x)$ in the form: $\dfrac{A}{(x + 2)^2} + \dfrac{B}{x + 2} + \dfrac{C}{3x + 4}$

where A, B and C are all integers to be found.

(4 marks)

b)   Hence, or otherwise, find the integral of $f(x)$, with respect to x.

(3 marks)

3   Use an appropriate identity to find $\displaystyle\int 2 \tan^2 3x + 2 \; dx$.

(3 marks)

4   A curve C is given by $x^2y + y^2x - 2y^2 - xy^3 = 0$.

a)   Use implicit differentiation to find the gradient $\dfrac{dy}{dx}$ of the curve.

(3 marks)

b)   Hence show that at the stationary points of the curve $x = \dfrac{y^2 - y}{2}$.

(2 marks)

c)   Show that when $x = 2$, $y = 0$ or $y = \pm\sqrt{2}$.

(2 marks)

d)   Find the equation of the tangent to the curve at $(2, \sqrt{2})$.

(4 marks)

5   The curve C has the equation $3e^x + 6y = 2x^2y$.

a)   (i)   Use implicit differentiation to find an expression for $\dfrac{dy}{dx}$.

(3 marks)

     (ii)   Show that at the stationary points of C, $y = \dfrac{3e^x}{4x}$.

(2 marks)

b)   Hence find the exact coordinates of the two stationary points of C.

(4 marks)

6   A curve, C, has parametric equations:
$$x = t^2 + 2t - 3, \ y = 2 - t^3.$$

a)   The line L is the tangent to C at $y = -6$.
Show that the equation of L is $y = -2x + 4$.

(4 marks)

b) L also meets C at point P.

(i)   Find the coordinates of P.

(4 marks)

(ii)   Find the equation of the normal to the curve at P.

(3 marks)

7   a)   Find the general solution to the differential equation
$$\frac{dy}{dx} = \frac{\cos x \cos^2 y}{\sin x}.$$

(4 marks)

b)   Given that $y = \pi$ when $x = \frac{\pi}{6}$, solve the differential equation above.

(2 marks)

8   The equation of curve C is $6x^2y - 7 = 5x - 4y^2 - x^2$.

a)   The line T has the equation $y = c$ and passes through a point on C where $x = 2$.
Find c, given that $c > 0$.

(2 marks)

b) T also crosses C at point Q.

(i)   Find the coordinates of Q.

(2 marks)

(ii)   Find the gradient of C at Q. Give your answer to 3 significant figures.

(6 marks)

9   Use an appropriate identity to find $\int 2\cot^2 x \ dx$.

(3 marks)

10   A supermarket sets up an advertising campaign to increase sales on the cheese counter.
After the start of the campaign, the number of kilograms of cheese sold each day, S,
increases over time, t days. The increase in sales is modelled by the differential equation
$\frac{dS}{dt} = k\sqrt{S} \ (k > 0)$.

a)   At the start of the campaign, the supermarket was selling 81 kg of cheese a day.
Use this information to solve the differential equation,
giving S in terms of k and t.

(4 marks)

b)   Given that $\frac{dS}{dt} = 18$ at the start of the campaign, calculate the number
of kg sold on the fifth day after the start of the campaign ($t = 5$).

(3 marks)

c)   How many days will it take before the sales reach 225 kg a day?

(2 marks)

1. Vectors

You might have seen vectors before in M1 — they've got a size and a direction. In this section you'll see how they work and what you can do with them.

Introducing vectors

Scalars are quantities **without a direction** — e.g. a speed of 2 m/s.

Vectors have both **size and direction** — e.g. a velocity of 2 m/s on a bearing of 050°.

- Vectors are drawn as **lines** with **arrowheads** on them.

The **length** of the line represents the **magnitude** (size) of the vector.

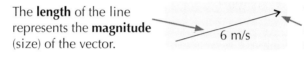

6 m/s

The **direction** of the arrowhead shows the direction of the vector.

- Sometimes vectors are drawn to **scale**:

4 m/s   8 m/s

- Vectors are usually **written** using either a **lowercase bold** letter or a **lowercase underlined** letter. When the **endpoints** of a vector are labelled, the vector can also be written by putting an **arrow** over the endpoints:

$\vec{a}$ $\underline{a}$

$\overrightarrow{AB}$

Tip: When a vector is typed it's usually bold, but if you're handwriting a vector you should always write it underlined, e.g. $\underline{a}$.

Adding vectors

- You can **add** vectors together by drawing the arrows **nose to tail**.

Tip: You might also see this referred to as the triangle rule.

- The single vector that goes from the start to the end of the combined vectors is called the **resultant vector**.

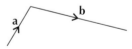

Resultant: **r** = **a** + **b**

- This method of adding is called the **parallelogram rule** because **a** and **b** form the sides of a parallelogram which has the resultant vector **r** = **a** + **b** as its diagonal.

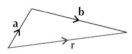

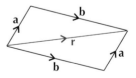

a + **b** = **r** = **b** + **a**

When you add two vectors you're really **combining** two **translations**:

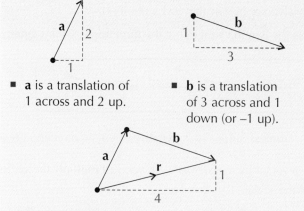

- **a** is a translation of 1 across and 2 up.
- **b** is a translation of 3 across and 1 down (or –1 up).

- So doing **a** then **b** gives you a combined translation of (1 + 3) = 4 across and (2 – 1) = 1 up.

Subtracting vectors

- The vector **–a** points in the opposite direction to the vector **a**. They're both exactly the **same size**.

- So **subtracting** a vector is the same as **adding the negative vector**:

To go from Q to P you can't just add the vectors **a** and **b** because the arrows don't run from end to end.

But replace vector **a** with **–a** (which goes in the opposite direction) and now you can add.

Tip: So when you're adding, going against the arrow on a vector is the same as subtracting that vector.

So: $\overrightarrow{QP} = \mathbf{b} + (-\mathbf{a}) = \mathbf{b} - \mathbf{a}$

You can use these rules to find a vector in terms of **other vectors**.

Example

Find $\overrightarrow{WZ}$ and $\overrightarrow{ZX}$ in terms of p, q and r.

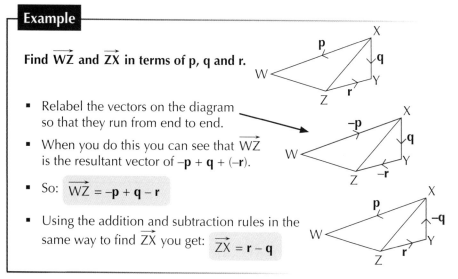

- Relabel the vectors on the diagram so that they run from end to end.

- When you do this you can see that $\overrightarrow{WZ}$ is the resultant vector of $-\mathbf{p} + \mathbf{q} + (-\mathbf{r})$.

- So: $\overrightarrow{WZ} = -\mathbf{p} + \mathbf{q} - \mathbf{r}$

- Using the addition and subtraction rules in the same way to find $\overrightarrow{ZX}$ you get: $\overrightarrow{ZX} = \mathbf{r} - \mathbf{q}$

Tip: You don't have to draw this diagram out — it's enough to know that if you want your vector to go from W to X and the vector **p** goes from X to W then you need to use **–p** instead.

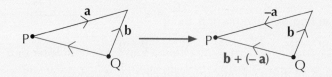

Scalar multiplication

- You can **multiply** a vector by a **scalar** (just a number).

- When you do this the **length changes** but the **direction** stays the **same**...

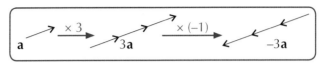

...unless the scalar is **negative**, then the direction's **reversed**.

- You can '**divide**' a vector by a scalar as well, you just **multiply** the vector by the **reciprocal** of the scalar. E.g. $\frac{\mathbf{a}}{3} = \frac{1}{3}\mathbf{a}$.

- **Multiplying** a vector by a **non-zero** scalar always produces a **parallel** vector.

> **Tip:** The number in these expressions is a scalar, the letter is a vector.

Example 1

X divides BC in the ratio 2:5. Find $\overrightarrow{AX}$ in terms of p and q.

- $\overrightarrow{AX} = \overrightarrow{AB} + \overrightarrow{BX}$. You know $\overrightarrow{AB} = \mathbf{p}$, so you just need to find $\overrightarrow{BX}$ in terms of **p** and **q**.

- X divides BC in the ratio 2:5, so BX is $\frac{2}{2+5} = \frac{2}{7}$ of BC. That means $\overrightarrow{BX} = \frac{2}{7}\overrightarrow{BC}$.

- Now to find $\overrightarrow{BC}$ in terms of **p** and **q**:
$$\overrightarrow{BC} = \overrightarrow{BA} + \overrightarrow{AC} = -\overrightarrow{AB} + \overrightarrow{AC} = -\mathbf{p} + \mathbf{q}$$

- Plugging all this back into your equation for $\overrightarrow{AX}$ gives:
$$\overrightarrow{AX} = \overrightarrow{AB} + \overrightarrow{BX} = \overrightarrow{AB} + \frac{2}{7}\overrightarrow{BC} = \mathbf{p} + \frac{2}{7}(-\mathbf{p} + \mathbf{q}) = \frac{5}{7}\mathbf{p} + \frac{2}{7}\mathbf{q}$$

> **Tip:** 'X divides **BC** in the ratio 2:5' means X is $\frac{2}{7}$ of the way from **B to C**. 'X divides **CB** in the ratio 2:5' would mean X is $\frac{2}{7}$ of the way from **C to B**.

- All **parallel** vectors are **scalar multiples** of each other, so showing that one vector is a scalar multiple of another is the same as showing they're parallel.

Example 2

Show that the vector 9a + 15b is parallel to the vector 6a + 10b.

- To show that they're **parallel** you need to try and write one as a **scalar multiple** of the other.

- To do this you need to find the **scalar factor** that you multiply by:

$$\frac{9\mathbf{a}}{6\mathbf{a}} = 1.5$$

$$\frac{15\mathbf{b}}{10\mathbf{b}} = 1.5$$

> Each **part** of the vector has the **same** scalar factor

- In this case the scalar factor is the **same** for **a** and **b**, so it's possible to write the first vector as a scalar multiple of the second.

- So $9\mathbf{a} + 15\mathbf{b} = 1.5(6\mathbf{a} + 10\mathbf{b})$ and the vectors are parallel.

> **Tip:** If you're asked to find whether or not two vectors are parallel then you need to check the scalar factor for each coefficient. If they're all the same then the vectors are parallel, if not then they're not.

Example 3

$\vec{CA} = \mathbf{p}$, $\vec{CB} = \mathbf{q}$, point M lies halfway along $\vec{CB}$, point N lies halfway along $\vec{AB}$. Show that $\vec{MN}$ is parallel to $\vec{CA}$.

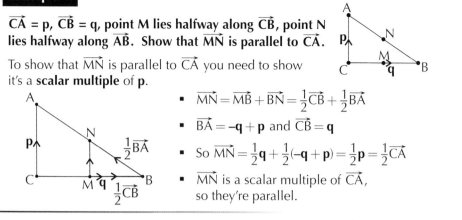

To show that $\vec{MN}$ is parallel to $\vec{CA}$ you need to show it's a **scalar multiple** of **p**.

- $\vec{MN} = \vec{MB} + \vec{BN} = \frac{1}{2}\vec{CB} + \frac{1}{2}\vec{BA}$
- $\vec{BA} = -\mathbf{q} + \mathbf{p}$ and $\vec{CB} = \mathbf{q}$
- So $\vec{MN} = \frac{1}{2}\mathbf{q} + \frac{1}{2}(-\mathbf{q} + \mathbf{p}) = \frac{1}{2}\mathbf{p} = \frac{1}{2}\vec{CA}$
- $\vec{MN}$ is a scalar multiple of $\vec{CA}$, so they're parallel.

- A vector can be **anywhere** in **space**.
- This means that vectors of the **same size** which are **parallel** and pointing in the **same direction** are the **same**, even if they're not in the same place.
- E.g. in a parallelogram, opposite sides have the **same vector**, so knowing one means you know the other:

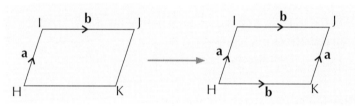

Tip: Look out for questions where you have to recognise that two lines are parallel in order to find a vector.

Collinear points

You can also use **vector addition** to show that three points are **collinear**.

- Three or more points are collinear if they all lie on a **single straight line**.
- If vectors $\vec{AB}$ and $\vec{BC}$ are **parallel**, then the points A, B and C must lie on a straight line, i.e. they are **collinear**.

Example

$\vec{AP} = \mathbf{m}$, $\vec{AQ} = \mathbf{m} + 2\mathbf{n}$, $\vec{AR} = \mathbf{m} + 6\mathbf{n}$. Show that P, Q and R are collinear.

First find $\vec{PQ}$ and $\vec{QR}$:

- $\vec{PQ} = -\vec{AP} + \vec{AQ}$
  $= -\mathbf{m} + \mathbf{m} + 2\mathbf{n} = 2\mathbf{n}$
- $\vec{QR} = -\vec{AQ} + \vec{AR}$
  $= -\mathbf{m} - 2\mathbf{n} + \mathbf{m} + 6\mathbf{n} = 4\mathbf{n}$

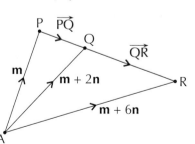

Now show that $\vec{QR}$ is a **scalar multiple** of $\vec{PQ}$:

- $\vec{QR} = 4\mathbf{n} = 2(2\mathbf{n}) = 2(\vec{PQ})$
- $\vec{QR}$ is a scalar multiple of $\vec{PQ}$ so the vectors are parallel, meaning the points P, Q and R lie on a **straight line** — i.e. the points P, Q and R are **collinear**.

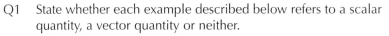
Q1 State whether each example described below refers to a scalar quantity, a vector quantity or neither.

    a) A pilot flies due south for a distance of 200 kilometres.

    b) The time taken to travel from London to Exeter is 3 hours.

    c) A force of 20 newtons is required to pull a sledge up the steepest section of a hill – the slope is at an angle of 5° to the horizontal.

Q2 Vectors **a** and **b** are represented by the lines below:

    Draw and label sketches that represent the following vectors:

    a) –**a**   b) 2**b**   c) **a** + **b**   d) **a** – **b**.

Q3 For the rectangle ABCD shown on the right, write down single vectors that are equivalent to:

    a) $\overrightarrow{AB} + \overrightarrow{BC}$ b) $\overrightarrow{BC} + \overrightarrow{CD} + \overrightarrow{DA}$ c) $\overrightarrow{DC} - \overrightarrow{BC}$

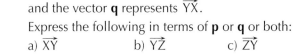

Q4 Hint: It helps to draw the shape out before you start answering the question.

Q4 In the triangle XYZ the vector **p** represents $\overrightarrow{XZ}$ and the vector **q** represents $\overrightarrow{YX}$.

    Express the following in terms of **p** or **q** or both:

    a) $\overrightarrow{XY}$ b) $\overrightarrow{YZ}$ c) $\overrightarrow{ZY}$

Q5 Group the following into sets of parallel vectors:

    2**a** + **b**   2**p** + **q**   2**a** – **b**   4**b** + 8**a**

           5(2**a** – **b**)   –**b** – 2**a** $\frac{1}{2}$**q** + **p**

Q6 In the rectangle ABCD, E is the midpoint of AD and F divides DC in the ratio 2:1.

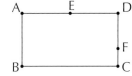

    If $\overrightarrow{AB}$ = **b** and $\overrightarrow{AD}$ = **d**, find the following vectors in terms of **b** and **d**.

    a) $\overrightarrow{DF}$ b) $\overrightarrow{BE}$ c) $\overrightarrow{EF}$

Q7 Hint: You need to prove that they all lie on the same straight line — which means that the vectors between them will be parallel.

Q7 $\overrightarrow{OA}$ = **a**, $\overrightarrow{OB}$ = **b**, $\overrightarrow{OC}$ = 5**a** – 4**b**. Show that A, B and C are collinear.

Q8 In triangle DEF, J and L are midpoints of ED and FD respectively.

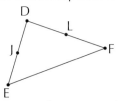

    a) Given that $\overrightarrow{EF}$ = **f** and $\overrightarrow{ED}$ = **d**, find $\overrightarrow{JL}$ in terms of **f** and **d**.

    b) What can you deduce about JL compared to EF?

Position vectors

You can use a vector to describe the **position** of a point in relation to the **origin**, O. This vector is called a **position vector**.

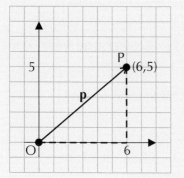

- One way of describing the position of the point P is with its **Cartesian coordinates** which are e.g. (6,5).
- This just tells you how far P is vertically and horizontally from the **origin** O.
- Another way of describing how far P is from the origin is using the **position vector** $\overrightarrow{OP} = \mathbf{p}$ which has **horizontal** and **vertical** components.

Tip: Position vectors always start at the origin and finish at the point they're describing the position of.

The position vector of any point A is $\overrightarrow{OA}$. It's usually called vector **a**.

You can write the vector from one point to another in **terms** of their **position vectors**:

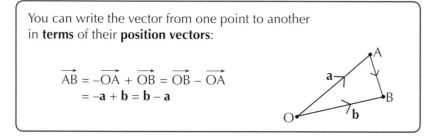

$$\overrightarrow{AB} = -\overrightarrow{OA} + \overrightarrow{OB} = \overrightarrow{OB} - \overrightarrow{OA}$$
$$= -\mathbf{a} + \mathbf{b} = \mathbf{b} - \mathbf{a}$$

Tip: This result will be used time after time for finding the vector from one point to another in this chapter.
Make sure you learn it in both its forms:
$$\overrightarrow{AB} = \overrightarrow{OB} - \overrightarrow{OA} = \mathbf{b} - \mathbf{a}$$

i + j units

- A **unit vector** is any vector with a **length of 1 unit**.
- The vectors **i** and **j** are **standard unit vectors**, so they each have a length of 1 unit. **i** is in the direction of the **positive x-axis**, and **j** is in the direction of the **positive y-axis**.

Every vector is made up of **horizontal** and **vertical components**, so you can express any vector as a **sum** of **i** and **j** unit vectors:

- Vector **a** goes from the origin O to the point A.

- To get from O to A you move **4** units **to the right** and **3** units **up**.

- So **a** is the **resultant** vector when you add a **horizontal vector** that goes **4 units** in the positive x direction and a **vertical vector** that goes **3 units** in the positive y direction.

- **i** and **j** are the **standard** unit vectors we use to express horizontal and vertical components. So **a** = 4**i** + 3**j**

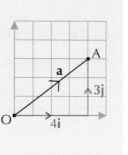

Tip: This only works for vectors which are two-dimensional. Three-dimensional vectors need an extra unit vector to describe them — you'll see more on this later on (p.114).

Example

a) **Write down the position vectors of A and B in i + j form.**
- Point A lies 5 units to the right and 7 units above the origin, so the position vector of point A is: $\boxed{\mathbf{a} = 5\mathbf{i} + 7\mathbf{j}}$

- The position vector of point B is: $$\boxed{\mathbf{b} = 4\mathbf{i} + \mathbf{j}}$$

b) **Hence find $\overrightarrow{AB}$ in terms of i and j.**
To find $\overrightarrow{AB}$:
- You know $\overrightarrow{AB} = -\overrightarrow{OA} + \overrightarrow{OB} = \overrightarrow{OB} - \overrightarrow{OA}$
$$= -\mathbf{a} + \mathbf{b} = \mathbf{b} - \mathbf{a}$$

- Add or subtract the **i** and **j** components **separately**:
Vector $\overrightarrow{AB} = \mathbf{b} - \mathbf{a} = (4\mathbf{i} + \mathbf{j}) - (5\mathbf{i} + 7\mathbf{j}) = \boxed{-\mathbf{i} - 6\mathbf{j}}$

Tip: This means that to go from A to B, you go 1 unit left and 6 units down. It's just like a translation.

Column vectors

Column vectors are another way of writing vectors in terms of their **horizontal** and **vertical components**.

- You just write the **horizontal (i) component** on **top** of the **vertical (j) component** and put a **bracket** around them:

$$x\mathbf{i} + y\mathbf{j} = \begin{pmatrix} x \\ y \end{pmatrix}$$

Tip: Unit vectors (see previous page) can also be written as column vectors: $\mathbf{i} = \begin{pmatrix} 1 \\ 0 \end{pmatrix}$ and $\mathbf{j} = \begin{pmatrix} 0 \\ 1 \end{pmatrix}$.

- **Calculating** with them is simple. Just add or subtract the **top** row, then add or subtract the **bottom** row **separately**:

$$\mathbf{a} = 5\mathbf{i} + 7\mathbf{j} = \begin{pmatrix} 5 \\ 7 \end{pmatrix} \quad \mathbf{b} = 4\mathbf{i} + \mathbf{j} = \begin{pmatrix} 4 \\ 1 \end{pmatrix}$$

$$\mathbf{b} - \mathbf{a} = \begin{pmatrix} 4 \\ 1 \end{pmatrix} - \begin{pmatrix} 5 \\ 7 \end{pmatrix} = \begin{pmatrix} 4 - 5 \\ 1 - 7 \end{pmatrix} = \begin{pmatrix} -1 \\ -6 \end{pmatrix}$$

Tip: Using column vectors is often quicker and easier than working with sums of **i** and **j** components.

- When you're **multiplying** a column vector by a **scalar** you multiply **each number** in the column vector by the scalar:

$$2\mathbf{b} - 3\mathbf{a} = 2\begin{pmatrix} 4 \\ 1 \end{pmatrix} - 3\begin{pmatrix} 5 \\ 7 \end{pmatrix} = \begin{pmatrix} 2 \times 4 \\ 2 \times 1 \end{pmatrix} - \begin{pmatrix} 3 \times 5 \\ 3 \times 7 \end{pmatrix} = \begin{pmatrix} 8 \\ 2 \end{pmatrix} - \begin{pmatrix} 15 \\ 21 \end{pmatrix} = \begin{pmatrix} -7 \\ -19 \end{pmatrix}$$

Three-dimensional vectors

- **Three-dimensional vectors** have components in the direction of the **x-, y-** and **z-axes**. Imagine that the x- and y-axes lie flat on the page. Then imagine a **third axis** sticking straight through the page at right angles to it — this is the **z-axis**.

- The points in three dimensions are given **(x, y, z) coordinates**.

- The **unit vector** in the direction of the z-axis is **k**, so three-dimensional vectors can be written like this: $x\mathbf{i} + y\mathbf{j} + z\mathbf{k}$ or $\begin{pmatrix} x \\ y \\ z \end{pmatrix}$

Tip: Three-dimensional vectors are used to describe things in three-dimensional space, e.g. an aeroplane moving through the sky.

- Calculating with 3D vectors is just the same as with 2D vectors, as the next example shows.

Example

The diagram below shows the position of the points P and Q.

a) Write the position vectors $\overrightarrow{OP}$ and $\overrightarrow{OQ}$ as column vectors.

$$\overrightarrow{OP} = 4\mathbf{i} + 3\mathbf{j} + 0\mathbf{k} = \begin{pmatrix} 4 \\ 3 \\ 0 \end{pmatrix}$$

$$\overrightarrow{OQ} = 2\mathbf{i} + 5\mathbf{j} + 4\mathbf{k} = \begin{pmatrix} 2 \\ 5 \\ 4 \end{pmatrix}$$

b) Hence find $\overrightarrow{PQ}$ as a column vector.

$$\overrightarrow{PQ} = -\overrightarrow{OP} + \overrightarrow{OQ} = -\begin{pmatrix} 4 \\ 3 \\ 0 \end{pmatrix} + \begin{pmatrix} 2 \\ 5 \\ 4 \end{pmatrix} = \begin{pmatrix} 2-4 \\ 5-3 \\ 4-0 \end{pmatrix} = \begin{pmatrix} -2 \\ 2 \\ 4 \end{pmatrix}$$

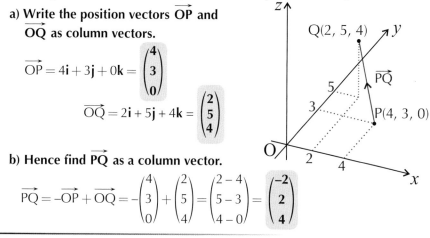

Tip: Don't get confused between a point and its position vector. Points are given by (x, y, z) coordinates and position vectors are the movement needed to get to the point from the origin, given in the form $x\mathbf{i} + y\mathbf{j} + z\mathbf{k}$. You'll need to be able to swap between the forms.

Tip: Just add along each row of the column as you do with 2D column vectors — don't forget that you've multiplied $\overrightarrow{OP}$ by the scalar '–1' so all its entries will change signs.

Exercise 1.2

Q1 A is the point (2, 3) and B is the point (4, –5). Write down the position vectors of A and B, giving your answers as column vectors.

Q2 R is the point (4, –5, 1) and S is the point (–3, 0, –1). Write down the position vectors of R and S, giving your answers in unit vector form.

Q3 C has position vector $-\mathbf{i} + 2\mathbf{j}$ and D has position vector $4\mathbf{i} - 3\mathbf{j}$.
    a) What are the Cartesian coordinates of the points C and D?
    b) Write the vectors $\overrightarrow{CD}$ and $\overrightarrow{DC}$ in unit vector form.

Q3 Hint: Remember the rule for writing the vector from A to B (see p.113):
$$\overrightarrow{AB} = \overrightarrow{OB} - \overrightarrow{OA} = \mathbf{b} - \mathbf{a}$$

Q4 Give $\overrightarrow{GH}$ and $\overrightarrow{HG}$ as column vectors, where $\overrightarrow{OG} = \begin{pmatrix} 2 \\ -3 \\ 4 \end{pmatrix}$ and $\overrightarrow{OH} = \begin{pmatrix} -1 \\ 4 \\ 9 \end{pmatrix}$.

Q5 M is the midpoint of the line PQ, where P has position vector $-3\mathbf{i} + \mathbf{j}$ and M has position vector $2\mathbf{i} - 5\mathbf{j}$.
What is the position vector of Q?

Q6 Triangle ABC is shown on the right.

Find the vectors $\overrightarrow{AB}$, $\overrightarrow{BC}$ and $\overrightarrow{CA}$.

Q6 Hint: The question doesn't mention **i** and **j** components or column vectors so you can answer it using either.

Q7 Quadrilateral DEFG has vertices at the points D (–7, –2), E (–3, –1), F (–1, 5) and G (–3, 10).
    a) State the vectors $\overrightarrow{DE}$, $\overrightarrow{EF}$, $\overrightarrow{FG}$ and $\overrightarrow{GD}$.
    b) Is this quadrilateral a parallelogram, a trapezium, or neither of these? Explain the reasons for your answer.

Q8 Triangle JKL has vertices at the points J (4, 0, –3), K (–1, 3, 0), L (2, 2, 7). Find the vectors $\overrightarrow{JK}$, $\overrightarrow{KL}$ and $\overrightarrow{LJ}$.

Q8 Hint: You answer questions about shapes in 3 dimensions in exactly the same way as shapes in 2 dimensions.

2. Magnitude of Vectors

Learning Objectives:

- Be able to find the magnitude of any vector in two or three dimensions.
- Be able to find the unit vector in the direction of any vector in two or three dimensions.
- Be able to find the distance between any two two-dimensional or three-dimensional points using vectors.

The magnitude of a vector is a scalar that tells you the vector's length. In this section you'll see how to calculate it and what you can use it for.

Magnitude of two-dimensional vectors

- The **magnitude** of a vector is the **distance** between its start point and end point. It's sometimes called **modulus** instead of magnitude.

> The **magnitude** of a vector **a** is written $|\mathbf{a}|$

> The **magnitude** of a vector $\overrightarrow{AB}$ is written $|\overrightarrow{AB}|$.

- Magnitude is a **scalar**, and it's **always positive**.
- The **horizontal** and **vertical** components of a vector form a **right-angled triangle**, so you can use **Pythagoras' theorem** to find a vector's magnitude.

Example 1

Find the magnitude of the vector a = 5i + 3j.

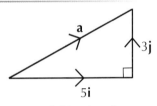

- You know the length of two sides of the right-angled triangle formed by **a** and its **horizontal** and **vertical** components.
- The magnitude of **a** is the length of the **hypotenuse** of this triangle.
- So find $|\mathbf{a}|$ using **Pythagoras**:

$$|\mathbf{a}| = \sqrt{5^2 + 3^2} = \sqrt{34} = \boxed{5.83} \text{ to 3 s.f.}$$

Tip: You don't need to draw the triangle out every time, just plug the lengths (i.e. the coefficients of **i** and **j**) into the Pythagoras formula.

You can use a vector's magnitude to find the **distance** between two **points**:

Example 2

$$\overrightarrow{JK} = \begin{pmatrix} 4 \\ -7 \end{pmatrix}$$

Find the distance between J and K. Give your answer in surd form.

The distance between J and K is $|\overrightarrow{JK}|$. Find the magnitude using **Pythagoras**:

$$|\overrightarrow{JK}| = \sqrt{4^2 + (-7)^2} = \boxed{\sqrt{65}}$$

You can find **missing components** of the vector using its magnitude:

Example 3

$$\overrightarrow{OP} = \begin{pmatrix} 3 \\ 5 \end{pmatrix}, \ \overrightarrow{OQ} = \begin{pmatrix} -2 \\ b \end{pmatrix}, \text{ given that } |\overrightarrow{PQ}| = \sqrt{29} \text{ and } |\overrightarrow{OQ}| = \sqrt{13}, \text{ find } b.$$

- First find $\overrightarrow{PQ}$: $\overrightarrow{PQ} = \overrightarrow{OQ} - \overrightarrow{OP} = \begin{pmatrix} -2 \\ b \end{pmatrix} - \begin{pmatrix} 3 \\ 5 \end{pmatrix} = \begin{pmatrix} -5 \\ b-5 \end{pmatrix}$
- Now find the magnitude of $\overrightarrow{PQ}$ in terms of b and compare it with the value given:

$$|\overrightarrow{PQ}| = \sqrt{25 + (b-5)^2}$$
$$\Rightarrow 29 = 25 + (b-5)^2$$
$$\Rightarrow 4 = (b-5)^2$$
$$\Rightarrow \pm 2 = b - 5$$
$$\Rightarrow b = 3 \text{ or } b = 7$$

- Do the same with $\overrightarrow{OQ}$:

$$|\overrightarrow{OQ}| = \sqrt{(-2)^2 + b^2}$$
$$\Rightarrow 13 = 4 + b^2$$
$$\Rightarrow 9 = b^2$$
$$\Rightarrow b = \pm 3$$

- Both statements '$b = \pm 3$' and '$b = 3$ or $b = 7$' must hold, so **$b = 3$**

- To find a **unit vector** in the direction of a particular vector you just **divide** the vector by its **magnitude** (i.e. multiply by the magnitude's reciprocal).

- So the unit vector in the direction of the vector **a** is: $\frac{1}{|\mathbf{a}|}\mathbf{a} = \frac{\mathbf{a}}{|\mathbf{a}|}$.

- Its magnitude is $\frac{1}{|\mathbf{a}|} \times |\mathbf{a}| = 1$.

- It's a **positive scalar multiple** of **a** (because magnitude is always positive), so it has the **same direction** as **a**.

Tip: Remember, a unit vector always has a magnitude of 1.

Tip: Remember, a unit vector always has a magnitude of 1.

Tip: Positive scalar multiples of **a** are parallel to **a** and have the same direction as **a**. Negative scalar multiples of **a** are parallel to **a** and have the opposite direction (the direction of **–a**).

Example 4

Find the unit vector in the direction of q = 5i – 12j.

- First find the magnitude of **q**:

$$|\mathbf{q}| = \sqrt{5^2 + (-12)^2} = \sqrt{169} = 13$$

- So the unit vector is:

$$\frac{\mathbf{q}}{|\mathbf{q}|} = \frac{1}{13}(5\mathbf{i} - 12\mathbf{j}) = \frac{5}{13}\mathbf{i} - \frac{12}{13}\mathbf{j}$$

Exercise 2.1

Q1 Find the exact magnitude of each of the following vectors.

a) $6\mathbf{i} + 8\mathbf{j}$ b) $12\mathbf{i} - 5\mathbf{j}$ c) $\begin{pmatrix} 2 \\ 4 \end{pmatrix}$ d) $\begin{pmatrix} -3 \\ -1 \end{pmatrix}$

e) $\begin{pmatrix} 24 \\ -7 \end{pmatrix}$ f) $\begin{pmatrix} -\sqrt{13} \\ 6 \end{pmatrix}$ g) $3\mathbf{i} + \sqrt{7}\mathbf{j}$ h) $-7\mathbf{j}$

Q1-3 Hint: Remember 'exact magnitude' or 'exact length' suggests some of the answers will include surds.

Q2 S has position vector $10\mathbf{i} + 5\mathbf{j}$.
Find the exact length of the line that joins point S to the origin.

Q3 For each of the pairs of vectors given below, find the exact magnitude of the resultant when the two vectors are added together.

a) $\mathbf{a} = 2\mathbf{i} + \mathbf{j}$ and $\mathbf{b} = 2\mathbf{i} - 4\mathbf{j}$ b) $\mathbf{u} = -5\mathbf{i} + \mathbf{j}$ and $\mathbf{v} = 9\mathbf{i} - 5\mathbf{j}$

c) $\mathbf{f} = \begin{pmatrix} 7 \\ 2 \end{pmatrix}$ and $\mathbf{g} = \begin{pmatrix} 17 \\ -12 \end{pmatrix}$ d) $\mathbf{d} = \begin{pmatrix} 4 \\ -2 \end{pmatrix}$ and $\mathbf{e} = \begin{pmatrix} -1 \\ -4 \end{pmatrix}$

Q4 $\overrightarrow{AB} = 3\mathbf{i} - 2\mathbf{j}$ and $\overrightarrow{BC} = \mathbf{i} + 5\mathbf{j}$. Find $|\overrightarrow{AC}|$.

Q5 If $\mathbf{a} = 4\mathbf{i} + 12\mathbf{j}$ and $\mathbf{b} = 13\mathbf{i}$, find the magnitude of $\mathbf{b} - \mathbf{a}$.

Q6 M has position vector $32\mathbf{i} - 48\mathbf{j}$ and N has position vector $21\mathbf{i} + 12\mathbf{j}$. Find the distance between points M and N.

Q7 Find the unit vector in the direction of the vector $\begin{pmatrix} 16 \\ -12 \end{pmatrix}$.

Q8 Find the unit vector in the direction of $\overrightarrow{TU}$ where T has position vector $\mathbf{t} = 3\mathbf{i} - 7\mathbf{j}$ and U has position vector $\mathbf{u} = -5\mathbf{i} - \mathbf{j}$.

Q9 $|\overrightarrow{FG}| = 13$. Given that $\overrightarrow{OF} = \begin{pmatrix} 4 \\ 7 \end{pmatrix}$ and $\overrightarrow{OG} = \begin{pmatrix} a \\ -5 \end{pmatrix}$, find the 2 possible values of a.

Magnitude of three-dimensional vectors

Pythagoras' theorem works in **three dimensions** too:

> The **distance** of point (a, b, c) from the origin is:
> $$\sqrt{a^2 + b^2 + c^2}$$

Tip: Remember the position vector of the point (a, b, c) is $a\mathbf{i} + b\mathbf{j} + c\mathbf{k}$, or as a column vector: $\begin{pmatrix} a \\ b \\ c \end{pmatrix}$

You can **derive** this formula from the **two-dimensional** Pythagoras' theorem:

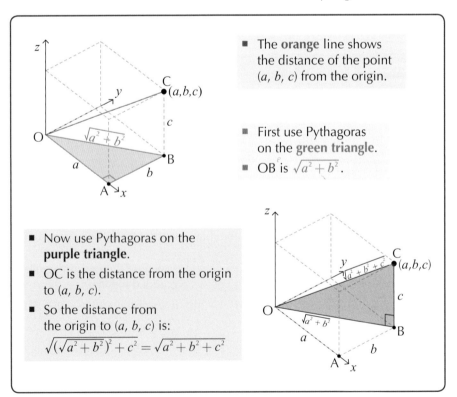

- The **orange** line shows the distance of the point (a, b, c) from the origin.

- First use Pythagoras on the **green triangle**.
- OB is $\sqrt{a^2 + b^2}$.

- Now use Pythagoras on the **purple triangle**.
- OC is the distance from the origin to (a, b, c).
- So the distance from the origin to (a, b, c) is:
$$\sqrt{\left(\sqrt{a^2 + b^2}\right)^2 + c^2} = \sqrt{a^2 + b^2 + c^2}$$

The **magnitude** of the position vector $a\mathbf{i} + b\mathbf{j} + c\mathbf{k}$ is the same as the distance of point (a, b, c) from the origin:

$$|a\mathbf{i} + b\mathbf{j} + c\mathbf{k}| = \sqrt{a^2 + b^2 + c^2}$$

Example 1

The diagram below shows the position of point Q.
Find $|\overrightarrow{OQ}|$, giving your answer in reduced surd form.

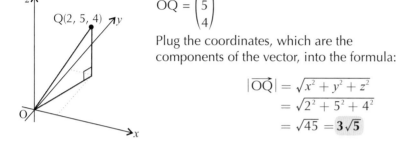

$$\overrightarrow{OQ} = \begin{pmatrix} 2 \\ 5 \\ 4 \end{pmatrix}$$

Plug the coordinates, which are the components of the vector, into the formula:

$$\begin{aligned} |\overrightarrow{OQ}| &= \sqrt{x^2 + y^2 + z^2} \\ &= \sqrt{2^2 + 5^2 + 4^2} \\ &= \sqrt{45} = \mathbf{3\sqrt{5}} \end{aligned}$$

Tip: As in two dimensions, there's no need to draw a triangle out to use Pythagoras — you can just plug the coordinates into the formula.

The formula can also be used to find the **distance** between **two points**:

The **distance** between any **two points** (x_1, y_1, z_1) and (x_2, y_2, z_2) is:

$$\sqrt{(x_2 - x_1)^2 + (y_2 - y_1)^2 + (z_2 - z_1)^2}$$

You can **prove** this formula as follows:

- The **distance** between the two points $P(x_1, y_1, z_1)$ and $Q(x_2, y_2, z_2)$ is the **magnitude** of the vector $\overrightarrow{PQ}$.

- $\overrightarrow{PQ} = \overrightarrow{OQ} - \overrightarrow{OP} = (x_2\mathbf{i} + y_2\mathbf{j} + z_2\mathbf{k}) - (x_1\mathbf{i} + y_1\mathbf{j} + z_1\mathbf{k})$
  $= (x_2 - x_1)\mathbf{i} + (y_2 - y_1)\mathbf{j} + (z_2 - z_1)\mathbf{k}$

- So the magnitude of the vector $\overrightarrow{PQ} = (x_2 - x_1)\mathbf{i} + (y_2 - y_1)\mathbf{j} + (z_2 - z_1)\mathbf{k}$
  is $\sqrt{(x_2 - x_1)^2 + (y_2 - y_1)^2 + (z_2 - z_1)^2}$, by Pythagoras' theorem.

Tip: To see visually why this formula works draw a diagram with two right-angled triangles like the one on the opposite page. The triangles will have sides whose lengths are the distances between the two points in the x, y and z directions.

Example 2

The position vector of point A is $3\mathbf{i} + 2\mathbf{j} + 4\mathbf{k}$,
and the position vector of point B is $2\mathbf{i} + 6\mathbf{j} - 5\mathbf{k}$.
Find $|\overrightarrow{AB}|$ to 1 decimal place.

- A has the coordinates $(3, 2, 4)$, B has the coordinates $(2, 6, -5)$.

- $\begin{aligned} |\overrightarrow{AB}| &= \sqrt{(x_2 - x_1)^2 + (y_2 - y_1)^2 + (z_2 - z_1)^2} \\ &= \sqrt{(2 - 3)^2 + (6 - 2)^2 + (-5 - 4)^2} \\ &= \sqrt{1 + 16 + 81} \\ &= \sqrt{98} = \mathbf{9.9} \text{ to 1 d.p.} \end{aligned}$

Example 3

A = (–3, –6, 4), B = (2t, 1, –t). $|\vec{AB}| = 3\sqrt{11}$.
Find the possible values of t.

$$|\vec{AB}| = \sqrt{(2t+3)^2 + (1+6)^2 + (-t-4)^2}$$

So: $\quad \sqrt{(2t+3)^2 + (1+6)^2 + (-t-4)^2} = 3\sqrt{11}$

$\Rightarrow 4t^2 + 12t + 9 + 49 + t^2 + 8t + 16 = 99$

$\Rightarrow \qquad\qquad 5t^2 + 20t + 74 = 99$

$\Rightarrow \qquad\qquad 5t^2 + 20t - 25 = 0$

$\Rightarrow \qquad\qquad\quad t^2 + 4t - 5 = 0$

$\Rightarrow \qquad\qquad (t+5)(t-1) = 0$

$\Rightarrow \qquad\qquad \boxed{t = -5 \text{ or } t = 1}$

Exercise 2.2

Unless specified, give each answer in this exercise as an integer or as a simplified surd.

Q1 Find the magnitude of each of the following vectors.

a) $\mathbf{i} + 4\mathbf{j} + 8\mathbf{k}$ b) $\begin{pmatrix} 4 \\ 2 \\ 4 \end{pmatrix}$ c) $\begin{pmatrix} -4 \\ -5 \\ 20 \end{pmatrix}$ d) $7\mathbf{i} + \mathbf{j} - 7\mathbf{k}$ e) $\begin{pmatrix} -2 \\ 4 \\ -6 \end{pmatrix}$

Q2 Find the magnitude of the resultant of each pair of vectors.

a) $\mathbf{i} + \mathbf{j} + 2\mathbf{k}$ and $\mathbf{i} + 2\mathbf{j} + 4\mathbf{k}$ b) $2\mathbf{i} + 11\mathbf{j} + 25\mathbf{k}$ and $3\mathbf{j} - 2\mathbf{k}$

c) $\begin{pmatrix} 4 \\ 2 \\ 8 \end{pmatrix}$ and $\begin{pmatrix} -2 \\ 4 \\ 1 \end{pmatrix}$ d) $\begin{pmatrix} 3 \\ 0 \\ 10 \end{pmatrix}$ and $\begin{pmatrix} -1 \\ 5 \\ 4 \end{pmatrix}$ e) $\begin{pmatrix} 8 \\ 4 \\ 10 \end{pmatrix}$ and $\begin{pmatrix} 2 \\ -2 \\ 4 \end{pmatrix}$

Q3 Find the distances between each of the following pairs of points.

a) (3, 4, 5), (5, 6, 6)   b) (7, 2, 9), (–11, 1, 15)
c) (10, –2, –1), (6, 10, –4)   d) (0, –4, 10), (7, 0, 14)
e) (–4, 7, 10), (2, 4, –12)   f) (7, –1, 4), (30, 9, –6)

Q4 $\mathbf{m} = \begin{pmatrix} -5 \\ -2 \\ 6 \end{pmatrix}$ and $\mathbf{n} = \begin{pmatrix} -4 \\ 1 \\ 2 \end{pmatrix}$, find $|2\mathbf{m} - \mathbf{n}|$ to 4 significant figures.

Q5 Hint: If the lengths of a triangle's sides satisfy Pythagoras' theorem then the triangle must be right-angled.

Q5 $\vec{OA} = \mathbf{i} - 4\mathbf{j} + 3\mathbf{k}$ and $\vec{OB} = -\mathbf{i} - 3\mathbf{j} + 5\mathbf{k}$. Find $|\vec{AO}|$, $|\vec{BO}|$ and $|\vec{BA}|$. Show that triangle AOB is right-angled.

Q6 Find the unit vector in the direction of $\mathbf{v}$ where $\mathbf{v} = \begin{pmatrix} 4 \\ -4 \\ -7 \end{pmatrix}$.

Q7 P is the point (2, –1, 4) and Q is the point (q – 2, 5, 2q + 1). Given that the length of the line PQ is 11, find the possible coordinates of the point Q.

3. Vector Equations of Lines

You can use vectors to give the equation of a straight line. In this section you'll see how to convert between the Cartesian equation of a line ($y = mx + c$) and a vector equation, as well as how to work with lines written in vector form.

Learning Objectives:

- Be able to find the vector equation of a 2D line from its Cartesian equation.
- Be able to find the vector equation of a line from a point on the line and a parallel vector.
- Be able to find the vector equation of a line from two points on the line.
- Be able to find the intersection point of two lines from their vector equations.
- Be able to show whether two lines are parallel, skew or intersecting.

Vector equations of lines in 2D

You've seen straight lines represented in **Cartesian coordinates** by an **equation** '$y = mx + c$' that includes the **gradient** (m) of the line and a **point** that it passes through (the y-intercept, c).

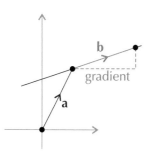

You can also use **vectors** to give the equation of a line. Just like the Cartesian equation, the **vector equation** uses the **gradient** of the line and a **point** it passes through.

The **position** of a point on the line is given as a **position vector**, usually called vector **a**.

The **gradient** is given by a **vector in the direction of the line**, usually called vector **b**.

- The vector **a** goes from the origin to the line and the vector **b** goes along the line, so you can reach any point on the line by following **a** then some scalar multiple of **b**.

- For example, by following vector **a** then vector **b** you get to point P, which has position vector $\mathbf{p} = \mathbf{a} + \mathbf{b}$.

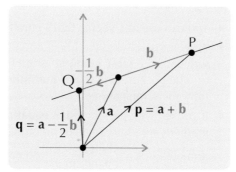

- And by following vector **a** then $-\frac{1}{2}\mathbf{b}$ you get to point Q which has position vector $\mathbf{q} = \mathbf{a} - \frac{1}{2}\mathbf{b}$.

- The equation $\mathbf{r} = \mathbf{a} + t\mathbf{b}$ gives the **position vector** of any point, R, on the line, just as $y = mx + c$ gives the **coordinates** of any point on the line. So $\mathbf{r} = \mathbf{a} + t\mathbf{b}$ is the vector equation of the **whole line**.

The **vector equation of a straight line** through point A and parallel to vector **b** is:

$$\mathbf{r} = \mathbf{a} + t\mathbf{b}$$

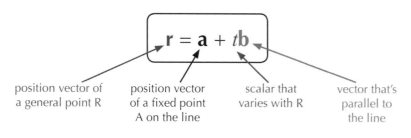

position vector of a general point R · position vector of a fixed point A on the line · scalar that varies with R · vector that's parallel to the line

Tip: Vector equations of lines aren't unique — you can use any point on the line for **a** and any vector parallel to the line for **b**.

Example

The diagram on the right shows the positions of points P and Q on a line with vector equation $r = a + tb$.

Find t when: a) $r = \overrightarrow{OP}$ b) $r = \overrightarrow{OQ}$

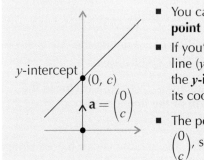

a) The position vector of P is $\overrightarrow{OP} = \mathbf{a} - \mathbf{b}$,
   so when $\mathbf{r} = \overrightarrow{OP}$, $t = $ **−1**

b) The position vector of Q is $\overrightarrow{OQ} = \mathbf{a} + 2\mathbf{b}$,
   so when $\mathbf{r} = \overrightarrow{OQ}$, $t = $ **2**

Finding vector a

- You can use the **position vector of any point** on the line as your vector **a**.
- If you're given the **Cartesian equation** of a line ($y = mx + c$) the easiest point to use is the **y-intercept**, because you already know its coordinates: $(0, c)$.
- The position vector of the point $(0, c)$ is $\begin{pmatrix} 0 \\ c \end{pmatrix}$, so in this case $\mathbf{a} = \begin{pmatrix} 0 \\ c \end{pmatrix} = 0\mathbf{i} + c\mathbf{j}$.

Finding vector b

- You can use any **vector that's parallel to the line** for vector **b**.
- A vector parallel to the line (i.e. with the same direction as the line) will have the **same gradient** as the line itself. The vector **b** isn't unique because **any scalar multiple** of **b** (i.e. any parallel vector) will have the same gradient.
- If you're given the **Cartesian equation** of a line you can use the **gradient** m to find a vector pointing in the same direction as the line. Remember $m = \dfrac{\text{change in } y}{\text{change in } x}$, you can use this to find the horizontal (**i**) and vertical (**j**) components of the vector **b**:

Tip: It doesn't matter whether **b** is pointing up or down the line because this includes negative scalar multiples (i.e. vectors that are parallel but pointing in the opposite direction).

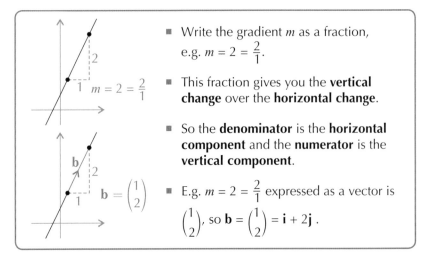

- Write the gradient m as a fraction, e.g. $m = 2 = \frac{2}{1}$.

- This fraction gives you the **vertical change** over the **horizontal change**.

- So the **denominator** is the **horizontal component** and the **numerator** is the **vertical component**.

- E.g. $m = 2 = \frac{2}{1}$ expressed as a vector is $\begin{pmatrix} 1 \\ 2 \end{pmatrix}$, so $\mathbf{b} = \begin{pmatrix} 1 \\ 2 \end{pmatrix} = \mathbf{i} + 2\mathbf{j}$.

So you can find a **vector equation** of a line from its **Cartesian equation**.

Example 1

Line *l* has Cartesian equation $y = \frac{1}{2}x + 2$.

a) **Express as a vector**

   (i) **the position of the *y* intercept**

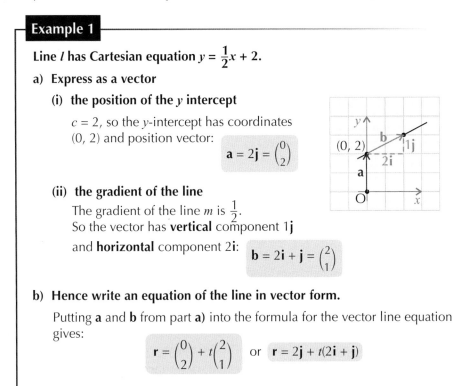

      $c = 2$, so the *y*-intercept has coordinates (0, 2) and position vector:

$$\mathbf{a} = 2\mathbf{j} = \begin{pmatrix} 0 \\ 2 \end{pmatrix}$$

   (ii) **the gradient of the line**

      The gradient of the line *m* is $\frac{1}{2}$.
      So the vector has **vertical** component $1\mathbf{j}$
      and **horizontal** component $2\mathbf{i}$:

$$\mathbf{b} = 2\mathbf{i} + \mathbf{j} = \begin{pmatrix} 2 \\ 1 \end{pmatrix}$$

b) **Hence write an equation of the line in vector form.**

   Putting **a** and **b** from part **a)** into the formula for the vector line equation gives:

$$\mathbf{r} = \begin{pmatrix} 0 \\ 2 \end{pmatrix} + t\begin{pmatrix} 2 \\ 1 \end{pmatrix} \quad \text{or} \quad \mathbf{r} = 2\mathbf{j} + t(2\mathbf{i} + \mathbf{j})$$

> **Tip:** You could also express this line as a single column vector — just add up along each row of the columns:
> $$\mathbf{r} = \begin{pmatrix} 2t \\ 2 + t \end{pmatrix}$$

You can also find the **Cartesian equation** of a line from its **vector equation**.

Example 2

The vector equation of line *l* is $\mathbf{r} = \begin{pmatrix} 3 \\ 2 \end{pmatrix} + t\begin{pmatrix} -2 \\ 7 \end{pmatrix}$.

Find the Cartesian equation of line *l* in the form $y = mx + c$.

You need to find the gradient *m* and the *y*-intercept *c*.

- You work out the gradient by putting the vertical component of vector **b** over the horizontal component, so $m = \frac{7}{-2} = -\frac{7}{2}$

- So the Cartesian equation of the line is $y = -\frac{7}{2}x + c$.

- $\begin{pmatrix} 3 \\ 2 \end{pmatrix}$ is the position vector of a point on the line, so (3, 2) lies on the line.

   This means that when $x = 3$, $y = 2$.
   So plug these values into the equation $y = -\frac{7}{2}x + c$:

$$2 = -\frac{7}{2}(3) + c \implies \frac{4}{2} + \frac{21}{2} = c$$

$$\implies \frac{25}{2} = c$$

> **Tip:** If the vector **a** had zero in the top row you'd already have the position vector of the *y*-intercept and you'd just read the value of *c* from the bottom row.

So the Cartesian equation of the line is: $y = -\frac{7}{2}x + \frac{25}{2}$

You can use the **position vectors** of **two points C and D** on a line to find the line's **equation**:

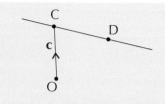

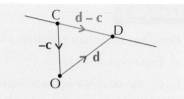

- You take one of the position vectors (e.g. **c**) as your vector for a point on the line (**a**).

- Then you take the vector $\overrightarrow{CD} = \mathbf{d} - \mathbf{c}$ as your direction vector (**b**).

Plugging these vectors into the formula $\mathbf{r} = \mathbf{a} + t\mathbf{b}$ gives you a **formula** for the line in **terms of the position vectors** of C and D:

$$\mathbf{r} = \mathbf{c} + t(\mathbf{d} - \mathbf{c})$$

You can use this formula to **quickly find the equation** of a line from two points, without having to work out which vectors to use each time.

Tip: In fact you could use **c** or **d** as the position vector and (**c** – **d**) or (**d** – **c**) as the direction vector. Using different combinations will give you different vector equations of the same line.

Tip: You can use column vectors or unit vector form to give the vector equation of a line, but column vectors are usually quicker to work with.

Tip: This is a different method of finding c to the one on p.123.

Example 3

M and N have position vectors m = 3i – 4j and n = –2i + 3j.

a) Find a vector equation of the line that passes through M and N.

Using the formula:
$$\mathbf{r} = \mathbf{m} + t(\mathbf{n} - \mathbf{m}) = \begin{pmatrix} 3 \\ -4 \end{pmatrix} + t\left(\begin{pmatrix} -2 \\ 3 \end{pmatrix} - \begin{pmatrix} 3 \\ -4 \end{pmatrix}\right) = \begin{pmatrix} 3 \\ -4 \end{pmatrix} + t\begin{pmatrix} -5 \\ 7 \end{pmatrix}$$

b) Write the Cartesian equation of this line in the form $y = mx + c$.

- First find the gradient: $m = \dfrac{\mathbf{j} \text{ component of direction vector}}{\mathbf{i} \text{ component of direction vector}} = \dfrac{7}{-5} = -\dfrac{7}{5}$

- Now the y-intercept:
$$\begin{pmatrix} 0 \\ c \end{pmatrix} = \begin{pmatrix} 3 \\ -4 \end{pmatrix} + t\begin{pmatrix} -5 \\ 7 \end{pmatrix} \Rightarrow 0 = 3 - 5t \Rightarrow 5t = 3 \Rightarrow t = \dfrac{3}{5}$$
$$c = -4 + 7t = -4 + 7\left(\dfrac{3}{5}\right) = \dfrac{-20 + 21}{5} = \dfrac{1}{5}$$

- So the equation is: $y = -\dfrac{7}{5}x + \dfrac{1}{5}$

Exercise 3.1

Q1 State the gradient and the y-intercept of each straight line below.

a) $\mathbf{r} = \begin{pmatrix} 0 \\ 2 \end{pmatrix} + t\begin{pmatrix} 1 \\ 3 \end{pmatrix}$ b) $\mathbf{r} = \begin{pmatrix} 0 \\ -5 \end{pmatrix} - t\begin{pmatrix} 1 \\ 2 \end{pmatrix}$ c) $\mathbf{r} = \begin{pmatrix} 0 \\ 0 \end{pmatrix} + t\begin{pmatrix} 3 \\ 15 \end{pmatrix}$

Q2 Write equations for the following straight lines in vector form.

a) $y = x + 2$ b) $y = 7$ c) $y = -4x$ d) $y = -3x + 5$

Q3 Hint: This is like using the Cartesian equation to find a vector equation, but vector **a** won't be $\begin{pmatrix} 0 \\ c \end{pmatrix}$.

Q3 For each of the following write a vector equation of the straight line with gradient m passing through point A.

a) $m = -3$, A (2, 6)   b) $m = \dfrac{1}{2}$, A (2, 2)   c) $m = 0$, A (1, –5)

Q4 Write equations for the following straight lines in the form $y = mx + c$.

a) $\mathbf{r} = \begin{pmatrix} 0 \\ 0 \end{pmatrix} + t\begin{pmatrix} 1 \\ 1 \end{pmatrix}$

b) $\mathbf{r} = \begin{pmatrix} 0 \\ -4 \end{pmatrix} + t\begin{pmatrix} -1 \\ 2 \end{pmatrix}$

c) $\mathbf{r} = \begin{pmatrix} 6 \\ 0 \end{pmatrix} + t\begin{pmatrix} 2 \\ 1 \end{pmatrix}$

d) $\mathbf{r} = \begin{pmatrix} 1 \\ 2 \end{pmatrix} + t\begin{pmatrix} 3 \\ 0 \end{pmatrix}$

e) $\mathbf{r} = \begin{pmatrix} -2 \\ 3 \end{pmatrix} + t\begin{pmatrix} 2 \\ 5 \end{pmatrix}$

f) $\mathbf{r} = \begin{pmatrix} 5 \\ 0 \end{pmatrix} + t\begin{pmatrix} 0 \\ 1 \end{pmatrix}$

Q5 For each of the following write a vector equation of the straight line that passes through point A and is parallel to vector **b**. Give your answers in **i** + **j** form.

a) A (2, 5), **b** = –**i** + 2**j**
b) A (–1, 0), **b** = 3**i** + 4**j**
c) A (–3, –1), **b** = 6**i** – **j**
d) A (0, 4), **b** = –3**i** – 5**j**

Q6 For each of the following, find a vector equation of the straight line that passes through the two points whose position vectors are given. Give your answers in **i** + **j** form.

a) **p** = **i**, **q** = 2**i** + **j**
b) **f** = 3**i** – 4**j**, **g** = 2**i** + 5**j**
c) **n** = –**i** + 3**j**, **m** = –5**i** – $\frac{3}{2}$**j**

Vector equations of lines in 3D

You've seen that the vector equation of a line passing **through point A** in the **direction** of **vector b** is $\mathbf{r} = \mathbf{a} + t\mathbf{b}$, where t is a variable scalar.

This isn't just true for 2D lines — it works in **three dimensions** as well.

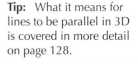

So just like in 2D you can find the vector equation of a line in 3D from a **point** on the line and a **parallel vector**.

You've also seen that the equation for a 2D line passing through **two points** C and D is $\mathbf{r} = \mathbf{c} + t(\mathbf{d} - \mathbf{c})$ — this works just the **same** in **three dimensions** too:

Tip: What it means for lines to be parallel in 3D is covered in more detail on page 128.

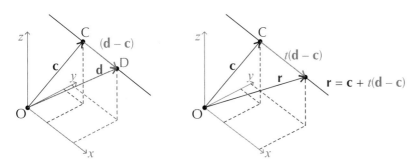

- C and D have position vectors **c** and **d** respectively.
- **c** is the position vector of a point on the line.
- $\overrightarrow{CD} = \mathbf{d} - \mathbf{c}$ is a vector in the direction of the line.

So you can also find the vector equation of a 3D line from the position vectors of **two points** on the line.

All this is exactly the same as in two dimensions — the only difference is that the vectors **r**, **a** and **b** (or **r**, **c** and **d**) have three components instead of two.

Example 1

A line passes through points with the coordinates (3, 2, 4) and (2, –2, 0). Find a vector equation for this line.

Call (3, 2, 4) point C and (2, –2, 0) point D.

Then $\mathbf{c} = \begin{pmatrix} 3 \\ 2 \\ 4 \end{pmatrix}$, and $\mathbf{d} = \begin{pmatrix} 2 \\ -2 \\ 0 \end{pmatrix}$.

Plugging these vectors into the equation $\mathbf{r} = \mathbf{c} + t(\mathbf{d} - \mathbf{c})$ gives:

$$\mathbf{r} = \begin{pmatrix} 3 \\ 2 \\ 4 \end{pmatrix} + t\left(\begin{pmatrix} 2 \\ -2 \\ 0 \end{pmatrix} - \begin{pmatrix} 3 \\ 2 \\ 4 \end{pmatrix}\right) \Rightarrow \mathbf{r} = \begin{pmatrix} 3 \\ 2 \\ 4 \end{pmatrix} + t\begin{pmatrix} -1 \\ -4 \\ -4 \end{pmatrix}$$

Tip: You don't need to draw a diagram to answer the question, but it's a good idea to sketch one if it helps you picture what's going on.

Given a point P with position vector **p** you can show that P lies on the line $\mathbf{r} = \mathbf{a} + t\mathbf{b}$ if you can **solve** the equation $\mathbf{p} = \mathbf{a} + t\mathbf{b}$ to find t.

Example 2

Show that the point M (–1, 3, –1) lies on the line $\mathbf{r} = \begin{pmatrix} 2 \\ -6 \\ 5 \end{pmatrix} + \mu\begin{pmatrix} -1 \\ 3 \\ -2 \end{pmatrix}$.

We want to solve:
$$\mathbf{m} = \begin{pmatrix} -1 \\ 3 \\ -1 \end{pmatrix} = \begin{pmatrix} 2 \\ -6 \\ 5 \end{pmatrix} + \mu\begin{pmatrix} -1 \\ 3 \\ -2 \end{pmatrix} = \begin{pmatrix} 2 - \mu \\ -6 + 3\mu \\ 5 - 2\mu \end{pmatrix}$$

Solve along each row to find μ:

first row: $-1 = 2 - \mu \Rightarrow -3 = -\mu \Rightarrow \mu = 3$
second row: $3 = -6 + 3\mu \Rightarrow 9 = 3\mu \Rightarrow \mu = 3$
third row: $-1 = 5 - 2\mu \Rightarrow -6 = -2\mu \Rightarrow \mu = 3$

All of the equations give the same μ value so there is a solution:

$$\mathbf{m} = \begin{pmatrix} -1 \\ 3 \\ -1 \end{pmatrix} = \begin{pmatrix} 2 \\ -6 \\ 5 \end{pmatrix} + 3\begin{pmatrix} -1 \\ 3 \\ -2 \end{pmatrix}$$ so M lies on the line $\mathbf{r} = \begin{pmatrix} 2 \\ -6 \\ 5 \end{pmatrix} + \mu\begin{pmatrix} -1 \\ 3 \\ -2 \end{pmatrix}$.

Tip: The variable in a vector line equation isn't always represented by t. Sometimes other letters are used, including Greek letters λ (lambda) and μ (mu).

Example 3

The point with coordinates (–4, 10, b) lies on the line $\mathbf{r} = \begin{pmatrix} 2 \\ 0 \\ 1 \end{pmatrix} + t\begin{pmatrix} 3 \\ a \\ 1 \end{pmatrix}$. Find a and b.

You know that $\begin{pmatrix} -4 \\ 10 \\ b \end{pmatrix} = \begin{pmatrix} 2 \\ 0 \\ 1 \end{pmatrix} + t\begin{pmatrix} 3 \\ a \\ 1 \end{pmatrix} = \begin{pmatrix} 2 + 3t \\ ta \\ 1 + t \end{pmatrix}$, for some value of t.

- Solve along the top row to find t:
  $-4 = 2 + 3t \Rightarrow -6 = 3t \Rightarrow t = -2$

- Now replace t with –2 in the second and third rows to find a and b:
  $10 = -2a \Rightarrow a = -5$ $b = 1 - 2 \Rightarrow b = -1$

Tip: In this example you have to solve along the top row to find t first because both of the other rows have more than one unknown.

Q1 Line L passes through point A and is parallel to vector **b**.
The vectors **a** and **b** are given by

$$\mathbf{a} = \begin{pmatrix} 4 \\ -3 \\ -2 \end{pmatrix} \text{ and } \mathbf{b} = \begin{pmatrix} 1 \\ 2 \\ 3 \end{pmatrix}$$

a) Find the position vectors of points
X, Y, Z and Q, where:
$\overrightarrow{OX} = \mathbf{a} + \mathbf{b}$, $\overrightarrow{OY} = \mathbf{a} + 2\mathbf{b}$,
$\overrightarrow{OZ} = \mathbf{a} + 3\mathbf{b}$, $\overrightarrow{OQ} = \mathbf{a} - \mathbf{b}$

b) Write a vector equation for line L.

Q2 Points C, D, E and F lie on the line with equation $\mathbf{r} = \begin{pmatrix} 2 \\ 1 \\ 3 \end{pmatrix} + \lambda \begin{pmatrix} 1 \\ -1 \\ 4 \end{pmatrix}$
and correspond to $\lambda = 0$, $\lambda = 1$, $\lambda = 4$ and $\lambda = -2$
respectively. Write down the coordinates of each point.

Q3 Give the coordinates of any 3 points on the line $\mathbf{r} = 3\mathbf{j} - 4\mathbf{k} + t(-\mathbf{i} + 2\mathbf{j})$.

Q4 Point S $(-1, 4, 5)$ lies on a straight line that passes through the origin O.
a) Give a vector equation of this line.
b) State the coordinates of 2 other points that lie on the line.

> **Q4 Hint:** The origin is $(0, 0, 0)$ so you've got the coordinates of two points on the line.

Q5 a) Find a vector equation for the straight line that passes through the
point with position vector **a**, and which is parallel to vector **b**,
where:

$$\text{(i) } \mathbf{a} = \begin{pmatrix} 4 \\ 2 \\ -1 \end{pmatrix}, \mathbf{b} = \begin{pmatrix} -2 \\ 0 \\ 3 \end{pmatrix} \qquad \text{(ii) } \mathbf{a} = \begin{pmatrix} 0 \\ 0 \\ 1 \end{pmatrix}, \mathbf{b} = \begin{pmatrix} 1 \\ -1 \\ 0 \end{pmatrix}$$

$$\text{(iii) } \mathbf{a} = 2\mathbf{i} + \mathbf{j}, \mathbf{b} = 5\mathbf{i} - \mathbf{k}$$

b) Each of the points P $(-2, 2, 1)$, Q $(2, 2, 2)$ and R $(-3, 1, 1)$
lies on just one of the lines from part a).
Determine which point lies on which line.

Q6 Line L has equation $\mathbf{r} = -6\mathbf{i} - \mathbf{j} + \mathbf{k} + t(\mathbf{i} - 3\mathbf{k})$. Write down an
equation for the line parallel to L that passes through $(5, -1, 3)$.

Q7 Points P $(-4, a, 10)$ and Q $(b, c, -11)$ lie on a line $\mathbf{r} = \begin{pmatrix} -2 \\ 5 \\ 4 \end{pmatrix} + s \begin{pmatrix} 1 \\ 2 \\ -3 \end{pmatrix}$.
Find the values of a, b and c.

> **Q7 Hint:** For each point find s first by solving along a line with no other unknowns, then find the missing coordinates.

Q8 $\mathbf{r} = \begin{pmatrix} -4 \\ 0 \\ 1 \end{pmatrix} + s \begin{pmatrix} 3 \\ 2 \\ -1 \end{pmatrix}$ is an equation for line L.

Write an equation for the line L in the form $\mathbf{r} = \mathbf{a} + t\mathbf{b}$, where:

a) **b** is not $\begin{pmatrix} 3 \\ 2 \\ -1 \end{pmatrix}$ b) **a** is not $\begin{pmatrix} -4 \\ 0 \\ 1 \end{pmatrix}$

Q9 Find equations for the lines that pass through the following pairs of points:
a) $(7, 0, -3)$ and $(-1, 1, -3)$ b) $(-1, 1, 4)$ and $(-4, 1, 0)$
c) $(2, 5, 0)$ and $(-2, -1, 2)$

Intersecting, parallel and skew lines

In **two dimensions**, given **two distinct lines** there are only **two possibilities**:

1. The lines are **intersecting** — they **meet** at a single **point**.

2. The lines are **parallel** — they never intersect and the shortest **distance** between them is always the **same**.

In **three dimensions** there are **three possibilities**:

1. The lines are **intersecting**.

2. The lines are **parallel**.

In 2D, parallel lines are lines that never intersect. **Parallel** lines in **3D** are similar, but not all non-intersecting lines are parallel in 3D.

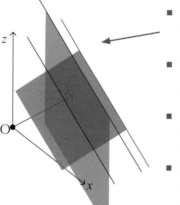

- In three-dimensional space two lines are parallel when the **smallest distance** from one line to the other is **constant** along the line.

- 3D **parallel lines** are **translations** of each other in the x, y and z directions, just like 2D parallel lines are translations of each other in the x and y directions.

- Another way to think of it is that any two lines that lie in the **same plane** and **don't intersect** are parallel.

- The **purple** and **blue** lines on the left are parallel because they both lie in the **blue plane** and they don't intersect.

- The **purple** and **orange** lines are also parallel — they lie in the **orange plane** and don't intersect.

- Just like in 2D, **two lines** that are both **parallel to a third line** are **parallel** to each other, so the blue and orange lines are also parallel to each other.

3. The lines are **neither parallel nor intersecting**. These lines are called **skew**. The two lines shown on the right are skew.

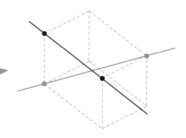

You can **work out** whether two lines are parallel, intersecting or skew from their **vector equations**.

Intersecting lines

- **Intersecting lines** meet somewhere, so they must **share a point**.
- For lines with equations $\mathbf{r} = \mathbf{c} + \lambda\mathbf{d}$ and $\mathbf{r} = \mathbf{e} + \mu\mathbf{f}$ this means that there's a value for λ and a value for μ so that $\mathbf{c} + \lambda\mathbf{d} = \mathbf{e} + \mu\mathbf{f}$, i.e. you get the same point for each line. This point is the **point of intersection**.

Tip: To prove that two lines intersect you just solve this equation to show that they have a point in common.

Example

Determine whether Line 1, $\mathbf{r} = \begin{pmatrix} 5 \\ 2 \\ -1 \end{pmatrix} + \mu\begin{pmatrix} 1 \\ -2 \\ -3 \end{pmatrix}$ and Line 2, $\mathbf{r} = \begin{pmatrix} 2 \\ 0 \\ 4 \end{pmatrix} + \lambda\begin{pmatrix} 1 \\ 2 \\ -1 \end{pmatrix}$ intersect.

If they do, find the coordinates of the point of intersection.

If the two lines intersect then at the point of intersection we'll have:

$$\begin{pmatrix} 5 \\ 2 \\ -1 \end{pmatrix} + \mu\begin{pmatrix} 1 \\ -2 \\ -3 \end{pmatrix} = \begin{pmatrix} 2 \\ 0 \\ 4 \end{pmatrix} + \lambda\begin{pmatrix} 1 \\ 2 \\ -1 \end{pmatrix}$$

So take the equation from **each row**:

① $5 + \mu = 2 + \lambda$
② $2 - 2\mu = 0 + 2\lambda$
③ $-1 - 3\mu = 4 - \lambda$

Tip: If you've got two equations that describe the same line then there'll be a solution to this equation for every value of the two variables, because they intersect everywhere. You show that two lines are the same by giving a solution for an intersection point and showing their direction vectors are parallel.

If you can find a value for μ and a value for λ which **solve all** of these equations **at once** then there's a **point** that lies on **both lines**. If not then there's no intersection point.

- Solve the first two **simultaneously**: $\quad 2 \times$① $: 10 + 2\mu = 4 + 2\lambda$ ④
  $\quad\quad$ ④$-$② $: 8 + 4\mu = 4 \Rightarrow \mu = -1$

- Now **substitute** μ into equation ②: $\quad 2 - 2(-1) = 0 + 2\lambda \Rightarrow \lambda = 2$

- If these values of μ and λ also solve equation ③ then the lines intersect. So substitute the values for μ and λ into equation ③:
  $$-1 - (3 \times -1) = 4 - 2 \Rightarrow 2 = 2$$
  — this is **true**, so $\boxed{\text{the lines } \textbf{do intersect}}$.

Now you can find the **intersection point** by plugging the value for μ into the **equation of Line 1**:

$$\mathbf{r} = \begin{pmatrix} 5 \\ 2 \\ -1 \end{pmatrix} + \mu\begin{pmatrix} 1 \\ -2 \\ -3 \end{pmatrix} = \begin{pmatrix} 5 \\ 2 \\ -1 \end{pmatrix} - 1\begin{pmatrix} 1 \\ -2 \\ -3 \end{pmatrix} \Rightarrow \mathbf{r} = \begin{pmatrix} 4 \\ 4 \\ 2 \end{pmatrix} = 4\mathbf{i} + 4\mathbf{j} + 2\mathbf{k}$$

This is the **position vector** of the intersection point.

The **coordinates** are $\boxed{(4, 4, 2)}$.

Tip: You could plug the value for λ into the equation of Line 2 instead, either will give you the position vector of the intersection point.

Parallel lines

- Every line with equation $\mathbf{r} = \mathbf{a} + t\mathbf{b}$ is parallel to any scalar multiple of the vector $\mathbf{b}$.
- If two lines are both parallel to a third line then they must be parallel to each other, so to prove that the **two lines** $\mathbf{r} = \mathbf{c} + \lambda\mathbf{d}$ and $\mathbf{r} = \mathbf{e} + \mu\mathbf{f}$ are parallel you just need to show that the **vectors d and f** are **parallel**.

Example

Show that the lines L_1: $r = \begin{pmatrix} 0 \\ 3 \\ -5 \end{pmatrix} + \lambda \begin{pmatrix} -1 \\ 0 \\ 2 \end{pmatrix}$ and L_2: $r = \begin{pmatrix} -2 \\ 3 \\ 1 \end{pmatrix} + \mu \begin{pmatrix} -2 \\ 0 \\ 4 \end{pmatrix}$ are parallel.

- Let $b_1 = \begin{pmatrix} -1 \\ 0 \\ 2 \end{pmatrix}$ and $b_2 = \begin{pmatrix} -2 \\ 0 \\ 4 \end{pmatrix}$, then $b_2 = 2b_1$.

- So the direction vectors of L_1 and L_2 (b_1 and b_2) are scalar multiples of one another, which means they're parallel.

- Therefore L_1 and L_2 are parallel as they're parallel, respectively, to their direction vectors b_1 and b_2.

Skew lines

To prove that two lines are **skew** you just show that they're **not parallel** and they **don't intersect**.

Example

Lines l_1 and l_2 are given by $\quad l_1$: $r = (-1 + 2\lambda)i + (4 + \lambda)j + (1 - 2\lambda)k$
$\qquad\qquad\qquad\qquad\qquad\qquad l_2$: $r = (2 + 3\mu)i + (-5 - 2\mu)j + (-4 + 3\mu)k$

Prove that l_1 and l_2 are skew.

Rewrite the equations in **column vector** form:

Tip: For questions where the line equation is given in a different form you'll probably find it easier to write it in the standard column vector form before you answer the question.

$$r = \begin{pmatrix} -1 \\ 4 \\ 1 \end{pmatrix} + \lambda \begin{pmatrix} 2 \\ 1 \\ -2 \end{pmatrix} \text{ and } r = \begin{pmatrix} 2 \\ -5 \\ -4 \end{pmatrix} + \mu \begin{pmatrix} 3 \\ -2 \\ 3 \end{pmatrix}$$

First show that l_1 and l_2 **don't intersect**:

- You need to show that there's no solution to the equation:

$$\begin{pmatrix} -1 \\ 4 \\ 1 \end{pmatrix} + \lambda \begin{pmatrix} 2 \\ 1 \\ -2 \end{pmatrix} = \begin{pmatrix} 2 \\ -5 \\ -4 \end{pmatrix} + \mu \begin{pmatrix} 3 \\ -2 \\ 3 \end{pmatrix}$$

- The three rows give the equations:
$$-1 + 2\lambda = 2 + 3\mu$$
$$4 + \lambda = -5 - 2\mu$$
$$1 - 2\lambda = -4 + 3\mu$$

- Solve the first two **simultaneously**:
$$-1 + 2\lambda = 2 + 3\mu \Rightarrow -1 + \tfrac{2}{3}\lambda = \mu$$
$$4 + \lambda = -5 - 2\mu \Rightarrow 4 + \lambda = -5 - 2\left(-1 + \tfrac{2}{3}\lambda\right) \Rightarrow 7 = -\tfrac{7}{3}\lambda \Rightarrow \lambda = -3$$
$$\Rightarrow \mu = -1 + \tfrac{2}{3}(-3) = -3$$

- Now plug these values into the third equation:
$$1 - 2\lambda = -4 + 3\mu \Rightarrow 1 - 2(-3) = -4 + 3(-3) \Rightarrow 1 + 6 = -4 - 9 \Rightarrow 7 = -13$$

- This is false so l_1 and l_2 **don't intersect**.

Tip: Note that the direction vectors of l_1 and l_2 are:

$$b_1 = \begin{pmatrix} 2 \\ 1 \\ -2 \end{pmatrix} \text{ and } b_2 = \begin{pmatrix} 3 \\ -2 \\ 3 \end{pmatrix}$$

So for the **i, j** and **k** components to share a common factor you'll need $\tfrac{2}{3} = \tfrac{1}{-2} = \tfrac{-2}{3}$.

Now show that they're **not parallel**:

- If l_1 and l_2 are parallel then their direction vectors are parallel, i.e. scalar multiples of one another.

- In that case their **i, j** and **k** components will have a common scalar factor, so $\tfrac{2}{3} = \tfrac{1}{-2} = \tfrac{-2}{3}$ will hold. This isn't true so l_1 and l_2 **aren't parallel**.

As they're **neither intersecting nor parallel** l_1 and l_2 are **skew**.

Exercise 3.3

Q1 State whether or not each of the following pairs of lines are parallel.

a) $\mathbf{r} = \begin{pmatrix} 1 \\ 0 \\ 1 \end{pmatrix} + p\begin{pmatrix} 0 \\ 7 \\ 0 \end{pmatrix}$, $\mathbf{r} = \begin{pmatrix} 2 \\ -4 \\ 1 \end{pmatrix} + q\begin{pmatrix} 0 \\ -2 \\ 0 \end{pmatrix}$

b) $\mathbf{r} = (\mathbf{i} + \mathbf{k}) + \lambda(\mathbf{j} + \mathbf{k})$
   $\mathbf{r} = (\mathbf{j} + \mathbf{k}) + \lambda(2\mathbf{i} + 2\mathbf{k})$

Q2 Find the values of a, b, c and d, given that each pair of lines is parallel.

a) $\mathbf{r} = \begin{pmatrix} -5 \\ 4 \\ 2 \end{pmatrix} + s\begin{pmatrix} a \\ 0 \\ -1 \end{pmatrix}$, $\mathbf{r} = \begin{pmatrix} 9 \\ 8 \\ -4 \end{pmatrix} + t\begin{pmatrix} 10 \\ b \\ -5 \end{pmatrix}$

b) $\mathbf{r} = (3\mathbf{i} - \mathbf{j}) + \lambda(2\mathbf{i} + c\mathbf{j} - 4\mathbf{k})$, $\mathbf{r} = (5\mathbf{i} + \mathbf{j} - \mathbf{k}) + \mu(d\mathbf{i} + 3\mathbf{j} + 2\mathbf{k})$

> **Q2 Hint:** You don't need to worry about s and t in this question — so just focus on the direction vectors.

Q3 Show that each pair of lines below intersects at a point, and find the coordinates of the point of intersection.

a) $\mathbf{r} = (2\mathbf{i} + \mathbf{j}) + \lambda(\mathbf{i} - 2\mathbf{j} + \mathbf{k})$, $\mathbf{r} = (-3\mathbf{i} - \mathbf{k}) + \mu(4\mathbf{i} + 3\mathbf{j})$

b) $\mathbf{r} = \begin{pmatrix} -1 \\ 7 \\ 1 \end{pmatrix} + \lambda\begin{pmatrix} 2 \\ -2 \\ 1 \end{pmatrix}$, $\mathbf{r} = \begin{pmatrix} 1 \\ 3 \\ 2 \end{pmatrix} + \mu\begin{pmatrix} 2 \\ -1 \\ 1 \end{pmatrix}$

c) $\mathbf{r} = (5\mathbf{i} + 7\mathbf{j} - 3\mathbf{k}) + s(\mathbf{i} + 3\mathbf{j} - 2\mathbf{k})$, $\mathbf{r} = (-4\mathbf{i} + 15\mathbf{j} - 10\mathbf{k}) + t(\mathbf{i} - 4\mathbf{j} + 3\mathbf{k})$

Q4 Lines L_1 and L_2 have equations $\mathbf{r} = \begin{pmatrix} 1 \\ 0 \\ a \end{pmatrix} + \lambda\begin{pmatrix} -1 \\ b \\ 2 \end{pmatrix}$ and $\mathbf{r} = \begin{pmatrix} 0 \\ c \\ 3 \end{pmatrix} + \mu\begin{pmatrix} 2 \\ 1 \\ d \end{pmatrix}$.
L_1 meets L_2 at $(2, -3, 2)$.
Find the values of a, b, c and d.

> **Q4 Hint:** Use the intersection point to find λ and μ first, then find the other unknowns.

Q5 Show that each pair of lines is skew:

a) $\mathbf{r} = \begin{pmatrix} 4 \\ 0 \\ 1 \end{pmatrix} + \lambda\begin{pmatrix} 1 \\ 2 \\ 1 \end{pmatrix}$, $\mathbf{r} = \begin{pmatrix} -1 \\ 3 \\ 2 \end{pmatrix} + \mu\begin{pmatrix} -1 \\ 1 \\ 0 \end{pmatrix}$

b) $\mathbf{r} = (\mathbf{i} + \mathbf{j} - \mathbf{k}) + \lambda(-\mathbf{i} + 2\mathbf{j} + 3\mathbf{k})$, $\mathbf{r} = (-2\mathbf{i} + 4\mathbf{j} + \mathbf{k}) + \mu(\mathbf{i} - \mathbf{j} + 3\mathbf{k})$

c) $\mathbf{r} = (3\mathbf{i} + \mathbf{j} + \mathbf{k}) + s(-\mathbf{i} + 2\mathbf{j} + \mathbf{k})$, $\mathbf{r} = (2\mathbf{i} - 2\mathbf{j}) + t(\mathbf{i} + \mathbf{j} - 3\mathbf{k})$

Q6 Determine whether the pair of equations $\mathbf{r} = (3\mathbf{i} + 4\mathbf{j}) + \lambda(-\mathbf{i} + \mathbf{j} - \mathbf{k})$ and $\mathbf{r} = (-6\mathbf{i} - 8\mathbf{j}) + \mu(-\mathbf{i} + \mathbf{j} - \mathbf{k})$ represent two different parallel lines, or the same line written in two different ways.

Q7 Find whether each pair of non-parallel lines below are intersecting or skew. Give the position vector of their intersection where possible.

a) $\mathbf{r} = \begin{pmatrix} 4 \\ -5 \\ 1 \end{pmatrix} + p\begin{pmatrix} 2 \\ 4 \\ 3 \end{pmatrix}$, $\mathbf{r} = \begin{pmatrix} 2 \\ -1 \\ 0 \end{pmatrix} + q\begin{pmatrix} 1 \\ 3 \\ 2 \end{pmatrix}$

b) $\mathbf{r} = (\mathbf{i} - \mathbf{j} + 4\mathbf{k}) + \lambda(\mathbf{i} - \mathbf{j} + \mathbf{k})$, $\mathbf{r} = (2\mathbf{i} + 4\mathbf{j} + 7\mathbf{k}) + \mu(2\mathbf{i} + \mathbf{j} + 3\mathbf{k})$

Q8 Quadrilateral ABCD is shown on the right.
a) Obtain vector equations for the lines containing diagonals AC and BD.
b) The diagonals meet at point E. Find the coordinates of E.

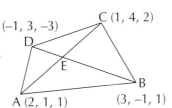

$(-1, 3, -3)$ D C $(1, 4, 2)$ E B A $(2, 1, 1)$ $(3, -1, 1)$

4. Scalar Product

Learning Objectives:

- Be able to find the scalar product of two vectors.
- Be able to find the angle between two vectors using the scalar product.
- Be able to find the angle between two lines from their vector equations.
- Be able to use the scalar product to find if two lines are parallel or perpendicular.
- Be able to find the shortest distance between a line and a point (and other complex vector problems).

The scalar product of two vectors is a method that combines (or 'multiplies') together two vectors to get a scalar. There is another method of 'multiplying' vectors, the cross product, which gives a vector instead. This section only covers finding the scalar product of two vectors, as well as how to use the scalar product to calculate the angle between two lines.

The scalar product

The **scalar product** of two vectors **a** and **b** is written **a.b** (you read this as 'a dot b'). The scalar product is sometimes called the **dot product**.

The **scalar product** of two vectors is **always** a **scalar** quantity, it's never a vector.

Given two vectors **a** and **b** the definition of the **scalar product** is:

$$\mathbf{a.b} = |\mathbf{a}|\,|\mathbf{b}|\cos\theta$$

where θ is the angle between **a** and **b**.

Tip: Make sure you know which angle θ is when you've got two vectors — the correct angle might not always be obvious.

- For **position vectors** it's clear what we mean by the angle between **a** and **b**.

- For other vectors θ is the angle between the vectors when **drawn away** from the **same point**.

Tip: This means that when you're finding the angle between two 3D vectors you can draw a 2D diagram to help you see what's going on.

- When you're working with two **3D vectors** there'll be some **plane** that they **both lie in**.
- The **angle** between the two vectors (e.g. angle ABC) is just the **angle in this plane**.
- Because you're working in a plane the angle between 3D vectors is just like the angle between 2D vectors.

Tip: It's really important you write the dot in **a.b** to make it clear you mean scalar product (instead of cross product — you don't need to know about the cross product for C4).

Example

The diagram on the right shows the vectors a and b.
Given that $|a| = 7$ and $|b| = 6$,
find the scalar product of a and b.
Give your answer to 1 decimal place.

Using the formula for the scalar product you get:

$\mathbf{a.b} = |\mathbf{a}|\,|\mathbf{b}|\cos\theta = 7 \times 6 \times \cos30° = \boxed{36.4}$ to 1 decimal place.

Parallel vectors don't intersect, but you can still find their scalar product. The **scalar product** of two **parallel** vectors is **plus or minus** the **product** of the **magnitudes** of the vectors:

■ If two vectors are **parallel**, the angle between them is **0° or 180°**:

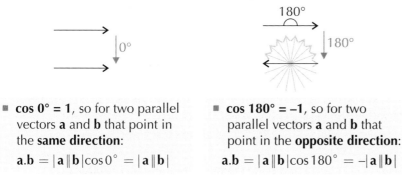

Tip: The angle between parallel vectors is 180° when one is a negative scalar multiple of the other, so they have opposite directions.

■ **cos 0° = 1**, so for two parallel vectors **a** and **b** that point in the **same direction**:
$$\mathbf{a}.\mathbf{b} = |\mathbf{a}\|\mathbf{b}|\cos 0° = |\mathbf{a}\|\mathbf{b}|$$

■ **cos 180° = –1**, so for two parallel vectors **a** and **b** that point in the **opposite direction**:
$$\mathbf{a}.\mathbf{b} = |\mathbf{a}\|\mathbf{b}|\cos 180° = -|\mathbf{a}\|\mathbf{b}|$$

So for any two **parallel** vectors **a** and **b**:

$\mathbf{a}.\mathbf{b} = |\mathbf{a}\|\mathbf{b}|$ when the vectors point in the **same** direction.
$\mathbf{a}.\mathbf{b} = -|\mathbf{a}\|\mathbf{b}|$ when the vectors point in **opposite** directions.

If the **scalar product** of two vectors is **zero** then the vectors are **perpendicular** (or one of the vectors is zero).

■ **Perpendicular** vectors are at **90°** to each other.
■ **Cos 90° = 0**, so for perpendicular vectors **a** and **b**:
$$\mathbf{a}.\mathbf{b} = |\mathbf{a}\|\mathbf{b}|\cos 90° = 0$$

So for any two **perpendicular** vectors **a** and **b**: $\boxed{\mathbf{a}.\mathbf{b} = 0}$

■ Having $|\mathbf{a}| = 0$ or $|\mathbf{b}| = 0$ is the only other way to make the scalar product 0, and this can only happen if the vector itself is **zero**.
■ So if the **scalar product** of two vectors is **zero** either one of the vectors is zero or the two vectors are **perpendicular**.

Tip: This means that if you can show the scalar product of two non-zero vectors is zero then you've proved they're perpendicular.

Example

Find the following scalar products
a)   **j.j**

Two identical vectors are **parallel** and point in the **same direction**, so:
$$\mathbf{j}.\mathbf{j} = |\mathbf{j}|\times|\mathbf{j}| = 1 \times 1 = \boxed{1}$$

b)   **3k.–4k**

3**k** is **parallel** to –4**k**, but they're pointing in **opposite directions**, so:
$$\mathbf{3k}.-\mathbf{4k} = -|3\mathbf{k}| \times |-4\mathbf{k}| = -(3 \times 4) = \boxed{-12}$$

c)   **i.j**

i and **j** are **perpendicular** to one another, so: $\mathbf{i}.\mathbf{j} = \boxed{0}$

d)   **3j.–4k**

j and **k** are **perpendicular** to one another, so: $\mathbf{3j}.-\mathbf{4k} = \boxed{0}$

Tip: The unit vectors **i**, **j** and **k** are all perpendicular to each other.

Q1 Each diagram below shows the magnitudes of two vectors and an angle between them. For each diagram find the scalar product of the two vectors in exact form.

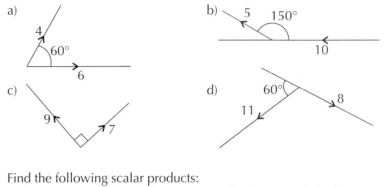

a)

b)

c)

d)

Q2 Find the following scalar products:

a) $\mathbf{i}.3\mathbf{j}$ b) $2\mathbf{j}.-\mathbf{j}$ c) $4\mathbf{k}.\ \mathbf{i}$ d) $\mathbf{k}.6\mathbf{k}$

Q3 Each diagram below show the magnitudes of two vectors whose scalar product is 3. In each case find θ to the nearest degree.

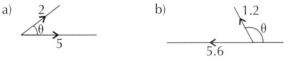

a)

b)

Scalar product from vector components

Tip: You can only use the formula $\mathbf{a}.\mathbf{b} = |\mathbf{a}||\mathbf{b}|\cos\theta$ to find $\mathbf{a}.\mathbf{b}$ if you already know the angle between $\mathbf{a}$ and $\mathbf{b}$.

The formula $\mathbf{a}.\mathbf{b} = |\mathbf{a}||\mathbf{b}|\cos\theta$ tells you what the scalar product is, but to work it out straight from the vectors $\mathbf{a}$ and $\mathbf{b}$ you need another formula.

Scalar products work like multiplication, so the normal laws of multiplication apply to scalar products:

- The **commutative** law: $\mathbf{a}.\mathbf{b} = \mathbf{b}.\mathbf{a}$
- The **distributive** law: $\mathbf{a}.(\mathbf{b} + \mathbf{c}) = \mathbf{a}.\mathbf{b} + \mathbf{a}.\mathbf{c}$

You can apply these laws to find a formula for working out the scalar product.

The scalar product of vectors $\mathbf{a} = a_1\mathbf{i} + a_2\mathbf{j} + a_3\mathbf{k}$ and $\mathbf{b} = b_1\mathbf{i} + b_2\mathbf{j} + b_3\mathbf{k}$ is:
$$\mathbf{a}.\mathbf{b} = (a_1\mathbf{i} + a_2\mathbf{j} + a_3\mathbf{k}).(b_1\mathbf{i} + b_2\mathbf{j} + b_3\mathbf{k})$$

Applying the **distributive law** to **multiply** out the brackets gives:

$$= (a_1\mathbf{i}).(b_1\mathbf{i}) + (a_1\mathbf{i}).(b_2\mathbf{j}) + (a_1\mathbf{i}).(b_3\mathbf{k}) + (a_2\mathbf{j}).(b_1\mathbf{i}) + (a_2\mathbf{j}).(b_2\mathbf{j})$$
$$+ (a_2\mathbf{j}).(b_3\mathbf{k}) + (a_3\mathbf{k}).(b_1\mathbf{i}) + (a_3\mathbf{k}).(b_2\mathbf{j}) + (a_3\mathbf{k}).(b_3\mathbf{k})$$

Now use the **scalar product** definition to work out each of these terms. Unit vectors $\mathbf{i}$, $\mathbf{j}$ and $\mathbf{k}$ are all **perpendicular** to each other, so their scalar product is always **zero**:

$$= (a_1\mathbf{i}).(b_1\mathbf{i}) + 0 + 0 + 0 + (a_2\mathbf{j}).(b_2\mathbf{j}) + 0 + 0 + 0 + (a_3\mathbf{k}).(b_3\mathbf{k})$$
$$= (a_1\mathbf{i}).(b_1\mathbf{i}) + (a_2\mathbf{j}).(b_2\mathbf{j}) + (a_3\mathbf{k}).(b_3\mathbf{k})$$

Use the scalar product definition on each term that's left:

$$(a_1\mathbf{i}).(b_1\mathbf{i}) = |a_1\mathbf{i}||b_1\mathbf{i}|\cos\theta = |a_1|\|\mathbf{i}\||b_1|\|\mathbf{i}|\cos\theta = |a_1 b_1|\cos\theta$$

Now either a_1 and b_1 have the same sign, so $\theta = 0°$

$$\Rightarrow (a_1\mathbf{i}).(b_1\mathbf{i}) = |a_1 b_1|\cos 0° = |a_1 b_1| = a_1 b_1 \ (a_1 b_1 \text{ is positive}),$$

or a_1 and b_1 have opposite signs, so $\theta = 180°$

$$\Rightarrow (a_1\mathbf{i}).(b_1\mathbf{i}) = |a_1 b_1|\cos 180° = -|a_1 b_1| = a_1 b_1 \ (a_1 b_1 \text{ is negative}).$$

Either way $(a_1\mathbf{i}) . (b_1\mathbf{i}) = a_1 b_1$, and the same is true for the $\mathbf{j}$ and $\mathbf{k}$ vectors. So, going back to the formula for the scalar product:

$$\mathbf{a}.\mathbf{b} = (a_1\mathbf{i}) . (b_1\mathbf{i}) + (a_2\mathbf{j}) . (b_2\mathbf{j}) + (a_3\mathbf{k}) . (b_3\mathbf{k})$$
$$= a_1 b_1 + a_2 b_2 + a_3 b_3$$

Tip: Remember, the magnitude of unit vectors is always 1.

Tip: The rules $|ab| = |a||b|$ and $|cd| = |c||d|$ are used here. You might not have been formally introduced to them before, but they make sense if you think about the value of each magnitude.

So we've got another formula for the scalar product:
For two vectors $\mathbf{a} = a_1\mathbf{i} + a_2\mathbf{j} + a_3\mathbf{k}$ and $\mathbf{b} = b_1\mathbf{i} + b_2\mathbf{j} + b_3\mathbf{k}$, the scalar product of $\mathbf{a}$ and $\mathbf{b}$ is:

$$\boxed{\mathbf{a}.\mathbf{b} = a_1 b_1 + a_2 b_2 + a_3 b_3}$$

Tip: For 2D vectors the formula is just:
$$\mathbf{a}.\mathbf{b} = a_1 b_1 + a_2 b_2$$
because 2D vectors have no $\mathbf{k}$ components.

Examples

a) **Find** $\begin{pmatrix} 3 \\ -4 \\ 2 \end{pmatrix}.\begin{pmatrix} -5 \\ -1 \\ 5 \end{pmatrix}$

Use the formula $\mathbf{a}.\mathbf{b} = a_1 b_1 + a_2 b_2 + a_3 b_3$:

$$\begin{pmatrix} 3 \\ -4 \\ 2 \end{pmatrix}.\begin{pmatrix} -5 \\ -1 \\ 5 \end{pmatrix} = (3 \times (-5)) + ((-4) \times (-1)) + (2 \times 5) = -15 + 4 + 10 = \boxed{-1}$$

b) $(2\mathbf{i} + 3\mathbf{j} + \mathbf{k}) . (\alpha\mathbf{i} - \mathbf{j} - 5\mathbf{k}) = -12$. **Find the value of α.**

- Let $\mathbf{a} = 2\mathbf{i} + 3\mathbf{j} + \mathbf{k}$ and $\mathbf{b} = \alpha\mathbf{i} - \mathbf{j} - 5\mathbf{k}$.
- Work out their scalar product $\mathbf{a}.\mathbf{b}$ in terms of α using the formula $\mathbf{a}.\mathbf{b} = a_1 b_1 + a_2 b_2 + a_3 b_3$:

$$\mathbf{a}.\mathbf{b} = (2 \times \alpha) + (3 \times (-1)) + (1 \times (-5)) = 2\alpha - 8$$

- So: $-12 = \mathbf{a}.\mathbf{b} = 2\alpha - 8 \Rightarrow -4 = 2\alpha \Rightarrow \boxed{\alpha = -2}$

Knowing that the **scalar product** of **perpendicular** vectors is always **zero** gives you an easy way to check if vectors are perpendicular.

You could also check if vectors are **parallel** using the scalar product.
If $\mathbf{a}.\mathbf{b} = |\mathbf{a}||\mathbf{b}|$ or $-|\mathbf{a}||\mathbf{b}|$ then the vectors $\mathbf{a}$ and $\mathbf{b}$ are parallel, but if $\mathbf{a}.\mathbf{b} \neq |\mathbf{a}||\mathbf{b}|$ or $-|\mathbf{a}||\mathbf{b}|$ they're not.

Tip: It's usually quicker to find out if two vectors are parallel by checking if they're scalar multiples of one another, but this is a handy check if you already know the vectors' magnitudes and scalar product.

a) **Determine if vectors a** $= \begin{pmatrix} 5 \\ 0 \\ -7 \end{pmatrix}$ **and b** $= \begin{pmatrix} -2 \\ -4 \\ -3 \end{pmatrix}$ **are perpendicular to one another.**

Find the scalar product of the two vectors — if they're **perpendicular**, the scalar product will be **zero**.

$$\mathbf{a.b} = a_1b_1 + a_2b_2 + a_3b_3 = (5 \times -2) + (0 \times -4) + (-7 \times -3)$$
$$= -10 + 0 + 21 = 11 \neq 0$$

The scalar product **isn't zero**, so the vectors are **not perpendicular**.

b) **Calculate the scalar product of 2i + 3j – k and 4i – 6j + 2k, and hence show that they are neither parallel nor perpendicular.**

- Let $\mathbf{a} = 2\mathbf{i} + 3\mathbf{j} - \mathbf{k}$ and $\mathbf{b} = 4\mathbf{i} - 6\mathbf{j} + 2\mathbf{k}$
$$\mathbf{a.b} = a_1b_1 + a_2b_2 + a_3b_3 = (2 \times 4) + (3 \times -6) + (-1 \times 2)$$
$$= 8 - 18 - 2 = -12 \neq 0$$

- So $\boxed{\mathbf{a} \text{ and } \mathbf{b} \text{ are not perpendicular as } \mathbf{a.b} \neq 0}$.

- Now prove they're not parallel by showing $\mathbf{a.b} \neq \pm|\mathbf{a}\|\mathbf{b}|$
$$|\mathbf{a}| = \sqrt{2^2 + 3^2 + (-1)^2} = \sqrt{14}$$
$$|\mathbf{b}| = \sqrt{4^2 + (-6)^2 + 2^2} = \sqrt{56} = \sqrt{4}\sqrt{14} = 2\sqrt{14}$$
$$\text{So } |\mathbf{a}\|\mathbf{b}| = 2\sqrt{14}\sqrt{14} = 28$$
Then $\mathbf{a.b} = -12 \neq |\mathbf{a}\|\mathbf{b}|$ or $-|\mathbf{a}\|\mathbf{b}|$

- So $\boxed{\mathbf{a} \text{ and } \mathbf{b} \text{ are not parallel as } \mathbf{a.b} \neq |\mathbf{a}\|\mathbf{b}| \text{ or } -|\mathbf{a}\|\mathbf{b}|}$

Tip: The question says 'hence show', which is a hint that you're meant to use the scalar product you've just worked out to show the vectors aren't parallel or perpendicular.

Exercise 4.2

Q1 Find the scalar product of these pairs of vectors.

a) $\begin{pmatrix} 1 \\ 4 \end{pmatrix}, \begin{pmatrix} -2 \\ 1 \end{pmatrix}$

b) $2\mathbf{i} - \mathbf{j}, \mathbf{i} + 3\mathbf{j}$

c) $-2\mathbf{i} - 6\mathbf{j} + \mathbf{k}, -\mathbf{i} + 2\mathbf{j} + 9\mathbf{k}$

d) $\begin{pmatrix} 3 \\ 1 \\ -4 \end{pmatrix}, \begin{pmatrix} 2 \\ 3 \\ 1 \end{pmatrix}$

e) $5\mathbf{j} - 6\mathbf{k}, 6\mathbf{i} + 5\mathbf{k}$

Q2 These pairs of vectors all have scalar products that are equal to 8. Find the values of e, f and g.

a) $\begin{pmatrix} 4 \\ e \end{pmatrix}, \begin{pmatrix} -2 \\ 4 \end{pmatrix}$

b) $7\mathbf{i} + f\mathbf{j} - 3\mathbf{k}, -2\mathbf{i} - \mathbf{j} - 5\mathbf{k}$

c) $\begin{pmatrix} -2 \\ 5 \\ 1 \end{pmatrix}, \begin{pmatrix} g \\ -2 \\ 12 \end{pmatrix}$

Q3 Determine which pairs of vectors are perpendicular to one another.

a) $4\mathbf{i} - 5\mathbf{j}, 10\mathbf{i} - 8\mathbf{j}$

b) $\begin{pmatrix} 4 \\ 0 \\ -5 \end{pmatrix}, \begin{pmatrix} 0 \\ 2 \\ 0 \end{pmatrix}$

c) $\begin{pmatrix} 3 \\ 6 \\ -5 \end{pmatrix}, \begin{pmatrix} -2 \\ 4 \\ 2 \end{pmatrix}$

d) $-\mathbf{i} - 2\mathbf{j} + \mathbf{k}, 2\mathbf{i} + \mathbf{j} + 4\mathbf{k}$

e) $5\mathbf{j} + 2\mathbf{k}, -4\mathbf{i} + 10\mathbf{j}$

Q4 The following pairs of vectors are perpendicular.
Find the values of a, b, c and d.

a) $4\mathbf{i} + a\mathbf{j}$, $5\mathbf{i} - 10\mathbf{j}$

b) $5b\mathbf{i} - 6\mathbf{j} + 9\mathbf{k}$, $2\mathbf{i} - \mathbf{j} - 4\mathbf{k}$

c) $\begin{pmatrix} 2 \\ 3 \\ 1 \end{pmatrix}$, $\begin{pmatrix} -1 \\ 1 \\ c \end{pmatrix}$

d) $\begin{pmatrix} -3 \\ 9 \\ 8 \end{pmatrix}\begin{pmatrix} d \\ 3 \\ -6 \end{pmatrix}$

Q5 Use the scalar product to show that $\begin{pmatrix} 4 \\ -1 \\ 3 \end{pmatrix}$ and $\begin{pmatrix} -12 \\ 3 \\ -9 \end{pmatrix}$ are parallel.

Q6 Find 3 non-parallel vectors that are perpendicular to $3\mathbf{i} - \mathbf{j} - 2\mathbf{k}$.

Q6 Hint: Start by finding an equation for the scalar product of the vector $3\mathbf{i} - \mathbf{j} - 2\mathbf{k}$ and a vector with unknown coefficients.

Finding angles between vectors

$\mathbf{a.b} = |\mathbf{a}\|\mathbf{b}|\cos\theta$ can be rearranged to get:

$$\cos\theta = \frac{\mathbf{a.b}}{|\mathbf{a}\|\mathbf{b}|}$$

Using this formula you can work out the angle θ between two vectors $\mathbf{a}$ and $\mathbf{b}$ straight from their $\mathbf{i}$, $\mathbf{j}$ and $\mathbf{k}$ components:

■ Find the scalar product using the formula: $\mathbf{a.b} = a_1b_1 + a_2b_2 + a_3b_3$.

■ Find the magnitude of $\mathbf{a}$ and of $\mathbf{b}$ using Pythagoras: $|\mathbf{a}| = \sqrt{a_1^2 + a_2^2 + a_3^2}$.

■ Plug these values into the formula $\cos\theta = \frac{\mathbf{a.b}}{|\mathbf{a}\|\mathbf{b}|}$.

Example 1

Find the angle between the vectors $\begin{pmatrix} -1 \\ -6 \\ 0 \end{pmatrix}$ **and** $\begin{pmatrix} 4 \\ 2 \\ 8 \end{pmatrix}$.

Let $\mathbf{a} = \begin{pmatrix} -1 \\ -6 \\ 0 \end{pmatrix}$ and $\mathbf{b} = \begin{pmatrix} 4 \\ 2 \\ 8 \end{pmatrix}$. We're looking for θ, where $\cos\theta = \frac{\mathbf{a.b}}{|\mathbf{a}\|\mathbf{b}|}$.

■ Find the **scalar product** of the vectors:

$\mathbf{a.b} = a_1b_1 + a_2b_2 + a_3b_3 = (-1 \times 4) + (-6 \times 2) + (0 \times 8)$

$= -4 - 12 + 0 = \boxed{-16}$

■ Find the **magnitude** of each vector:

$|\mathbf{a}| = \sqrt{(-1)^2 + (-6)^2 + (0)^2} = \boxed{\sqrt{37}}$

$|\mathbf{b}| = \sqrt{(4)^2 + (2)^2 + (8)^2} = \boxed{\sqrt{84}}$

■ Now put these values into the formula and find the **angle**:

$\cos\theta = \frac{\mathbf{a.b}}{|\mathbf{a}\|\mathbf{b}|} = \frac{-16}{\sqrt{37}\sqrt{84}} \Rightarrow \boxed{\theta = 106.7°}$ to 1 d.p.

Tip: It's good to give your vectors names, it'll save you having to write them out every time you want to refer to them.

You can also use this formula for answering **geometric questions**, the key is figuring out which vectors you need to use:

Example 2

The coordinates of A, B and C are (–2, 0, 3), (1, 5, 2) and (3, –2, 1) respectively. Find the size of angle ABC to one decimal place.

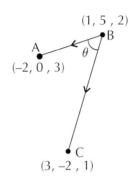

(1, 5 , 2)

A
(–2, 0 , 3)

B

θ

C
(3, –2 , 1)

- The **angle** you're looking for is ABC, so it's the angle **between** lines **AB and BC**.

- Both vectors need to be directed **away from the angle** so the vectors you need are $\overrightarrow{BA}$ and $\overrightarrow{BC}$.

- You can then use the formula $\cos\theta = \dfrac{\overrightarrow{BA}.\overrightarrow{BC}}{|\overrightarrow{BA}||\overrightarrow{BC}|}$ to **find θ**.

- Find the vectors first:

$$\overrightarrow{BA} = \overrightarrow{OA} - \overrightarrow{OB} = \begin{pmatrix} -2 \\ 0 \\ 3 \end{pmatrix} - \begin{pmatrix} 1 \\ 5 \\ 2 \end{pmatrix} = \begin{pmatrix} -3 \\ -5 \\ 1 \end{pmatrix}$$

$$\overrightarrow{BC} = \overrightarrow{OC} - \overrightarrow{OB} = \begin{pmatrix} 3 \\ -2 \\ 1 \end{pmatrix} - \begin{pmatrix} 1 \\ 5 \\ 2 \end{pmatrix} = \begin{pmatrix} 2 \\ -7 \\ -1 \end{pmatrix}$$

- Now find the scalar product and the magnitudes as before:

$$\overrightarrow{BA}.\overrightarrow{BC} = (-3 \times 2) + (-5 \times (-7)) + (1 \times (-1)) = -6 + 35 - 1 = \boxed{28}$$

$$|\overrightarrow{BA}| = \sqrt{(-3)^2 + (-5)^2 + 1^2} = \boxed{\sqrt{35}}$$

$$|\overrightarrow{BC}| = \sqrt{2^2 + (-7)^2 + (-1)^2} = \boxed{\sqrt{54}}$$

- Stick these values into the formula to find θ:

$$\cos\theta = \frac{\overrightarrow{BA}.\overrightarrow{BC}}{|\overrightarrow{BA}||\overrightarrow{BC}|} = \frac{28}{\sqrt{35}\sqrt{54}} \quad \Rightarrow \quad \boxed{\theta = 49.9°} \text{ to 1 d.p.}$$

Exercise 4.3

Q1 Find the angle between each of the following pairs of vectors. In each case, give your answer in degrees correct to 1 d.p.

a) $\mathbf{p} = 4\mathbf{i} + 3\mathbf{j},$
$\mathbf{q} = 12\mathbf{i} + 5\mathbf{j}$

b) $\mathbf{r} = \begin{pmatrix} 2 \\ -1 \end{pmatrix}, \mathbf{s} = \begin{pmatrix} -6 \\ 3 \end{pmatrix}$

c) $\mathbf{a} = \begin{pmatrix} -2 \\ -4 \end{pmatrix}, \mathbf{b} = \begin{pmatrix} 3 \\ -1 \end{pmatrix}$

Q2 Find the angle between each of the following pairs of vectors. In each case, give your answer in degrees correct to 1 d.p.

a) $\mathbf{a} = \begin{pmatrix} 2 \\ -2 \\ 1 \end{pmatrix}, \mathbf{b} = \begin{pmatrix} 6 \\ 3 \\ 2 \end{pmatrix}$

b) $\mathbf{c} = \begin{pmatrix} -7 \\ -4 \\ 4 \end{pmatrix}, \mathbf{d} = \begin{pmatrix} -6 \\ 7 \\ 6 \end{pmatrix}$

c) $\mathbf{e} = 9\mathbf{i} + 6\mathbf{j} - 2\mathbf{k}, \mathbf{f} = \mathbf{i} + 4\mathbf{j} - 8\mathbf{k}$

d) $\mathbf{g} = 7\mathbf{i} + \mathbf{j} - \mathbf{k}, \mathbf{h} = \mathbf{i} - 18\mathbf{j} - 6\mathbf{k}$

e) $\mathbf{t} = \begin{pmatrix} 23 \\ -10 \\ 10 \end{pmatrix}, \mathbf{u} = \begin{pmatrix} 2 \\ -4 \\ 4 \end{pmatrix}$

Q3 Triangle ABC has vertices at the points A $(-4, -1)$, B $(-1, 3)$ and C $(4, 5)$.

a) Find the vectors $\overrightarrow{AB}$ and $\overrightarrow{AC}$.

b) Find $|\overrightarrow{AB}|$ and $|\overrightarrow{AC}|$.

c) Find $(\overrightarrow{AB}) \cdot (\overrightarrow{AC})$.

d) Hence calculate angle BAC, correct to the nearest degree.

Q3 Hint: Draw a diagram if it helps you to see what's going on.

Q4 Points P, Q and R have position vectors $\mathbf{p} = -4\mathbf{i} - 7\mathbf{j} - 9\mathbf{k}$, $\mathbf{q} = -2\mathbf{i} + 2\mathbf{j} + 5\mathbf{k}$ and $\mathbf{r} = -2\mathbf{i} - \mathbf{j} - 11\mathbf{k}$ respectively.

a) Find the vectors $\overrightarrow{PQ}$ and $\overrightarrow{PR}$.

b) Find the magnitudes $|\overrightarrow{PQ}|$ and $|\overrightarrow{PR}|$.

c) Find $(\overrightarrow{PQ}) \cdot (\overrightarrow{PR})$.

d) Hence find the angle QPR, giving your answer in degrees correct to 3 s.f.

Q5 The isosceles triangle TRU shown has TR = TU.

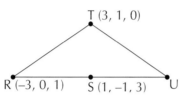

T $(3, 1, 0)$

R $(-3, 0, 1)$ S $(1, -1, 3)$ U

a) Find $(\overrightarrow{TS}) \cdot (\overrightarrow{RS})$.

b) Show that S is the midpoint of RU.

c) Write down the coordinates of U.

Q6 ABCD is a parallelogram where A, B and C have position vectors $\mathbf{a} = -4\mathbf{i} + 5\mathbf{j} - 6\mathbf{k}$, $\mathbf{b} = 4\mathbf{j} + 2\mathbf{k}$ and $\mathbf{c} = 6\mathbf{i} + 13\mathbf{j}$ respectively.

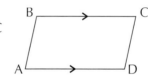

a) Write down the position vector of D.

b) Find the vectors $\overrightarrow{AB}$ and $\overrightarrow{AD}$ in $\mathbf{i}, \mathbf{j}, \mathbf{k}$ form.

c) Find the magnitudes of $\overrightarrow{AB}$ and $\overrightarrow{AD}$.

d) Hence find the angle BAD, giving your answer in degrees correct to 4 s.f.

Q7

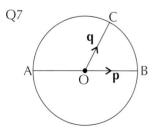

AB is the diameter of a circle centre O, radius r. C is a point on the circumference of the circle. $\overrightarrow{OB} = \mathbf{p}$ and $\overrightarrow{OC} = \mathbf{q}$.

a) Find the vectors $\overrightarrow{AC}$ and $\overrightarrow{CB}$ in terms of $\mathbf{p}$ and $\mathbf{q}$.

b) Show that $(\overrightarrow{AC}) \cdot (\overrightarrow{CB}) = \mathbf{p} \cdot \mathbf{p} - \mathbf{q} \cdot \mathbf{q}$.

c) Hence explain why angle ACB = $90°$.

Q7 b) Hint: Remember the commutative and distributive laws (p.134) and you'll also need to know that: $(c_1\mathbf{d}) \cdot (c_2\mathbf{b}) = c_1 c_2(\mathbf{d} \cdot \mathbf{b})$

Finding the angle between two lines

You can find the **angle between two lines** from the **vector equations** of the lines, or from **two points** on each line.

If you're given the **vector equations** you just use the **b** vectors in the equations $\mathbf{r}_1 = \mathbf{a}_1 + s\mathbf{b}_1$ and $\mathbf{r}_2 = \mathbf{a}_2 + t\mathbf{b}_2$ (the 'parallel to' or the 'direction' bits), and find the angle between them using $\cos\theta = \dfrac{\mathbf{b}_1.\mathbf{b}_2}{|\mathbf{b}_1\|\mathbf{b}_2|}$.

- This formula gives you the **angle** that both vectors are **pointing away from**, which could be up to 180°.

- The **angle between two lines** is the **smallest angle** you can rotate one line by to get it onto the other line, so it **can't be more than 90°**.

Tip: If you rotate a line by more than 90° clockwise it's the same as a rotation of less than 90° anticlockwise.

- So you might have to **subtract** the angle you get from the formula **from 180°** to find the angle between the lines:

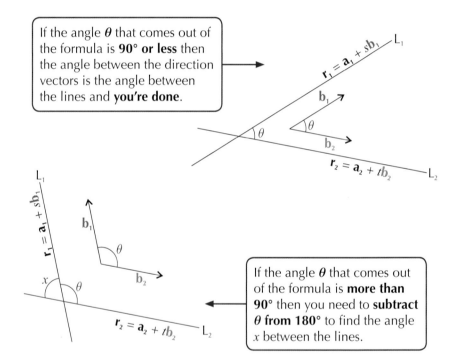

If the angle θ that comes out of the formula is **90° or less** then the angle between the direction vectors is the angle between the lines and **you're done**.

If the angle θ that comes out of the formula is **more than 90°** then you need to **subtract** θ from **180°** to find the angle x between the lines.

If you're given **two points** on a line you'll have to **find a vector parallel to the line** before you can plug it into the formula.

Tip: This is what you do when you're finding the vector equation of a line from two points. If you're only asked to find the angle there's no need to write the whole equation out (though you can do if it helps).

This is nice and simple because the vector that joins the two points is parallel to the line, so given two points P and Q with position vectors **p** and **q** you just use the vector $\overrightarrow{PQ} = \mathbf{q} - \mathbf{p}$.

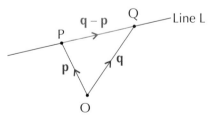

Example 1

Line *l* has the equation r = (2i + 4k) + λ(i + 2j –k).
Point A and point B have coordinates (4, 4, 2) and (1, 0, 3) respectively.
Point A lies on *l*.

a) **Find the acute angle between *l* and line segment AB.**

- First draw a **diagram**, it'll make everything clearer:

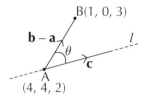

Tip: Don't worry about drawing everything accurately, it's just to give you an idea of what's going on.

- Find the vectors that you want to **know the angle** between.
  The vector parallel to line segment AB is $\overrightarrow{AB}$.

$$\overrightarrow{AB} = \mathbf{b} - \mathbf{a} = \begin{pmatrix} 1 \\ 0 \\ 3 \end{pmatrix} - \begin{pmatrix} 4 \\ 4 \\ 2 \end{pmatrix} = \begin{pmatrix} -3 \\ -4 \\ 1 \end{pmatrix}$$

The direction vector of *l* (which we've called **c**) is: $\mathbf{c} = \begin{pmatrix} 1 \\ 2 \\ -1 \end{pmatrix}$

- Next you need to find the scalar product of your two vectors:

$$\overrightarrow{AB} \cdot \mathbf{c} = (-3 \times 1) + (-4 \times 2) + (1 \times -1) = -3 - 8 - 1 = -12$$

- And the magnitudes of each vector:

$$|\overrightarrow{AB}| = \sqrt{(-3)^2 + (-4)^2 + (1)^2} = \sqrt{26}$$
$$|\mathbf{c}| = \sqrt{(1)^2 + (2)^2 + (-1)^2} = \sqrt{6}$$

- Now plug these values into the equation and find the angle:

$$\cos\theta = \frac{\overrightarrow{AB} \cdot \mathbf{c}}{|\overrightarrow{AB}||\mathbf{c}|} = \frac{-12}{\sqrt{26}\sqrt{6}} \Rightarrow \theta = 163.897...°$$

- The formula's given us the **obtuse angle**, so the situation must have been more like this:

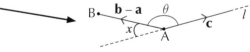

Tip: Remember, the vectors always point away from the angle θ that the formula gives you.

- So you just **subtract this angle from 180°** to get the acute angle (that's *x*) between the lines:

$$180° - 163.897...° = \mathbf{16.1°} \text{ to 1 d.p.}$$

b) **P is the point on *l* such that BP is the shortest distance from B to *l*.**
   Find the distance BP to two decimal places.

Draw a diagram.
BP is the shortest distance from B to *l*,
so it must be perpendicular to *l*:

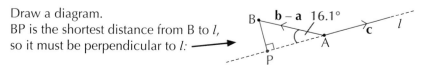

Tip: The shortest distance between a point and a line is always the perpendicular line segment.

APB is a right-angled triangle, so you can find the length of BP using trig.

- You know from part **a)** that the vector $\vec{AB}$ is $\begin{pmatrix} -3 \\ -4 \\ 1 \end{pmatrix}$, and $|\vec{AB}| = \sqrt{26}$
- Angle PAB is 16.1°.
- You want to find side BP, the side opposite PAB.
  opposite = $\sin\theta \times$ hypotenuse, so:

$$BP = \sin(16.1...) \times \sqrt{26} = \boxed{1.41} \text{ to 2 d.p.}$$

You can prove **lines are perpendicular** by showing that their direction vectors are perpendicular, i.e. by showing the **scalar product** of their direction vectors is **zero**:

L_1 and L_2 are **perpendicular** if $\mathbf{b_1} \cdot \mathbf{b_2} = 0$

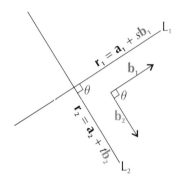

Example 2

Show that the lines $\mathbf{r_1} = (\mathbf{i} + 6\mathbf{j} + 2\mathbf{k}) + \lambda(\mathbf{i} + 2\mathbf{j} + 2\mathbf{k})$ and $\mathbf{r_2} = (3\mathbf{i} - \mathbf{j} + \mathbf{k}) + \mu(4\mathbf{i} - 3\mathbf{j} + \mathbf{k})$ are perpendicular.

- $\mathbf{r_1}$ and $\mathbf{r_2}$ are **parallel** to their direction vectors $\mathbf{b_1} = \mathbf{i} + 2\mathbf{j} + 2\mathbf{k}$ and $\mathbf{b_2} = 4\mathbf{i} - 3\mathbf{j} + \mathbf{k}$ respectively.
- The **scalar product** of $\mathbf{b_1}$ and $\mathbf{b_2}$ is:
$$(\mathbf{i} + 2\mathbf{j} + 2\mathbf{k}).(4\mathbf{i} - 3\mathbf{j} + \mathbf{k}) = 4 - 6 + 2 = 0$$
- So $\mathbf{b_1}$ and $\mathbf{b_2}$ are perpendicular, therefore $\mathbf{r_1}$ and $\mathbf{r_2}$ are **perpendicular**.

Exercise 4.4

Q1 Hint: You don't need to use the scalar product to decide if the lines are parallel or not.

Q1 For each pair of lines whose equations are given below, state whether the lines are parallel, perpendicular or neither.

a) $\mathbf{r} = (\mathbf{i} - 2\mathbf{j} + \mathbf{k}) + s(2\mathbf{i} - 4\mathbf{j} - 6\mathbf{k})$, $\mathbf{r} = (2\mathbf{i} + 3\mathbf{j} + 4\mathbf{k}) + t(-\mathbf{i} + 2\mathbf{j} + 3\mathbf{k})$

b) $\mathbf{r} = \begin{pmatrix} -5 \\ 3 \\ 2 \end{pmatrix} + p\begin{pmatrix} 4 \\ -1 \\ 1 \end{pmatrix}$, $\mathbf{r} = \begin{pmatrix} 2 \\ 1 \\ 0 \end{pmatrix} + q\begin{pmatrix} 1 \\ -4 \\ 0 \end{pmatrix}$

c) $\mathbf{r} = \lambda(2\mathbf{j} - 7\mathbf{k})$, $\mathbf{r} = 3\mathbf{k} + \mu(2\mathbf{i} - 7\mathbf{k})$

d) $\mathbf{r} = (\mathbf{j} + \mathbf{k}) + p(\mathbf{i} + \mathbf{j})$, $\mathbf{r} = (\mathbf{i} + \mathbf{k}) + q(\mathbf{i} - \mathbf{j} + 2\mathbf{k})$

e) $\mathbf{r} = \begin{pmatrix} 1 \\ 0 \\ 0 \end{pmatrix} + \lambda\begin{pmatrix} 0 \\ 0 \\ 4 \end{pmatrix}$, $\mathbf{r} = \begin{pmatrix} 0 \\ 1 \\ 0 \end{pmatrix} + \mu\begin{pmatrix} -4 \\ 8 \\ 0 \end{pmatrix}$

Q2 Find the acute angle between each pair of intersecting lines below.

a) $\mathbf{r} = \begin{pmatrix} 4 \\ 0 \\ 4 \end{pmatrix} + \lambda \begin{pmatrix} 2 \\ 2 \\ 1 \end{pmatrix}$, $\mathbf{r} = \begin{pmatrix} 1 \\ -4 \\ 3 \end{pmatrix} + \mu \begin{pmatrix} 2 \\ 3 \\ 6 \end{pmatrix}$

b) $\mathbf{r} = (-\mathbf{i} - \mathbf{j} - 3\mathbf{k}) + p(4\mathbf{i} + 4\mathbf{j} - 7\mathbf{k})$, $\mathbf{r} = (2\mathbf{i} + 4\mathbf{j} + \mathbf{k}) + q(8\mathbf{i} + \mathbf{j} - 4\mathbf{k})$

c) $\mathbf{r} = \begin{pmatrix} 5 \\ -7 \\ 11 \end{pmatrix} + s \begin{pmatrix} 6 \\ -7 \\ 5 \end{pmatrix}$, $\mathbf{r} = \begin{pmatrix} 9 \\ 0 \\ -9 \end{pmatrix} + t \begin{pmatrix} 2 \\ 1 \\ -1 \end{pmatrix}$

d) $\mathbf{r} = 4\mathbf{i} + \alpha(7\mathbf{i} - 6\mathbf{j} + 6\mathbf{k})$, $\mathbf{r} = 4\mathbf{j} + \beta(-4\mathbf{i} + 2\mathbf{j} - 2\mathbf{k})$

e) $\mathbf{r} = (4\mathbf{i} - \mathbf{j}) + u(-3\mathbf{i} - 5\mathbf{j} + 2\mathbf{k})$, $\mathbf{r} = 5\mathbf{k} + v(2\mathbf{i} + \mathbf{k})$

Q3 The lines given by equations $\mathbf{r} = (4\mathbf{i} + \mathbf{j} + 2\mathbf{k}) + \lambda(4\mathbf{i} + 6\mathbf{j} - \mathbf{k})$ and $\mathbf{r} = (4\mathbf{i} + \mathbf{j} + 2\mathbf{k}) + \mu(5\mathbf{i} - 2\mathbf{j} + z\mathbf{k})$ are perpendicular. Find z.

Q4 A $(-1, -2, 6)$, B $(p, -1, 3)$ and C $(-1, 0, 2)$ are the vertices of a triangle where angle ABC is $90°$.

a) Write down vector equations for the lines containing AB and BC in terms of p.

b) Find 2 possible values of p.

Q5 The position vectors of points A and B are $\begin{pmatrix} 4 \\ 2 \\ -2 \end{pmatrix}$ and $\begin{pmatrix} -1 \\ 3 \\ 1 \end{pmatrix}$ respectively.

The points C and D are such that $\overrightarrow{OD} = 2\overrightarrow{OB}$ and $\overrightarrow{OC} = \frac{3}{2}\overrightarrow{OA}$.

a) Write down the position vectors of C and D.

b) Line L_1 passes through A and D, line L_2 passes through B and C. Write down vector equations for L_1 and L_2.

c) Determine whether the lines are skew or intersecting.

d) Find the acute angle between the directions of the 2 lines, correct to 1 decimal place.

Q6 a) Find an equation for the line L which passes through A $(3, 8, -5)$ and B $(8, -2, 0)$.

b) Find the co-ordinates of the point P, lying on line L, such that OP is perpendicular to line L.

c) Find the distance of P from O in the form $m\sqrt{n}$.

Q7 Points A, B and C have position vectors $(4\mathbf{i} - 6\mathbf{j} + 2\mathbf{k})$, $(-3\mathbf{i} + 2\mathbf{j} + 4\mathbf{k})$ and $(5\mathbf{i} - \mathbf{j} - \mathbf{k})$ respectively. The line l passes through B and C.

a) Find a vector equation for the line l.

b) Find the acute angle between the line segment AB and line l to 1 d.p.

c) Find the shortest distance from the point A to the line l to 2 d.p.

Q7 c) Hint:
You're looking for the perpendicular line segment.

Review Exercise — Chapter 6

Q1 Give two vectors that are parallel to each of the following:

a) 2**a**   b) 3**i** + 4**j** − 2**k**   c) $\begin{pmatrix} 1 \\ 2 \\ -1 \end{pmatrix}$

Q2 Using the diagram on the right find these vectors in terms of vectors **a**, **b** and **c**.

a) $\overrightarrow{AB}$ b) $\overrightarrow{BA}$ c) $\overrightarrow{CB}$ d) $\overrightarrow{AC}$

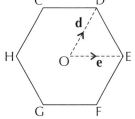

Q3 CDEFGH is a regular hexagon whose centre is O.

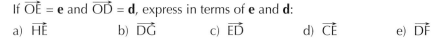

If $\overrightarrow{OE}$ = **e** and $\overrightarrow{OD}$ = **d**, express in terms of **e** and **d**:

a) $\overrightarrow{HE}$ b) $\overrightarrow{DG}$ c) $\overrightarrow{ED}$ d) $\overrightarrow{CE}$ e) $\overrightarrow{DF}$

Q4 Give, in unit vector form, the position vector of point P, which has the coordinates (2, −4, 5).

Q5 X is the point (6, −1, 0) and Y is the point (4, −4, 7).
Write the vectors $\overrightarrow{XO}$ and $\overrightarrow{YO}$ in unit vector form and in column vector form.

Q6 R has position vector $\begin{pmatrix} 3 \\ -1 \end{pmatrix}$ and S has position vector $\begin{pmatrix} -5 \\ -7 \end{pmatrix}$.
Find the magnitude of $\overrightarrow{RS}$.

Q7 Find the magnitudes of these vectors: a) 3**i** + 4**j** − 2**k**   b) $\begin{pmatrix} 1 \\ 2 \\ -1 \end{pmatrix}$

Q8 If A is (1, 2, 3) and B is (3, −1, −2), find: a) $|\overrightarrow{OA}|$ b) $|\overrightarrow{OB}|$ c) $|\overrightarrow{AB}|$

Q9 X is the point (−2, 1, 0).

The distance between X and Y is 6. The unit vector in the direction $\overrightarrow{XY}$ is $\begin{pmatrix} \frac{2}{3} \\ \frac{2}{3} \\ -\frac{1}{3} \end{pmatrix}$.

Find the coordinates of Y.

Q10 Find vector equations for the following lines in unit and in column vector form.
a) a straight line through (4, 1, 2), parallel to vector 3**i** + **j** − **k**.
b) a straight line through (2, −1, 1) and (0, 2, 3).

Q11 Find three points that lie on the line with vector equation $\mathbf{r} = \begin{pmatrix} 3 \\ 2 \\ 4 \end{pmatrix} + t \begin{pmatrix} -1 \\ 3 \\ 0 \end{pmatrix}$.

Q12 Line L passes through the origin and contains the point A whose position vector is $2\mathbf{i} + 8\mathbf{j} - 4\mathbf{k}$. Points B, C and D also lie on the line, where B is the midpoint of OA, A is the midpoint of OC and O is the midpoint of DA.
a) Draw a sketch of the positions of O, A, B, C and D on the line.
b) Write down the position vectors of B, C and D.
c) Give a vector equation for line L.

Q13 Point P has position vector $\begin{pmatrix} 3 \\ -5 \\ 2 \end{pmatrix}$ and point Q has position vector $\begin{pmatrix} 5 \\ -2 \\ -1 \end{pmatrix}$.
a) Write down the vector $\overrightarrow{PQ}$ in column vector form.
b) Find a vector equation for the straight line that passes through P and Q.

Q14 Points A and B have coordinates (1, 1, 3) and (9, –3, 9) respectively.
Line m passes through A and is parallel to the vector $3\mathbf{i} - \mathbf{j} + 4\mathbf{k}$.
Line n passes through B and is parallel to the vector $-\mathbf{i} + \mathbf{j} + \mathbf{k}$.
a) Show that line m and line n intersect,
   and find the coordinates of the point of intersection C.
b) Show that triangle ABC is right-angled.

Q15 Find $\mathbf{a.b}$ if: a) $\mathbf{a} = 3\mathbf{i} + 4\mathbf{j}$ and $\mathbf{b} = \mathbf{i} - 2\mathbf{j} + 3\mathbf{k}$ b) $\mathbf{a} = \begin{pmatrix} 4 \\ 2 \\ 1 \end{pmatrix}$ and $\mathbf{b} = \begin{pmatrix} 3 \\ -4 \\ -3 \end{pmatrix}$

Q16

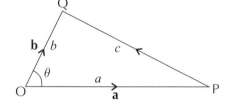

O is the origin and points P and Q have position vectors $\mathbf{a}$ and $\mathbf{b}$ respectively.
Triangle OPQ has sides whose lengths are given by OP = a, OQ = b, PQ = c. Angle POQ = θ.
a) Write down the vector $\overrightarrow{PQ}$ in terms of $\mathbf{a}$ and $\mathbf{b}$.
b) Obtain an expression for $(\mathbf{b} - \mathbf{a}) . (\mathbf{b} - \mathbf{a})$ in terms of $\mathbf{a}$, $\mathbf{b}$ and θ.
c) Hence deduce that $c^2 = a^2 + b^2 - 2ab\cos\theta$.

Q17 $\mathbf{r_1} = \begin{pmatrix} 2 \\ -1 \\ 2 \end{pmatrix} + t \begin{pmatrix} -4 \\ 6 \\ -2 \end{pmatrix}$ and $\mathbf{r_2} = \begin{pmatrix} 3 \\ 2 \\ 4 \end{pmatrix} + u \begin{pmatrix} -1 \\ 3 \\ 0 \end{pmatrix}$
a) Show that these lines intersect and find the position vector of their intersection point.
b) Find the angle between these lines.

Q18 Find a vector that is perpendicular to $3\mathbf{i} + 4\mathbf{j} - 2\mathbf{k}$.

Q19 Two lines L$_1$ and L$_2$ have vector equations $\mathbf{r_1} = (x\mathbf{i} + \mathbf{j} + 5\mathbf{k}) + \lambda(2\mathbf{i} + 2\mathbf{j} + 3\mathbf{k})$ and $\mathbf{r_2} = (-\mathbf{i} - 2\mathbf{j} + 3\mathbf{k}) + \mu(3\mathbf{i} - \mathbf{j} - 2\mathbf{k})$. Given that the two lines intersect:
a) Find the value of x.
b) Find the coordinates of the point of intersection.
c) Find the acute angle between the two lines.

1   The quadrilateral ABCD has vertices A(1, 5, 9), B(3, 2, 1), C(–2, 4, 3) and D(5, –1, –7).

    a)   Find the vector $\overrightarrow{AB}$.

(2 marks)

    b)   C and D lie on line l_1. Using the parameter μ, find the vector equation of l_1.

(2 marks)

    c)   Find the coordinates of the intersection point of l_1 and the line that passes through AB.

(5 marks)

    d)   (i)   Find the acute angle between l_1 and AB.
            Give your answer to 1 decimal place.

(4 marks)

        (ii) Find the shortest distance from point A to l_1.

(4 marks)

2   The lines l_1 and l_2 are given by the vector equations:

$$l_1 : \mathbf{r} = \begin{pmatrix} 3 \\ -3 \\ -2 \end{pmatrix} + \mu \begin{pmatrix} 1 \\ -4 \\ 2 \end{pmatrix} \qquad l_2 : \mathbf{r} = \begin{pmatrix} 10 \\ -21 \\ 11 \end{pmatrix} + \lambda \begin{pmatrix} -3 \\ 12 \\ -6 \end{pmatrix}$$

    a)   Show that l_1 and l_2 are parallel.

(1 mark)

    b)   Show that point A(2, 1, –4) lies on l_1.

(2 marks)

    c)   Point B lies on l_2 and is such that the line segment AB is perpendicular to l_1 and l_2.
        Find the position vector of point B.

(6 marks)

    d)   Find $|\overrightarrow{AB}|$.

(2 marks)

3   Point A has the position vector $\begin{pmatrix} 3 \\ 2 \\ 1 \end{pmatrix}$ and point B has position vector $\begin{pmatrix} 3 \\ -4 \\ -1 \end{pmatrix}$.

    a)   Show that AOB is a right-angled triangle.

(3 marks)

    b)   Find angle ABO in the triangle using the scalar product definition.

(5 marks)

    c)   (i)   Point C has the position vector $3\mathbf{i} - \mathbf{j}$.
            Show that triangle OAC is isosceles.

(3 marks)

        (ii) Calculate the area of triangle OAC.

(4 marks)

    d)   (i)   Find the vector equation for line l, which passes through points A and B.

(2 marks)

        (ii) The point D lies on line l and has the position vector $a\mathbf{i} + b\mathbf{j}$.
            Find a and b.

(3 marks)

4   The point A has coordinates $(-5, -4, 6)$, the point B has coordinates $(-1, 1, 8)$ and the point D has coordinates $(-7, 0, 5)$.

Given that ABCD is a parallelogram, find

a)   the position vector of point C

(3 marks)

b)   a vector equation for the line L_1 that contains the line segment DC

(2 marks)

c)   a vector equation for the line L_2 that contains the points A and C

(3 marks)

d)   the shortest distance between L_1 and the origin, to 3 significant figures.

(6 marks)

5   The line l passes through points J and K, where J has position vector $\begin{pmatrix} 2 \\ -2 \\ 1 \end{pmatrix}$

and K has position vector $\begin{pmatrix} 3 \\ 1 \\ -1 \end{pmatrix}$.

a)   Obtain a vector equation for the line l.

(2 marks)

b)   Find the acute angle between the line l and the line segment OJ.
Give your answer to the nearest degree.

(4 marks)

Determine, showing your reasons clearly, whether the following sets of points are collinear

c)   J, K and G, where point G has coordinates $(1, -5, 3)$

(2 marks)

d)   J, K and H, where point H has coordinates $(5, 11, -2)$

(2 marks)

6   The lines l_1 and l_2 are given by the equations:

$$l_1 : \mathbf{r} = \begin{pmatrix} 3 \\ 0 \\ -2 \end{pmatrix} + \lambda \begin{pmatrix} 1 \\ 3 \\ -2 \end{pmatrix} \qquad l_2 : \mathbf{r} = \begin{pmatrix} 0 \\ 2 \\ 1 \end{pmatrix} + \mu \begin{pmatrix} 2 \\ -5 \\ -3 \end{pmatrix}$$

a)   Show that l_1 and l_2 do not intersect.

(4 marks)

b)   Point P has coordinates $(5, 8, -3)$.
Point Q is the image of point P after reflection in line l_1.
Points P and Q both lie on the line which has equation $\mathbf{r} = \begin{pmatrix} 5 \\ 4 \\ -9 \end{pmatrix} + t \begin{pmatrix} 0 \\ 2 \\ 3 \end{pmatrix}$.

(i)   Find the intersection point of line segment PQ and line l_1.

(4 marks)

(ii)   Show that the line segment PQ and line l_1 are perpendicular.

(2 marks)

(iii)   Find the position vector of point Q.

(3 marks)

Answers

Chapter 1: Algebra and Functions

1. Simplifying Expressions

Exercise 1.1 — Simplifying algebraic fractions

Q1 $\dfrac{4}{2x + 10} = \dfrac{4}{2(x + 5)} = \dfrac{2}{x + 5}$

Q2 $\dfrac{5x}{x^2 + 2x} = \dfrac{5x}{x(x + 2)} = \dfrac{5}{x + 2}$

Q3 $\dfrac{6x^2 - 3x}{3x^2} = \dfrac{3x(2x - 1)}{3x^2} = \dfrac{2x - 1}{x}$

Q4 $\dfrac{4x^3}{x^3 + 3x^2} = \dfrac{4x^3}{x^2(x + 3)} = \dfrac{4x}{x + 3}$

Q5 $\dfrac{3x + 6}{x^2 + 3x + 2} = \dfrac{3(x + 2)}{(x + 1)(x + 2)} = \dfrac{3}{x + 1}$

Q6 $\dfrac{x^2 + 3x}{x^2 + x - 6} = \dfrac{x(x + 3)}{(x - 2)(x + 3)} = \dfrac{x}{x - 2}$

Q7 $\dfrac{2x - 6}{x^2 - 9} = \dfrac{2(x - 3)}{(x - 3)(x + 3)} = \dfrac{2}{x + 3}$

Q8 $\dfrac{5x^2 - 20x}{2x^2 - 5x - 12} = \dfrac{5x(x - 4)}{(2x + 3)(x - 4)} = \dfrac{5x \cdot}{2x + 3}$

Q9 $\dfrac{3x^2 - 7x - 6}{2x^2 - x - 15} = \dfrac{(3x + 2)(x - 3)}{(2x + 5)(x - 3)} = \dfrac{3x + 2}{2x + 5}$

Q10 $\dfrac{x^3 - 4x^2 - 19x - 14}{x^2 - 6x - 7}$

$= \dfrac{(x + 1)(x + 2)(x - 7)}{(x + 1)(x - 7)} = x + 2$

To factorise the cubic, try a few different values for x — once you've spotted that f(−1) = 0 (and so (x + 1) is a factor) you can take that out and see what's left to factorise.

Q11 $\dfrac{x^3 - 2x^2}{x^3 - 4x} = \dfrac{x^2(x - 2)}{x(x^2 - 4)} = \dfrac{x^2(x - 2)}{x(x - 2)(x + 2)} = \dfrac{x}{x + 2}$

Q12 $\dfrac{1 + \frac{1}{x}}{x + 1} = \dfrac{\left(1 + \frac{1}{x}\right)x}{(x + 1)x} = \dfrac{x + 1}{x(x + 1)} = \dfrac{1}{x}$

Q13 $\dfrac{3 + \frac{1}{x}}{2 + \frac{1}{x}} = \dfrac{\left(3 + \frac{1}{x}\right)x}{\left(2 + \frac{1}{x}\right)x} = \dfrac{3x + 1}{2x + 1}$

Q14 $\dfrac{1 + \frac{1}{2x}}{2 + \frac{1}{x}} = \dfrac{\left(1 + \frac{1}{2x}\right)2x}{\left(2 + \frac{1}{x}\right)2x} = \dfrac{2x + 1}{4x + 2} = \dfrac{2x + 1}{2(2x + 1)} = \dfrac{1}{2}$

Q15 $\dfrac{\frac{1}{3x} - 1}{3x^2 - x} = \dfrac{\left(\frac{1}{3x} - 1\right)3x}{(3x^2 - x)3x} = \dfrac{-(3x - 1)}{3x^2(3x - 1)} = -\dfrac{1}{3x^2}$

Q16 $\dfrac{2 + \frac{1}{x}}{6x^2 + 3x} = \dfrac{\left(2 + \frac{1}{x}\right)x}{(6x^2 + 3x)x} = \dfrac{2x + 1}{3x^2(2x + 1)} = \dfrac{1}{3x^2}$

Q17 $\dfrac{\frac{3x}{x + 2}}{\frac{x}{x + 2} + \frac{1}{x + 2}} = \dfrac{\left(\frac{3x}{x + 2}\right)(x + 2)}{\left(\frac{x}{x + 2} + \frac{1}{x + 2}\right)(x + 2)} = \dfrac{3x}{x + 1}$

Q18 $\dfrac{2 + \frac{1}{x + 1}}{3 + \frac{1}{x + 1}} = \dfrac{\left(2 + \frac{1}{x + 1}\right)(x + 1)}{\left(3 + \frac{1}{x + 1}\right)(x + 1)} = \dfrac{2(x + 1) + 1}{3(x + 1) + 1}$

$= \dfrac{2x + 3}{3x + 4}$

Q19 $\dfrac{1 - \frac{2}{x + 3}}{x + 2} = \dfrac{\left(1 - \frac{2}{x + 3}\right)(x + 3)}{(x + 2)(x + 3)} = \dfrac{x + 3 - 2}{(x + 2)(x + 3)}$

$= \dfrac{x + 1}{(x + 2)(x + 3)}$

Q20 $\dfrac{4 - \frac{1}{x^2}}{2 - \frac{1}{x} - \frac{1}{x^2}} = \dfrac{\left(4 - \frac{1}{x^2}\right)x^2}{\left(2 - \frac{1}{x} - \frac{1}{x^2}\right)x^2} = \dfrac{4x^2 - 1}{2x^2 - x - 1}$

$= \dfrac{(2x + 1)(2x - 1)}{(x - 1)(2x + 1)} = \dfrac{2x - 1}{x - 1}$

Exercise 1.2 — Adding and subtracting algebraic fractions

Q1 $\dfrac{2x}{3} + \dfrac{x}{5} = \dfrac{10x}{15} + \dfrac{3x}{15} = \dfrac{13x}{15}$

Q2 $\dfrac{2}{3x} - \dfrac{1}{5x} = \dfrac{10}{15x} - \dfrac{3}{15x} = \dfrac{7}{15x}$

Q3 $\dfrac{3}{x^2} + \dfrac{2}{x} = \dfrac{3}{x^2} + \dfrac{2x}{x^2} = \dfrac{3 + 2x}{x^2}$

Q4 $\dfrac{x + 1}{3} + \dfrac{x + 2}{4} = \dfrac{4(x + 1)}{12} + \dfrac{3(x + 2)}{12}$

$= \dfrac{4x + 4 + 3x + 6}{12} = \dfrac{7x + 10}{12}$

Q5 $\dfrac{2x}{3} + \dfrac{x - 1}{7x} = \dfrac{14x^2}{21x} + \dfrac{3(x - 1)}{21x}$

$= \dfrac{14x^2 + 3x - 3}{21x}$

Q6 $\dfrac{3x}{4} - \dfrac{2x - 1}{5x} = \dfrac{15x^2}{20x} - \dfrac{4(2x - 1)}{20x}$

$= \dfrac{15x^2 - 8x + 4}{20x}$

Q7 $\dfrac{2}{x - 1} + \dfrac{3}{x} = \dfrac{2x}{x(x - 1)} + \dfrac{3(x - 1)}{x(x - 1)}$

$= \dfrac{2x + 3x - 3}{x(x - 1)} = \dfrac{5x - 3}{x(x - 1)}$

Q8 $\dfrac{3}{x + 1} + \dfrac{2}{x + 2} = \dfrac{3(x + 2)}{(x + 1)(x + 2)} + \dfrac{2(x + 1)}{(x + 1)(x + 2)}$

$= \dfrac{3x + 6 + 2x + 2}{(x + 1)(x + 2)} = \dfrac{5x + 8}{(x + 1)(x + 2)}$

Q9 $\dfrac{4}{x - 3} - \dfrac{1}{x + 4} = \dfrac{4(x + 4)}{(x - 3)(x + 4)} - \dfrac{x - 3}{(x - 3)(x + 4)}$

$= \dfrac{4x + 16 - x + 3}{(x - 3)(x + 4)} = \dfrac{3x + 19}{(x - 3)(x + 4)}$

Q10 $\dfrac{6}{x+2} + \dfrac{6}{x-2} = \dfrac{6(x-2)}{(x+2)(x-2)} + \dfrac{6(x+2)}{(x+2)(x-2)}$

$= \dfrac{6x - 12 + 6x + 12}{(x+2)(x-2)} = \dfrac{12x}{(x+2)(x-2)}$

Q11 $\dfrac{3}{x-2} - \dfrac{5}{2x+3} = \dfrac{3(2x+3)}{(x-2)(2x+3)} - \dfrac{5(x-2)}{(x-2)(2x+3)}$

$= \dfrac{6x + 9 - 5x + 10}{(x-2)(2x+3)} = \dfrac{x+19}{(x-2)(2x+3)}$

Q12 $\dfrac{3}{x+2} + \dfrac{x}{x+1} = \dfrac{3(x+1)}{(x+2)(x+1)} + \dfrac{x(x+2)}{(x+2)(x+1)}$

$= \dfrac{3x + 3 + x^2 + 2x}{(x+2)(x+1)} = \dfrac{x^2 + 5x + 3}{(x+2)(x+1)}$

Q13 $\dfrac{5x}{(x+1)^2} - \dfrac{3}{x+1} = \dfrac{5x}{(x+1)^2} - \dfrac{3(x+1)}{(x+1)^2}$

$= \dfrac{5x - 3x - 3}{(x+1)^2} = \dfrac{2x-3}{(x+1)^2}$

Q14 $\dfrac{5}{x(x+3)} + \dfrac{3}{x+2}$

$= \dfrac{5(x+2)}{x(x+3)(x+2)} + \dfrac{3x(x+3)}{x(x+3)(x+2)}$

$= \dfrac{5x + 10 + 3x^2 + 9x}{x(x+3)(x+2)} = \dfrac{3x^2 + 14x + 10}{x(x+3)(x+2)}$

Q15 $\dfrac{x}{x^2-4} - \dfrac{1}{x+2} = \dfrac{x}{(x+2)(x-2)} - \dfrac{1}{x+2}$

$= \dfrac{x}{(x+2)(x-2)} - \dfrac{x-2}{(x+2)(x-2)}$

$= \dfrac{x - x + 2}{(x+2)(x-2)} = \dfrac{2}{(x+2)(x-2)}$

Q16 $\dfrac{3}{x+1} + \dfrac{6}{2x^2 + x - 1} = \dfrac{3}{x+1} + \dfrac{6}{(x+1)(2x-1)}$

$= \dfrac{3(2x-1)}{(x+1)(2x-1)} + \dfrac{6}{(x+1)(2x-1)}$

$= \dfrac{6x - 3 + 6}{(x+1)(2x-1)} = \dfrac{3(2x+1)}{(x+1)(2x-1)}$

Q17 $\dfrac{2}{x} + \dfrac{3}{x+1} + \dfrac{4}{x+2}$

$= \dfrac{2(x+1)(x+2)}{x(x+1)(x+2)} + \dfrac{3x(x+2)}{x(x+1)(x+2)}$

$\qquad + \dfrac{4x(x+1)}{x(x+1)(x+2)}$

$= \dfrac{2x^2 + 6x + 4 + 3x^2 + 6x + 4x^2 + 4x}{x(x+1)(x+2)}$

$= \dfrac{9x^2 + 16x + 4}{x(x+1)(x+2)}$

Q18 $\dfrac{3}{x+4} - \dfrac{2}{x+1} + \dfrac{1}{x-2}$

$= \dfrac{3(x+1)(x-2)}{(x+4)(x+1)(x-2)} - \dfrac{2(x+4)(x-2)}{(x+4)(x+1)(x-2)}$

$\qquad + \dfrac{(x+4)(x+1)}{(x+4)(x+1)(x-2)}$

$= \dfrac{3x^2 - 3x - 6 - 2x^2 - 4x + 16 + x^2 + 5x + 4}{(x+4)(x+1)(x-2)}$

$= \dfrac{2(x^2 - x + 7)}{(x+4)(x+1)(x-2)}$

Q19 $2 - \dfrac{3}{x+1} + \dfrac{4}{(x+1)^2}$

$= \dfrac{2(x+1)^2}{(x+1)^2} - \dfrac{3(x+1)}{(x+1)^2} + \dfrac{4}{(x+1)^2}$

$= \dfrac{2x^2 + 4x + 2 - 3x - 3 + 4}{(x+1)^2} = \dfrac{2x^2 + x + 3}{(x+1)^2}$

Q20 $\dfrac{2x^2 - x - 3}{x^2 - 1} + \dfrac{1}{x(x-1)}$

$= \dfrac{(x+1)(2x-3)}{(x+1)(x-1)} + \dfrac{1}{x(x-1)}$

$= \dfrac{2x-3}{x-1} + \dfrac{1}{x(x-1)}$

$= \dfrac{x(2x-3)}{x(x-1)} + \dfrac{1}{x(x-1)}$

$= \dfrac{2x^2 - 3x + 1}{x(x-1)} = \dfrac{(x-1)(2x-1)}{x(x-1)} = \dfrac{2x-1}{x}$

Exercise 1.3 — Multiplying and dividing algebraic fractions

Q1 a) $\dfrac{2x}{3} \times \dfrac{5x}{4} = \dfrac{x}{3} \times \dfrac{5x}{2} = \dfrac{x \times 5x}{3 \times 2} = \dfrac{5x^2}{6}$

b) $\dfrac{6x^3}{7} \times \dfrac{2}{x^2} = \dfrac{6x}{7} \times \dfrac{2}{1} = \dfrac{6x \times 2}{7 \times 1} = \dfrac{12x}{7}$

c) $\dfrac{8x^2}{3y^2} \times \dfrac{x^3}{4y} = \dfrac{2x^2}{3y^2} \times \dfrac{x^3}{y} = \dfrac{2x^2 \times x^3}{3y^2 \times y} = \dfrac{2x^5}{3y^3}$

d) $\dfrac{8x^4}{3y} \times \dfrac{6y^2}{5x} = \dfrac{8x^3}{1} \times \dfrac{2y}{5} = \dfrac{8x^3 \times 2y}{1 \times 5} = \dfrac{16x^3 y}{5}$

Q2 a) $\dfrac{x}{3} \div \dfrac{3}{x} = \dfrac{x}{3} \times \dfrac{x}{3} = \dfrac{x \times x}{3 \times 3} = \dfrac{x^2}{9}$

b) $\dfrac{4x^3}{3} \div \dfrac{x}{2} = \dfrac{4x^3}{3} \times \dfrac{2}{x} = \dfrac{4x^2}{3} \times \dfrac{2}{1} = \dfrac{4x^2 \times 2}{3 \times 1} = \dfrac{8x^2}{3}$

c) $\dfrac{3}{2x} \div \dfrac{6}{x^3} = \dfrac{3}{2x} \times \dfrac{x^3}{6} = \dfrac{1}{2} \times \dfrac{x^2}{2} = \dfrac{1 \times x^2}{2 \times 2} = \dfrac{x^2}{4}$

d) $\dfrac{2x^3}{3y} \div \dfrac{4x}{y^2} = \dfrac{2x^3}{3y} \times \dfrac{y^2}{4x} = \dfrac{x^2}{3} \times \dfrac{y}{2} = \dfrac{x^2 \times y}{3 \times 2} = \dfrac{x^2 y}{6}$

Q3 $\dfrac{x+2}{4} \times \dfrac{x}{3x+6} = \dfrac{x+2}{4} \times \dfrac{x}{3(x+2)}$

$= \dfrac{1}{4} \times \dfrac{x}{3} = \dfrac{1 \times x}{4 \times 3} = \dfrac{x}{12}$

Q4 $\dfrac{4x}{5} \div \dfrac{4x^2 + 8x}{15} = \dfrac{4x}{5} \times \dfrac{15}{4x(x+2)}$

$= \dfrac{1}{1} \times \dfrac{3}{(x+2)} = \dfrac{3}{(x+2)}$

Q5 $\dfrac{2x^2 - 2}{x} \times \dfrac{5x}{3x-3} = \dfrac{2(x-1)(x+1)}{x} \times \dfrac{5x}{3(x-1)}$

$= \dfrac{2(x+1)}{1} \times \dfrac{5}{3} = \dfrac{2(x+1) \times 5}{1 \times 3} = \dfrac{10(x+1)}{3}$

Q6 $\dfrac{2x^2 + 8x}{x^2 - 2x} \times \dfrac{x-1}{x+4} = \dfrac{2x(x+4)}{x(x-2)} \times \dfrac{x-1}{x+4}$

$= \dfrac{2}{x-2} \times \dfrac{x-1}{1} = \dfrac{2(x-1)}{x-2}$

Q7 $\dfrac{x^2 - 4}{9} \div \dfrac{x-2}{3} = \dfrac{(x+2)(x-2)}{9} \times \dfrac{3}{x-2}$

$= \dfrac{x+2}{3} \times \dfrac{1}{1} = \dfrac{x+2}{3}$

Q8 $\dfrac{2}{x^2 + 4x} \div \dfrac{1}{x+4} = \dfrac{2}{x(x+4)} \times \dfrac{x+4}{1} = \dfrac{2}{x} \times \dfrac{1}{1} = \dfrac{2}{x}$

Q9 $\dfrac{x^2 + 4x + 3}{x^2 + 5x + 6} \times \dfrac{x^2 + 2x}{x+1} = \dfrac{(x+1)(x+3)}{(x+2)(x+3)} \times \dfrac{x(x+2)}{x+1}$

$= \dfrac{1}{1} \times \dfrac{x}{1} = x$

Q10 $\dfrac{x^2 + 5x + 6}{x^2 - 2x - 3} \times \dfrac{3x+3}{x^2 + 2x} = \dfrac{(x+2)(x+3)}{(x-3)(x+1)} \times \dfrac{3(x+1)}{x(x+2)}$

$= \dfrac{x+3}{x-3} \times \dfrac{3}{x} = \dfrac{3(x+3)}{x(x-3)}$

Q11 $\dfrac{x^2 - 4}{6x - 3} \times \dfrac{2x^2 + 5x - 3}{x^2 + 2x}$

$= \dfrac{(x + 2)(x - 2)}{3(2x - 1)} \times \dfrac{(2x - 1)(x + 3)}{x(x + 2)}$

$= \dfrac{x - 2}{3} \times \dfrac{x + 3}{x} = \dfrac{(x - 2)(x + 3)}{3x}$

Q12 $\dfrac{x^2 + 7x + 6}{4x - 4} \div \dfrac{x^2 + 8x + 12}{x^2 - x}$

$= \dfrac{(x + 1)(x + 6)}{4(x - 1)} \times \dfrac{x(x - 1)}{(x + 2)(x + 6)}$

$= \dfrac{x + 1}{4} \times \dfrac{x}{x + 2} = \dfrac{x(x + 1)}{4(x + 2)}$

Q13 $\dfrac{x^2 + 4x + 4}{x^2 - 4x + 3} \times \dfrac{x^2 - 2x - 3}{2x^2 - 2x} \times \dfrac{4x - 4}{x^2 + 2x}$

$= \dfrac{(x + 2)^2}{(x - 3)(x - 1)} \times \dfrac{(x - 3)(x + 1)}{2x(x - 1)} \times \dfrac{4(x - 1)}{x(x + 2)}$

$= \dfrac{x + 2}{x - 1} \times \dfrac{x + 1}{x} \times \dfrac{2}{x} = \dfrac{2(x + 2)(x + 1)}{x^2(x - 1)}$

Q14 $\dfrac{x}{6x + 12} \div \dfrac{x^2 - x}{x + 2} \times \dfrac{3x - 3}{x + 1}$

$= \dfrac{x}{6(x + 2)} \times \dfrac{x + 2}{x(x - 1)} \times \dfrac{3(x - 1)}{x + 1}$

$= \dfrac{1}{2} \times \dfrac{1}{1} \times \dfrac{1}{x + 1} = \dfrac{1}{2(x + 1)}$

Q15 $\dfrac{x^2 + 5x}{2x^2 + 7x + 3} \times \dfrac{2x + 1}{x^3 - x^2} \div \dfrac{x + 5}{x^2 + x - 6}$

$= \dfrac{x(x + 5)}{(2x + 1)(x + 3)} \times \dfrac{2x + 1}{x^2(x - 1)} \times \dfrac{(x + 3)(x - 2)}{x + 5}$

$= \dfrac{1}{1} \times \dfrac{1}{x(x - 1)} \times \dfrac{x - 2}{1} = \dfrac{x - 2}{x(x - 1)}$

2. Algebraic Division

Exercise 2.1 — Algebraic division

Q1 a) $x^3 - 14x^2 + 6x + 11 \equiv (Ax^2 + Bx + C)(x + 1) + D$

The degree of the quotient is the difference between the degrees of the polynomial and the divisor, in this case $3 - 1 = 2$. The degree of the remainder must be less than the degree of the divisor (1) so it must be 0.

Set $x = -1$: $-1 - 14 - 6 + 11 = D$, so $D = -10$.

Set $x = 0$: $11 = C + D$, so $C = 21$.

Equating the coefficients of x^3 gives $1 = A$.

Equating the coefficients of x^2 gives:
$-14 = A + B$, so $B = -15$.

So $x^3 - 14x^2 + 6x + 11 \equiv (x^2 - 15x + 21)(x + 1) - 10$.

Quotient: $x^2 - 15x + 21$
Remainder: -10

b) $2x^3 + 5x^2 - 8x - 17 \equiv (Ax^2 + Bx + C)(x - 2) + D$

Set $x = 2$: $16 + 20 - 16 - 17 = D$, so $D = 3$.

Set $x = 0$: $-17 = -2C + D$, so $C = 10$.

Equating the coefficients of x^3 gives $2 = A$.

Equating the coefficients of x^2 gives:
$5 = -2A + B$, so $B = 9$.

So $2x^3 + 5x^2 - 8x - 17 \equiv (2x^2 + 9x + 10)(x - 2) + 3$.

Quotient: $2x^2 + 9x + 10$
Remainder: 3

c) $2x^3 + 4x^2 - 5x + 2 \equiv (Ax + B)(x^2 - 2x + 1) + Cx + D$
$\equiv (Ax + B)(x - 1)^2 + Cx + D$

Equating the coefficients of x^3 gives $2 = A$.

Equating the coefficients of x^2 gives $4 = B - 2A$, so $B = 8$.

Set $x = 0$: $2 = B + D$, so $D = -6$.

Set $x = 1$: $2 + 4 - 5 + 2 = C + D$, so $C = 9$.

So $2x^3 + 4x^2 - 5x + 2 \equiv (2x + 8)(x^2 - 2x + 1) + 9x - 6$.

Quotient: $2x + 8$
Remainder: $9x - 6$

Q2 $6x^4 + 11x^3 + 9x^2 + 15x - 2$
$\equiv (Ax^2 + Bx + C)(2x^2 + x + 3) + Dx + E$

Equating the coefficients of x^4 gives $6 = 2A$, so $A = 3$.

Equating the coefficients of x^3 gives $11 = A + 2B$,
so $B = 4$.

Equating the coefficients of x^2 gives $9 = 3A + B + 2C$,
so $C = -2$.

Set $x = 0$: $-2 = 3C + E$, so $E = 4$.

Set $x = 1$: $6 + 11 + 9 + 15 - 2 = 34 + D$, so $D = 5$.

So $6x^4 + 11x^3 + 9x^2 + 15x - 2$
$\equiv (3x^2 + 4x - 2)(2x^2 + x + 3) + 5x + 4$

Quotient: $3x^2 + 4x - 2$
Remainder: $5x + 4$

Q3 a)

$$
\begin{array}{r}
x^2 - 15x + 21 \text{ r } -10 \\
x + 1 \overline{)\, x^3 - 14x^2 + 6x + 11} \\
-\ \underline{x^3 + x^2} \\
-15x^2 + 6x \\
-\ \underline{-15x^2 - 15x} \\
21x + 11 \\
-\ \underline{21x + 21} \\
-10
\end{array}
$$

Quotient: $x^2 - 15x + 21$
Remainder: -10

b)

$$
\begin{array}{r}
x^2 + 7x - 6 \text{ r } 5 \\
x + 3 \overline{)\, x^3 + 10x^2 + 15x - 13} \\
-\ \underline{x^3 + 3x^2} \\
7x^2 + 15x \\
-\ \underline{7x^2 + 21x} \\
-6x - 13 \\
-\ \underline{-6x - 18} \\
5
\end{array}
$$

Quotient: $x^2 + 7x - 6$
Remainder: 5

c)

$$
\begin{array}{r}
2x^2 + 9x + 10 \text{ r } 3 \\
x - 2 \overline{)\, 2x^3 + 5x^2 - 8x - 17} \\
-\ \underline{2x^3 - 4x^2} \\
9x^2 - 8x \\
-\ \underline{9x^2 - 18x} \\
10x - 17 \\
-\ \underline{10x - 20} \\
3
\end{array}
$$

Quotient: $2x^2 + 9x + 10$
Remainder: 3

d)

$$x + 5 \overline{)3x^3 + 0x^2 - 78x + 9} \quad \frac{3x^2 - 15x - 3 \quad \text{r } 24}{}$$

$$\begin{array}{r} 3x^2 - 15x - 3 \quad \text{r } 24 \\ x + 5 \overline{)3x^3 + 0x^2 - 78x + 9} \\ -\underline{3x^3 + 15x^2} \\ -15x^2 - 78x \\ -\underline{-15x^2 - 75x} \\ -3x + 9 \\ -\underline{-3x - 15} \\ 24 \end{array}$$

Quotient: $3x^2 - 15x - 3$
Remainder: 24

e)

$$\begin{array}{r} x^3 + x^2 + x + 1 \\ x - 1 \overline{)x^4 + 0x^3 + 0x^2 + 0x - 1} \\ -\underline{x^4 - x^3} \\ x^3 + 0x^2 \\ -\underline{x^3 - x^2} \\ x^2 + 0x \\ -\underline{x^2 - x} \\ x - 1 \\ -\underline{x - 1} \\ 0 \end{array}$$

Quotient: $x^3 + x^2 + x + 1$
Remainder: 0

f)

$$\begin{array}{r} 4x^2 + 3x + 5 \quad \text{r } 25 \\ 2x - 3 \overline{)8x^3 - 6x^2 + x + 10} \\ -\underline{8x^3 - 12x^2} \\ 6x^2 + x \\ -\underline{6x^2 - 9x} \\ 10x + 10 \\ -\underline{10x - 15} \\ 25 \end{array}$$

Quotient: $4x^2 + 3x + 5$
Remainder: 25

g)

$$\begin{array}{r} 2x + 8 \quad \text{r } 9x - 6 \\ x^2 - 2x + 1 \overline{)2x^3 + 4x^2 - 5x + 2} \\ -\underline{2x^3 - 4x^2 + 2x} \\ 8x^2 - 7x + 2 \\ -\underline{8x^2 - 16x + 8} \\ 9x - 6 \end{array}$$

Quotient: $2x + 8$
Remainder: $9x - 6$

h)

$$\begin{array}{r} 3x^2 + 4x - 2 \quad \text{r } 5x + 4 \\ 2x^2 + x + 3 \overline{)6x^4 + 11x^3 + 9x^2 + 15x - 2} \\ -\underline{6x^4 + 3x^3 + 9x^2} \\ 8x^3 + 0x^2 + 15x \\ -\underline{8x^3 + 4x^2 + 12x} \\ -4x^2 + 3x - 2 \\ -\underline{-4x^2 - 2x - 6} \\ 5x + 4 \end{array}$$

Quotient: $3x^2 + 4x - 2$
Remainder: $5x + 4$

Q4 Quotient: $5x^2 + x - 3$
Remainder: 24

Q5 Quotient: $3x - 11$
Remainder: $32x - 34$

Q6 Quotient: $3x^2 + 1$
Remainder: 0

3. Partial Fractions

Exercise 3.1 — Expressing in partial fractions

Q1
$$\frac{3x + 3}{(x - 1)(x - 4)} \equiv \frac{A}{(x - 1)} + \frac{B}{(x - 4)}$$
$$\Rightarrow \frac{3x + 3}{(x - 1)(x - 4)} \equiv \frac{A(x - 4) + B(x - 1)}{(x - 1)(x - 4)}$$
$$\Rightarrow \quad 3x + 3 \equiv A(x - 4) + B(x - 1)$$

Substitution:
$x = 4 \Rightarrow 15 = 3B \Rightarrow B = 5$
$x = 1 \Rightarrow 6 = -3A \Rightarrow A = -2$
This gives: $\dfrac{3x + 3}{(x - 1)(x - 4)} \equiv -\dfrac{2}{(x - 1)} + \dfrac{5}{(x - 4)}$

Q2
$$\frac{5x - 1}{x(2x + 1)} \equiv \frac{A}{x} + \frac{B}{(2x + 1)}$$
$$\Rightarrow 5x - 1 \equiv A(2x + 1) + Bx$$

Equating coefficients:
x terms: $\quad 5 = 2A + B$
constants: $\quad -1 = A$
$A = -1$, putting this into the first equation gives:
$5 = -2 + B \Rightarrow B = 7$
This gives: $\dfrac{5x - 1}{x(2x + 1)} \equiv -\dfrac{1}{x} + \dfrac{7}{(2x + 1)}$

Q3
$$\frac{3x - 2}{x^2 + x - 12} \equiv \frac{3x - 2}{(x + 4)(x - 3)} \equiv \frac{A}{(x + 4)} + \frac{B}{(x - 3)}$$
$$\Rightarrow \frac{3x - 2}{(x + 4)(x - 3)} \equiv \frac{A(x - 3) + B(x + 4)}{(x + 4)(x - 3)}$$
$$\Rightarrow \quad 3x - 2 \equiv A(x - 3) + B(x + 4)$$

Equating coefficients:
x terms: $\quad 3 = A + B$
constants: $-2 = -3A + 4B$
Solving simultaneously gives: $A = 2, B = 1$
This gives: $\dfrac{3x - 2}{x^2 + x - 12} \equiv \dfrac{2}{(x + 4)} + \dfrac{1}{(x - 3)}$

Q4
$$\frac{2}{x^2 - 16} \equiv \frac{2}{(x + 4)(x - 4)} \equiv \frac{A}{(x + 4)} + \frac{B}{(x - 4)}$$
$$\Rightarrow \quad 2 \equiv A(x - 4) + B(x + 4)$$

Substitution:
$x = 4 \Rightarrow 2 = 8B \Rightarrow B = \dfrac{1}{4}$
$x = -4 \Rightarrow 2 = -8A \Rightarrow A = -\dfrac{1}{4}$
This gives: $\dfrac{2}{x^2 - 16} \equiv -\dfrac{1}{4(x + 4)} + \dfrac{1}{4(x - 4)}$

Don't worry if you get fractions for your coefficients — just put the numerator on the top of your partial fraction and the denominator on the bottom.

Q5 $x^2 - x - 6 = (x - 3)(x + 2)$
$$\frac{5}{(x - 3)(x + 2)} \equiv \frac{A}{(x - 3)} + \frac{B}{(x + 2)}$$
$$\Rightarrow \quad 5 \equiv A(x + 2) + B(x - 3)$$

Equating coefficients:
x terms: $\quad 0 = A + B$
constants: $5 = 2A - 3B$
Solving simultaneously gives: $A = 1, B = -1$
This gives: $\dfrac{5}{x^2 - x - 6} \equiv \dfrac{1}{(x - 3)} - \dfrac{1}{(x + 2)}$

Q6 $\dfrac{11x}{2x^2 + 5x - 12} \equiv \dfrac{11x}{(2x-3)(x+4)} \equiv \dfrac{A}{(2x-3)} + \dfrac{B}{(x+4)}$

$\Rightarrow \qquad 11x \equiv A(x+4) + B(2x-3)$

Equating coefficients:

x terms: $\qquad 11 = A + 2B$

constants: $0 = 4A - 3B$

Solving simultaneously gives: $A = 3$, $B = 4$

This gives $\dfrac{11x}{2x^2 + 5x - 12} \equiv \dfrac{3}{(2x-3)} + \dfrac{4}{(x+4)}$

Q7 a) $x^3 - 9x = x(x^2 - 9) = x(x+3)(x-3)$

b) $\dfrac{x^2 - 3x + 2}{x(x+3)(x-3)} \equiv \dfrac{A}{x} + \dfrac{B}{(x+3)} + \dfrac{C}{(x-3)}$

$\Rightarrow x^2 - 3x + 2$
$\equiv A(x+3)(x-3) + Bx(x-3) + Cx(x+3)$

Equating coefficients:

x^2 terms: $\quad 1 = A + B + C$

x terms: $\quad -3 = -3B + 3C$

constants: $\quad 2 = -9A$

The third equation gives that $A = -\dfrac{2}{9}$

Then solving the first two simultaneously gives:

$B = \dfrac{10}{9}$, $C = \dfrac{1}{9}$

This gives: $\dfrac{x^2 - 3x + 2}{x^3 - 9x} \equiv -\dfrac{2}{9x} + \dfrac{10}{9(x+3)} + \dfrac{1}{9(x-3)}$

Q8 $\dfrac{4x^2 - 14}{x^3 - 36x} \equiv \dfrac{4x^2 - 14}{x(x^2 - 36)} \equiv \dfrac{4x^2 - 14}{x(x+6)(x-6)}$

$\dfrac{4x^2 - 14}{x(x+6)(x-6)} \equiv \dfrac{A}{x} + \dfrac{B}{(x+6)} + \dfrac{C}{(x-6)}$

$\Rightarrow \quad 4x^2 - 14 \equiv A(x+6)(x-6) + Bx(x-6) + Cx(x+6)$

Substitution:

$x = 0 \Rightarrow -14 = -36A \Rightarrow A = \dfrac{14}{36} = \dfrac{7}{18}$

$x = 6 \Rightarrow 130 = 72C \Rightarrow C = \dfrac{130}{72} = \dfrac{65}{36}$

$x = -6 \Rightarrow 130 = 72B \Rightarrow B = \dfrac{130}{72} = \dfrac{65}{36}$

This gives: $\dfrac{4x^2 - 14}{x^3 - 36x} \equiv \dfrac{7}{18x} + \dfrac{65}{36(x+6)} + \dfrac{65}{36(x-6)}$

Q9 a) $f(x) = x^3 - 7x - 6$

$f(-1) = -1 + 7 - 6 = 0 \Rightarrow (x+1)$ is a factor

Once you've found one factor using the Factor Theorem you can use this method:

$(x+1)$ is a factor of $x^3 - 7x - 6$, so:

$x^3 - 7x - 6 = (x+1)(\qquad)$

There's an x^3 on the LHS, so there's an x^2 term in the bracket:

$x^3 - 7x - 6 = (x+1)(x^2 \qquad)$

There's -6 on the LHS, so you need -6 in the bracket to multiply with the 1 in $(x+1)$ and give -6:

$x^3 - 7x - 6 = (x+1)(x^2 \qquad -6)$

Now you've got $-7x$ on the LHS and $-6x$ (from multiplying x by -6) on the RHS. So you need $-x$ in the middle of the bracket to get another $-x$ on the RHS (from multiplying 1 by $-x$):

$x^3 - 7x - 6 = (x+1)(x^2 - x - 6)$

When you multiply out the RHS you get the LHS (the terms in x^2 cancel), so this is the right quadratic. Finally, factorise the quadratic:

$x^3 - 7x - 6 = (x+1)(x^2 - x - 6) = (x+1)(x+2)(x-3)$

This method looks a bit involved, but it's just laid out like this to show you what's going on — if you did it yourself you'd just write:

'$x^3 - 7x - 6 = (x+1)(x^2 - x - 6) = (x+1)(x+2)(x-3)$'

So $x^3 - 7x - 6 = (x+1)(x-3)(x+2)$

Or you can keep using trial and error to find the other factors, but this could take a while:

$f(3) = 27 - 21 - 6 = 0 \Rightarrow (x-3)$ is a factor

$f(-2) = -8 + 14 - 6 = 0 \Rightarrow (x+2)$ is a factor

So $x^3 - 7x - 6 = (x+1)(x-3)(x+2)$

b) $\dfrac{5x^2 - 7x - 4}{x^3 - 7x - 6} \equiv \dfrac{5x^2 - 7x - 4}{(x+1)(x-3)(x+2)}$

$\dfrac{5x^2 - 7x - 4}{(x+1)(x-3)(x+2)} \equiv \dfrac{A}{(x+1)} + \dfrac{B}{(x-3)} + \dfrac{C}{(x+2)}$

$\Rightarrow 5x^2 - 7x - 4$
$\equiv A(x-3)(x+2) + B(x+1)(x+2)$
$\qquad\qquad + C(x+1)(x-3)$

Substitution:

$x = -1 \Rightarrow 8 = -4A \Rightarrow A = -2$

$x = 3 \Rightarrow 20 = 20B \Rightarrow B = 1$

$x = -2 \Rightarrow 30 = 5C \Rightarrow C = 6$

This gives:

$\dfrac{5x^2 - 7x - 4}{x^3 - 7x - 6} \equiv -\dfrac{2}{(x+1)} + \dfrac{1}{(x-3)} + \dfrac{6}{(x+2)}$

Q10 $\dfrac{6x^2 - x + 5}{(x+4)(x-1)(x+1)} \equiv \dfrac{A}{(x+4)} + \dfrac{B}{(x-1)} + \dfrac{C}{(x+1)}$

$\Rightarrow 6x^2 - x + 5$
$\equiv A(x-1)(x+1) + B(x+4)(x+1) + C(x+4)(x-1)$

$x = 1 \Rightarrow 10 = 10B \Rightarrow B = 1$

$x = -1 \Rightarrow 12 = -6C \Rightarrow C = -2$

$x = -4 \Rightarrow 105 = 15A \Rightarrow A = 7$

This gives:

$\dfrac{6x^2 - x + 5}{(x+4)(x-1)(x+1)} \equiv \dfrac{7}{(x+4)} + \dfrac{1}{(x-1)} - \dfrac{2}{(x+1)}$

Q11 $\dfrac{3x^2 - 6x + 3}{x^3 - 6x^2 + 3x + 10} \equiv \dfrac{3x^2 - 6x + 3}{(x+1)(x-2)(x-5)}$

You get this by using the factor theorem, as in Q9.

$\dfrac{3x^2 - 6x + 3}{(x+1)(x-2)(x-5)} \equiv \dfrac{A}{(x+1)} + \dfrac{B}{(x-2)} + \dfrac{C}{(x-5)}$

$\Rightarrow 3x^2 - 6x + 3$
$\equiv A(x-2)(x-5) + B(x+1)(x-5) + C(x+1)(x-2)$

Substitution:

$x = 2 \Rightarrow 3 = -9B \Rightarrow B = -\dfrac{1}{3}$

$x = 5 \Rightarrow 48 = 18C \Rightarrow C = \dfrac{8}{3}$

$x = -1 \Rightarrow 12 = 18A \Rightarrow A = \dfrac{2}{3}$

This gives:

$\dfrac{3x^2 - 6x + 3}{x^3 - 6x^2 + 3x + 10} \equiv \dfrac{2}{3(x+1)} - \dfrac{1}{3(x-2)} + \dfrac{8}{3(x-5)}$

Exercise 3.2 — Repeated factors

Q1 $\dfrac{3x}{(x+5)^2} \equiv \dfrac{A}{(x+5)} + \dfrac{B}{(x+5)^2} \equiv \dfrac{A(x+5)+B}{(x+5)^2}$

$\Rightarrow \quad 3x \equiv A(x+5) + B$

Equating coefficients:

x terms: $\quad 3 = A$

constants: $0 = 5A + B$

The first equation gives $A = 3$, putting this into the second equation gives $B = -15$.

This gives: $\dfrac{3x}{(x+5)^2} \equiv \dfrac{3}{(x+5)} - \dfrac{15}{(x+5)^2}$

Q2 $\dfrac{x^2 - 5x + 2}{x^2(x+1)} \equiv \dfrac{A}{x} + \dfrac{B}{x^2} + \dfrac{C}{(x+1)}$

$\Rightarrow x^2 - 5x + 2 \equiv Ax(x+1) + B(x+1) + Cx^2$

Equating coefficients:

x^2 terms: $\quad 1 = A + C$

x terms: $\quad -5 = A + B$

constants: $\quad 2 = B$

The third equation gives $B = 2$, putting this into the second equation gives $A = -7$, putting this into the first equation gives $C = 8$.

This gives: $\dfrac{x^2 - 5x + 2}{x^2(x+1)} \equiv -\dfrac{7}{x} + \dfrac{2}{x^2} + \dfrac{8}{(x+1)}$

Q3 $\dfrac{x^2 + 5x - 1}{(x-2)^3} \equiv \dfrac{A}{(x-2)} + \dfrac{B}{(x-2)^2} + \dfrac{C}{(x-2)^3}$

$\Rightarrow x^2 + 5x - 1 \equiv A(x-2)^2 + B(x-2) + C$

Substitution: $\quad x = 2 \Rightarrow 13 = C$

Equating coefficients:

x^2 terms: $1 = A$

x terms: $\quad 5 = -4A + B \Rightarrow B = 9$

This gives: $\dfrac{x^2 + 5x - 1}{(x-2)^3} \equiv \dfrac{1}{(x-2)} + \dfrac{9}{(x-2)^2} + \dfrac{13}{(x-2)^3}$

Q4 a) $\dfrac{2x - 7}{(x-3)^2} \equiv \dfrac{A}{(x-3)} + \dfrac{B}{(x-3)^2}$

$\Rightarrow 2x - 7 \equiv A(x-3) + B$

Substitution: $\quad x = 3 \Rightarrow -1 = B$

Equating coefficients of the x terms: $2 = A$

This gives: $\dfrac{2x - 7}{(x-3)^2} \equiv \dfrac{2}{(x-3)} - \dfrac{1}{(x-3)^2}$

b) $\dfrac{x + 4}{(x+2)^2} \equiv \dfrac{A}{(x+2)} + \dfrac{B}{(x+2)^2}$

$\Rightarrow x + 4 \equiv A(x+2) + B$

Substitution: $x = -2 \Rightarrow 2 = B$

Equating coefficients of x: $A = 1$

This gives: $\dfrac{x + 4}{(x+2)^2} \equiv \dfrac{1}{(x+2)} + \dfrac{2}{(x+2)^2}$

c) $\dfrac{2x^2 - 9x + 5}{(x-4)^2(x+2)} \equiv \dfrac{A}{(x-4)} + \dfrac{B}{(x-4)^2} + \dfrac{C}{(x+2)}$

$\Rightarrow 2x^2 - 9x + 5 \equiv A(x-4)(x+2)$
$\qquad\qquad\qquad\qquad + B(x+2) + C(x-4)^2$

Substitution:

$x = 4 \Rightarrow 1 = 6B \Rightarrow B = \dfrac{1}{6}$

$x = -2 \Rightarrow 31 = 36C \Rightarrow C = \dfrac{31}{36}$

Equating coefficients: x^2 terms:

$2 = A + C \Rightarrow A = \dfrac{41}{36}$

This gives:

$\dfrac{2x^2 - 9x + 5}{(x-4)^2(x+2)} \equiv \dfrac{41}{36(x-4)} + \dfrac{1}{6(x-4)^2} + \dfrac{31}{36(x+2)}$

d) $\dfrac{3x^2 - 7x - 25}{x(x-5)^2} \equiv \dfrac{A}{x} + \dfrac{B}{(x-5)} + \dfrac{C}{(x-5)^2}$

$\Rightarrow 3x^2 - 7x - 25 \equiv A(x-5)^2 + Bx(x-5) + Cx$

Substituting:

$x = 5 \Rightarrow 15 = 5C \Rightarrow C = 3$

$x = 0 \Rightarrow -25 = 25A \Rightarrow A = -1$

Equating the coefficients of x^2:

$3 = A + B = -1 + B \Rightarrow B = 4$

This gives:

$\dfrac{3x^2 - 7x - 25}{x(x-5)^2} \equiv -\dfrac{1}{x} + \dfrac{4}{(x-5)} + \dfrac{3}{(x-5)^2}$

Q5 $x^3 - 10x^2 + 25x = x(x^2 - 10x + 25) = x(x-5)(x-5)$

So $\dfrac{5x^2 - 10x - 5}{x^3 - 10x^2 + 25x} = \dfrac{5x^2 - 10x - 5}{x(x-5)^2}$

$\dfrac{5x^2 - 10x - 5}{x(x-5)^2} \equiv \dfrac{A}{x} + \dfrac{B}{(x-5)} + \dfrac{C}{(x-5)^2}$

$\Rightarrow 5x^2 - 10x - 5 \equiv A(x-5)^2 + Bx(x-5) + Cx$

Substitution: $x = 0 \Rightarrow -5 = 25A \Rightarrow A = -\dfrac{1}{5}$

Equating coefficients:

x^2 terms: $\quad 5 = A + B = -\dfrac{1}{5} + B \Rightarrow B = \dfrac{26}{5}$

x terms: $\quad -10 = -10A - 5B + C = 2 - 26 + C$
$\qquad\qquad\qquad\qquad\qquad \Rightarrow C = 14$

This gives: $\dfrac{5x^2 - 10x - 5}{x^3 - 10x^2 + 25x} \equiv -\dfrac{1}{5x} + \dfrac{26}{5(x-5)} + \dfrac{14}{(x-5)^2}$

Exercise 3.3 — Improper fractions as partial fractions

Q1 a) $(x-3)(x+1) = x^2 - 2x - 3$

$$x^2 - 2x - 3 \overline{\smash{\big)}\,2x^2 - 4x + 6} \quad \begin{array}{c} 2 \\ \end{array}$$
$$\underline{-(2x^2 - 4x - 6)}$$
$$\qquad\qquad\qquad 12$$

So: $\dfrac{2x^2 - 4x + 6}{(x-3)(x+1)} \equiv 2 + \dfrac{12}{(x-3)(x+1)}$

Here q(x) = 2, r(x) = 12 and d(x) = $(x-3)(x+1)$.

b) $\dfrac{12}{(x-3)(x+1)} \equiv \dfrac{A}{(x-3)} + \dfrac{B}{(x+1)}$

$\Rightarrow \qquad 12 \equiv A(x+1) + B(x-3)$

Substitution: $\quad x = -1 \Rightarrow 12 = -4B \Rightarrow B = -3$
$\qquad\qquad\qquad\quad x = 3 \Rightarrow 12 = 4A \Rightarrow A = 3$

This gives: $\dfrac{12}{(x-3)(x+1)} \equiv \dfrac{3}{(x-3)} - \dfrac{3}{(x+1)}$

So: $\dfrac{2x^2 - 4x + 6}{(x-3)(x+1)} \equiv 2 + \dfrac{3}{(x-3)} - \dfrac{3}{(x+1)}$

Q2 $(x+2)(x+3) \equiv x^2 + 5x + 6$

$$x^2 + 5x + 6 \overline{\smash{\big)}\,3x^3 + 4x^2 + 2x - 5} \quad \begin{array}{c} 3x - 11 \\ \end{array}$$
$$\underline{-(3x^3 + 15x^2 + 18x)}$$
$$\qquad\qquad -11x^2 - 16x - 5$$
$$\qquad\qquad \underline{-(-11x^2 - 55x - 66)}$$
$$\qquad\qquad\qquad\qquad 39x + 61$$

So: $\dfrac{3x^3 + 4x^2 + 2x - 5}{(x+2)(x+3)} \equiv 3x - 11 + \dfrac{39x + 61}{(x+2)(x+3)}$

Here $q(x) = 3x - 11$, $r(x) = 39x + 61$
and $d(x) = (x + 2)(x + 3)$.
Now, converting to partial fractions:

$$\frac{39x + 61}{(x + 2)(x + 3)} \equiv \frac{A}{(x + 2)} + \frac{B}{(x + 3)}$$
$$\Rightarrow \quad 39x + 61 \equiv A(x + 3) + B(x + 2)$$

Substitution:
$x = -3 \Rightarrow -56 = -B \Rightarrow B = 56$
$x = -2 \Rightarrow -17 = A \Rightarrow A = -17$

This gives: $\dfrac{39x + 61}{(x + 2)(x + 3)} \equiv -\dfrac{17}{(x + 2)} + \dfrac{56}{(x + 3)}$

So: $\dfrac{3x^3 + 4x^2 + 2x - 5}{(x^2 + 5x + 6)} \equiv 3x - 11 - \dfrac{17}{(x + 2)} + \dfrac{56}{(x + 3)}$

Q3 By algebraic division:

$$\frac{2x^2 + 4x + 7}{(x - 1)(x + 2)} \equiv 2 + \frac{2x + 11}{(x - 1)(x + 2)}$$

Just use the same method you've used in Q1 and Q2 for this first bit.

$$\frac{2x + 11}{(x - 1)(x + 2)} \equiv \frac{B}{(x - 1)} + \frac{C}{(x + 2)}$$
$$\Rightarrow \quad 2x + 11 \equiv B(x + 2) + C(x - 1)$$

Substitution:

$x = 1 \Rightarrow 13 = 3B \Rightarrow B = \dfrac{13}{3}$

$x = -2 \Rightarrow 7 = -3C \Rightarrow C = -\dfrac{7}{3}$

This gives: $\dfrac{2x + 11}{(x - 1)(x + 2)} \equiv \dfrac{13}{3(x - 1)} - \dfrac{7}{3(x + 2)}$

So: $\dfrac{2x^2 + 4x + 7}{(x - 1)(x + 2)} \equiv 2 + \dfrac{13}{3(x - 1)} - \dfrac{7}{3(x + 2)}$

Q4 By algebraic division:

$$\frac{3x^2 - 5x + 2}{(x - 3)^2} \equiv 3 + \frac{13x - 25}{(x - 3)^2}$$

$$\frac{13x - 25}{(x - 3)^2} \equiv \frac{B}{(x - 3)} + \frac{C}{(x - 3)^2}$$

$$\Rightarrow 13x - 25 \equiv B(x - 3) + C$$

Substitution: $x = 3 \Rightarrow 14 = C$
Equating coefficients of the x terms: $13 = B$

This gives: $\dfrac{13x - 25}{(x - 3)^2} \equiv \dfrac{13}{(x - 3)} + \dfrac{14}{(x - 3)^2}$

So: $\dfrac{3x^2 - 5x + 2}{(x - 3)^2} \equiv 3 + \dfrac{13}{(x - 3)} + \dfrac{14}{(x - 3)^2}$

Q5 By algebraic division:

$$\frac{x^3 - 3x^2 - 3x + 9}{x^2 + 3x - 4} \equiv x - 6 + \frac{19x - 15}{(x + 4)(x - 1)}$$

So $A = 1$ and $B = -6$.
The remainder can be split as follows:

$$\frac{19x - 15}{(x + 4)(x - 1)} \equiv \frac{C}{(x + 4)} + \frac{D}{(x - 1)}$$
$$\Rightarrow \quad 19x - 15 \equiv C(x - 1) + D(x + 4)$$

Substitution:

$x = 1 \Rightarrow 4 = 5D \Rightarrow D = \dfrac{4}{5}$

$x = -4 \Rightarrow -91 = -5C \Rightarrow C = \dfrac{91}{5}$

This gives: $\dfrac{19x - 15}{(x + 4)(x - 1)} \equiv \dfrac{91}{5(x + 4)} + \dfrac{4}{5(x - 1)}$

So: $\dfrac{x^3 - 3x^2 - 3x + 9}{x^2 + 3x - 4} \equiv x - 6 + \dfrac{91}{5(x + 4)} + \dfrac{4}{5(x - 1)}$

Q6 By algebraic division:

$$\frac{x^3 + 4x^2 - 3x + 8}{x^2(x - 2)} \equiv 1 + \frac{6x^2 - 3x + 8}{x^2(x - 2)}$$

$$\frac{6x^2 - 3x + 8}{x^2(x - 2)} \equiv \frac{A}{x} + \frac{B}{x^2} + \frac{C}{(x - 2)}$$

$$\Rightarrow 6x^2 - 3x + 8 \equiv Ax(x - 2) + B(x - 2) + Cx^2$$

Substitution:
$x = 0 \Rightarrow 8 = -2B \Rightarrow B = -4$

$x = 2 \Rightarrow 26 = 4C \Rightarrow C = \dfrac{13}{2}$

Equate coefficients of the x^2 terms:

$$6 = A + C \Rightarrow 6 = A + \frac{13}{2} \Rightarrow A = -\frac{1}{2}$$

This gives: $\dfrac{6x^2 - 3x + 8}{x^2(x - 2)} \equiv -\dfrac{1}{2x} - \dfrac{4}{x^2} + \dfrac{13}{2(x - 2)}$

So: $\dfrac{x^3 + 4x^2 - 3x + 8}{x^2(x - 2)} \equiv 1 - \dfrac{1}{2x} - \dfrac{4}{x^2} + \dfrac{13}{2(x - 2)}$

4. Exponential Growth and Decay
Exercise 4.1 — Modelling growth and decay

Q1 When $t = 10$, $M = \dfrac{M_0}{2}$ so $\dfrac{M_0}{2} = M_0 e^{-10k} \Rightarrow \dfrac{1}{2} = e^{-10k}$
$\Rightarrow k = -\dfrac{1}{10} \ln\left(\dfrac{1}{2}\right) = 0.0693... = 0.0693$ (3 s.f.)

a) Want to find t when $M = \dfrac{M_0}{4}$,

so $\dfrac{M_0}{4} = M_0 e^{(-0.0693... \times t)} \Rightarrow \dfrac{1}{4} = e^{(-0.0693... \times t)} \Rightarrow$

$t = -\dfrac{1}{0.0693...} \ln\left(\dfrac{1}{4}\right) = 20.0$ years (3 s.f.).

So after 20 years the substance will be reduced to a quarter of its mass.

Note that a much easier way to do this would be to think of it as 'half and half again'. The substance will be a quarter of its mass after two half lives which is 2 × 10 = 20 years.

b) When $t = 5$, $M = 200$, so $200 = M_0 e^{(-0.0693... \times 5)}$ so
$M_0 = 200 e^{(0.0693... \times 5)} = 283$ grams (3 s.f.).
So the original mass is 283 grams.

c) Let $t = 15$, then $M = 283 \times e^{(-0.0693... \times 15)} = 100$
(3 s.f.). So after 15 years, 100 g is remaining.

Q2 When $t = 0$, $V = 300$, so $300 = Ak^0 \Rightarrow A = 300$.
When $t = 3$, $V = 500$, so $500 = 300k^3 \Rightarrow k^3 = \dfrac{5}{3}$
$\Rightarrow k = \sqrt[3]{\dfrac{5}{3}} = 1.185...$
When the value has tripled, $V = 900$.
So $900 = 300(1.185...)^t \Rightarrow 3 = (1.185...)^t$.
Now solve for t: $\ln 3 = \ln(1.185...)^t = t \ln 1.185...$
$\Rightarrow t = \dfrac{\ln 3}{\ln 1.185...} = 6.4519... = 6.45$ (3 s.f.)
So after 7 whole years, the value of the painting will be triple its original value.

Q3 a) If $t = 0$, $T = 225 - 207e^0 = 18$. So the oven was 18 °C to begin with.

b) As $t \to \infty$, $e^{\left(-\frac{t}{8}\right)} \to 0$ so $T \to 225 - 0 = 225$.
The oven would approach 225 °C if left on indefinitely.

c) Let $t = 5$, then $T = 225 - 207e^{\left(-\frac{5}{8}\right)} = 114\ °C$. (3 s.f.). So after 5 minutes the oven will be at 114 °C.

d) Let $T = 190\ °C$. Then $190 = 225 - 207e^{\left(-\frac{t}{8}\right)}$

$\Rightarrow e^{\left(-\frac{t}{8}\right)} = \dfrac{190 - 225}{-207} = \dfrac{35}{207}$

$\Rightarrow -\dfrac{t}{8} = \ln\left(\dfrac{35}{207}\right) \Rightarrow t = -8\ln\left(\dfrac{35}{207}\right) = 14.2\ \text{min}$
(to 3 s.f.). So the oven reaches 190 °C just after 12:14.

e)

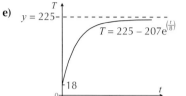

$y = 225$

$T = 225 - 207e^{\left(\frac{t}{8}\right)}$

18

t

Q4 When $t = 0$, $N = 3$. So $3 = Ae^0$ so $A = 3$.

a) Let $t = 0.5$ (hours).
Then $N = 3e^{-t} = 3e^{-0.5} = 1.82\ \text{mg/l}$.
The concentration after 30 minutes is 1.82 mg/l.

b) Let $N = 0.1$. Then $0.1 = 3e^{-t}$ so
$t = -\ln\left(\dfrac{0.1}{3}\right) = 3.40\ \text{hours}$ (3 s.f.).

c)

N

3

$N = 3e^{-t}$

0   t

Q5 **a)** $b = \ln 1.8 = 0.5877... = 0.588$ (3 s.f.)

b) Let $t = 3$ then $H = 20e^{(0.5877... \times 3)} = 117$ (3 s.f.).
So after 3 hours, 117 hectares will be burnt.

c) If $H = 500$, $500 = 20e^{(0.5877... \times t)} \Rightarrow 25 = e^{(0.5877... \times t)}$
$\Rightarrow \ln 25 = 0.5877... \times t$
$\Rightarrow t = \dfrac{1}{0.5877...}\ln 25 = 5.48$ (3 s.f.)
So it would take 5.48 hours to burn 500 hectares of land.

d) At $t = k$, $H = H_k = 20e^{(\ln 1.8)k}$
At $t = k + 1$, $H = H_{k+1} = 20e^{(\ln 1.8)(k + 1)}$
$= 20e^{(\ln 1.8)k + \ln 1.8} = 20e^{(\ln 1.8)k}e^{\ln 1.8} = H_k \times 1.8$
Every hour the burnt area is multiplied by 1.8.
This represents a percentage increase of 80%.

Q6 **a)** If $t = 0$, then $\theta = 65e^0 + 18 = 83\ °C$. The initial temperature is 83 °C.

b) When $t = 60$, $\theta = 83 - 8 = 75 \Rightarrow$
$75 = 65e^{-60c} + 18$
$\Rightarrow 65e^{-60c} = 75 - 18 = 57 \Rightarrow e^{-60c} = \dfrac{57}{65}$
$\Rightarrow 60c = -\ln\left(\dfrac{57}{65}\right) \Rightarrow c = -\dfrac{1}{60}\ln\left(\dfrac{57}{65}\right) = 0.002188...$
$c = 0.00219$ (3 s.f.)

c) Let $t = 3$ min $= 3 \times 60$ seconds $= 180$ seconds.
$\Rightarrow \theta = 65e^{(-0.002188... \times 180)} + 18 = 61.8$ (3 s.f.)
After 3 minutes the soup will be 61.8 °C.

d) Let $\theta = 40$. Then $40 = 65e^{(-0.002188... \times t)} + 18$
$\Rightarrow \dfrac{40 - 18}{65} = e^{(-0.002188... \times t)}$
$\Rightarrow \ln\left(\dfrac{22}{65}\right) = -0.002188... \times t$
$\Rightarrow t = -\dfrac{1}{0.002188...}\ln\left(\dfrac{22}{65}\right) = 495$ (3 s.f.)
So the soup will take 495 seconds to cool down.

e)

θ

$\theta = 65\ e^{-ct} + 18$

83

$\theta = 18$

0   t

Q7 **a)** At 8:00, let $t = 0$. Then at $t = 0$, $p = 0.05$.
So $0.05 = \dfrac{1}{1 + Re^0} = \dfrac{1}{1 + R} \Rightarrow 1 + R = \dfrac{1}{0.05} = 20$
$R = 19$
At 10:00, $t = 2$ and $p = 0.3$
So $0.3 = \dfrac{1}{1 + 19e^{-2q}} \Rightarrow 0.3(1 + 19e^{-2q}) = 1$
$\Rightarrow 19e^{-2q} = \dfrac{1}{0.3} - 1 = \dfrac{7}{3} \Rightarrow e^{-2q} = \dfrac{7}{57}$
$\Rightarrow q = -0.5\ln\dfrac{7}{57} = 1.048... = 1.05$ (3 s.f.)

b) At 14:00, $t = 6$. $p = \dfrac{1}{1 + 19e^{(-1.048... \times 6)}} = 0.966$
By 14:00, 96.6% of the population have heard of the King's death.

c) Let $p = 0.7$ then $0.7 = \dfrac{1}{1 + 19e^{(-1.048... \times t)}} \Rightarrow$
$1 + 19e^{(-1.048... \times t)} = \dfrac{1}{0.7} \Rightarrow 19e^{(-1.048... \times t)} = \dfrac{1}{0.7} - 1$
$\Rightarrow e^{(-1.048... \times t)} = \dfrac{1}{19}\left(\dfrac{1}{0.7} - 1\right) = 0.0225...$
$= 0.0226$ (3 s.f.)
$\Rightarrow -1.048... \times t = \ln(0.0225...)$
$\Rightarrow t = -\dfrac{1}{1.048...}\ln(0.0225...) = 3.62$ (3 s.f.)
So the time taken is 3.62 hours
$= 3$ hours 37 minutes. So the time will be 11:37.

Review Exercise — Chapter 1

Q1 **a)** $\dfrac{\dfrac{x}{x - 5}}{\dfrac{2x}{x - 5} + \dfrac{3}{x - 5}} = \dfrac{\left(\dfrac{x}{x - 5}\right)(x - 5)}{\left(\dfrac{2x}{x - 5} + \dfrac{3}{x - 5}\right)(x - 5)}$
$= \dfrac{x}{2x + 3}$

b) $\dfrac{5 - \dfrac{2}{2x + 3}}{7 + \dfrac{1}{2x + 3}} = \dfrac{\left(5 - \dfrac{2}{2x + 3}\right)(2x + 3)}{\left(7 + \dfrac{1}{2x + 3}\right)(2x + 3)}$
$= \dfrac{5(2x + 3) - 2}{7(2x + 3) + 1} = \dfrac{10x + 13}{14x + 22}$

c) $\dfrac{\dfrac{4}{2x + 7} + 6}{x + 2} = \dfrac{\left(\dfrac{4}{2x + 7} + 6\right)(2x + 7)}{(x + 2)(2x + 7)}$
$= \dfrac{4 + 12x + 42}{(x + 2)(2x + 7)} = \dfrac{12x + 46}{(x + 2)(2x + 7)}$

Q2 **a)** $\dfrac{4x^2 - 25}{6x - 15} = \dfrac{(2x + 5)(2x - 5)}{3(2x - 5)} = \dfrac{2x + 5}{3}$

b) $\dfrac{2x + 3}{x - 2} \times \dfrac{4x - 8}{2x^2 - 3x - 9}$

$= \dfrac{2x + 3}{x - 2} \times \dfrac{4(x - 2)}{(2x + 3)(x - 3)}$

$= \dfrac{4}{x - 3}$

c) $\dfrac{x^2 - 3x}{x + 1} \div \dfrac{x}{2} = \dfrac{x(x - 3)}{x + 1} \times \dfrac{2}{x}$

$= \dfrac{x - 3}{x + 1} \times 2 = \dfrac{2(x - 3)}{x + 1}$

Q3 a) $\dfrac{x}{2x + 1} + \dfrac{3}{x^2} + \dfrac{1}{x}$

$= \dfrac{x^2(x)}{x^2(2x + 1)} + \dfrac{3(2x + 1)}{x^2(2x + 1)} + \dfrac{x(2x + 1)}{x^2(2x + 1)}$

$= \dfrac{x^3 + 6x + 3 + 2x^2 + x}{x^2(2x + 1)}$

$= \dfrac{x^3 + 2x^2 + 7x + 3}{x^2(2x + 1)}$

b) $\dfrac{2}{x^2 - 1} - \dfrac{3x}{x - 1} + \dfrac{x}{x + 1}$

$= \dfrac{2}{(x + 1)(x - 1)} - \dfrac{3x(x + 1)}{(x + 1)(x - 1)}$

$+ \dfrac{x(x - 1)}{(x + 1)(x - 1)}$

$= \dfrac{2 - 3x^2 - 3x + x^2 - x}{(x + 1)(x - 1)} = \dfrac{2 - 2x^2 - 4x}{(x + 1)(x - 1)}$

$= \dfrac{2(1 - x^2 - 2x)}{(x + 1)(x - 1)}$

Q4 a) $x^3 + 8x^2 - 3x + 13 \equiv (Ax^2 + Bx + C)(x + 2) + D$

Set $x = -2$: $-8 + 32 + 6 + 13 = D$, so $D = 43$.

Set $x = 0$: $13 = 2C + D$, so $C = -15$.

Equating the coefficients of x^3 gives $1 = A$.

Equating the coefficients of x^2 gives:
$8 = 2A + B$, so $B = 6$.

So $x^3 + 8x^2 - 3x + 13 \equiv (x^2 + 6x - 15)(x + 2) + 43$.

Quotient: $x^2 + 6x - 15$
Remainder: 43

b) $3x^3 - 4x^2 - 12x + 9 \equiv (Ax^2 + Bx + C)(x - 3) + D$

Set $x = 3$: $81 - 36 - 36 + 9 = D$, so $D = 18$.

Set $x = 0$: $9 = -3C + D$, so $C = 3$.

Equating the coefficients of x^3 gives $3 = A$.

Equating the coefficients of x^2 gives:
$-4 = -3A + B$, so $B = 5$.

So $3x^3 - 4x^2 - 12x + 9 \equiv (3x^2 + 5x + 3)(x - 3) + 18$.

Quotient: $3x^2 + 5x + 3$
Remainder: 18

Q5 a)

$$\begin{array}{r} x^2 - 2x + 7 \text{ r } -9 \\ x + 4\overline{)x^3 + 2x^2 - x + 19} \\ -\underline{ x^3 + 4x^2} \\ -2x^2 - x \\ -\underline{-2x^2 - 8x} \\ 7x + 19 \\ -\underline{7x + 28} \\ -9 \end{array}$$

so $(x^3 + 2x^2 - x + 19) \div (x + 4)$
$= x^2 - 2x + 7$ remainder -9.

b)

$$\begin{array}{r} 2x^2 + 2x + 1 \text{ r } 5 \\ x + 3\overline{)2x^3 + 8x^2 + 7x + 8} \\ -\underline{2x^3 + 6x^2} \\ 2x^2 + 7x \\ -\underline{2x^2 + 6x} \\ x + 8 \\ -\underline{x + 3} \\ 5 \end{array}$$

so $(2x^3 + 8x^2 + 7x + 8) \div (x + 3)$
$= 2x^2 + 2x + 1$ remainder 5.

For questions 6-12 you can use the substitution method or the equating coefficients method, but only one method has been shown for each.

Q6 $\dfrac{2x}{(x - 5)(x + 5)} \equiv \dfrac{A}{(x - 5)} + \dfrac{B}{(x + 5)}$

$\Rightarrow \qquad 2x \equiv A(x + 5) + B(x - 5)$

Substitution:
$x = -5 \Rightarrow -10 = -10B \Rightarrow B = 1$
$x = 5 \Rightarrow 10 = 10A \Rightarrow A = 1$

This gives: $\dfrac{2x}{(x - 5)(x + 5)} \equiv \dfrac{1}{(x - 5)} + \dfrac{1}{(x + 5)}$

Q7 $\dfrac{2 - x}{(3x + 2)(x + 1)} \equiv \dfrac{A}{(3x + 2)} + \dfrac{B}{(x + 1)}$

$\Rightarrow \qquad 2 - x \equiv A(x + 1) + B(3x + 2)$

Substitution:
$x = -1 \Rightarrow 3 = -B \Rightarrow B = -3$
$x = -\dfrac{2}{3} \Rightarrow \dfrac{8}{3} = \dfrac{1}{3}A \Rightarrow A = 8$

This gives: $\dfrac{2 - x}{(3x + 2)(x + 1)} \equiv \dfrac{8}{(3x + 2)} - \dfrac{3}{(x + 1)}$

Q8 $\dfrac{x^2 - 3x - 8}{x^3 + 3x^2 + 2x} \equiv \dfrac{x^2 - 3x - 8}{x(x + 1)(x + 2)}$

$\equiv \dfrac{A}{x} + \dfrac{B}{(x + 1)} + \dfrac{C}{(x + 2)}$

$\Rightarrow x^2 - 3x - 8$

$\equiv A(x + 1)(x + 2) + Bx(x + 2) + Cx(x + 1)$

Equating coefficients:
x^2 terms: $1 = A + B + C$
x terms: $-3 = 3A + 2B + C$
constants: $-8 = 2A$
the equation for the constant terms gives $A = -4$.
Then solving simultaneously gives: $B = 4$, $C = 1$

This gives $\dfrac{x^2 - 3x - 8}{x^3 + 3x^2 + 2x} \equiv -\dfrac{4}{x} + \dfrac{4}{(x + 1)} + \dfrac{1}{(x + 2)}$

Q9 a) $\dfrac{2x + 2}{(x + 3)^2} \equiv \dfrac{A}{(x + 3)} + \dfrac{B}{(x + 3)^2}$

$\Rightarrow \qquad 2x + 2 \equiv A(x + 3) + B$

Substitution:
$x = -3 \Rightarrow -4 = B$
$x = 0 \Rightarrow 2 = 3A - 4 \Rightarrow A = 2$

This gives: $\dfrac{2x + 2}{(x + 3)^2} \equiv \dfrac{2}{(x + 3)} - \dfrac{4}{(x + 3)^2}$

b) $\dfrac{6x^2 + 17x + 5}{x(x + 2)^2} \equiv \dfrac{A}{x} + \dfrac{B}{(x + 2)} + \dfrac{C}{(x + 2)^2}$

$\Rightarrow 6x^2 + 17x + 5 \equiv A(x + 2)^2 + Bx(x + 2) + Cx$

Substitution:

$x = -2 \Rightarrow -5 = -2C \Rightarrow C = \dfrac{5}{2}$

$x = 0 \Rightarrow 5 = 4A \Rightarrow A = \dfrac{5}{4}$

Equating coefficients of the x^2 terms:

$6 = A + B \Rightarrow 6 = \dfrac{5}{4} + B \Rightarrow B = \dfrac{19}{4}$

This gives:

$\dfrac{6x^2 + 17x + 5}{x(x+2)^2} \equiv \dfrac{5}{4x} + \dfrac{19}{4(x+2)} + \dfrac{5}{2(x+2)^2}$

c) $\dfrac{-18x + 14}{(2x-1)^2(x+2)}$

$\equiv \dfrac{A}{(2x-1)} + \dfrac{B}{(2x-1)^2} + \dfrac{C}{(x+2)}$

$\Rightarrow -18x + 14$

$\equiv A(2x-1)(x+2) + B(x+2) + C(2x-1)^2$

Substitution:

$x = -2 \Rightarrow 50 = 25C \Rightarrow C = 2$

$x = 0.5 \Rightarrow 5 = 2.5B \Rightarrow B = 2$

Equating coefficients of the x^2 terms:

$0 = 2A + 4C \Rightarrow 0 = 2A + 8 \Rightarrow A = -4$

This gives:

$\dfrac{-18x + 14}{(2x-1)^2(x+2)} \equiv \dfrac{-4}{(2x-1)} + \dfrac{2}{(2x-1)^2} + \dfrac{2}{(x+2)}$

d) $\dfrac{8x^2 - x - 5}{x^3 - x^2} = \dfrac{8x^2 - x - 5}{x^2(x-1)} = \dfrac{A}{x} + \dfrac{B}{x^2} + \dfrac{C}{(x-1)}$

$\Rightarrow 8x^2 - x - 5 \equiv Ax(x-1) + B(x-1) + Cx^2$

Equating coefficients:

x^2 terms: $8 = A + C$

x terms: $-1 = -A + B$

constants: $-5 = -B$

The third equation gives $B = 5$, putting this into the second equation gives $A = 6$, putting this into the first equation gives $C = 2$.

This gives: $\dfrac{8x^2 - x - 5}{x^3 - x^2} \equiv \dfrac{6}{x} + \dfrac{5}{x^2} + \dfrac{2}{(x-1)}$

Q10 Using algebraic division gives:

$\dfrac{5x^2 - 10x + 42}{(5x-1)(x+2)} \equiv 1 + \dfrac{-19x + 44}{(5x-1)(x+2)}$

$\dfrac{-19x + 44}{(5x-1)(x+2)} \equiv \dfrac{B}{(5x-1)} + \dfrac{C}{(x+2)}$

$\Rightarrow -19x + 44 \equiv B(x+2) + C(5x-1)$

Substitution:

$x = -2 \Rightarrow 82 = -11C \Rightarrow C = -\dfrac{82}{11}$

$x = \dfrac{1}{5} \Rightarrow \dfrac{201}{5} = \dfrac{11}{5}B \Rightarrow B = \dfrac{201}{11}$

This gives: $\dfrac{-19x + 44}{(5x-1)(x+2)} \equiv \dfrac{201}{11(5x-1)} - \dfrac{82}{11(x+2)}$

So: $\dfrac{5x^2 - 10x + 42}{(5x-1)(x+2)} \equiv 1 + \dfrac{201}{11(5x-1)} - \dfrac{82}{11(x+2)}$

Q11 By algebraic division:

$\dfrac{4x^3 + 12x^2 - x - 5}{(x+1)(2x-1)} \equiv 2x + 5 - \dfrac{4x}{(x+1)(2x-1)}$

Writing the remainder as partial fractions:

$\dfrac{-4x}{(x+1)(2x-1)} \equiv \dfrac{A}{(x+1)} + \dfrac{B}{(2x-1)}$

$\Rightarrow -4x \equiv A(2x-1) + B(x+1)$

Substitution:

$x = -1 \Rightarrow -4 = -3A \Rightarrow A = \dfrac{4}{3}$

$x = \dfrac{1}{2} \Rightarrow -2 = \dfrac{3}{2}B \Rightarrow B = -\dfrac{4}{3}$

This gives: $\dfrac{-4x}{(x+1)(2x-1)} \equiv \dfrac{4}{3(x+1)} - \dfrac{4}{3(2x-1)}$

So: $\dfrac{4x^3 + 12x^2 - x - 5}{(x+1)(2x-1)} \equiv 2x + 5 + \dfrac{4}{3(x+1)} - \dfrac{4}{3(2x-1)}$

Q12 a) By algebraic division:

$\dfrac{2x^2 + 18x + 26}{(x+2)(x+4)} \equiv 2 + \dfrac{6x + 10}{(x+2)(x+4)}$

$\dfrac{6x + 10}{(x+2)(x+4)} \equiv \dfrac{A}{(x+2)} + \dfrac{B}{(x+4)}$

$\Rightarrow 6x + 10 \equiv A(x+4) + B(x+2)$

Substitution:

$x = -4 \Rightarrow -14 = -2B \Rightarrow B = 7$

$x = -2 \Rightarrow -2 = 2A \Rightarrow A = -1$

This gives: $\dfrac{6x + 10}{(x+2)(x+4)} \equiv -\dfrac{1}{(x+2)} + \dfrac{7}{(x+4)}$

So: $\dfrac{2x^2 + 18x + 26}{(x+2)(x+4)} \equiv 2 - \dfrac{1}{(x+2)} + \dfrac{7}{(x+4)}$

b) By algebraic division:

$\dfrac{3x^2 + 9x + 2}{x(x+1)} \equiv 3 + \dfrac{6x + 2}{x(x+1)}$

$\dfrac{6x + 2}{x(x+1)} \equiv \dfrac{A}{x} + \dfrac{B}{(x+1)}$

$\Rightarrow 6x + 2 \equiv A(x+1) + Bx$

Substitution:

$x = -1 \Rightarrow -4 = -B \Rightarrow B = 4$

$x = 0 \Rightarrow 2 = A$

This gives: $\dfrac{6x + 2}{x(x+1)} \equiv \dfrac{2}{x} + \dfrac{4}{(x+1)}$

So: $\dfrac{3x^2 + 9x + 2}{x(x+1)} \equiv 3 + \dfrac{2}{x} + \dfrac{4}{(x+1)}$

c) By algebraic division:

$\dfrac{3x^3 - 2x^2 - 2x - 3}{(x+1)(x-2)} \equiv 3x + 1 + \dfrac{5x - 1}{(x+1)(x-2)}$

$\dfrac{5x - 1}{(x+1)(x-2)} \equiv \dfrac{A}{(x+1)} + \dfrac{B}{(x-2)}$

$\Rightarrow 5x - 1 \equiv A(x-2) + B(x+1)$

Substitution:

$x = 2 \Rightarrow 9 = 3B \Rightarrow B = 3$

$x = -1 \Rightarrow -6 = -3A \Rightarrow A = 2$

This gives: $\dfrac{5x - 1}{(x+1)(x-2)} \equiv \dfrac{2}{(x+1)} + \dfrac{3}{(x-2)}$

So:

$\dfrac{3x^3 - 2x^2 - 2x - 3}{(x+1)(x-2)} \equiv 3x + 1 + \dfrac{2}{(x+1)} + \dfrac{3}{(x-2)}$

d) By algebraic division:

$\dfrac{24x^2 - 70x + 53}{(2x-3)^2} \equiv 6 + \dfrac{2x - 1}{(2x-3)^2}$

$\dfrac{2x - 1}{(2x-3)^2} \equiv \dfrac{A}{(2x-3)} + \dfrac{B}{(2x-3)^2}$

$\Rightarrow 2x - 1 \equiv A(2x-3) + B$

Substitution:

$x = 1.5 \Rightarrow 2 = B$

$x = 0 \Rightarrow -1 = -3A + B \Rightarrow A = 1$

This gives: $\dfrac{2x - 1}{(2x-3)^2} \equiv \dfrac{1}{(2x-3)} + \dfrac{2}{(2x-3)^2}$

So: $\dfrac{24x^2 - 70x + 53}{(2x-3)^2} \equiv 6 + \dfrac{1}{(2x-3)} + \dfrac{2}{(2x-3)^2}$

Q13 a) When $t = 0$, $y = 5 \Rightarrow 5 = pe^0 = p \Rightarrow p = 5$.
When $t = 3$, $y = 20 \Rightarrow 20 = 5e^{3q} \Rightarrow 4 = e^{3q} \Rightarrow$
$\ln 4 = 3q \Rightarrow q = \frac{1}{3}\ln 4 = 0.462... = 0.462$ (3 s.f.).

b) When $t = 6$, $y = 5 \Rightarrow 5 = pe^{6q}$
When $t = 9$, $y = 20 \Rightarrow 20 = pe^{9q}$
$\frac{20}{5} = \frac{pe^{9q}}{pe^{6q}} \Rightarrow 4 = e^{3q}$
$3q = \ln 4 \Rightarrow q = \left(\frac{1}{3}\right)\ln 4$
$q = 0.462... = 0.462$ (3 s.f.)
So $5 = p\,e^{(6 \times 0.462...)}$ and $p = 5\,e^{-(6 \times 0.462...)} = 0.3125$
$= 0.313$ (3 s.f.). So $y = 0.313\,e^{0.462... \times t}$

You could also do this question by noticing that the graph for part a) has been translated up the x-axis by 6, giving the equation $y = 5e^{0.462...\times(t-6)}$.

Q14 a) $V = 7500k^{-0.2t}$, so when $t = 0$,
$V = 7500 \times k^0 = £7500$.

b) $3000 = 7500k^{-0.2 \times 5} \Rightarrow 0.4 = k^{-1} \Rightarrow k = 2.5$.

c) $V = 7500 \times 2.5^{(-0.2 \times 10)} = £1200$.

d) When $V = 500$, $500 = 7500(2.5)^{-0.2t}$
$\Rightarrow 2.5^{-0.2t} = \frac{500}{7500} \Rightarrow 2.5^{0.2t} = \frac{7500}{500} = 15$
$\Rightarrow 0.2t\ln 2.5 = \ln 15$
$\Rightarrow t = 2.9554... \div 0.2 = 14.777...$ years.
So it will be 15 years old before the value falls below £500.

Q15 a) $L = 20e^{\left(\frac{10}{12}\right)} = 46.02$, so the model predicts the reserve will have 46 leopards after 10 years.

b) Let $L = 60$, then $60 = 20e^{\frac{t}{12}} \Rightarrow 3 = e^{\frac{t}{12}}$
$\Rightarrow t = 12\ln 3 = 13.18$. So the reserve will run out of space after 13 years.

c) $W = 15e^{\left(-\frac{5}{3}\right)} = 2.83$. So the model predicts that only 2 or 3 leopards will be left in the wild after 5 years.

Q16 a) $Z = 10 + 20e^0 = 30$. There were 30 zombies to begin with.

b) $Z = 10 + 20e^2 = 157.8$, so around 160 people will have been turned into zombies after 2 weeks.

c) $60\,000\,000 = 10 + 20e^t$
$\Rightarrow t = \ln\left(\frac{60\,000\,000 - 10}{20}\right) = 14.9$
So after 15 weeks more than 60 million will be zombies.

d) A graph of $Z = 10 + 20e^t$ with intersect at $Z = 30$

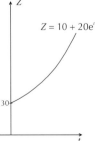

Exam-Style Questions — Chapter 1

Q1 Add the partial fractions and equate the numerators:
$5 + 9x \equiv A + B(1 + 3x)$ *[1 mark]*
Substitution:
$x = -\frac{1}{3}$: $2 = A \Rightarrow A = 2$ *[1 mark]*
$x = 0$: $5 = 2 + B \Rightarrow B = 3$ *[1 mark]*

Q2 $\frac{2x^2 - 9x - 35}{x^2 - 49} = \frac{(2x + 5)(x - 7)}{(x + 7)(x - 7)} = \frac{2x + 5}{x + 7}$

[3 marks available — 1 mark for factorising the numerator, 1 mark for factorising the denominator and 1 mark for correct answer (after cancelling)]

Q3 a) $\frac{x^2 - x - 20}{2x + 4} \div \frac{x^2 - 16}{x + 2}$
$= \frac{(x + 4)(x - 5)}{2(x + 2)} \times \frac{x + 2}{(x + 4)(x - 4)}$
$= \frac{x - 5}{2} \times \frac{1}{x - 4} = \frac{x - 5}{2(x - 4)}$

[3 marks available — 1 mark for turning the second fraction upside down, 1 mark for correct factorisations and 1 mark for correct answer (after cancelling)]

b) $\frac{x^2 - x - 20}{2x + 4} - \frac{x^2 - 16}{x + 2}$
$= \frac{x^2 - x - 20}{2(x + 2)} - \frac{2x^2 - 32}{2(x + 2)}$
$= \frac{x^2 - x - 20 - 2x^2 + 32}{2(x + 2)}$
$= \frac{-x^2 - x + 12}{2(x + 2)} = \frac{-(x^2 + x - 12)}{2(x + 2)}$
$= \frac{-(x - 3)(x + 4)}{2(x + 2)}$

[3 marks available — 1 mark for correctly writing the fractions over a common denominator, 1 mark for correct subtraction of the numerators and 1 mark for correct answer (allow unfactorised answer)]

Q4 First put $x = -6$ into the identity
$x^3 + 15x^2 + 43x - 30 \equiv (Ax^2 + Bx + C)(x + 6) + D$:
$(-6)^3 + 15(-6)^2 + 43(-6) - 30 = D \Rightarrow 36 = D$
[1 mark]
Now set $x = 0$: $-30 = 6C + D$, so $C = -11$ *[1 mark]*.
Equating the coefficients of x^3 gives $1 = A$. Equating the coefficients of x^2 gives $15 = 6A + B$, so $B = 9$ *[1 mark]*.
So:
$x^3 + 15x^2 + 43x - 30 = (x^2 + 9x - 11)(x + 6) + 36$.
You could also do this question by algebraic long division — you just have to use your answer to work out A, B, C and D.

Q5 To use algebraic long division, first expand the denominator:
$\frac{18x^2 - 15x - 62}{(3x + 4)(x - 2)} \equiv \frac{18x^2 - 15x - 62}{3x^2 - 2x - 8}$
Then divide the fraction:

$$3x^2 - 2x - 8 \overline{\smash{)}\begin{array}{r} 6 \\ 18x^2 - 15x - 62 \\ \underline{-(18x^2 - 12x - 48)} \\ -3x - 14 \end{array}}$$

Watch out for the negative signs here. You're subtracting the bottom line from the top, so be sure to get it right. You could use alternative methods for the division. You'll still get the marks, so use the one you're happiest with unless they tell you otherwise.

$$\frac{18x^2 - 15x - 62}{(3x + 4)(x - 2)} \equiv 6 + \frac{-3x - 14}{(3x + 4)(x - 2)}$$

So $A = 6$ *[1 mark]*

$$\frac{-3x - 14}{(3x + 4)(x - 2)} \equiv \frac{B}{(3x + 4)} + \frac{C}{(x - 2)}$$

$\Rightarrow \quad -3x - 14 \equiv B(x - 2) + C(3x + 4)$ *[1 mark]*

Substitution:

$$x = 2 \Rightarrow -20 = 10C \Rightarrow C = -2 \text{ [1 mark]}$$

You could carry on using the substitution method for the last bit but you'd need to substitute $-\frac{4}{3}$ in for x, so it's easier to equate coefficients.

Equating coefficients of the x terms:

$$-3 = B + 3C \quad \Rightarrow \quad -3 = B - 6 \quad \Rightarrow \quad B = 3 \text{ [1 mark]}$$

Q6 $5x^2 + 3x + 6 \equiv A(2x - 1)^2 + B(3 - x) + C(2x - 1)(3 - x)$ *[1 mark]*

Substitution:

$$x = 3 \Rightarrow 60 = 25A \Rightarrow A = \frac{12}{5} \text{ [1 mark]}$$

$$x = \frac{1}{2} \Rightarrow \frac{35}{4} = \frac{5}{2}B \Rightarrow B = \frac{7}{2} \text{ [1 mark]}$$

Equating coefficients of the x^2 terms:

$$5 = 4A - 2C$$

$$\Rightarrow 5 = \frac{48}{5} - 2C \Rightarrow -\frac{23}{5} = -2C \Rightarrow C = \frac{23}{10} \text{ [1 mark]}$$

Q7 Divide the fraction:

$$x^2 + 2x - 3 \overline{\smash{\big)}\ {\begin{array}{l} {-2x} \\ -2x^3 - 4x^2 + 18x + 6 \end{array}}}$$
$$\underline{-(-2x^3 - 4x^2 + 6x)}$$
$$12x + 6$$

$$\frac{-2x^3 - 4x^2 + 18x + 6}{x^2 + 2x - 3} \equiv -2x + \frac{12x + 6}{x^2 + 2x - 3}$$

$$\equiv -2x + \frac{12x + 6}{(x + 3)(x - 1)}$$

So $A = -2$ *[1 mark]* and $B = 0$ *[1 mark]*

$$\frac{12x + 6}{(x + 3)(x - 1)} \equiv \frac{C}{(x + 3)} + \frac{D}{(x - 1)}$$

$\Rightarrow \quad 12x + 6 \equiv C(x - 1) + D(x + 3)$ *[1 mark]*

Substitution:

$$x = 1 \Rightarrow 18 = 4D \Rightarrow D = \frac{9}{2} \text{ [1 mark]}$$

$$x = -3 \Rightarrow -30 = -4C \Rightarrow C = \frac{15}{2} \text{ [1 mark]}$$

Q8 a) When $t = 0$ (i.e. when the mink were introduced to the habitat) $M = 74 \times e^0 = 74$, so there were 74 mink originally *[1 mark]*.

b) After 3 years, $M = 74 \times e^{0.6 \times 3}$ *[1 mark]* = 447.67 i.e. 447 mink (rounding down) *[1 mark]*.

c) For $M = 10\ 000$: $10\ 000 = 74e^{0.6t}$

$\Rightarrow e^{0.6t} = 10\ 000 \div 74 = 135.1351$

$\Rightarrow 0.6t = \ln 135.1351 = 4.9063$ *[1 mark]*

$\Rightarrow t = 4.9063 \div 0.6 = 8.2$ years to reach 10 000, so it would take 9 complete years for the population to exceed 10 000 *[1 mark]*.

d)

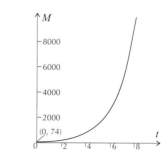

[2 marks available — 1 mark for correct shape, 1 mark for (0, 74) as a point on the graph.]

Q9 a) Using the Factor Theorem from C1:

$f(x) = 2x^3 - 19x^2 + 32x + 21$

$f(3) = 0 \Rightarrow (x - 3)$ is a factor *[1 mark]*

$$2x^3 - 19x^2 + 32x + 21 = (x - 3)(2x^2 \qquad)$$
$$= (x - 3)(2x^2 \qquad -7)$$
$$= (x - 3)(2x^2 - 13x - 7)$$
$$= (x - 3)(2x + 1)(x - 7)$$

[1 mark]

This method is explained in Exercise 3.1, Question 9 a) — your other option is to use the Factor Theorem to find the other factors.

b) $\frac{x^2 - 9x - 21}{2x^3 - 19x^2 + 32x + 21} \equiv \frac{A}{(x - 3)} + \frac{B}{(x - 7)} + \frac{C}{(2x + 1)}$

$\Rightarrow x^2 - 9x - 21$
$\equiv A(x - 7)(2x + 1) + B(x - 3)(2x + 1)$
$\qquad\qquad + C(x - 3)(x - 7)$

[1 mark]

Substitution:

$$x = 7 \Rightarrow -35 = 60B \Rightarrow B = -\frac{7}{12} \text{ [1 mark]}$$

$$x = -\frac{1}{2} \Rightarrow -\frac{65}{4} = \frac{105}{4}C \Rightarrow C = \frac{-13}{21} \text{ [1 mark]}$$

$$x = 3 \Rightarrow -39 = -28A \Rightarrow A = \frac{39}{28} \text{ [1 mark]}$$

So:

$$\frac{x^2 - 9x - 21}{2x^3 - 19x^2 + 32x + 21}$$

$$\equiv \frac{39}{28(x - 3)} - \frac{7}{12(x - 7)} - \frac{13}{21(2x + 1)}$$

Q10 $\frac{6x - 1}{x^2 + 4x + 4} \equiv \frac{6x - 1}{(x + 2)^2} \equiv \frac{A}{(x + 2)} + \frac{B}{(x + 2)^2}$

$\Rightarrow \qquad\qquad 6x - 1 \equiv A(x + 2) + B$ *[1 mark]*

Equating coefficients:

x terms: $\qquad 6 = A$ *[1 mark]*

constants: $-1 = 2A + B \Rightarrow B = -13$ *[1 mark]*

This gives: $\frac{6x - 1}{x^2 + 4x + 4} \equiv \frac{6}{(x + 2)} - \frac{13}{(x + 2)^2}$ *[1 mark]*

Q11 $\frac{18x^3 - 57x^2 + 0x + 38}{3x^2 - 7x - 6} \equiv \frac{18x^3 - 57x^2 + 0x + 38}{(x - 3)(3x + 2)}$

$$3x^2 - 7x - 6 \overline{\smash{\big)}\ {\begin{array}{l} {6x - 5} \\ 18x^3 - 57x^2 + 0x + 38 \end{array}}}$$
$$\underline{-(18x^3 - 42x^2 - 36x)}$$
$$-15x^2 + 36x + 38$$
$$\underline{-(-15x^2 + 35x + 30)}$$
$$x + 8$$

So: $\frac{18x^3 - 57x^2 + 0x + 38}{(x - 3)(3x + 2)} \equiv 6x - 5 + \frac{x + 8}{(x - 3)(3x + 2)}$

So $A = 6$ *[1 mark]* and $B = -5$ *[1 mark]*

$$\frac{x+8}{(x-3)(3x+2)} \equiv \frac{C}{(x-3)} + \frac{D}{(3x+2)}$$
$$\Rightarrow \quad x+8 \equiv C(3x+2) + D(x-3) \quad \text{*[1 mark]*}$$

Substitution:
$x = 3 \Rightarrow 11 = 11C \Rightarrow C = 1 \qquad$ *[1 mark]*

Equating coefficients of constant terms:
$8 = 2C - 3D \Rightarrow 8 = 2 - 3D \Rightarrow 6 = -3D \Rightarrow D = -2$
$$\text{*[1 mark]*}$$

Q12 a) B is the value of A when $t = 0$.
From the table, $B = 50$ *[1 mark]*.

b) Substitute $t = 5$ and $A = 42$ into $A = 50e^{-kt}$:
$42 = 50e^{-5k} \Rightarrow e^{-5k} = \frac{42}{50} \Rightarrow e^{5k} = \frac{50}{42}$ *[1 mark]*
$\Rightarrow 5k = \ln\left(\frac{50}{42}\right) = 0.17435$
$\Rightarrow k = 0.17435 \div 5 = 0.0349$ to 3 s.f. *[1 mark]*.

c) $A = 50e^{-0.0349t}$ (using values from (a) and (b)),
so when $t = 10$, $A = 50 \times e^{-0.0349 \times 10}$ *[1 mark]*
$= 35$ to the nearest whole *[1 mark]*.

d) The half-life will be the value of t when A reaches half of the original value of 50, i.e. when $A = 25$.
$25 = 50e^{-0.0349t} \Rightarrow \frac{25}{50} = e^{-0.0349t} \Rightarrow \frac{50}{25} = e^{0.0349t}$
$\Rightarrow e^{0.0349t} = 2$ *[1 mark]* $\Rightarrow 0.0349t = \ln 2$ *[1 mark]*
$\Rightarrow t = \ln 2 \div 0.0349 = 20$ days to the nearest day
[1 mark].

Chapter 2: Trigonometry

1. The Addition Formulas

Exercise 1.1 — Finding exact values

Q1 a) $\cos 72° \cos 12° + \sin 72° \sin 12°$
$= \cos (72° - 12°) = \cos 60° = \frac{1}{2}$

b) $\cos 13° \cos 17° - \sin 13° \sin 17°$
$= \cos (13° + 17°) = \cos 30° = \frac{\sqrt{3}}{2}$

c) $\frac{\tan 12° + \tan 18°}{1 - \tan 12° \tan 18°} = \tan (12° + 18°)$
$= \tan 30° = \frac{1}{\sqrt{3}}$

d) $\frac{\tan 500° - \tan 140°}{1 + \tan 500° \tan 140°} = \tan (500° - 140°)$
$= \tan 360° = 0$

e) $\sin 35° \cos 10° + \cos 35° \sin 10°$
$= \sin (35° + 10°) = \sin 45° = \frac{1}{\sqrt{2}}$

f) $\sin 69° \cos 9° - \cos 69° \sin 9°$
$= \sin (69° - 9°) = \sin 60° = \frac{\sqrt{3}}{2}$

Q2 a) $\sin \frac{2\pi}{3} \cos \frac{\pi}{2} - \cos \frac{2\pi}{3} \sin \frac{\pi}{2} = \sin \left(\frac{2\pi}{3} - \frac{\pi}{2}\right)$
$= \sin \frac{\pi}{6} = \frac{1}{2}$

b) $\cos 4\pi \cos 3\pi + \sin 4\pi \sin 3\pi$
$= \cos (4\pi - 3\pi) = \cos \pi = -1$

c) $\frac{\tan \frac{5\pi}{12} + \tan \frac{5\pi}{4}}{1 - \tan \frac{5\pi}{12} \tan \frac{5\pi}{4}} = \tan \left(\frac{5\pi}{12} + \frac{5\pi}{4}\right)$
$= \tan \frac{5\pi}{3} = \tan \left(2\pi - \frac{\pi}{3}\right) = -\tan \frac{\pi}{3} = -\sqrt{3}$

Q3 a) $\sin (5x - 2x) = \sin 3x$

b) $\cos (4x + 6x) = \cos 10x$

c) $\tan (7x + 3x) = \tan 10x$

d) $5 \sin (2x + 3x) = 5 \sin 5x$

e) $8 \cos (7x - 5x) = 8 \cos 2x$

Q4 Before answering a)-d), calculate $\cos x$ and $\sin y$:
$\sin x = \frac{3}{4} \Rightarrow \sin^2 x = \frac{9}{16} \Rightarrow \cos^2 x = 1 - \frac{9}{16} = \frac{7}{16}$
$\Rightarrow \cos x = \frac{\sqrt{7}}{4}$

x is acute, so cos x must be positive, therefore take the positive square root.

$\cos y = \frac{3}{\sqrt{10}} \Rightarrow \cos^2 y = \frac{9}{10}$
$\Rightarrow \sin^2 y = 1 - \frac{9}{10} = \frac{1}{10} \Rightarrow \sin y = \frac{1}{\sqrt{10}}$

Again, y is acute, so sin y must be positive, so you can take the positive square root. If you don't like using this method, you can use the triangle method to work out sin y and cos x.

a) $\sin (x + y) = \sin x \cos y + \cos x \sin y$
$= \left(\frac{3}{4} \times \frac{3}{\sqrt{10}}\right) + \left(\frac{\sqrt{7}}{4} \times \frac{1}{\sqrt{10}}\right)$
$= \frac{9 + \sqrt{7}}{4\sqrt{10}} = \frac{9\sqrt{10} + \sqrt{70}}{40}$

b) $\cos(x - y) = \cos x \cos y + \sin x \sin y$

$$= \left(\frac{\sqrt{7}}{4} \times \frac{3}{\sqrt{10}}\right) + \left(\frac{3}{4} \times \frac{1}{\sqrt{10}}\right)$$

$$= \frac{3\sqrt{7} + 3}{4\sqrt{10}} = \frac{3\sqrt{70} + 3\sqrt{10}}{40}$$

c) $\operatorname{cosec}(x + y) = \dfrac{1}{\sin(x + y)} = \dfrac{40}{9\sqrt{10} + \sqrt{70}}$

$$= \frac{18\sqrt{10} - 2\sqrt{70}}{37}$$

d) $\sec(x - y) = \dfrac{1}{\cos(x - y)} = \dfrac{40}{3\sqrt{70} + 3\sqrt{10}}$

$$= \frac{2\sqrt{70} - 2\sqrt{10}}{9}$$

Q5 $\cos \dfrac{\pi}{12} = \cos\left(\dfrac{\pi}{4} - \dfrac{\pi}{6}\right) = \cos \dfrac{\pi}{4} \cos \dfrac{\pi}{6} + \sin \dfrac{\pi}{4} \sin \dfrac{\pi}{6}$

$$= \left(\frac{1}{\sqrt{2}} \times \frac{\sqrt{3}}{2}\right) + \left(\frac{1}{\sqrt{2}} \times \frac{1}{2}\right) = \frac{\sqrt{3} + 1}{2\sqrt{2}}$$

Now rationalise the denominator...

$$= \frac{(\sqrt{3} + 1) \times \sqrt{2}}{(2\sqrt{2}) \times \sqrt{2}} = \frac{\sqrt{6} + \sqrt{2}}{4}$$

Q6 $\sin 75° = \sin(30° + 45°)$

$$= \sin 30° \cos 45° + \cos 30° \sin 45°$$

$$= \left(\frac{1}{2} \times \frac{1}{\sqrt{2}}\right) + \left(\frac{\sqrt{3}}{2} \times \frac{1}{\sqrt{2}}\right)$$

$$= \frac{1 + \sqrt{3}}{2\sqrt{2}} = \frac{(1 + \sqrt{3}) \times \sqrt{2}}{(2\sqrt{2}) \times \sqrt{2}} = \frac{\sqrt{6} + \sqrt{2}}{4}$$

Q7 $\tan 75° = \tan(45° + 30°) = \dfrac{\tan 45° + \tan 30°}{1 - \tan 45° \tan 30°} =$

$$\frac{1 + \frac{1}{\sqrt{3}}}{1 - 1 \times \frac{1}{\sqrt{3}}} = \frac{\left(\frac{\sqrt{3} + 1}{\sqrt{3}}\right)}{\left(\frac{\sqrt{3} - 1}{\sqrt{3}}\right)} = \frac{\sqrt{3} + 1}{\sqrt{3} - 1}.$$

Exercise 1.2 — Simplifying, solving equations and proving identities

Q1 $\tan(A - B) \equiv \dfrac{\sin(A - B)}{\cos(A - B)}$

$$\equiv \frac{\sin A \cos B - \cos A \sin B}{\cos A \cos B + \sin A \sin B}$$

Divide through by cos A cos B...

$$\equiv \frac{\left(\frac{\sin A \cos B}{\cos A \cos B}\right) - \left(\frac{\cos A \sin B}{\cos A \cos B}\right)}{\left(\frac{\cos A \cos B}{\cos A \cos B}\right) + \left(\frac{\sin A \sin B}{\cos A \cos B}\right)}$$

$$\equiv \frac{\left(\frac{\sin A}{\cos A}\right) - \left(\frac{\sin B}{\cos B}\right)}{1 + \left(\frac{\sin A}{\cos A}\right)\left(\frac{\sin B}{\cos B}\right)}$$

Now use tan = sin / cos...

$$\equiv \frac{\tan A - \tan B}{1 + \tan A \tan B}$$

Q2 a) $\dfrac{\cos(A - B) - \cos(A + B)}{\cos A \sin B}$

$$\equiv \frac{(\cos A \cos B + \sin A \sin B) - (\cos A \cos B - \sin A \sin B)}{\cos A \sin B}$$

$$\equiv \frac{2 \sin A \sin B}{\cos A \sin B} \equiv \frac{2 \sin A}{\cos A} \equiv 2 \tan A$$

b) $\dfrac{1}{2}[\cos(A - B) - \cos(A + B)]$

$$\equiv \frac{1}{2}[(\cos A \cos B + \sin A \sin B) - (\cos A \cos B - \sin A \sin B)]$$

$$\equiv \frac{1}{2}(2 \sin A \sin B) \equiv \sin A \sin B$$

c) $\sin(x + 90°)$

$$\equiv \sin x \cos 90° + \cos x \sin 90°$$

$$\equiv \sin x (0) + \cos x (1) \equiv \cos x$$

Q3 $4 \sin x \cos \dfrac{\pi}{3} - 4 \cos x \sin \dfrac{\pi}{3} = \cos x$

$$\Rightarrow 2 \sin x - 2\sqrt{3} \cos x = \cos x$$

$$\Rightarrow 2 \sin x = (1 + 2\sqrt{3}) \cos x$$

$$\Rightarrow \frac{\sin x}{\cos x} = \frac{1 + 2\sqrt{3}}{2} = \tan x$$

$$\Rightarrow x = -1.99 \text{ and } 1.15 \text{ to 2 d.p.}$$

Q4 a) $\tan\left(-\dfrac{\pi}{12}\right) = \tan\left(\dfrac{\pi}{6} - \dfrac{\pi}{4}\right) \equiv \dfrac{\tan \frac{\pi}{6} - \tan \frac{\pi}{4}}{1 + \tan \frac{\pi}{6} \tan \frac{\pi}{4}}$

$$\equiv \frac{\frac{1}{\sqrt{3}} - 1}{1 + \frac{1}{\sqrt{3}}}$$

$$\equiv \frac{1 - \sqrt{3}}{\sqrt{3} + 1}$$

Now rationalise the denominator...

$$\equiv \frac{1 - \sqrt{3}}{\sqrt{3} + 1} \times \frac{\sqrt{3} - 1}{\sqrt{3} - 1}$$

$$\equiv \frac{2\sqrt{3} - 4}{2} \equiv \sqrt{3} - 2$$

b) $\cos x = \cos x \cos \dfrac{\pi}{6} - \sin x \sin \dfrac{\pi}{6}$

$$\Rightarrow \cos x = \frac{\sqrt{3}}{2} \cos x - \frac{1}{2} \sin x$$

$$\Rightarrow (2 - \sqrt{3}) \cos x = -\sin x$$

$$\Rightarrow \frac{\sin x}{\cos x} = \tan x = \sqrt{3} - 2$$

From a), $\tan\left(-\dfrac{\pi}{12}\right) = \sqrt{3} - 2$, so one solution for x is $-\dfrac{\pi}{12}$. To get an answer in the correct interval, add π, since $\tan x$ repeats itself every π radians. So $x = \dfrac{11\pi}{12}$.

Q5 $2 \sin(x + 30°) \equiv 2 \sin x \cos 30° + 2 \cos x \sin 30°$

$$\equiv 2 \sin x \left(\frac{\sqrt{3}}{2}\right) + 2 \cos x \left(\frac{1}{2}\right)$$

$$\equiv \sqrt{3} \sin x + \cos x$$

Q6 $\tan\left(\dfrac{\pi}{3} - x\right) \equiv \dfrac{\tan \frac{\pi}{3} - \tan x}{1 + \tan \frac{\pi}{3} \tan x} \equiv \dfrac{\sqrt{3} - \tan x}{1 + \sqrt{3} \tan x}$

Q7 $\tan(A + B) = \dfrac{\tan A + \tan B}{1 - \tan A \tan B} = \dfrac{1}{4}$

$$\Rightarrow \frac{\frac{3}{8} + \tan B}{1 - \frac{3}{8} \tan B} = \frac{1}{4}$$

$$\Rightarrow \frac{3}{8} + \tan B = \frac{1}{4}\left(1 - \frac{3}{8} \tan B\right)$$

$\Rightarrow \frac{3}{8} + \tan B = \frac{1}{4} - \frac{3}{32}\tan B$

$\Rightarrow \tan B + \frac{3}{32}\tan B = \frac{1}{4} - \frac{3}{8} = -\frac{1}{8}$

$\Rightarrow \frac{35}{32}\tan B = -\frac{1}{8} \Rightarrow \tan B = -\frac{1}{8} \times \frac{32}{35} = -\frac{4}{35}$

Q8 **a)** $\sin x \cos y + \cos x \sin y$

$= 4 \cos x \cos y + 4 \sin x \sin y$

Dividing through by $\cos x \cos y$ gives:

$\frac{\sin x}{\cos x} + \frac{\sin y}{\cos y} = 4 + \frac{4 \sin x \sin y}{\cos x \cos y}$

$\Rightarrow \tan x + \tan y = 4 + 4 \tan x \tan y$

$\Rightarrow \tan x - 4 \tan x \tan y = 4 - \tan y$

$\Rightarrow \tan x (1 - 4 \tan y) = 4 - \tan y$

$\Rightarrow \tan x = \frac{4 - \tan y}{1 - 4 \tan y}$

b) $\tan x = \frac{4 - \tan \frac{\pi}{4}}{1 - 4 \tan \frac{\pi}{4}}$

Comparing the equation you have to solve to the one in part a) you can see that $y = \frac{\pi}{4}$.

$\Rightarrow \tan x = \frac{4 - 1}{1 - 4} = -1$

$\Rightarrow x = \frac{3\pi}{4}$ and $\frac{7\pi}{4}$

Q9 **a)** Use the sin addition formula on $\sin(\theta + 45°)$:

$\sqrt{2}(\sin \theta \cos 45° + \cos \theta \sin 45°) = 3 \cos \theta$

$\sqrt{2}\left(\frac{1}{\sqrt{2}}\sin \theta + \frac{1}{\sqrt{2}}\cos \theta\right) = 3 \cos \theta$

$\sin \theta + \cos \theta = 3 \cos \theta$

$\sin \theta = 2 \cos \theta$

$\frac{\sin \theta}{\cos \theta} = 2$

$\tan \theta = 2$

So $\theta = 63.43°$ and $63.43° + 180° = 243.43°$.

b) Use the cos addition formula:

$2\cos\left(\theta - \frac{2\pi}{3}\right) - 5 \sin \theta = 0$

$2\left(\cos \theta \cos\frac{2\pi}{3} + \sin \theta \sin\frac{2\pi}{3}\right) - 5 \sin \theta = 0$

$2\left(-\frac{1}{2}\cos \theta + \frac{\sqrt{3}}{2}\sin \theta\right) - 5 \sin \theta = 0$

$-\cos \theta + \sqrt{3}\sin \theta - 5 \sin \theta = 0$

$-\cos \theta + (\sqrt{3} - 5)\sin \theta = 0$

$\cos \theta = (\sqrt{3} - 5)\sin \theta$

$\frac{1}{(\sqrt{3} - 5)} = \frac{\sin \theta}{\cos \theta} = \tan \theta$

So $\theta = -0.296... + \pi = 2.84$ to 2 d.p.
and $-0.296... + 2\pi = 5.99$ to 2 d.p.

c) Use the addition formulas:

$\sin(\theta - 30°) - \cos(\theta + 60°) = 0$

$(\sin \theta \cos 30° - \cos \theta \sin 30°)$
$\qquad - (\cos \theta \cos 60° - \sin \theta \sin 60°) = 0$

$\left(\frac{\sqrt{3}}{2}\sin \theta - \frac{1}{2}\cos \theta\right) - \left(\frac{1}{2}\cos \theta - \frac{\sqrt{3}}{2}\sin \theta\right) = 0$

$\frac{\sqrt{3}}{2}\sin \theta - \frac{1}{2}\cos \theta - \frac{1}{2}\cos \theta + \frac{\sqrt{3}}{2}\sin \theta = 0$

$\sqrt{3}\sin \theta - \cos \theta = 0$

$\sqrt{3}\sin \theta = \cos \theta$

$\frac{\sin \theta}{\cos \theta} = \frac{1}{\sqrt{3}} \Rightarrow \tan \theta = \frac{1}{\sqrt{3}}$

$\theta = 30°$ and $30° + 180° = 210°$

2. The Double Angle Formulas

Exercise 2.1 — Using the double angle formulas

Q1 **a)** $\sin 2A \equiv 2 \sin A \cos A$

$\Rightarrow 4 \sin A \cos A \equiv 2 \sin 2A$

$\Rightarrow 4 \sin\frac{\pi}{12}\cos\frac{\pi}{12} = 2 \sin\frac{\pi}{6} = 2 \times \frac{1}{2} = 1$

b) $\cos 2A \equiv 2 \cos^2 A - 1$

$\Rightarrow \cos\frac{2\pi}{3} = 2 \cos^2\frac{\pi}{3} - 1 = 2\left(\frac{1}{2}\right)^2 - 1 = -\frac{1}{2}$

c) $\sin 2A \equiv 2 \sin A \cos A$

$\Rightarrow \frac{\sin 2A}{2} \equiv \sin A \cos A$

$\Rightarrow \frac{\sin 120°}{2} \equiv \sin 60° \cos 60° = \frac{\sqrt{3}}{2} \times \frac{1}{2} = \frac{\sqrt{3}}{4}$

d) $\tan 2A \equiv \frac{2 \tan A}{1 - \tan^2 A}$

$\Rightarrow \frac{\tan A}{2 - 2\tan^2 A} \equiv \frac{\tan 2A}{4}$

$\Rightarrow \frac{\tan 15°}{2 - 2\tan^2 15°} = \frac{\tan 30°}{4} = \frac{1}{4\sqrt{3}} = \frac{\sqrt{3}}{12}$

e) $\cos 2A \equiv 1 - 2 \sin^2 A$

$\Rightarrow 2 \sin^2 A - 1 \equiv -\cos 2A$

$\Rightarrow 2 \sin^2 15° - 1 = -\cos 30° = -\frac{\sqrt{3}}{2}$

Q2 **a)** $\cos 2A \equiv 1 - 2 \sin^2 A$

$\Rightarrow \cos 2x = 1 - 2 \sin^2 x = 1 - 2\left(\frac{1}{6}\right)^2 = \frac{17}{18}$

b) First find $\cos x$:

$\cos^2 x = 1 - \sin^2 x = 1 - \left(\frac{1}{6}\right)^2 = \frac{35}{36}$

$\Rightarrow \cos x = \frac{\sqrt{35}}{6}$

x is acute so take the positive root for cos x. Again, if you find it easier you can use the triangle method here.

$\sin 2A \equiv 2 \sin A \cos A$

$\Rightarrow \sin 2x = 2\left(\frac{1}{6} \times \frac{\sqrt{35}}{6}\right) = \frac{\sqrt{35}}{18}$

c) $\tan 2x = \frac{\sin 2x}{\cos 2x} = \frac{\sqrt{35}}{17}$

Q3 **a)** $\cos 2x = 1 - 2 \sin^2 x = 1 - 2\left(-\frac{1}{4}\right)^2 = \frac{7}{8}$

b) First find $\cos x$:

$\cos^2 x = 1 - \sin^2 x = 1 - \left(-\frac{1}{4}\right)^2 = \frac{15}{16}$

$\Rightarrow \cos x = -\frac{\sqrt{15}}{4}$

x is in the 3rd quadrant of the CAST diagram where cos x is negative, so take the negative root for cos x.

$\sin 2A \equiv 2 \sin A \cos A$

$\Rightarrow \sin 2x = 2\left(-\frac{1}{4} \times -\frac{\sqrt{15}}{4}\right) = \frac{\sqrt{15}}{8}$

c) $\tan 2x = \frac{\sin 2x}{\cos 2x} = \frac{\sqrt{15}}{7}$

Q4 **a)** Using the sin double angle formula:

$\frac{\sin 3\theta \cos 3\theta}{3} \equiv \frac{\sin 6\theta}{6}$

b) Using the cos double angle formula:

$\sin^2\left(\frac{2y}{3}\right) - \cos^2\left(\frac{2y}{3}\right) \equiv -\cos\left(\frac{4y}{3}\right)$

c) Using the tan double angle formula:

$\frac{1 - \tan^2\left(\frac{x}{2}\right)}{2\tan\left(\frac{x}{2}\right)} \equiv \frac{1}{\tan x} \equiv \cot x$

Exercise 2.2 — Solving equations and proving identities

Q1 **a)** Using the double angle formula for cos involving sin:

$4(1 - 2\sin^2 x) - 14 \sin x = 0$

$\Rightarrow 4 - 8 \sin^2 x - 14 \sin x = 0$

$\Rightarrow 8 \sin^2 x + 14 \sin x - 4 = 0$

$\Rightarrow 4 \sin^2 x + 7 \sin x - 2 = 0$

$\Rightarrow (4 \sin x - 1)(\sin x + 2) = 0$

So $\sin x = \frac{1}{4}$ or $\sin x = -2$ (not valid)

Solving $\sin x = \frac{1}{4}$ in the interval $0 \le x \le 360°$:

$x = 14.5°$ and $(180° - 14.5°) = 165.5°$

b) Using the double angle formula for cos involving cos:

$5(2\cos^2 x - 1) + 9 \cos x + 7 = 0$

$\Rightarrow 10 \cos^2 x + 9 \cos x + 2 = 0$

$\Rightarrow (2 \cos x + 1)(5 \cos x + 2) = 0$

$\Rightarrow \cos x = -\frac{1}{2}$ or $\cos x = -\frac{2}{5}$

$\Rightarrow x = 113.6°, 120°, 240°, 246.4°$

c) Using the double angle formula for tan.

$\frac{4(1 - \tan^2 x)}{2 \tan x} + \frac{1}{\tan x} = 5$

$\Rightarrow 2(1 - \tan^2 x) + 1 = 5 \tan x$

$\Rightarrow 3 - 2 \tan^2 x = 5 \tan x$

$\Rightarrow 0 = 2 \tan^2 x + 5 \tan x - 3$

$\Rightarrow 0 = (2 \tan x - 1)(\tan x + 3)$

$\Rightarrow \tan x = \frac{1}{2}$ or $\tan x = -3$

$\Rightarrow x = 26.6°, 108.4°, 206.6°, 288.4°$

d) $\tan x - 5 (2 \sin x \cos x) = 0$

$\Rightarrow \frac{\sin x}{\cos x} = 10 \sin x \cos x$

$\Rightarrow \sin x = 10 \sin x \cos^2 x$

$\Rightarrow \sin x - 10 \sin x \cos^2 x = 0$

$\Rightarrow \sin x(1 - 10 \cos^2 x) = 0$

$\Rightarrow \sin x = 0$ or $\cos x = \pm\frac{1}{\sqrt{10}}$

Don't forget to find $\cos^{-1}$ of both the positive and negative root...

$x = 0°, 71.6°, 108.4°, 180°, 251.6°, 288.4°, 360°$.

Q2 **a)** $4(2 \cos^2 x - 1) - 10 \cos x + 1 = 0$

$\Rightarrow 8 \cos^2 x - 10 \cos x - 3 = 0$

$\Rightarrow (4 \cos x + 1)(2 \cos x - 3) = 0$

$\Rightarrow \cos x = -\frac{1}{4}$ or $\cos x = \frac{3}{2}$ (not valid)

$\Rightarrow x = 1.82$ and 4.46

b) $\cos 2x - 3 = 6 \sin^2 x - 3$

$\Rightarrow (1 - 2 \sin^2 x) - 3 - 6 \sin^2 x + 3 = 0$

$\Rightarrow 1 - 8 \sin^2 x = 0$

$\Rightarrow \sin x = \pm\frac{1}{2\sqrt{2}}$

$\Rightarrow x = 0.361, 2.78, 3.50, 5.92$

Q3 **a)** $2 \cos^2 x - 1 + 7 \cos x = -4$

$\Rightarrow 2 \cos^2 x + 7 \cos x + 3 = 0$

$\Rightarrow (2 \cos x + 1)(\cos x + 3) = 0$

$\Rightarrow \cos x = -\frac{1}{2}$ or $\cos x = -3$ (not valid)

$\Rightarrow x = \frac{2\pi}{3}$ and $\frac{4\pi}{3}$

b) $2 \sin \frac{x}{2} \cos \frac{x}{2} + \cos \frac{x}{2} = 0$

$\Rightarrow \cos \frac{x}{2} \left(2 \sin \frac{x}{2} + 1\right) = 0$

$\Rightarrow \cos \frac{x}{2} = 0$ or $\sin \frac{x}{2} = -\frac{1}{2}$

There are no solutions for $\sin \frac{x}{2} = -\frac{1}{2}$ in the interval $0 \le x \le \pi$ (they both lie in the 3rd and 4th quadrants of the CAST diagram, $\pi \le x \le 2\pi$) so...

$\Rightarrow \frac{x}{2} = \frac{\pi}{2} \Rightarrow x = \pi$

Q4 **a)** $\sin 2x \sec^2 x \equiv (2 \sin x \cos x)\left(\frac{1}{\cos^2 x}\right)$

$\equiv \frac{2 \sin x}{\cos x} \equiv 2 \tan x$

b) $\frac{2}{1 + \cos 2x} \equiv \frac{2}{1 + 2\cos^2 x - 1}$

$\equiv \frac{2}{2 \cos^2 x} \equiv \frac{1}{\cos^2 x} \equiv \sec^2 x$

c) $\cot x - 2 \cot 2x \equiv \frac{1}{\tan x} - \frac{2}{\tan 2x}$

$\equiv \frac{1}{\tan x} - \frac{2(1 - \tan^2 x)}{2 \tan x} \equiv \frac{1 - (1 - \tan^2 x)}{\tan x}$

$\equiv \frac{\tan^2 x}{\tan x} \equiv \tan x$

d) $\tan 2x + \cot 2x \equiv \frac{\sin 2x}{\cos 2x} + \frac{\cos 2x}{\sin 2x}$

$\equiv \frac{\sin^2 2x + \cos^2 2x}{\sin 2x \cos 2x}$

Use $\sin^2 x + \cos^2 x \equiv 1$, and $\sin 4x = 2 \sin 2x \cos 2x$...

$\equiv \frac{1}{\frac{1}{2}\sin 4x} \equiv \frac{2}{\sin 4x} \equiv 2 \csc 4x$

Q5 a) $\dfrac{1 + \cos 2x}{\sin 2x} \equiv \dfrac{1 + (2\cos^2 x - 1)}{2 \sin x \cos x}$

$\equiv \dfrac{2 \cos^2 x}{2 \sin x \cos x} \equiv \dfrac{\cos x}{\sin x} \equiv \cot x$

b) Use $4\theta = 2x$, so $x = 2\theta$ and so $\dfrac{1 + \cos 4\theta}{\sin 4\theta} \equiv \cot 2\theta$

Solve $\cot 2\theta = 7$

$\Rightarrow \tan 2\theta = \dfrac{1}{7}$

$\Rightarrow 2\theta = 8.130°, 188.130°, 368.130°, 548.130°$

$\Rightarrow \theta = 4.1°, 94.1°, 184.1°, 274.1°$

Q6 a) $\operatorname{cosec} x - \cot \dfrac{x}{2} \equiv \dfrac{1}{\sin x} - \dfrac{\cos \frac{x}{2}}{\sin \frac{x}{2}}$

$\equiv \dfrac{1}{2 \sin \frac{x}{2} \cos \frac{x}{2}} - \dfrac{\cos \frac{x}{2}}{\sin \frac{x}{2}} \equiv \dfrac{1 - 2\cos^2 \frac{x}{2}}{2 \sin \frac{x}{2} \cos \frac{x}{2}}$

Here we've let $2A = x$ so $x = \dfrac{A}{2}$.

$\equiv \dfrac{-\left(2 \cos^2 \frac{x}{2} - 1\right)}{2 \sin \frac{x}{2} \cos \frac{x}{2}} \equiv \dfrac{-\cos x}{\sin x}$

$-\dfrac{1}{\left(\frac{\sin x}{\cos x}\right)} \equiv -\dfrac{1}{\tan x} \equiv -\cot x.$

b) Rearranging, $\operatorname{cosec} y - \cot \dfrac{y}{2} = -2 = -\cot y$

$\Rightarrow \cot y = 2 \Rightarrow \tan y = \dfrac{1}{2}.$

There are 2 solutions in the interval $-\pi \le y \le \pi$, at $y = 0.464$ and $y = 0.464 - \pi = -2.68.$

3. The R Addition Formulas

Exercise 3.1 — Expressions of the form $a \cos \theta + b \sin \theta$

Q1 $3 \sin x - 2 \cos x \equiv R \sin (x - \alpha)$

$\Rightarrow 3 \sin x - 2 \cos x \equiv R \sin x \cos \alpha - R \cos x \sin \alpha$

$\Rightarrow$ **(1)** $R \cos \alpha = 3$ and **(2)** $R \sin \alpha = 2$

(2) ÷ **(1)** gives $\tan \alpha = \dfrac{2}{3} \Rightarrow \alpha = 33.7°$ (to 1 d.p.)

(1)² + **(2)²** gives:

$R^2 \cos^2 \alpha + R^2 \sin^2 \alpha = 3^2 + 2^2 = 13$

$\Rightarrow R^2 (\cos^2 \alpha + \sin^2 \alpha) = 13 \Rightarrow R^2 = 13 \Rightarrow R = \sqrt{13}$

So $3 \sin x - 2 \cos x \equiv \sqrt{13} \sin (x - 33.7°)$.

Q2 $6 \cos x - 5 \sin x \equiv R \cos (x + \alpha)$

$\Rightarrow 6 \cos x - 5 \sin x \equiv R \cos x \cos \alpha - R \sin x \sin \alpha$

$\Rightarrow$ **(1)** $R \cos \alpha = 6$ and **(2)** $R \sin \alpha = 5$

(2) ÷ **(1)** gives $\tan \alpha = \dfrac{5}{6} \Rightarrow \alpha = 39.8°$ (to 1 d.p.)

(1)² + **(2)²** gives:

$R^2 \cos^2 \alpha + R^2 \sin^2 \alpha = 6^2 + 5^2 = 61 \Rightarrow R = \sqrt{61}$

So $6 \cos x - 5 \sin x \equiv \sqrt{61} \cos (x + 39.8°)$

Q3 $\sin x + \sqrt{7} \cos x \equiv R \sin (x + \alpha)$

$\Rightarrow \sin x + \sqrt{7} \cos x \equiv R \sin x \cos \alpha + R \cos x \sin \alpha$

$\Rightarrow$ **(1)** $R \cos \alpha = 1$ and **(2)** $R \sin \alpha = \sqrt{7}$

(2) ÷ **(1)** gives $\tan \alpha = \sqrt{7} \Rightarrow \alpha = 1.21$ (to 3 s.f.)

(1)² + **(2)²** gives:

$R^2 \cos^2 \alpha + R^2 \sin^2 \alpha = 1^2 + (\sqrt{7})^2 = 8$

$\Rightarrow R = \sqrt{8} = \sqrt{4 \times 2} = \sqrt{4} \times \sqrt{2} = 2\sqrt{2}$

So $\sin x + \sqrt{7} \cos x \equiv 2\sqrt{2} \sin (x + 1.21)$

Q4 $\sqrt{2} \sin x - \cos x \equiv R \sin (x - \alpha)$

$\Rightarrow \sqrt{2} \sin x - \cos x \equiv R \sin x \cos \alpha - R \cos x \sin \alpha$

$\Rightarrow$ **(1)** $R \cos \alpha = \sqrt{2}$ and **(2)** $R \sin \alpha = 1$

(2) ÷ **(1)** gives $\tan \alpha = \dfrac{1}{\sqrt{2}}$

(1)² + **(2)²** gives:

$R^2 \cos^2 \alpha + R^2 \sin^2 \alpha = (\sqrt{2})^2 + 1^2 = 3$

$\Rightarrow R^2 (\cos^2 \alpha + \sin^2 \alpha) = 3$

$\Rightarrow R^2 = 3 \Rightarrow R = \sqrt{3}$

So $\sqrt{2} \sin x - \cos x \equiv \sqrt{3} \sin (x - \alpha)$, where $\tan \alpha = \dfrac{1}{\sqrt{2}}$.

Q5 $3 \cos 2x + 5 \sin 2x \equiv R \cos (2x - \alpha)$

$\Rightarrow 3 \cos 2x + 5 \sin 2x \equiv R \cos 2x \cos \alpha + R \sin 2x \sin \alpha$

$\Rightarrow$ **(1)** $R \cos \alpha = 3$ and **(2)** $R \sin \alpha = 5$

(2) ÷ **(1)** gives $\tan \alpha = \dfrac{5}{3}$

(1)² + **(2)²** gives:

$R^2 \cos^2 \alpha + R^2 \sin^2 \alpha = 3^2 + 5^2 = 34 \Rightarrow R = \sqrt{34}$

So $3 \cos 2x + 5 \sin 2x \equiv \sqrt{34} \cos (2x - \alpha)$, where $\tan \alpha = \dfrac{5}{3}$.

Q6 a) $\sqrt{3} \sin x + \cos x \equiv R \sin (x + \alpha)$

$\Rightarrow \sqrt{3} \sin x + \cos x \equiv R \sin x \cos \alpha + R \cos x \sin \alpha$

$\Rightarrow$ **(1)** $R \cos \alpha = \sqrt{3}$ and **(2)** $R \sin \alpha = 1$

(2) ÷ **(1)** gives $\tan \alpha = \dfrac{1}{\sqrt{3}} \Rightarrow \alpha = \dfrac{\pi}{6}$

(1)² + **(2)²** gives:

$R^2 \cos^2 \alpha + R^2 \sin^2 \alpha = (\sqrt{3})^2 + 1^2 = 4$

$\Rightarrow R = \sqrt{4} = 2$

So $\sqrt{3} \sin x + \cos x \equiv 2 \sin (x + \dfrac{\pi}{6})$

b) The graph of $y = 2 \sin (x + \dfrac{\pi}{6})$ is the graph of $y = \sin x$ transformed in the following way: a horizontal translation left by $\dfrac{\pi}{6}$, then a vertical stretch by a factor of 2.

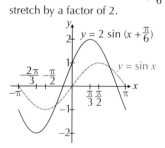

c) The graph of $y = \sin x$ has a minimum at $(-\frac{\pi}{2}, -1)$, a maximum at $(\frac{\pi}{2}, 1)$, and cuts the x-axis at $(-\pi, 0)$, $(0, 0)$ and $(\pi, 0)$.

To describe the graph of $y = 2 \sin (x + \frac{\pi}{6})$, each of these points needs to have $\frac{\pi}{6}$ subtracted from the x-coordinates, and the y-coordinates multiplied by 2.

So the graph of $y = 2 \sin (x + \frac{\pi}{6})$ has a minimum at $(-\frac{2\pi}{3}, -2)$, a maximum at $(\frac{\pi}{3}, 2)$, and cuts the x-axis at $(-\frac{\pi}{6}, 0)$ and $(\frac{5\pi}{6}, 0)$.

To find the y-intercept, put $x = 0$ into the equation:
$$y = 2 \sin (0 + \frac{\pi}{6}) = 2 \times \frac{1}{2} = 1$$
So the y-intercept is at $(0, 1)$.

Exercise 3.2 — Applying the R addition formulas

For each of the questions below, use the methods shown in Exercise 3.1 to express the equations in R form.

Q1 a) $5 \cos \theta - 12 \sin \theta \equiv 13 \cos (\theta + 67.4°)$

b) $13 \cos (\theta + 67.4°) = 4$, in the interval $67.4° \leq (\theta + 67.4°) \leq 427.4°$.

$$\cos (\theta + 67.4°) = \frac{4}{13}$$
$$\Rightarrow \theta + 67.4° = \cos^{-1} \frac{4}{13}$$
$$= 72.1° \text{ and } (360° - 72.1°) = 287.9°$$
$$\Rightarrow \theta = (72.1° - 67.4°) \text{ and } (287.9° - 67.4°)$$
$$= 4.7° \text{ and } 220.5°$$

c) The maximum and minimum values of $\cos \theta$ are at ± 1. So the maximum and minimum values of $13 \cos (\theta + 67.4°)$ are at ± 13.

Q2 a) $2 \sin 2\theta + 3 \cos 2\theta \equiv \sqrt{13} \sin (2\theta + 0.983)$

b) $\sqrt{13} \sin (2\theta + 0.983) = 1$ in the interval $0.983 \leq (2\theta + 0.983) \leq 13.549$.

$$\sin (2\theta + 0.983) = \frac{1}{\sqrt{13}}$$
$$\Rightarrow 2\theta + 0.983 = 0.281 \text{ (not in correct interval)},$$
$$(\pi - 0.281), (2\pi + 0.281),$$
$$(3\pi - 0.281), (4\pi + 0.281).$$

There will be 4 solutions for θ between 0 and 2π because you're dealing with $\sin 2\theta$.

$$\Rightarrow 2\theta + 0.983 = 2.861, 6.564, 9.144, 12.847$$
$$\Rightarrow \theta = 0.939, 2.79, 4.08, 5.93$$

Q3 a) $3 \sin \theta - 2\sqrt{5} \cos \theta \equiv \sqrt{29} \sin (\theta - 56.1°)$

b) $\sqrt{29} \sin (\theta - 56.1°) = 5$ in the interval $-56.1° \leq (\theta - 56.1°) \leq 303.9°$.

$$\sin (\theta - 56.1°) = \frac{5}{\sqrt{29}}$$
$$\Rightarrow \theta - 56.1° = 68.2°, \text{ and } (180° - 68.2°) = 111.8°$$
$$\Rightarrow \theta = 124.3° \text{ and } 167.9°$$

c) $f(x) = \sqrt{29} \sin (x - 56.1°)$. The maximum of $\sin x$ is at 1, so the maximum value of $f(x)$ is at $f(x) = \sqrt{29}$.

When $f(x) = \sqrt{29}$, $\sin (x - 56.1°) = 1$
$$\Rightarrow x - 56.1° = 90° \Rightarrow x = 146.1°$$

Q4 a) $3 \sin x + \cos x \equiv \sqrt{10} \sin (x + 18.4°)$

b) $\sqrt{10} \sin (x + 18.4°) = 2$ in the interval $18.4° \leq (x + 18.4°) \leq 378.4°$.

$$\sin (x + 18.4°) = \frac{2}{\sqrt{10}}$$
$$\Rightarrow x + 18.4° = 39.2° \text{ or } (180° - 39.2°) = 140.8°.$$
$$\Rightarrow x = 20.8° \text{ and } 122.4°.$$

c) The maximum and minimum values of $f(x)$ are at $\pm\sqrt{10}$.

Q5 a) $4 \sin x + \cos x \equiv \sqrt{17} \sin (x + 0.245)$

b) Maximum value of $4 \sin x + \cos x = \sqrt{17}$, so the greatest value of $(4 \sin x + \cos x)^4 = (\sqrt{17})^4 = 289$.

c) $\sqrt{17} \sin (x + 0.245) = 1$ in the interval $0.245 \leq (x + 0.245) \leq 3.387$.

$$\sin (x + 0.245) = \frac{1}{\sqrt{17}}$$
$$\Rightarrow x + 0.245 = 0.245 \text{ and } (\pi - 0.245) = 2.897$$
$$\Rightarrow x = 0 \text{ and } 2.65$$

Q6 a) $f(x) = 8 \cos x + 15 \sin x = 17 \cos (x - 1.08)$.

b) So solve for $17 \cos (x - 1.08) = 5$ in the interval $-1.08 \leq (x - 1.08) \leq 5.20$.

$$\cos (x - 1.08) = \frac{5}{17}$$
$$\Rightarrow x - 1.08 = 1.27 \text{ or } (2\pi - 1.27) = 5.01$$
$$\Rightarrow x = 2.35 \text{ and } 6.09.$$

c) $g(x) = (8 \cos x + 15 \sin x)^2 = 17^2 \cos^2 (x - 1.08)$
$$= 289 \cos^2 (x - 1.08)$$

The function $\cos^2 x$ has a minimum value of 0 (since all negative values of $\cos x$ become positive when you square it) so the minimum of $g(x)$ is 0.
This minimum occurs when $\cos^2(x - 1.08) = 0$ so $\cos(x - 1.08) = 0$ so $x - 1.08 = \pi$ and $x = 2.06$.

Q7 a) $2 \cos x + \sin x \equiv R \cos (x - \alpha)$
$$\equiv R \cos x \cos \alpha + R \sin x \sin \alpha$$
$$\Rightarrow \textbf{(1)} \; R \cos \alpha = 2 \text{ and } \textbf{(2)} \; R \sin \alpha = 1$$

(2) $\div$ **(1)** gives $\tan \alpha = \frac{1}{2} \Rightarrow \alpha = 26.6°$ (to 3 s.f.)
(1)^2 + **(2)**^{2} gives:
$$R^2 \cos^2 \alpha + R^2 \sin^2 \alpha = 2^2 + 1^2 = 5$$
$$\Rightarrow R^2 (\cos^2 \alpha + \sin^2 \alpha) = 5$$
$$\Rightarrow R^2 = 5 \Rightarrow R = \sqrt{5}$$
So $2 \cos x + \sin x \equiv \sqrt{5} \cos (x - 26.6°)$.

b) The range of $g(x)$ is between the maximum and minimum values, which are at $\pm\sqrt{5}$. So $-\sqrt{5} \leq g(x) \leq \sqrt{5}$.

Q8 $3 \sin \theta - \dfrac{3}{2}\cos \theta \equiv \dfrac{3\sqrt{5}}{2}\sin(\theta - 0.464)$

So solve $\dfrac{3\sqrt{5}}{2}\sin(\theta - 0.464) = 3$ in the interval
$-0.464 \le (\theta - 0.464) \le 5.819$.

$\sin(\theta - 0.464) = \dfrac{2}{\sqrt{5}}$

$\Rightarrow \theta - 0.464 = 1.107$ and $(\pi - 1.107) = 2.034$

$\Rightarrow \theta = 1.57$ and 2.50

Q9 $4 \sin 2\theta + 3 \cos 2\theta \equiv 5 \sin(2\theta + 0.644)$

So solve $5 \sin(2\theta + 0.644) = 2$ in the interval
$0.644 \le (2\theta + 0.644) \le 6.927$.

$\sin(2\theta + 0.644) = \dfrac{2}{5}$

$\Rightarrow 2\theta + 0.644 = 0.412$ (not in the interval),
$(\pi - 0.412) = 2.730$, and $(2\pi + 0.412) = 6.695$

$\Rightarrow \theta = 1.04$ and 3.03

4. The Factor Formulas

Exercise 4.1 — Proving and using the factor formulas

Q1 Starting with the addition formulas for sin:
$\sin(x + y) \equiv \sin x \cos y + \cos x \sin y$
$\sin(x - y) \equiv \sin x \cos y - \cos x \sin y$

So $\sin(x + y) + \sin(x - y)$
$\equiv \sin x \cos y + \cos x \sin y + \sin x \cos y - \cos x \sin y$
$\equiv 2 \sin x \cos y$

Substitute $A = x + y$ and $B = x - y$

Then $A + B = 2x$ and $A - B = 2y$,
so $x = \left(\dfrac{A + B}{2}\right)$ and $y = \left(\dfrac{A - B}{2}\right)$.

Putting this back into the identity gives:
$\sin A + \sin B \equiv 2 \sin\left(\dfrac{A + B}{2}\right)\cos\left(\dfrac{A - B}{2}\right)$

Q2 Starting again with the addition formulas for sin, but subtracting this time gives:
$\sin(x + y) - \sin(x - y)$
$\equiv \sin x \cos y + \cos x \sin y - \sin x \cos y + \cos x \sin y$
$\equiv 2 \cos x \sin y$

Substituting as before for
$x = \left(\dfrac{A + B}{2}\right)$ and $y = \left(\dfrac{A - B}{2}\right)$, gives:

$\sin A - \sin B \equiv 2 \cos\left(\dfrac{A + B}{2}\right)\sin\left(\dfrac{A - B}{2}\right)$

Q3 Starting with the addition formulas for cos:
$\cos(x + y) \equiv \cos x \cos y - \sin x \sin y$
$\cos(x - y) \equiv \cos x \cos y + \sin x \sin y$

So $\cos(x + y) - \cos(x - y)$
$\equiv \cos x \cos y - \sin x \sin y - \cos x \cos y - \sin x \sin y$
$\equiv -2 \sin x \sin y$

Substitute $A = x + y$ and $B = x - y$

Then $A + B = 2x$ and $A - B = 2y$,
so $x = \left(\dfrac{A + B}{2}\right)$ and $y = \left(\dfrac{A - B}{2}\right)$.

Putting this back into the identity gives:
$\cos A - \cos B \equiv -2 \sin\left(\dfrac{A + B}{2}\right)\sin\left(\dfrac{A - B}{2}\right)$

Q4 $\sin 75° - \sin 15° = 2 \cos\left(\dfrac{75° + 15°}{2}\right)\sin\left(\dfrac{75° - 15°}{2}\right)$
$= 2 \cos 45° \sin 30°$
$= 2\left(\dfrac{1}{\sqrt{2}}\right)\left(\dfrac{1}{2}\right) = \dfrac{1}{\sqrt{2}}\left(\dfrac{\sqrt{2}}{\sqrt{2}}\right) = \dfrac{\sqrt{2}}{2}$

Q5 $\cos 165° - \cos 75°$
$= -2 \sin\left(\dfrac{165° + 75°}{2}\right)\sin\left(\dfrac{165° - 75°}{2}\right)$
$= -2 \sin 120° \sin 45° = -2 \sin 60° \sin 45°$
$= -2\left(\dfrac{\sqrt{3}}{2}\right)\left(\dfrac{1}{\sqrt{2}}\right) = -\dfrac{\sqrt{3}}{\sqrt{2}}\left(\text{or} -\dfrac{\sqrt{6}}{2}\right)$

Q6 a) $\cos\left(\dfrac{A + B}{2}\right)\cos\left(\dfrac{A - B}{2}\right) \equiv \dfrac{1}{2}(\cos A + \cos B)$

$\left(\dfrac{A + B}{2}\right) = 140° \Rightarrow A + B = 280°$

$\left(\dfrac{A - B}{2}\right) = 50° \Rightarrow A - B = 100°$

Solving these equations: $A = 190°$ and $B = 90°$.

So $\cos 140° \cos 50° = \dfrac{1}{2}(\cos 190° + \cos 90°)$

$= \dfrac{1}{2}(\cos 190° + 0) = \dfrac{1}{2}\cos 190°$

So $\dfrac{\cos 140° \cos 50°}{\cos 190°} = \dfrac{\frac{1}{2}\cos 190°}{\cos 190°} = \dfrac{1}{2}$

b) $2 \cos\left(\dfrac{A + B}{2}\right)\sin\left(\dfrac{A - B}{2}\right) \equiv \sin A - \sin B$

So $2 \cos 75° \sin 15° = \sin A - \sin B$, where:

$\left(\dfrac{A + B}{2}\right) = 75° \Rightarrow A + B = 150°$

$\left(\dfrac{A - B}{2}\right) = 15° \Rightarrow A - B = 30°$

Solving these equations: $A = 90°$ and $B = 60°$.

So $2 \cos 75° \sin 15° = \sin 90° - \sin 60°$
$= 1 - \dfrac{\sqrt{3}}{2} = \dfrac{2 - \sqrt{3}}{2}$

Q7 $4 \sin\left(\dfrac{A + B}{2}\right)\cos\left(\dfrac{A - B}{2}\right) \equiv 2 \sin A + 2 \sin B$

So $4 \sin 52.5° \cos 7.5° = 2 \sin A + 2 \sin B$, where:

$\left(\dfrac{A + B}{2}\right) = 52.5° \Rightarrow A + B = 105°$

$\left(\dfrac{A - B}{2}\right) = 7.5° \Rightarrow A - B = 15°$

Solving these equations: $A = 60°$ and $B = 45°$

So $4 \sin 52.5° \cos 7.5° = 2 \sin 60° + 2 \sin 45°$
$= 2\left(\dfrac{\sqrt{3}}{2}\right) + 2\left(\dfrac{\sqrt{2}}{2}\right) = \sqrt{3} + \sqrt{2}$

Q8
$\dfrac{\cos \frac{\pi}{12} - \cos \frac{5\pi}{12}}{\sin \frac{5\pi}{12} + \sin \frac{\pi}{12}} = \dfrac{-\left(\cos \frac{5\pi}{12} - \cos \frac{\pi}{12}\right)}{\sin \frac{5\pi}{12} + \sin \frac{\pi}{12}}$

$= \dfrac{2 \sin\left(\frac{5\pi}{24} + \frac{\pi}{24}\right)\sin\left(\frac{5\pi}{24} - \frac{\pi}{24}\right)}{2 \sin\left(\frac{5\pi}{24} + \frac{\pi}{24}\right)\cos\left(\frac{5\pi}{24} - \frac{\pi}{24}\right)}$

$= \dfrac{\sin \frac{\pi}{6}}{\cos \frac{\pi}{6}} = \tan \frac{\pi}{6} = \dfrac{1}{\sqrt{3}}\left(\dfrac{\sqrt{3}}{\sqrt{3}}\right) = \dfrac{\sqrt{3}}{3}$

Exercise 4.2 — Solving equations and proving other identities

Q1 a) $2 \sin 6\theta \cos 3\theta = 2 \sin \left(\dfrac{9\theta + 3\theta}{2}\right) \cos \left(\dfrac{9\theta - 3\theta}{2}\right)$
$= \sin 9\theta + \sin 3\theta$

b) $2 \sin 8\theta \cos 4\theta = 2 \sin \left(\dfrac{12\theta + 4\theta}{2}\right) \cos \left(\dfrac{12\theta - 4\theta}{2}\right)$
$= \sin 12\theta + \sin 4\theta$

c) $2 \sin 3\theta \cos \theta = 2 \sin \left(\dfrac{4\theta + 2\theta}{2}\right) \cos \left(\dfrac{4\theta - 2\theta}{2}\right)$
$= \sin 4\theta + \sin 2\theta$

d) $2 \cos 5\theta \sin 2\theta = 2 \cos \left(\dfrac{7\theta + 3\theta}{2}\right) \sin \left(\dfrac{7\theta - 3\theta}{2}\right)$
$= \sin 7\theta - \sin 3\theta$

e) $2 \cos 7\theta \sin 3\theta = 2 \cos \left(\dfrac{10\theta + 4\theta}{2}\right) \sin \left(\dfrac{10\theta - 4\theta}{2}\right)$
$= \sin 10\theta - \sin 4\theta$

f) $2 \cos 12\theta \sin \dfrac{5}{2}\theta$
$= 2 \cos \left(\dfrac{\frac{29}{2}\theta + \frac{19}{2}\theta}{2}\right) \sin \left(\dfrac{\frac{29}{2}\theta - \frac{19}{2}\theta}{2}\right)$
$= \sin \dfrac{29}{2}\theta - \sin \dfrac{19}{2}\theta$

Q2 a) $\cos 18\theta + \cos 8\theta$

b) $\cos 4\theta + \cos 3\theta$

c) $\cos 15\theta + \cos 19\theta$

d) $2\cos 16\theta + 2\cos 4\theta$

e) $\cos 22\theta - \cos 4\theta$

f) $\cos \dfrac{31}{2}\theta - \cos \dfrac{29}{2}\theta$

Q3 a) $\cos 5x - \cos 4x = -2 \sin \dfrac{9}{2}x \sin \dfrac{1}{2}x$

b) $\dfrac{\cos 5x}{\cos 4x} = 1 \Rightarrow \cos 5x - \cos 4x = 0$

$\Rightarrow -2 \sin \dfrac{9}{2}x \sin \dfrac{1}{2}x = 0$

So either $\sin \dfrac{9}{2}x = 0$ or $\sin \dfrac{1}{2}x = 0$

Remember, $0 \le x \le 360°$ so $0 \le \dfrac{x}{2} \le 180°$
and $0 \le \dfrac{9x}{2} \le 1620°$.

$\Rightarrow \dfrac{9}{2}x = 0$, 180°, 360°, 540°, 720°, 900°, 1080°, 1260°, 1440°, 1620°.
and $\dfrac{1}{2}x = 0$, 180°
So $x = 0$, 40°, 80°, 120°, 160°, 200°, 240°, 280°, 320°, 360°

Q4 a) $\cos 2x + \cos 3x = 2 \cos \dfrac{5}{2}x \cos \dfrac{1}{2}x$

b) $\cos 2x + \cos 3x = 0 \Rightarrow 2 \cos \dfrac{5}{2}x \cos \dfrac{1}{2}x = 0$

So either $\cos \dfrac{5}{2}x = 0$ or $\cos \dfrac{1}{2}x = 0$

This time, $0 \le x \le 2\pi$ so $0 \le \dfrac{x}{2} \le \pi$
and $0 \le \dfrac{5x}{2} \le 5\pi$.

$\Rightarrow \dfrac{5}{2}x = \dfrac{\pi}{2}, \dfrac{3\pi}{2}, \dfrac{5\pi}{2}, \dfrac{7\pi}{2}, \dfrac{9\pi}{2}$
and $\dfrac{1}{2}x = \dfrac{\pi}{2}$. So $x = \dfrac{\pi}{5}, \dfrac{3\pi}{5}, \pi, \dfrac{7\pi}{5}, \dfrac{9\pi}{5}$

Q5 $\sin (x + 15°) \cos (x - 15°) = 0.5$
$2 \sin (x + 15°) \cos (x - 15°) = 1$
$\Rightarrow \sin A + \sin B = 1$, where:
$x + 15° = \left(\dfrac{A + B}{2}\right) \Rightarrow A = 2x + 30° - B$
and $x - 15° = \left(\dfrac{A - B}{2}\right)$
$\Rightarrow \left(\dfrac{2x + 30° - 2B}{2}\right) = x + 15° - B$
$\Rightarrow B = 30° \Rightarrow A = 2x$
So $\sin 2x + \sin 30° = 1 \Rightarrow \sin 2x = 0.5$
$\Rightarrow 2x = 30°, 150° \Rightarrow x = 15°, 75°$

Q6 $\cos 6x + \cos 4x = 2 \cos 5x \cos x$
So write the equation as:
$2 \cos 5x \cos x + \cos x = 0$
$\Rightarrow \cos x (2 \cos 5x + 1) = 0$
$\Rightarrow \cos x = 0 \Rightarrow x = \dfrac{\pi}{2}$
or $2 \cos 5x + 1 = 0 \Rightarrow \cos 5x = -\dfrac{1}{2}$
$\Rightarrow 5x = \dfrac{2\pi}{3}, \dfrac{4\pi}{3}, \dfrac{8\pi}{3}, \dfrac{10\pi}{3}, \dfrac{14\pi}{3}$
$\Rightarrow x = \dfrac{2\pi}{15}, \dfrac{4\pi}{15}, \dfrac{8\pi}{15}, \dfrac{2\pi}{3}, \dfrac{14\pi}{15}$

Q7 a) $\dfrac{\sin 9x + \sin x}{\sin 8x + \sin 2x} \equiv \dfrac{2 \sin 5x \cos 4x}{2 \sin 5x \cos 3x}$
$\equiv \dfrac{\cos 4x}{\cos 3x}$

b) $\dfrac{\sin 5x - \sin x}{\cos 5x + \cos x} \equiv \dfrac{2 \cos 3x \sin 2x}{2 \cos 3x \cos 2x}$
$\equiv \dfrac{\sin 2x}{\cos 2x} \equiv \tan 2x$

c) $\dfrac{\sin x + \sin y}{\cos x + \cos y} \equiv \dfrac{2 \sin \left(\frac{x + y}{2}\right) \cos \left(\frac{x - y}{2}\right)}{2 \cos \left(\frac{x + y}{2}\right) \cos \left(\frac{x - y}{2}\right)}$
$\equiv \dfrac{\sin \left(\frac{x + y}{2}\right)}{\cos \left(\frac{x + y}{2}\right)} \equiv \tan \left(\dfrac{x + y}{2}\right)$

Review Exercise — Chapter 2

Q1 $\cos 2\theta \equiv \cos^2 \theta - \sin^2 \theta$
$\cos 2\theta \equiv 2\cos^2 \theta - 1$
$\cos 2\theta \equiv 1 - 2\sin^2 \theta$

Q2 $\dfrac{\pi}{12} = \dfrac{\pi}{3} - \dfrac{\pi}{4}$, so use the addition formula for $\cos(A - B)$:
$\cos \dfrac{\pi}{12} = \cos \left(\dfrac{\pi}{3} - \dfrac{\pi}{4}\right)$
$= \cos \dfrac{\pi}{3} \cos \dfrac{\pi}{4} + \sin \dfrac{\pi}{3} \sin \dfrac{\pi}{4}$
As $\cos \dfrac{\pi}{3} = \dfrac{1}{2}$, $\cos \dfrac{\pi}{4} = \dfrac{1}{\sqrt{2}}$,
$\sin \dfrac{\pi}{3} = \dfrac{\sqrt{3}}{2}$ and $\sin \dfrac{\pi}{4} = \dfrac{1}{\sqrt{2}}$

Putting these values into the equation gives:

$\cos\frac{\pi}{3}\cos\frac{\pi}{4} + \sin\frac{\pi}{3}\sin\frac{\pi}{4}$

$= \left(\frac{1}{2} \times \frac{1}{\sqrt{2}}\right) + \left(\frac{\sqrt{3}}{2} \times \frac{1}{\sqrt{2}}\right)$

$= \frac{1}{2\sqrt{2}} + \frac{\sqrt{3}}{2\sqrt{2}} = \frac{1+\sqrt{3}}{2\sqrt{2}}$

$= \frac{\sqrt{2}(1+\sqrt{3})}{4} = \frac{\sqrt{2}+\sqrt{6}}{4}$

You could also have used $\frac{\pi}{12} = \frac{\pi}{4} - \frac{\pi}{6}$ in your answer.

Q3 $\sin(A+B) \equiv \sin A \cos B + \cos A \sin B$.

As $\sin A = \frac{4}{5}$, $\cos A = \frac{3}{5}$ (from the right-angled triangle with sides of length 3, 4 and 5) and as $\sin B = \frac{7}{25}$, $\cos B = \frac{24}{25}$ (from the right-angled triangle with sides of length 7, 24 and 25). Putting these values into the equation gives:

$\sin A \cos B + \cos A \sin B = \left(\frac{4}{5} \cdot \frac{24}{25}\right) + \left(\frac{3}{5} \cdot \frac{7}{25}\right)$

$= \frac{96}{125} + \frac{21}{125} = \frac{117}{125}$ $(= 0.936)$

Q4 $\sin 2\theta = -\sqrt{3}\sin\theta \Rightarrow \sin 2\theta + \sqrt{3}\sin\theta = 0$

$2\sin\theta\cos\theta + \sqrt{3}\sin\theta = 0$

$\sin\theta(2\cos\theta + \sqrt{3}) = 0$

So either $\sin\theta = 0$, so $\theta = 0°$, 180°, 360° or

$2\cos\theta + \sqrt{3} = 0 \Rightarrow \cos\theta = -\frac{\sqrt{3}}{2}$

so $\theta = 150°$ or $210°$. The set of values for θ is 0°, 150°, 180°, 210°, 360°.

Q5 a) $4(2\sin\frac{x}{2}\cos\frac{x}{2}) = \sin\frac{x}{2}$

$\Rightarrow 8\sin\frac{x}{2}\cos\frac{x}{2} - \sin\frac{x}{2} = 0$

$\Rightarrow \sin\frac{x}{2}(8\cos\frac{x}{2} - 1) = 0$

$\Rightarrow \sin\frac{x}{2} = 0$ or $\cos\frac{x}{2} = \frac{1}{8}$

$\Rightarrow \frac{x}{2} = 0, 1.445, 3.142 \Rightarrow x = 0, 2.89, 6.28$

As you're solving for $\frac{x}{2}$ remember to halve the interval you're finding solutions in, so that when you double them to get solutions for x they'll lie in the right interval.

b) $\frac{\tan\frac{x}{2}(2\tan\frac{x}{2})}{1-\tan^2\frac{x}{2}} = 2 \Rightarrow \frac{2\tan^2\frac{x}{2}}{1-\tan^2\frac{x}{2}} = 2$

$\Rightarrow 2\tan^2\frac{x}{2} = 2 - 2\tan^2\frac{x}{2} \Rightarrow \tan^2\frac{x}{2} = \frac{1}{2}$

$\Rightarrow \tan\frac{x}{2} = \pm\frac{1}{\sqrt{2}} \Rightarrow \frac{x}{2} = 0.615, 2.526$

$\Rightarrow x = 1.23, 5.05$

Q6 a) $\frac{4\tan x}{1-\tan^2 x} = \tan x \Rightarrow 4\tan x = \tan x(1-\tan^2 x)$

$\Rightarrow \tan^3 x + 3\tan x = 0 \Rightarrow \tan x(\tan^2 x + 3) = 0$

$\Rightarrow \tan x = 0$ or $\tan^2 x + 3 = 0$ (not valid because $\tan^2 x = -3$ so $\tan x = \sqrt{-3}$)

$\Rightarrow x = 0, \pi, 2\pi$

b) $2\sin 3x \cos 3x - \cos 3x = 0$

$\cos 3x(2\sin 3x - 1) = 0$

$\cos 3x = 0$ or $\sin 3x = \frac{1}{2}$

You're solving for 3x, so find solutions between 0 and 6π.

$3x = \frac{\pi}{2}, \frac{3\pi}{2}, \frac{5\pi}{2}, \frac{7\pi}{2}, \frac{9\pi}{2}, \frac{11\pi}{2}$ or

$\frac{\pi}{6}, \frac{5\pi}{6}, \frac{13\pi}{6}, \frac{17\pi}{6}, \frac{25\pi}{6}, \frac{29\pi}{6}$

$x = \frac{\pi}{6}, \frac{\pi}{2}, \frac{5\pi}{6}, \frac{7\pi}{6}, \frac{3\pi}{2}, \frac{11\pi}{6},$

$\frac{\pi}{18}, \frac{5\pi}{18}, \frac{13\pi}{18}, \frac{17\pi}{18}, \frac{25\pi}{18}, \frac{29\pi}{18}$

Q7 $a\cos\theta + b\sin\theta \equiv R\cos(\theta - \alpha)$ or $b\sin\theta + a\cos\theta \equiv R\sin(\theta + \alpha)$

Q8 $5\sin\theta - 6\cos\theta \equiv R\sin(\theta - \alpha)$
$\equiv R\sin\theta\cos\alpha - R\cos\theta\sin\alpha$ (using the addition rule for sin).
Equating coefficients of $\sin\theta$ and $\cos\theta$ gives:
1) $R\cos\alpha = 5$ and 2) $R\sin\alpha = 6$.

Dividing 2. by 1. to find α:
$\frac{R\sin\alpha}{R\cos\alpha} = \tan\alpha$, so $\frac{6}{5} = \tan\alpha$

Solving this gives $\alpha = 50.19°$.
To find R, square equations 1. and 2., add, then square root:
$R = \sqrt{5^2 + 6^2} = \sqrt{25+36} = \sqrt{61}$, so
$5\sin\theta - 6\cos\theta \equiv \sqrt{61}\sin(\theta - 50.19°)$.

Q9 Start by putting the LHS over a common denominator:
$\frac{\cos\theta}{\sin\theta} + \frac{\sin\theta}{\cos\theta} \equiv \frac{\cos\theta\cos\theta}{\sin\theta\cos\theta} + \frac{\sin\theta\sin\theta}{\sin\theta\cos\theta}$

$\equiv \frac{\cos^2\theta + \sin^2\theta}{\sin\theta\cos\theta} \equiv \frac{1}{\sin\theta\cos\theta}$

(using the identity $\sin^2\theta + \cos^2\theta \equiv 1$).
Now, $\sin 2\theta \equiv 2\sin\theta\cos\theta$, so $\sin\theta\cos\theta = \frac{1}{2}\sin 2\theta$.
So $\frac{1}{\sin\theta\cos\theta} \equiv \frac{1}{\frac{1}{2}\sin 2\theta} \equiv 2\csc 2\theta$,

which is the same as the RHS.

Exam-Style Questions — Chapter 2

Q1 **a)** $9\sin\theta + 12\cos\theta \equiv R\sin(\theta + \alpha)$.
Using the sin addition formula,
$9\sin\theta + 12\cos\theta \equiv R\sin\theta\cos\alpha + R\cos\theta\sin\alpha$.
Equating coefficients of $\sin\theta$ and $\cos\theta$ gives:
$R\cos\alpha = 9$ and $R\sin\alpha = 12$ *[1 mark]*.
$\dfrac{R\sin\alpha}{R\cos\alpha} = \tan\alpha$, so $\tan\alpha = \dfrac{12}{9} = \dfrac{4}{3}$
Solving this gives $\alpha = 0.927$
[1 mark — no other solutions in given range].
$R = \sqrt{9^2 + 12^2} = \sqrt{81 + 144} = \sqrt{225} = 15$
[1 mark],
so $9\sin\theta + 12\cos\theta = 15\sin(\theta + 0.927)$.

b) If $9\sin\theta + 12\cos\theta = 3$, then from part a),
$15\sin(\theta + 0.927) = 3$, so $\sin(\theta + 0.927) = 0.2$.
The range for θ is $0 \le \theta \le 2\pi$, which becomes
$0.927 \le \theta + 0.927 \le 7.210$. Solving the equation
gives $(\theta + 0.927) = 0.201$ *[1 mark]*.

As this is outside the range, use a sketch to find
values that are in the range:

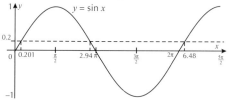

There are solutions at
$\pi - 0.201 = 2.94$ and at $2\pi + 0.201 = 6.48$, so
$(\theta + 0.927) = 2.940, 6.48$ *[1 mark for each]*,
so $\theta = 2.01, 5.56$ *[1 mark for each solution]*.

*Be careful with the range — if you hadn't extended the
range to $2\pi + 0.927$, you would have missed one of the
solutions.*

Q2 $\sin 3x \equiv \sin(2x + x)$
$\equiv \sin 2x\cos x + \cos 2x\sin x$ *[1 mark]*
$\equiv (2\sin x\cos x)\cos x + (1 - 2\sin^2 x)\sin x$
   [1 mark]
$\equiv 2\sin x\cos^2 x + \sin x - 2\sin^3 x$
$\equiv 2\sin x(1 - \sin^2 x) + \sin x - 2\sin^3 x$ *[1 mark]*
$\equiv 2\sin x - 2\sin^3 x + \sin x - 2\sin^3 x$
$\equiv 3\sin x - 4\sin^3 x$ *[1 mark]*

Q3 **a)** Use the double angle formula:
$\cos 2\theta \equiv 1 - 2\sin^2\theta$ to replace $\cos 2\theta$:
$DE^2 = 4 - 4(1 - 2\sin^2\theta)$ *[1 mark]*
$DE^2 = 4 - 4 + 8\sin^2\theta \Rightarrow DE^2 = 8\sin^2\theta$
$DE = \sqrt{8}\sin\theta = 2\sqrt{2}\sin\theta$ *[1 mark]*

b) $P = 2DE + 2DG$
To find DG, use triangle BDG:

$\cos\theta = \dfrac{DG}{\sqrt{2}}$, so $DG = \sqrt{2}\cos\theta$ *[1 mark]*

So $P = 2(2\sqrt{2}\sin\theta) + 2(\sqrt{2}\cos\theta)$
$\quad = 4\sqrt{2}\sin\theta + 2\sqrt{2}\cos\theta$ *[1 mark]*

c) $4\sqrt{2}\sin\theta + 2\sqrt{2}\cos\theta \equiv R\sin(\theta + \alpha)$
$\Rightarrow 4\sqrt{2}\sin\theta + 2\sqrt{2}\cos\theta$
$\equiv R\sin\theta\cos\alpha + R\cos\theta\sin\alpha$
$\Rightarrow$ **(1)** $R\cos\alpha = 4\sqrt{2}$
and **(2)** $R\sin\alpha = 2\sqrt{2}$ *[1 mark]*
(2) $\div$ **(1)** gives $\tan\alpha = \dfrac{1}{2}$
$\Rightarrow \alpha = 0.464$ (to 3 s.f.) *[1 mark]*
(1)^2 + **(2)**^{2} gives:
$R^2\cos^2\alpha + R^2\sin^2\alpha = (4\sqrt{2})^2 + (2\sqrt{2})^2 = 40$
$\Rightarrow R = \sqrt{40} = 2\sqrt{10}$ *[1 mark]*
So $4\sqrt{2}\sin\theta + 2\sqrt{2}\cos\theta \equiv 2\sqrt{10}\sin(\theta + 0.464)$

Q4 **a)** $5\cos\theta + 12\sin\theta \equiv R\cos(\theta - \alpha)$.
$5\cos\theta + 12\sin\theta \equiv R\cos\theta\cos\alpha + R\sin\theta\sin\alpha$.
Equating coefficients gives:
$R\cos\alpha = 5$ and $R\sin\alpha = 12$ *[1 mark]*.
$\dfrac{R\sin\alpha}{R\cos\alpha} = \tan\alpha$, so $\tan\alpha = \dfrac{12}{5}$ *[1 mark]*.
Solving this gives $\alpha = 67.38°$ *[1 mark]*.
$R = \sqrt{5^2 + 12^2} = \sqrt{25 + 144} = \sqrt{169} = 13$
[1 mark],
so $5\cos\theta + 12\sin\theta = 13\cos(\theta - 67.38°)$.

b) From part a), if $5\cos\theta + 12\sin\theta = 2$, that means
$13\cos(\theta - 67.38°) = 2$, so:
$\cos(\theta - 67.38°) = \dfrac{2}{13}$ *[1 mark]*.

The range for θ is $0 \le \theta \le 360°$, which becomes
$-67.38° \le \theta - 67.38° \le 292.62°$ *[1 mark]*.

Solving the equation gives
$\theta - 67.38 = 81.15, 278.85$ *[1 mark]*,
so $\theta = 148.53°, 346.23°$ *[1 mark for each value]*.
*You can look at the cos graph to get the second solution
of $\theta - 67.38°$ (or use the CAST diagram).*

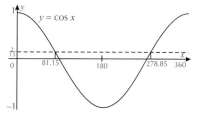

*There are two solutions, one at 81.15°, and the other
at $360 - 81.15 = 278.85°$.*

c) The minimum points of the cos curve have a
value of -1,
so as $5\cos\theta + 12\sin\theta = 13\cos(\theta - 67.38°)$,
the minimum value of $5\cos\theta + 12\sin\theta$ is -13
[1 mark]. Hence the minimum value of
$(5\cos\theta + 12\sin\theta)^3$ is $(-13)^3 = -2197$ *[1 mark]*.

Chapter 3: Coordinate Geometry in the (x, y) Plane

1. Parametric Equations of Curves
Exercise 1.1 — Finding coordinates from parametric equations

Q1 **a)** $x = 3t = 3 \times 5 = 15$
$y = t^2 = 5^2 = 25$
So coordinates are (15, 25).

b) $18 = 3t \Rightarrow t = 6$

c) $36 = t^2 \Rightarrow t = \pm 6 \Rightarrow x = \pm 18$

Q2 **a)** $x = 2t - 1 = (2 \times 7) - 1 = 13$
$y = 4 - t^2 = 4 - 7^2 = -45$
So coordinates are (13, −45).

b) $2t - 1 = 15 \Rightarrow t = 8$

c) $4 - t^2 = -5 \Rightarrow t = \pm 3 \Rightarrow x = -7$ or 5

Q3 **a)** $x = 2 + \sin \theta = 2 + \sin \dfrac{\pi}{4} = \dfrac{4 + \sqrt{2}}{2}$

$y = -3 + \cos \theta = -3 + \cos \dfrac{\pi}{4} = \dfrac{\sqrt{2} - 6}{2}$

So coordinates are $\left(\dfrac{4 + \sqrt{2}}{2}, \dfrac{\sqrt{2} - 6}{2} \right)$.

b) $2 + \sin \theta = \dfrac{4 + \sqrt{3}}{2} = 2 + \dfrac{\sqrt{3}}{2}$
$\Rightarrow \sin \theta = \dfrac{\sqrt{3}}{2} \Rightarrow \theta = \dfrac{\pi}{3}$

c) $-3 + \cos \theta = -\dfrac{7}{2} \Rightarrow \cos \theta = -\dfrac{1}{2} \Rightarrow \theta = \dfrac{2\pi}{3}$

The angle in a) was given in radians so make sure you use radians for b) and c). They're both cos values you should know an angle for off by heart. The cos value in part c) is negative so you can use the CAST diagram (see C2) to figure out which angle you need (cos is negative in the 2nd and 3rd quadrants).

Q4 **a)** $5 \cos 2t = \dfrac{5\sqrt{3}}{2} \Rightarrow \cos 2t = \dfrac{\sqrt{3}}{2}$
You'd normally double the domain when solving for 2t. In this case the domain for t is $0 < t < \dfrac{\pi}{2}$, so $0 < 2t < \pi$. There is only one positive solution for cos in this domain, as given below:
$2t = \dfrac{\pi}{6} \Rightarrow t = \dfrac{\pi}{12}$

b) $3 \sin t = -\dfrac{3\sqrt{3}}{2} \Rightarrow \sin t = -\dfrac{\sqrt{3}}{2}$
There are two values of t in the domain $0 \leq t \leq 2\pi$ that have $\sin t = -\dfrac{\sqrt{3}}{2}$ — you can find these using the CAST diagram (sin is negative in the 3rd and 4th quadrants).
Since $\sin \dfrac{\pi}{3} = \dfrac{\sqrt{3}}{2}$, then $t = \pi + \dfrac{\pi}{3} = \dfrac{4\pi}{3}$
and $t = 2\pi - \dfrac{\pi}{3} = \dfrac{5\pi}{3}$, are two possible solutions.
There are other possible solutions outside the range $0 \leq t \leq 2\pi$.

Q5

t	−5	−4	−3	−2	−1	0	1	2	3	4	5
x	−25	−20	−15	−10	−5	0	5	10	15	20	25
y	$-\frac{2}{5}$	$-\frac{1}{2}$	$-\frac{2}{3}$	−1	−2	—	2	1	$\frac{2}{3}$	$\frac{1}{2}$	$\frac{2}{5}$

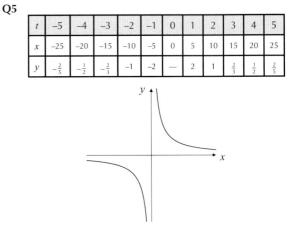

When t = 0, y is undefined, so there must be an asymptote.

Q6

t	−5	−4	−3	−2	−1	0	1	2	3	4	5
x	25	16	9	4	1	0	1	4	9	16	25
y	−4	−3	−2	−1	0	1	2	3	4	5	6

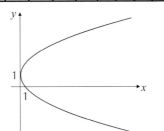

Q7

θ	0	$\frac{\pi}{4}$	$\frac{\pi}{3}$	$\frac{\pi}{2}$	$\frac{2\pi}{3}$	$\frac{3\pi}{4}$	π	$\frac{4\pi}{3}$	$\frac{3\pi}{2}$	$\frac{5\pi}{3}$	2π
x	1	1.71	1.87	2	1.87	1.71	1	0.13	0	0.13	1
y	3	2.71	2.5	2	1.5	1.29	1	1.5	2	2.5	3

Q8

t	0	$\frac{\pi}{4}$	$\frac{\pi}{2}$	$\frac{3\pi}{4}$	π	$\frac{5\pi}{4}$	$\frac{3\pi}{2}$	$\frac{7\pi}{4}$	2π
x	0	2.12	3	2.12	0	−2.12	−3	−2.12	0
y	5	3.54	0	−3.54	−5	−3.54	0	3.54	5

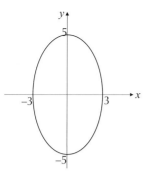

Q9 E.g.

t	−5	−4	−3	−2	−1	0	1	2	3	4	5
x	−6	−5	−4	−3	−2	−1	0	1	2	3	4
y	−9	0	7	12	15	16	15	12	7	0	−9

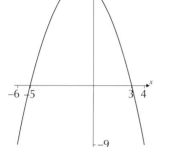

Exercise 1.2 — Finding intersections

Q1 At A: $y = 0 \Rightarrow -2 + t = 0 \Rightarrow t = 2$
  $x = 3 + t = 3 + 2 = 5$
  At B: $x = 0 \Rightarrow 3 + t = 0 \Rightarrow t = -3$
  $y = -2 + (-3) = -5$
  So the coordinates are A(5, 0) and B(0, −5).

Q2 a) The curve meets the x-axis when $y = 0$, so:
  $3t^3 - 24 = 0$
  $\Rightarrow 3(t^3 - 8) = 0$
  $\Rightarrow t^3 = 8 \Rightarrow t = 2$

  b) The curve meets the y-axis when $x = 0$, so:
  $2t^2 - 50 = 0$
  $\Rightarrow 2(t^2 - 25) = 0$
  $\Rightarrow t^2 = 25 \Rightarrow t = \pm 5$
  If you'd have been asked to give the coordinates you would then just put the t values into the parametric equations.

Q3 The curve meets the y-axis when $x = 0$, so:
  $64 - t^3 = 0 \Rightarrow t^3 = 64 \Rightarrow t = 4$
  $y = \frac{1}{t} = \frac{1}{4}$, so P is $\left(0, \frac{1}{4}\right)$.

Q4 $y = x - 3$
  $\Rightarrow 4t = (2t + 1) - 3$
  $\Rightarrow 2t = -2 \Rightarrow t = -1$
  To find the coordinates when t = −1, just put this value back into the parametric equations...
  $x = (2 \times -1) + 1 = -1$
  $y = 4 \times -1 = -4$
  So P is (−1, −4).

Q5 $y = x^2 + 32$
  $\Rightarrow 6t^2 = (2t)^2 + 32$
  $\Rightarrow 6t^2 = 4t^2 + 32$
  $\Rightarrow 2t^2 = 32$
  $\Rightarrow t^2 = 16 \Rightarrow t = \pm 4$
  When $t = 4$:
  $x = 2 \times 4 = 8$
  $y = 6 \times 4^2 = 96$
  So one point of intersection is (8, 96).
  When $t = -4$:
  $x = 2 \times -4 = -8$
  $y = 6 \times (-4)^2 = 96$
  So the other point of intersection is (−8, 96).

Q6 $x^2 + y^2 = 32$
  $\Rightarrow (t^2)^2 + (2t)^2 = 32$
  $\Rightarrow t^4 + 4t^2 - 32 = 0$
  $\Rightarrow (t^2 - 4)(t^2 + 8) = 0$
  $\Rightarrow t^2 = 4 \Rightarrow t = \pm 2$
  (there are no real solutions to $t^2 = -8$).
  When $t = 2$:
  $x = 2^2 = 4$
  $y = 2 \times 2 = 4$
  So one point of intersection is (4, 4).
  When $t = -2$:
  $x = (-2)^2 = 4$
  $y = 2 \times -2 = -4$
  So the other point of intersection is (4, −4).

Q7 a) At the point (0, 4):
  $x = 0 \Rightarrow a(t - 2) = 0 \Rightarrow t = 2$ (as $a \neq 0$)
  $y = 4 \Rightarrow 2at^2 + 3 = 4 \Rightarrow 2a(2^2) + 3 = 4$
  $\Rightarrow 8a + 3 = 4 \Rightarrow a = \frac{1}{8}$.

  b) The curve would meet the x-axis when $y = 0$.
  $y = 2at^2 + 3 = \frac{2t^2}{8} + 3 = \frac{t^2}{4} + 3$
  So at the x-axis, $\frac{t^2}{4} + 3 = 0 \Rightarrow t^2 = -12$.
  This has no real solutions, so the curve does not meet the x-axis.

Q8 a) The curve crosses the x-axis when $y = 0$.
  $t^2 - 9 = 0 \Rightarrow t = \pm 3$
  When $t = 3$, $x = \frac{2}{3}$, so one point is $\left(\frac{2}{3}, 0\right)$.
  When $t = -3$, $x = -\frac{2}{3}$, so the other point is $\left(-\frac{2}{3}, 0\right)$.

  b) The curve would meet the y-axis when $x = 0$, i.e. when $\frac{2}{t} = 0$. This has no solutions, so the curve does not meet the y-axis.

  c) $y = \frac{10}{x} - 3$
  $\Rightarrow t^2 - 9 = \frac{10t}{2} - 3$
  $\Rightarrow t^2 - 5t - 6 = 0$
  $\Rightarrow (t + 1)(t - 6) = 0$
  $\Rightarrow t = -1$ and $t = 6$
  When $t = -1$:
  $x = -2$
  $y = (-1)^2 - 9 = -8$
  So one point of intersection is (−2, −8).
  When $t = 6$:
  $x = \frac{2}{6} = \frac{1}{3}$
  $y = 6^2 - 9 = 27$
  So the other point of intersection is $\left(\frac{1}{3}, 27\right)$.

Q9 **a)** The curve meets the x-axis when $y = 0$.

$5 \cos t = 0 \Rightarrow \cos t = 0$

$\Rightarrow t = -\frac{3\pi}{2}, -\frac{\pi}{2}, \frac{\pi}{2}$ and $\frac{3\pi}{2}$.

It's easiest to check the symmetry of the cos t graph below to find all these solutions in the domain.

When $t = -\frac{3\pi}{2}$, $x = 3 \sin\left(-\frac{3\pi}{2}\right) = 3$, so $(3, 0)$.

When $t = -\frac{\pi}{2}$, $x = 3 \sin\left(-\frac{\pi}{2}\right) = -3$, so $(-3, 0)$.

When $t = \frac{\pi}{2}$, $x = 3 \sin\left(\frac{\pi}{2}\right) = 3$, so $(3, 0)$.

When $t = \frac{3\pi}{2}$, $x = 3 \sin\left(\frac{3\pi}{2}\right) = -3$, so $(-3, 0)$.

So the curve crosses the x-axis twice in the domain $-2\pi \le t \le 2\pi$, at $(-3, 0)$ and $(3, 0)$.

The curve meets the y-axis when $x = 0$.

$3 \sin t = 0 \Rightarrow \sin t = 0$

$\Rightarrow t = -2\pi, -\pi, 0, \pi$ and 2π.

Again, look at the symmetry of the sin t graph...

When $t = -2\pi$, $y = 5 \cos(-2\pi) = 5$, so $(0, 5)$.

When $t = -\pi$, $y = 5 \cos(-\pi) = -5$, so $(0, -5)$.

When $t = 0$, $y = 5 \cos 0 = 5$, so $(0, 5)$.

When $t = \pi$, $y = 5 \cos \pi = -5$, so $(0, -5)$.

When $t = 2\pi$, $y = 5 \cos 2\pi = 5$, so $(0, 5)$.

So the curve crosses the y-axis twice in the domain $-2\pi \le t \le 2\pi$, at $(0, -5)$ and $(0, 5)$.

b) $y = \left(\frac{5\sqrt{3}}{9}\right)x$

$\Rightarrow 5 \cos t = \left(\frac{5\sqrt{3}}{3}\right)\sin t$

$\Rightarrow \frac{15}{5\sqrt{3}} = \frac{\sin t}{\cos t} = \tan t$

$\Rightarrow \tan t = \frac{3}{\sqrt{3}} = \sqrt{3}$

$\Rightarrow t = \frac{\pi}{3}, \left(\pi + \frac{\pi}{3}\right), \left(\frac{\pi}{3} - \pi\right), \left(\frac{\pi}{3} - 2\pi\right)$

$\Rightarrow t = -\frac{5\pi}{3}, -\frac{2\pi}{3}, \frac{\pi}{3}, \frac{4\pi}{3}$

When $t = -\frac{5\pi}{3}$:

$x = 3 \sin\left(-\frac{5\pi}{3}\right) = \frac{3\sqrt{3}}{2}$

$y = 5 \cos\left(-\frac{5\pi}{3}\right) = \frac{5}{2}$

So one point of intersection is $\left(\frac{3\sqrt{3}}{2}, \frac{5}{2}\right)$.

When $t = -\frac{2\pi}{3}$:

$x = 3 \sin\left(-\frac{2\pi}{3}\right) = -\frac{3\sqrt{3}}{2}$

$y = 5 \cos\left(-\frac{2\pi}{3}\right) = -\frac{5}{2}$

So one point of intersection is $\left(-\frac{3\sqrt{3}}{2}, -\frac{5}{2}\right)$.

When $t = \frac{\pi}{3}$:

$x = 3 \sin\frac{\pi}{3} = \frac{3\sqrt{3}}{2}$

$y = 5 \cos\frac{\pi}{3} = \frac{5}{2}$

So one point of intersection is $\left(\frac{3\sqrt{3}}{2}, \frac{5}{2}\right)$ (already found).

When $t = \frac{4\pi}{3}$:

$x = 3 \sin\frac{4\pi}{3} = -\frac{3\sqrt{3}}{2}$

$y = 5 \cos\frac{4\pi}{3} = -\frac{5}{2}$

So one point of intersection is $\left(-\frac{3\sqrt{3}}{2}, -\frac{5}{2}\right)$ (already found).

In fact there's no need to work out the coordinates of these last two points. Their t-values are 2π away from the t-values of the first two points, so the coordinates will be the same as the ones you've already found. This is because cos and sin have a period of 2π, so $\sin\left(-\frac{5\pi}{3}\right) = \sin\frac{\pi}{3}$ and $\cos\left(-\frac{5\pi}{3}\right) = \cos\frac{\pi}{3}$.

2. Parametric and Cartesian Equations
Exercise 2.1 — Converting parametric equations to Cartesian equations

Q1 **a)** $x = t + 3 \Rightarrow t = x - 3$, so $y = t^2 = (x-3)^2 = x^2 - 6x + 9$
$y = x^2 - 6x + 9$

b) $x = 3t \Rightarrow t = \frac{x}{3}$ so $y = \frac{6}{t} = \frac{18}{x}$
$y = \frac{18}{x}$

c) $x = 2t^3 \Rightarrow t = \left(\frac{x}{2}\right)^{\frac{1}{3}}$, so $y = t^2 = \left(\frac{x}{2}\right)^{\frac{2}{3}}$
$y = \left(\frac{x}{2}\right)^{\frac{2}{3}}$

d) $x = t + 7 \Rightarrow t = x - 7$,
so $y = 12 - 2t = 12 - 2(x - 7) = 26 - 2x$
$y = 26 - 2x$

e) $x = t + 4 \Rightarrow t = x - 4$,
so $y = t^2 - 9 = (x - 4)^2 - 9 = x^2 - 8x + 7$
$y = x^2 - 8x + 7$

f) $x = \sin\theta$, $y = \cos\theta$
Use trig identities here rather than rearranging...
$\sin^2\theta + \cos^2\theta \equiv 1$
$\Rightarrow x^2 + y^2 = 1$

g) $x = 1 + \sin\theta \Rightarrow \sin\theta = x - 1$
$y = 2 + \cos\theta \Rightarrow \cos\theta = y - 2$
$\sin^2\theta + \cos^2\theta \equiv 1 \Rightarrow (x - 1)^2 + (y - 2)^2 = 1$
You can leave this equation in the form it's in — it's the equation of a circle radius 1, centre (1, 2).

h) $x = \sin\theta$, $y = \cos 2\theta$

The 2θ should make you think of the double angle formulae...

$\cos 2\theta \equiv 1 - 2\sin^2\theta \Rightarrow y = 1 - 2x^2$

i) $x = \cos\theta$, $y = \cos 2\theta$

$\cos 2\theta \equiv 2\cos^2\theta - 1 \Rightarrow y = 2x^2 - 1$

j) $x = \cos\theta - 5 \Rightarrow \cos\theta = x + 5$

$y = \cos 2\theta$

$\cos 2\theta \equiv 2\cos^2\theta - 1$

$\Rightarrow y = 2(x + 5)^2 - 1 = 2x^2 + 20x + 49$

$y = 2x^2 + 20x + 49$

Q2 $x = \tan\theta$, $y = \sec\theta$

Using the identity $\sec^2\theta \equiv 1 + \tan^2\theta$ gives:

$y^2 = 1 + x^2$

Q3 $x = 2\cot\theta \Rightarrow \cot\theta = \frac{x}{2}$

$y = 3\,\mathrm{cosec}\,\theta \Rightarrow \mathrm{cosec}\,\theta = \frac{y}{3}$

Using the identity $\mathrm{cosec}^2\theta \equiv 1 + \cot^2\theta$ gives:

$\frac{y^2}{9} = 1 + \frac{x^2}{4} \Rightarrow y^2 = 9 + \frac{9x^2}{4}$

Q4 a) From the parametric equations the centre of the circle is $(5, -3)$, and the radius is 1.

b) $x = 5 + \sin\theta \Rightarrow \sin\theta = x - 5$

$y = -3 + \cos\theta \Rightarrow \cos\theta = y + 3$

Using the identity $\sin^2\theta + \cos^2\theta \equiv 1$ gives:

$(x - 5)^2 + (y + 3)^2 = 1$

Q5 a) $x = \frac{1 + 2t}{t} \Rightarrow xt = 1 + 2t \Rightarrow xt - 2t = 1$

$\Rightarrow t(x - 2) = 1 \Rightarrow t = \frac{1}{(x - 2)}.$

b) $y = \frac{3 + t}{t^2} = \dfrac{3 + \dfrac{1}{(x - 2)}}{\dfrac{1}{(x - 2)^2}} = 3(x - 2)^2 + (x - 2)$

$= 3(x^2 - 4x + 4) + x - 2$

$= 3x^2 - 11x + 10$

$= (3x - 5)(x - 2)$

c)

Q6 $x = \frac{2 - 3t}{1 + t} \Rightarrow x(1 + t) = 2 - 3t \Rightarrow x + xt = 2 - 3t$

$\Rightarrow xt + 3t = 2 - x \Rightarrow t(x + 3) = 2 - x \Rightarrow t = \frac{2 - x}{x + 3}$

$y = \frac{5 - t}{4t + 1} = \dfrac{5 - \left(\dfrac{2 - x}{x + 3}\right)}{4\left(\dfrac{2 - x}{x + 3}\right) + 1} = \frac{5(x + 3) - (2 - x)}{4(2 - x) + (x + 3)}$

$\Rightarrow y = \frac{6x + 13}{11 - 3x}$

You could also write this as $6x - 11y + 3xy + 13 = 0$

Q7 $x = 5\sin^2\theta \Rightarrow \sin^2\theta = \frac{x}{5}$

$y = \cos\theta$

Using the identity $\sin^2\theta + \cos^2\theta \equiv 1$ gives:

$\frac{x}{5} + y^2 = 1 \Rightarrow y^2 = 1 - \frac{x}{5}$

Q8 a) $x = a\sin\theta \Rightarrow \sin\theta = \frac{x}{a}$

$y = b\cos\theta \Rightarrow \cos\theta = \frac{y}{b}$

Using the identity $\sin^2\theta + \cos^2\theta \equiv 1$ gives:

$\left(\frac{x}{a}\right)^2 + \left(\frac{y}{b}\right)^2 = 1$

b) To sketch the graph, find the x- and y-intercepts.

When $x = 0$, $\left(\frac{y}{b}\right)^2 = 1 \Rightarrow y = \pm b$.

When $y = 0$, $\left(\frac{x}{a}\right)^2 = 1 \Rightarrow x = \pm a$.

So the curve looks like this:

c) An ellipse.

If a and b were equal it would be a circle.

Q9 a) $y = 2t - 1 \Rightarrow t = \frac{y + 1}{2}$

$x = 3t^2 = 3\left(\frac{y + 1}{2}\right)^2 = \frac{3}{4}(y + 1)^2$

b) Substitute $y = 4x - 3$ into the equation above:

$x = \frac{3}{4}(4x - 3 + 1)^2$

$4x = 3(4x - 2)^2$

$4x = 3(16x^2 - 16x + 4)$

$4x = 48x^2 - 48x + 12$

$12x^2 - 13x + 3 = 0$

$(3x - 1)(4x - 3) = 0$

$x = \frac{1}{3}$ and $x = \frac{3}{4}$

$y = 4\left(\frac{1}{3}\right) - 3 = -\frac{5}{3}$ and $y = 4\left(\frac{3}{4}\right) - 3 = 0$

So the curve and the line intersect at $\left(\frac{1}{3}, -\frac{5}{3}\right)$ and $\left(\frac{3}{4}, 0\right)$.

Q10 $x = 7t + 2$ $t = \frac{x - 2}{7}$

$y = \frac{5}{t} = \frac{5}{\left(\frac{x - 2}{7}\right)} = \frac{35}{x - 2}$

This is the graph of $y = \frac{1}{x}$ stretched vertically by a factor of 35 and translated right by 2.

The y-intercept is at $x = 0$, so $y = \frac{35}{-2} = -17.5$.

Review Exercise — Chapter 3

Q1 a) $\frac{1}{t} = \frac{1}{4} \Rightarrow t = 4$

$y = \frac{2}{t^2} = \frac{2}{16} = \frac{1}{8}$

b) $\frac{1}{50} = \frac{2}{t^2} \Rightarrow t^2 = 100 \quad t = \pm 10$

Q2 a) Substitute the values of t into the parametric equations to find the corresponding values of x and y:

$t = 0 \Rightarrow x = \frac{6-0}{2} = 3, y = 2(0)^2 + 0 + 4 = 4$

$t = 1 \Rightarrow x = \frac{6-1}{2} = 2.5, y = 2(1)^2 + 1 + 4 = 7$

$t = 2 \Rightarrow x = \frac{6-2}{2} = 2, y = 2(2)^2 + 2 + 4 = 14$

$t = 3 \Rightarrow x = \frac{6-3}{2} = 1.5, y = 2(3)^2 + 3 + 4 = 25$

b) Use the given values in the parametric equations and solve for t:

(i) $\frac{6-t}{2} = -7 \Rightarrow t = 20$

(ii) $2t^2 + t + 4 = 19$
$\Rightarrow 2t^2 + t - 15 = 0$
$\Rightarrow (2t-5)(t+3) = 0$
$\Rightarrow t = 2.5, t = -3$

c) Rearrange the parametric equation for x to make t the subject:

$x = \frac{6-t}{2} \Rightarrow 2x = 6 - t \Rightarrow t = 6 - 2x$

Now substitute this into the parametric equation for y:

$y = 2t^2 + t + 4$
$= 2(6-2x)^2 + (6-2x) + 4$
$= 2(36 - 24x + 4x^2) + 10 - 2x$
$y = 8x^2 - 50x + 82.$

Q3 a) Substitute the values of θ into the parametric equations to find the corresponding values of x and y:

(i) $x = 2\sin\frac{\pi}{4} = \frac{2}{\sqrt{2}} = \sqrt{2}$

$y = \cos^2\frac{\pi}{4} + 4 = \left(\cos\frac{\pi}{4}\right)^2 + 4 = \left(\frac{1}{\sqrt{2}}\right)^2 + 4$
$= \frac{1}{2} + 4 = \frac{9}{2}$

So the coordinates are $\left(\sqrt{2}, \frac{9}{2}\right)$.

(ii) $x = 2\sin\frac{\pi}{6} = 2 \times \frac{1}{2} = 1$

$y = \cos^2\frac{\pi}{6} + 4 = \left(\cos\frac{\pi}{6}\right)^2 + 4 = \left(\frac{\sqrt{3}}{2}\right)^2 + 4$
$= \frac{3}{4} + 4 = \frac{19}{4}$

So the coordinates are $\left(1, \frac{19}{4}\right)$.

b) Use the identity $\cos^2\theta \equiv 1 - \sin^2\theta$ in the equation for y so both equations are in terms of $\sin\theta$:

$y = \cos^2\theta + 4$
$= 1 - \sin^2\theta + 4$
$= 5 - \sin^2\theta$

Rearrange the equation for x to get $\sin^2\theta$ in terms of x:

$x = 2\sin\theta \Rightarrow \frac{x}{2} = \sin\theta \Rightarrow \sin^2\theta = \frac{x^2}{4}$

So $y = 5 - \sin^2\theta \Rightarrow y = 5 - \frac{x^2}{4}$

c) $x = 2\sin\theta$, and $-1 \leq \sin\theta \leq 1$ so $-2 \leq x \leq 2$.

Q4 Use the identity $\cos 2\theta \equiv 1 - 2\sin^2\theta$ in the equation for y:

$y = 3 + 2\cos 2\theta$
$= 3 + 2(1 - 2\sin^2\theta)$
$= 5 - 4\sin^2\theta$

Rearrange the equation for x to get $\sin^2\theta$ in terms of x:

$x = \frac{\sin\theta}{3} \Rightarrow 3x = \sin\theta \Rightarrow \sin^2\theta = 9x^2$

So $y = 5 - 4\sin^2\theta$
$\Rightarrow y = 5 - 4(9x^2)$
$\Rightarrow y = 5 - 36x^2$

Q5 a) On the y-axis:

$x = 0 \Rightarrow t^2 - 1 = 0 \Rightarrow t = \pm 1$

If $t = 1, y = 4 + \frac{3}{1} = 7$

If $t = -1, y = 4 + \frac{3}{-1} = 1$

So the curve crosses the y-axis at $(0, 1)$ and $(0, 7)$.

b) Substitute the parametric equations into the equation of the line:

$x + 2y = 14$
$\Rightarrow (t^2 - 1) + 2(4 + \frac{3}{t}) = 14$
$\Rightarrow t^2 - 1 + 8 + \frac{6}{t} = 14$
$\Rightarrow t^2 - 7 + \frac{6}{t} = 0$
$\Rightarrow t^3 - 7t + 6 = 0$
$\Rightarrow (t-1)(t^2 + t - 6) = 0$
$\Rightarrow (t-1)(t-2)(t+3) = 0$
$\Rightarrow t = 1, t = 2, t = -3$

When $t = 1$, $x = 0$, $y = 7$ (from part (i))

When $t = 2$, $x = 2^2 - 1 = 3$, $y = 4 + \frac{3}{2} = 5.5$

When $t = -3$, $x = (-3)^2 - 1 = 8$,
$$y = 4 + \frac{3}{-3} = 3$$

So the curve crosses the line $x + 2y = 14$ at $(0, 7)$, $(3, 5.5)$ and $(8, 3)$.

Q6 a) Use the x- or y-coordinate of H in the relevant parametric equation to find θ:

At H, $3 + 4\sin\theta = 5$
$\Rightarrow 4\sin\theta = 2$
$\Rightarrow \sin\theta = \frac{1}{2}$
$\Rightarrow \theta = \frac{\pi}{6}$

OR

At H, $\frac{1 + \cos 2\theta}{3} = \frac{1}{2}$
$\Rightarrow 1 + \cos 2\theta = \frac{3}{2}$
$\Rightarrow \cos 2\theta = \frac{1}{2}$
$\Rightarrow 2\theta = \frac{\pi}{3}$
$\Rightarrow \theta = \frac{\pi}{6}$

b) Rearrange the parametric equation for x to make $\sin\theta$ the subject:

$x = 3 + 4\sin\theta \Rightarrow \sin\theta = \frac{x-3}{4}$

Use the identity $\cos 2\theta \equiv 1 - 2\sin^2\theta$ to rewrite the parametric equation for y in terms of $\sin\theta$:

$y = \frac{1 + \cos 2\theta}{3}$
$= \frac{1 + (1 - 2\sin^2\theta)}{3}$
$= \frac{2 - 2\sin^2\theta}{3}$
$= \frac{2}{3}(1 - \sin^2\theta)$

$$= \frac{2}{3}\left(1 - \left(\frac{x-3}{4}\right)^2\right)$$

$$= \frac{2}{3}\left(1 - \frac{(x-3)^2}{16}\right)$$

$$= \frac{2}{3}\left(\frac{16 - (x^2 - 6x + 9)}{16}\right)$$

$$= \frac{2}{3}\left(\frac{-x^2 + 6x + 7}{16}\right)$$

$$= \frac{-x^2 + 6x + 7}{24}$$

c) $-\frac{\pi}{2} \le \theta \le \frac{\pi}{2} \Rightarrow -1 \le \sin\theta \le 1$
$\Rightarrow -4 \le 4\sin\theta \le 4$
$\Rightarrow -1 \le 3 + 4\sin\theta \le 7$
$\Rightarrow -1 \le x \le 7$

Exam-Style Questions — Chapter 3

Q1 a) Substitute the given value of θ into the parametric equations:

$\theta = \frac{\pi}{3} \Rightarrow x = 1 - \tan\frac{\pi}{3} = 1 - \sqrt{3}$

$y = \frac{1}{2}\sin\left(\frac{2\pi}{3}\right) = \frac{1}{2}\left(\frac{\sqrt{3}}{2}\right) = \frac{\sqrt{3}}{4}$

So $P = \left(1 - \sqrt{3}, \frac{\sqrt{3}}{4}\right)$

[2 marks available — 1 mark for substituting
$\theta = \frac{\pi}{3}$ into the parametric equations, 1 mark for
both coordinates of P correct.]

b) Use $y = -\frac{1}{2}$ to find the value of θ:

$-\frac{1}{2} = \frac{1}{2}\sin 2\theta \Rightarrow \sin 2\theta = -1$

$\Rightarrow 2\theta = -\frac{\pi}{2}$

$\Rightarrow \theta = -\frac{\pi}{4}$

You can also find θ using the parametric equation for x,
with x = 2.
[2 marks available — 1 mark for substituting
given x- or y-value into the correct parametric
equation, 1 mark for finding the correct value
of θ.]

c) $x = 1 - \tan\theta \Rightarrow \tan\theta = 1 - x$

$y = \frac{1}{2}\sin 2\theta$

$= \frac{1}{2}\left(\frac{2\tan\theta}{1 + \tan^2\theta}\right)$

$= \frac{\tan\theta}{1 + \tan^2\theta}$

$= \frac{(1-x)}{1 + (1-x)^2}$

$= \frac{1-x}{1 + 1 - 2x + x^2}$

$= \frac{1-x}{x^2 - 2x + 2}$

[3 marks available — 1 mark for using the given
identity to rearrange one of the parametric
equations, 1 mark for eliminating θ from the
parametric equation for y, 1 mark for correctly
expanding to give the Cartesian equation given
in the question.]

Q2 a) Substitute $y = 1$ into the parametric equation for y:
$t^2 - 2t + 2 = 1$
$\Rightarrow t^2 - 2t + 1 = 0$
$\Rightarrow (t-1)^2 = 0$
$\Rightarrow t = 1$ *[1 mark]*
So a is the value of x when $t = 1$.
$a = t^3 + t = 1^3 + 1 = 2$ *[1 mark]*

b) Substitute the parametric equations for x and y into the equation of the line:
$8y = x + 6$
$\Rightarrow 8(t^2 - 2t + 2) = (t^3 + t) + 6$ *[1 mark]*
$\Rightarrow 8t^2 - 16t + 16 = t^3 + t + 6$
$\Rightarrow t^3 - 8t^2 + 17t - 10 = 0$
We know that this line passes through K, and from a) we know that $t = 1$ at K, so $t = 1$ is a solution of this equation, and $(t - 1)$ is a factor:
$\Rightarrow (t-1)(t^2 - 7t + 10) = 0$ *[1 mark]*
$\Rightarrow (t-1)(t-2)(t-5) = 0$
So $t = 2$ at L and $t = 5$ at M. *[1 mark]*
Substitute $t = 2$ and $t = 5$ back into the parametric equations: *[1 mark]*
If $t = 2$, then $x = 2^3 + 2 = 10$
and $y = 2^2 - 2(2) + 2 = 2$
If $t = 5$, then $x = 5^3 + 5 = 130$
and $y = 5^2 - 2(5) + 2 = 17$
So $L = (10, 2)$ *[1 mark]*
and $M = (130, 17)$ *[1 mark]*

Q3 a) Substitute $t = 0.5$ into the parametric equations for x and y:
$x = t^3 = 0.5^3 = 0.125$ *[1 mark]*
$y = t^2 - 4 = 0.5^2 - 4 = -3.75$ *[1 mark]*.
So the coordinates of F are $(0.125, -3.75)$.

b) First, put the parametric equations into the equation of the line and rearrange:
$3(t^2 - 4) = 2(t^3) - 11$
$3t^2 - 12 = 2t^3 - 11 \Rightarrow 2t^3 - 3t^2 + 1 = 0$. *[1 mark]*
Now solve for t: Putting $t = 1$ into the equation gives 0, so 1 is a root.
This means that $(t - 1)$ is a factor *[1 mark]*.
$(t-1)(2t^2 - t - 1) = 0 \Rightarrow (t-1)(2t+1)(t-1) = 0$.
So $t = 1$ *[1 mark]* and $t = -0.5$ *[1 mark]*
(ignore the repeated root).
Putting these values of t back into the parametric equations gives the coordinates $(1, -3)$ *[1 mark]*
and $(-0.125, -3.75)$ *[1 mark]*.

Chapter 4:
Sequences and Series

1. The Binomial Expansion
Exercise 1.1 — Expansions where n is a positive integer

Q1 $(1 + x)^3 = 1 + 3x + \dfrac{3(3-1)}{1 \times 2}x^2 + \dfrac{3(3-1)(3-2)}{1 \times 2 \times 3}x^3$

$= 1 + 3x + 3x^2 + x^3$

Q2 $(1 + x)^7 = 1 + 7x + \dfrac{7(7-1)}{1 \times 2}x^2 + \dfrac{7(7-1)(7-2)}{1 \times 2 \times 3}x^3 + ...$

$= 1 + 7x + 21x^2 + 35x^3 + ...$

This isn't the full expansion, so keep the dots at the end to show it carries on.

Q3 $(1 - x)^4 = 1 + 4(-x) + \dfrac{4(4-1)}{1 \times 2}(-x)^2$

$+ \dfrac{4(4-1)(4-2)}{1 \times 2 \times 3}(-x)^3$

$+ \dfrac{4(4-1)(4-2)(4-3)}{1 \times 2 \times 3 \times 4}(-x)^4$

$= 1 - 4x + 6x^2 - 4x^3 + x^4$

Q4 $(1 + 3x)^6 = 1 + 6(3x) + \dfrac{6(6-1)}{1 \times 2}(3x)^2 + ...$

$= 1 + 6(3x) + 15(9x^2) + ...$

$= 1 + 18x + 135x^2 + ...$

Q5 $(1 + 2x)^8 = 1 + 8(2x) + \dfrac{8(8-1)}{1 \times 2}(2x)^2$

$+ \dfrac{8(8-1)(8-2)}{1 \times 2 \times 3}(2x)^3 + ...$

$= 1 + 8(2x) + 28(4x^2) + 56(8x^3) + ...$

$= 1 + 16x + 112x^2 + 448x^3 + ...$

Q6 $(1 - 5x)^5 = 1 + 5(-5x) + \dfrac{5(5-1)}{1 \times 2}(-5x)^2 + ...$

$= 1 + 5(-5x) + 10(25x^2) + ...$

$= 1 - 25x + 250x^2 - ...$

Q7 $(1 - 4x)^3 = 1 + 3(-4x) + \dfrac{3(3-1)}{1 \times 2}(-4x)^2$

$+ \dfrac{3(3-1)(3-2)}{1 \times 2 \times 3}(-4x)^3$

$= 1 + 3(-4x) + 3(16x^2) + (-64x^3)$

$= 1 - 12x + 48x^2 - 64x^3$

Q8 $(1 + 6x)^6 = 1 + 6(6x) + \dfrac{6(6-1)}{1 \times 2}(6x)^2$

$+ \dfrac{6(6-1)(6-2)}{1 \times 2 \times 3}(6x)^3 + ...$

$= 1 + 6(6x) + 15(36x^2) + 20(216x^3)$

$= 1 + 36x + 540x^2 + 4320x^3 + ...$

Exercise 1.2 — Expansions where n is negative or a fraction

Q1 $(1 + x)^{-4} = 1 + (-4)x + \dfrac{-4(-4-1)}{1 \times 2}x^2$

$+ \dfrac{-4(-4-1)(-4-2)}{1 \times 2 \times 3}x^3 + ...$

$= 1 + (-4)x + \dfrac{-4 \times -5}{2}x^2$

$+ \dfrac{-4 \times -5 \times -6}{6}x^3 + ...$

$= 1 - 4x + 10x^2 - 20x^3 + ...$

Q2 a) $(1 - 6x)^{-3} = 1 + (-3)(-6x) + \dfrac{-3(-3-1)}{1 \times 2}(-6x)^2$

$+ \dfrac{-3(-3-1)(-3-2)}{1 \times 2 \times 3}(-6x)^3 + ...$

$= 1 + 18x + \dfrac{-3 \times -4}{2}(36x^2)$

$+ \dfrac{-3 \times -4 \times -5}{6}(-216x^3) + ...$

$= 1 + 18x + 6(36x^2) + (-10)(-216x^3) + ...$

$= 1 + 18x + 216x^2 + 2160x^3 + ...$

b) The expansion is valid for $\left|\dfrac{-6x}{1}\right| < 1$, so $|x| < \dfrac{1}{6}$.

Q3 a) $(1 + 4x)^{\frac{1}{3}} = 1 + \dfrac{1}{3}(4x) + \dfrac{\frac{1}{3}\left(\frac{1}{3}-1\right)}{1 \times 2}(4x)^2 + ...$

$= 1 + \dfrac{1}{3}(4x) + \dfrac{\frac{1}{3} \times -\frac{2}{3}}{2}(16x^2) + ...$

$= 1 + \dfrac{1}{3}(4x) + \left(-\dfrac{1}{9}\right)(16x^2) + ...$

$= 1 + \dfrac{4x}{3} - \dfrac{16x^2}{9} + ...$

b) $(1 + 4x)^{-\frac{1}{2}} = 1 + \left(-\dfrac{1}{2}\right)(4x) + \dfrac{-\frac{1}{2}\left(-\frac{1}{2}-1\right)}{1 \times 2}(4x)^2 + ...$

$= 1 - \dfrac{1}{2}(4x) + \dfrac{-\frac{1}{2} \times -\frac{3}{2}}{2}(16x^2) + ...$

$= 1 - \dfrac{1}{2}(4x) + \left(\dfrac{3}{8}\right)(16x^2) + ...$

$= 1 - 2x + 6x^2 - ...$

c) Both a) and b) are valid for $|x| < \dfrac{1}{4}$.

Q4 a) $\dfrac{1}{(1 - 4x)^2} = (1 - 4x)^{-2}$

$= 1 + (-2)(-4x) + \dfrac{-2(-2-1)}{1 \times 2}(-4x)^2$

$+ \dfrac{-2(-2-1)(-2-2)}{1 \times 2 \times 3}(-4x)^3 + ...$

$= 1 + (-2)(-4x) + \dfrac{-2 \times -3}{2}(16x^2)$

$+ \dfrac{-2 \times -3 \times -4}{6}(-64x^3) + ...$

$= 1 + 8x + 3(16x^2) + (-4)(-64x^3) + ...$

$= 1 + 8x + 48x^2 + 256x^3 + ...$

b) $\sqrt{1 + 6x} = (1 + 6x)^{\frac{1}{2}}$

$= 1 + \dfrac{1}{2}(6x) + \dfrac{\frac{1}{2}\left(\frac{1}{2}-1\right)}{1 \times 2}(6x)^2$

$+ \dfrac{\frac{1}{2}\left(\frac{1}{2}-1\right)\left(\frac{1}{2}-2\right)}{1 \times 2 \times 3}(6x)^3 + ...$

$= 1 + \dfrac{1}{2}(6x) + \dfrac{\frac{1}{2} \times -\frac{1}{2}}{2}(36x^2)$

$$+ \frac{\frac{1}{2} \times -\frac{1}{2} \times -\frac{3}{2}}{6}(216x^3) + ...$$

$$= 1 + \frac{1}{2}(6x) + \left(-\frac{1}{8}\right)(36x^2) + \frac{1}{16}(216x^3) + ...$$

$$= 1 + 3x - \frac{9x^2}{2} + \frac{27x^3}{2} - ...$$

c) $\dfrac{1}{\sqrt{1-3x}} = (1-3x)^{-\frac{1}{2}}$

$$= 1 + \left(-\frac{1}{2}\right)(-3x) + \frac{-\frac{1}{2}\left(-\frac{1}{2}-1\right)}{1 \times 2}(-3x)^2$$

$$+ \frac{-\frac{1}{2}\left(-\frac{1}{2}-1\right)\left(-\frac{1}{2}-2\right)}{1 \times 2 \times 3}(-3x)^3 + ...$$

$$= 1 + \left(-\frac{1}{2}\right)(-3x) + \frac{-\frac{1}{2} \times -\frac{3}{2}}{2}(9x^2)$$

$$+ \frac{-\frac{1}{2} \times -\frac{3}{2} \times -\frac{5}{2}}{6}(-27x^3) + ...$$

$$= 1 + \frac{3x}{2} + \frac{3}{8}(9x^2) + \left(-\frac{5}{16}\right)(-27x^3) + ...$$

$$= 1 + \frac{3x}{2} + \frac{27x^2}{8} + \frac{135x^3}{16} + ...$$

d) $\sqrt[3]{1 + \dfrac{x}{2}} = \left(1 + \dfrac{1}{2}x\right)^{\frac{1}{3}}$

$$= 1 + \frac{1}{3}\left(\frac{x}{2}\right) + \frac{\frac{1}{3}\left(\frac{1}{3}-1\right)}{1 \times 2}\left(\frac{x}{2}\right)^2$$

$$+ \frac{\frac{1}{3}\left(\frac{1}{3}-1\right)\left(\frac{1}{3}-2\right)}{1 \times 2 \times 3}\left(\frac{x}{2}\right)^3 ...$$

$$= 1 + \frac{1}{3}\left(\frac{x}{2}\right) + \frac{\frac{1}{3} \times -\frac{2}{3}}{2}\left(\frac{x}{2}\right)^2$$

$$+ \frac{\frac{1}{3} \times -\frac{2}{3} \times -\frac{5}{3}}{6}\left(\frac{x}{2}\right)^3 ...$$

$$= 1 + \frac{1}{3}\left(\frac{x}{2}\right) + \left(-\frac{1}{9}\right)\left(\frac{x}{2}\right)^2 + \frac{5}{81}\left(\frac{x}{2}\right)^3 ...$$

$$= 1 + \frac{x}{6} - \frac{x^2}{36} + \frac{5x^3}{648} ...$$

Q5 a) $\dfrac{1}{(1+7x)^4} = (1+7x)^{-4}$

The x^3 term is $\dfrac{-4(-4-1)(-4-2)}{1 \times 2 \times 3}(7x)^3$

$$= \frac{-4 \times -5 \times -6}{6}(343x^3)$$

$$= -20(343x^3) = -6860x^3$$

So the coefficient of the x^3 term is –6860.

b) The expansion is valid for $|x| < \dfrac{1}{7}$.

Q6 a) $\sqrt[4]{1-4x} = (1-4x)^{\frac{1}{4}}$

The x^5 term is :

$$\frac{\frac{1}{4}\left(\frac{1}{4}-1\right)\left(\frac{1}{4}-2\right)\left(\frac{1}{4}-3\right)\left(\frac{1}{4}-4\right)}{1 \times 2 \times 3 \times 4 \times 5}(-4x)^5$$

$$= \frac{\frac{1}{4} \times -\frac{3}{4} \times -\frac{7}{4} \times -\frac{11}{4} \times -\frac{15}{4}}{120}(-4)^5 x^5$$

$$= \frac{1 \times -3 \times -7 \times -11 \times -15}{120} \times \left(\frac{-4}{4}\right)^5 \times x^5$$

$$= \frac{3465}{120} \times -1 \times x^5 = -\frac{231x^5}{8}$$

So the coefficient of the x^5 term is $-\dfrac{231}{8}$.

b) The expansion is valid for $|x| < \dfrac{1}{4}$.

Q7 a) $(1-5x)^{\frac{1}{6}} = 1 + \dfrac{1}{6}(-5x) + \dfrac{\frac{1}{6}\left(\frac{1}{6}-1\right)}{1 \times 2}(-5x)^2 + ...$

$$= 1 + \frac{1}{6}(-5x) + \frac{\frac{1}{6} \times -\frac{5}{6}}{2}(25x^2) + ...$$

$$= 1 - \frac{5x}{6} + \left(-\frac{5}{72}\right)(25x^2) + ...$$

$$= 1 - \frac{5x}{6} - \frac{125x^2}{72} - ...$$

b) $(1+4x)^4 = 1 + 16x + 96x^2 + ...$

So $(1+4x)^4(1-5x)^{\frac{1}{6}}$

$$= (1 + 16x + 96x^2 + ...)\left(1 - \frac{5x}{6} - \frac{125x^2}{72} + ...\right)$$

$$= 1(1 + 16x + 96x^2) - \frac{5x}{6}(1 + 16x) - \frac{125x^2}{72}(1) + ...$$

$$= 1 + 16x + 96x^2 - \frac{5x}{6} - \frac{40x^2}{3} - \frac{125x^2}{72} + ...$$

$$= 1 + \frac{91x}{6} + \frac{5827x^2}{72} + ...$$

c) The expansion of $(1-5x)^{\frac{1}{6}}$ is valid for $|x| < \dfrac{1}{5}$.

The expansion of $(1+4x)^4$ is valid for all values of x, since n is a positive integer.

So overall, the expansion of $(1+4x)^4(1-5x)^{\frac{1}{6}}$ is valid for the narrower of these ranges, i.e. $|x| < \dfrac{1}{5}$.

Q8 a) $\dfrac{(1+3x)^4}{(1+x)^3} = (1+3x)^4(1+x)^{-3}$

$(1+3x)^4 = 1 + 12x + 54x^2 + ...$

$(1+x)^{-3} = 1 - 3x + 6x^2 - ...$

So $(1+3x)^4(1+x)^{-3}$

$$= 1 - 3x + 6x^2 + [12x(1-3x)] + 54x^2 + ...$$

$$= 1 - 3x + 6x^2 + 12x - 36x^2 + 54x^2 + ...$$

$$= 1 + 9x + 24x^2 + ...$$

b) The expansion of $(1+3x)^4$ is valid for all values of x, since n is a positive integer.

The expansion of $(1+x)^{-3}$ is valid for $|x| < 1$.

So overall, the expansion of $\dfrac{(1+3x)^4}{(1+x)^3}$ is valid for the narrower of these ranges, i.e. $|x| < 1$.

Exercise 1.3 — Expanding $(p + qx)^n$

Q1 a) $(2+4x)^3 = 2^3(1+2x)^3 = 8(1+2x)^3$

$$(1+2x)^3 = 1 + 3(2x) + \frac{3 \times 2}{1 \times 2}(2x)^2 + \frac{3 \times 2 \times 1}{1 \times 2 \times 3}(2x)^3$$

$$= 1 + 6x + 3(4x^2) + 8x^3$$

$$= 1 + 6x + 12x^2 + 8x^3$$

So $(2+4x)^3 = 8(1 + 6x + 12x^2 + 8x^3)$

$$= 8 + 48x + 96x^2 + 64x^3$$

b) $(3+4x)^5 = 3^5\left(1 + \dfrac{4}{3}x\right)^5 = 243\left(1 + \dfrac{4}{3}x\right)^5$

$$\left(1 + \frac{4}{3}x\right)^5 = 1 + 5\left(\frac{4}{3}x\right) + \frac{5 \times 4}{1 \times 2}\left(\frac{4}{3}x\right)^2$$

$$+ \frac{5 \times 4 \times 3}{1 \times 2 \times 3}\left(\frac{4}{3}x\right)^3 + ...$$

$$= 1 + \frac{20x}{3} + \frac{160x^2}{9} + \frac{640x^3}{27} + ...$$

$$(3+4x)^5 = 243\left(1 + \frac{20x}{3} + \frac{160x^2}{9} + \frac{640x^3}{27} + ...\right)$$

$$= 243 + 1620x + 4320x^2 + 5760x^3 + ...$$

c) $(4 + x)^{\frac{1}{2}} = 4^{\frac{1}{2}}\left(1 + \frac{x}{4}\right)^{\frac{1}{2}} = 2\left(1 + \frac{x}{4}\right)^{\frac{1}{2}}$

$\left(1 + \frac{x}{4}\right)^{\frac{1}{2}} = 1 + \frac{1}{2}\left(\frac{x}{4}\right) + \frac{\frac{1}{2} \times -\frac{1}{2}}{1 \times 2}\left(\frac{x}{4}\right)^2$

$\qquad + \frac{\frac{1}{2} \times -\frac{1}{2} \times -\frac{3}{2}}{1 \times 2 \times 3}\left(\frac{x}{4}\right)^3 + \dots$

$\qquad = 1 + \frac{x}{8} - \frac{x^2}{128} + \frac{x^3}{1024} - \dots$

$(4 + x)^{\frac{1}{2}} = 2\left(1 + \frac{x}{4}\right)^{\frac{1}{2}}$

$\qquad = 2(1 + \frac{x}{8} - \frac{x^2}{128} + \frac{x^3}{1024} - \dots)$

$\qquad = 2 + \frac{x}{4} - \frac{x^2}{64} + \frac{x^3}{512} - \dots$

d) $(8 + 2x)^{-\frac{1}{3}} = 8^{-\frac{1}{3}}\left(1 + \frac{2x}{8}\right)^{-\frac{1}{3}} = \frac{1}{2}\left(1 + \frac{x}{4}\right)^{-\frac{1}{3}}$

$\left(1 + \frac{x}{4}\right)^{-\frac{1}{3}} = 1 + \left(-\frac{1}{3}\right)\left(\frac{x}{4}\right) + \frac{-\frac{1}{3} \times -\frac{4}{3}}{1 \times 2}\left(\frac{x}{4}\right)^2$

$\qquad + \frac{-\frac{1}{3} \times -\frac{4}{3} \times -\frac{7}{3}}{1 \times 2 \times 3}\left(\frac{x}{4}\right)^3 + \dots$

$\qquad = 1 - \frac{x}{12} + \frac{x^2}{72} - \frac{7x^3}{2592} + \dots$

$(8 + 2x)^{-\frac{1}{3}} = \frac{1}{2}\left(1 + \frac{x}{4}\right)^{-\frac{1}{3}}$

$\qquad = \frac{1}{2}(1 - \frac{x}{12} + \frac{x^2}{72} - \frac{7x^3}{2592} + \dots)$

$\qquad = \frac{1}{2} - \frac{x}{24} + \frac{x^2}{144} - \frac{7x^3}{5184} + \dots)$

Q2 $(a + 5x)^5 = a^5\left(1 + \frac{5}{a}x\right)^5$

So the x^2 term is:

$a^5\left(\frac{5 \times 4}{1 \times 2}\right)\left(\frac{5}{a}x\right)^2 = 10a^5\left(\frac{25}{a^2}x^2\right) = \left(\frac{250a^5}{a^2}\right)x^2 = 250a^3x^2$

So $250a^3 = 2000 \Rightarrow a^3 = 8 \Rightarrow a = 2$.

Q3 a) $(2 - 5x)^7 = 2^7\left(1 - \frac{5}{2}x\right)^7 = 128\left(1 - \frac{5}{2}x\right)^7$

$\left(1 - \frac{5}{2}x\right)^7 = 1 + 7\left(-\frac{5}{2}x\right) + \frac{7 \times 6}{1 \times 2}\left(-\frac{5}{2}x\right)^2 + \dots$

$\qquad = 1 - \frac{35x}{2} + \frac{525x^2}{4} - \dots$

$(2 - 5x)^7 = 128(1 - \frac{35x}{2} + \frac{525x^2}{4} - \dots)$

$\qquad = 128 - 2240x + 16800x^2 - \dots$

b) $(1 + 6x)^3 = 1 + 18x + 108x^2 + \dots$

So $(1 + 6x)^3(2 - 5x)^7 =$

$128 - 2240x + 16800x^2 + 18x(128 - 2240x)$

$\qquad\qquad\qquad\qquad\qquad + 108x^2(128) + \dots$

$\qquad = 128 + 64x - 9696x^2 + \dots$

Q4 a) $\left(1 + \frac{6}{5}x\right)^{-\frac{1}{2}} = 1 + \left(-\frac{1}{2}\right)\left(\frac{6}{5}x\right)$

$\qquad + \frac{\left(-\frac{1}{2}\right) \times \left(-\frac{3}{2}\right)}{1 \times 2}\left(\frac{6}{5}x\right)^2$

$\qquad + \frac{\left(-\frac{1}{2}\right) \times \left(-\frac{3}{2}\right) \times \left(-\frac{5}{2}\right)}{1 \times 2 \times 3}\left(\frac{6}{5}x\right)^3 + \dots$

$\qquad = 1 - \frac{3x}{5} + \frac{27x^2}{50} - \frac{27x^3}{50} + \dots$

The expansion is valid for $\left|\frac{6x}{5}\right| < 1$, so $|x| < \frac{5}{6}$.

b) $\sqrt{\frac{20}{5 + 6x}} = \frac{\sqrt{20}}{\sqrt{5 + 6x}} = 20^{\frac{1}{2}}(5 + 6x)^{-\frac{1}{2}}$

$\qquad = (20^{\frac{1}{2}})(5^{-\frac{1}{2}})\left(1 + \frac{6}{5}x\right)^{-\frac{1}{2}}$

$\qquad = \left(\frac{20^{\frac{1}{2}}}{5^{\frac{1}{2}}}\right)\left(1 + \frac{6}{5}x\right)^{-\frac{1}{2}}$

$\qquad = \left(\frac{20}{5}\right)^{\frac{1}{2}}\left(1 + \frac{6}{5}x\right)^{-\frac{1}{2}}$

$\qquad = 4^{\frac{1}{2}}\left(1 + \frac{6}{5}x\right)^{-\frac{1}{2}}$

$\qquad = 2\left(1 + \frac{6}{5}x\right)^{-\frac{1}{2}}$

So, using the expansion in part a):

$\sqrt{\frac{20}{5 + 6x}} = 2(1 - \frac{3x}{5} + \frac{27x^2}{50} - \frac{27x^3}{50} + \dots)$

$\qquad = 2 - \frac{6x}{5} + \frac{27x^2}{25} - \frac{27x^3}{25} + \dots$

Q5 a) $\frac{1}{\sqrt{5 - 2x}} = (5 - 2x)^{-\frac{1}{2}} = 5^{-\frac{1}{2}}\left(1 - \frac{2}{5}x\right)^{-\frac{1}{2}}$

$\left(1 - \frac{2}{5}x\right)^{-\frac{1}{2}} = 1 + \left(-\frac{1}{2}\right)\left(-\frac{2}{5}x\right)$

$\qquad + \frac{\left(-\frac{1}{2}\right) \times \left(-\frac{3}{2}\right)}{1 \times 2}\left(-\frac{2}{5}x\right)^2 + \dots$

$\qquad = 1 + \frac{x}{5} + \left(\frac{3}{8}\right)\left(\frac{4}{25}x^2\right) + \dots$

$\qquad = 1 + \frac{x}{5} + \frac{3x^2}{50} + \dots$

So $\frac{1}{\sqrt{5 - 2x}} = 5^{-\frac{1}{2}}\left(1 - \frac{2}{5}x\right)^{-\frac{1}{2}}$

$\qquad = \frac{1}{\sqrt{5}}(1 + \frac{x}{5} + \frac{3x^2}{50} \dots)$

$\qquad = \frac{1}{\sqrt{5}} + \frac{x}{5\sqrt{5}} + \frac{3x^2}{50\sqrt{5}} + \dots$

b) $\frac{3 + x}{\sqrt{5 - 2x}} \approx (3 + x)\left(\frac{1}{\sqrt{5}} + \frac{x}{5\sqrt{5}} + \frac{3x^2}{50\sqrt{5}}\right)$

$\qquad \approx 3\left(\frac{1}{\sqrt{5}} + \frac{x}{5\sqrt{5}} + \frac{3x^2}{50\sqrt{5}}\right)$

$\qquad\qquad\qquad\qquad + x\left(\frac{1}{\sqrt{5}} + \frac{x}{5\sqrt{5}}\right)$

$\qquad = \frac{3}{\sqrt{5}} + \frac{3x}{5\sqrt{5}} + \frac{9x^2}{50\sqrt{5}} + \frac{x}{\sqrt{5}} + \frac{x^2}{5\sqrt{5}}$

$\qquad = \frac{3}{\sqrt{5}} + \frac{8x}{5\sqrt{5}} + \frac{19x^2}{50\sqrt{5}}$

Q6 a) $(9 + 4x)^{-\frac{1}{2}} = 9^{-\frac{1}{2}}\left(1 + \frac{4}{9}x\right)^{-\frac{1}{2}}$

$\left(1 + \frac{4}{9}x\right)^{-\frac{1}{2}} = 1 + \left(-\frac{1}{2}\right)\left(\frac{4}{9}x\right)$

$\qquad + \frac{\left(-\frac{1}{2}\right) \times \left(-\frac{3}{2}\right)}{1 \times 2}\left(\frac{4}{9}x\right)^2 + \dots$

$\qquad = 1 - \frac{2x}{9} + \frac{2x^2}{27} - \dots$

So $(9 + 4x)^{-\frac{1}{2}} = \frac{1}{\sqrt{9}}\left(1 - \frac{2x}{9} + \frac{2x^2}{27} - \dots\right)$

$\qquad = \frac{1}{3} - \frac{2x}{27} + \frac{2x^2}{81} - \dots$

b) $(1 + 6x)^4 = 1 + 24x + 216x^2 + \dots$

So $\dfrac{(1 + 6x)^4}{\sqrt{9 + 4x}} = (1 + 6x)^4(9 + 4x)^{-\frac{1}{2}}$

$\approx (1 + 24x + 216x^2)\left(\dfrac{1}{3} - \dfrac{2x}{27} + \dfrac{2x^2}{81}\right)$

$\approx \dfrac{1}{3} - \dfrac{2x}{27} + \dfrac{2x^2}{81} + 24x\left(\dfrac{1}{3} - \dfrac{2x}{27}\right) + 216x^2\left(\dfrac{1}{3}\right)$

$= \dfrac{1}{3} - \dfrac{2x}{27} + \dfrac{2x^2}{81} + 8x - \dfrac{16x^2}{9} + 72x^2$

$= \dfrac{1}{3} + \dfrac{214x}{27} + \dfrac{5690x^2}{81}$

2. Using the Binomial Expansion as an Approximation

Exercise 2.1 — Approximating with binomial expansions

Q1 a) $(1 + 6x)^{-1} = 1 + (-1)(6x) + \dfrac{-1 \times -2}{1 \times 2}(6x)^2 + \dots$

$= 1 - 6x + 36x^2 - \dots$

b) The expansion is valid if $|x| < \dfrac{1}{6}$.

c) $\dfrac{100}{106} = \dfrac{1}{1.06} = \dfrac{1}{1 + 0.06} = (1 + 0.06)^{-1}$

This is the same as $(1 + 6x)^{-1}$ with $x = 0.01$.

$0.01 < \dfrac{1}{6}$ so the approximation is valid.

$(1 + 6(0.01))^{-1} \approx 1 - 6(0.01) + 36(0.01^2)$

$= 1 - 0.06 + 0.0036 = 0.9436$

d) $\left|\dfrac{\left(\dfrac{100}{106}\right) - 0.9436}{\left(\dfrac{100}{106}\right)}\right| \times 100 = 0.02 \text{ \% (to 1 s.f.)}$

In the answers that follow, the expansions will just be stated. Look back at the previous sections of this chapter to check how to set out the working if you need to.

Q2 a) $(1 + 3x)^{\frac{1}{4}} = 1 + \dfrac{3x}{4} - \dfrac{27x^2}{32} + \dfrac{189x^3}{128} - \dots$

b) The expansion is valid if $|x| < \dfrac{1}{3}$.

c) $\sqrt[4]{1.9} = 1.9^{\frac{1}{4}} = (1 + 0.9)^{\frac{1}{4}}$

This is the same as $(1 + 3x)^{\frac{1}{4}}$ with $x = 0.3$.

$0.3 < \dfrac{1}{3}$ so the approximation is valid.

$(1 + 3(0.3))^{\frac{1}{4}} \approx 1 + \dfrac{3(0.3)}{4} - \dfrac{27(0.3^2)}{32} + \dfrac{189(0.3^3)}{128}$

$= 1.1889 \text{ (to 4 d.p.)}$

d) $\left|\dfrac{(\sqrt[4]{1.9}) - 1.1889}{(\sqrt[4]{1.9})}\right| \times 100 = 1.26\% \text{ (to 3 s.f.)}$

Q3 a) $(1 - 2x)^{-\frac{1}{2}} = 1 + x + \dfrac{3x^2}{2} + \dfrac{5x^3}{2} + \dots$

b) The expansion is valid if $|x| < \dfrac{1}{2}$.

c) Using $x = \dfrac{1}{10}$ gives:

$\left(1 - \dfrac{2}{10}\right)^{-\frac{1}{2}} \approx 1 + \dfrac{1}{10} + \dfrac{3}{200} + \dfrac{5}{2000}$

$\left(\dfrac{4}{5}\right)^{-\frac{1}{2}} \approx 1 + 0.1 + 0.015 + 0.0025$

$\left(\dfrac{5}{4}\right)^{\frac{1}{2}} \approx 1.1175$

$\sqrt{\dfrac{5}{4}} \approx 1.1175$

$\dfrac{\sqrt{5}}{\sqrt{4}} \approx 1.1175$

$\dfrac{\sqrt{5}}{2} \approx 1.1175$

$\sqrt{5} \approx 2 \times 1.1175 = 2.235$

d) $\left|\dfrac{\sqrt{5} - 2.235}{\sqrt{5}}\right| \times 100 = 0.048\% \text{ (to 2 s.f.)}$

Q4 a) $(2 - 5x)^6 = 2^6\left(1 - \dfrac{5}{2}x\right)^6$

$= 64\left(1 - 15x + \dfrac{375x^2}{4} - \dots\right)$

$= 64 - 960x + 6000x^2 - \dots$

b) $1.95^6 = (2 - 0.05)^6$

This is the same as $(2 - 5x)^6$ with $x = 0.01$.

$(2 - 5(0.01))^6 \approx 64 - 960(0.01) + 6000(0.01)^2$

$= 64 - 9.6 + 0.6 = 55$

c) $\left|\dfrac{1.95^6 - 55}{1.95^6}\right| \times 100 = 0.036\% \text{ (to 2 s.f.)}$

Q5 a) $\sqrt{3 - 4x} = (3 - 4x)^{\frac{1}{2}} = \sqrt{3}\left(1 - \dfrac{4}{3}x\right)^{\frac{1}{2}}$

$= \sqrt{3}\left(1 - \dfrac{2x}{3} - \dfrac{2x^2}{9} - \dfrac{4x^3}{27} - \dots\right)$

$= \sqrt{3} - \dfrac{2\sqrt{3}x}{3} - \dfrac{2\sqrt{3}x^2}{9} - \dfrac{4\sqrt{3}x^3}{27} - \dots$

Remember to factorise the original expression to get it in the form $(1 + ax)^n$.

b) The expansion is valid if $|x| < \dfrac{3}{4}$.

c) $\sqrt{3 - 4\left(\dfrac{9}{20}\right)}$

$\approx \sqrt{3} - \dfrac{2\sqrt{3}}{3}\left(\dfrac{9}{20}\right) - \dfrac{2\sqrt{3}}{9}\left(\dfrac{9}{20}\right)^2 - \dfrac{4\sqrt{3}}{27}\left(\dfrac{9}{20}\right)^3$

$\sqrt{3 - \dfrac{18}{10}} \approx \sqrt{3}\left(1 - \dfrac{3}{10} - \dfrac{9}{200} - \dfrac{27}{2000}\right)$

$\sqrt{\dfrac{12}{10}} \approx \dfrac{1283\sqrt{3}}{2000}$

$\dfrac{2\sqrt{3}}{\sqrt{10}} \approx \dfrac{1283\sqrt{3}}{2000}$

$\dfrac{2}{\sqrt{10}} \approx \dfrac{1283}{2000}$

d) $\left|\dfrac{\dfrac{2}{\sqrt{10}} - \dfrac{1283}{2000}}{\dfrac{2}{\sqrt{10}}}\right| \times 100 = 1.43\% \text{ (to 3 s.f.)}$

3. Binomial Expansion and Partial Fractions

Exercise 3.1 — Finding binomial expansions using partial fractions

Q1 a) $5 - 12x \equiv A(4 + 3x) + B(1 + 6x)$

Using the substitution method:

Let $x = -\dfrac{4}{3}$, then $5 + 16 = -7B \Rightarrow B = -3$.

Let $x = -\dfrac{1}{6}$, then $5 + 2 = \dfrac{7A}{2} \Rightarrow A = 2$.

You could also use the 'equating coefficients' method if you prefer.

b) (i) $(1 + 6x)^{-1} = 1 - 6x + 36x^2 - \dots$

(ii) $(4 + 3x)^{-1} = 4^{-1}\left(1 + \frac{3}{4}x\right)^{-1}$

$\qquad = \frac{1}{4}\left(1 - \frac{3x}{4} + \frac{9x^2}{16} - \dots\right)$

$\qquad = \frac{1}{4} - \frac{3x}{16} + \frac{9x^2}{64} - \dots$

c) From a):

$\dfrac{5 - 12x}{(1 + 6x)(4 + 3x)} \equiv \dfrac{2}{(1 + 6x)} - \dfrac{3}{(4 + 3x)}$

$\qquad\qquad\qquad \equiv 2(1 + 6x)^{-1} - 3(4 + 3x)^{-1}$

$2(1 + 6x)^{-1} - 3(4 + 3x)^{-1} \approx$

$2(1 - 6x + 36x^2) - 3\left(\frac{1}{4} - \frac{3x}{16} + \frac{9x^2}{64}\right)$

$= 2 - 12x + 72x^2 - \frac{3}{4} + \frac{9x}{16} - \frac{27x^2}{64}$

$= \frac{5}{4} - \frac{183x}{16} + \frac{4581x^2}{64}$

d) $(1 + 6x)^{-1}$ is valid if $|x| < \frac{1}{6}$.

$(4 + 3x)^{-1}$ is valid if $|x| < \frac{4}{3}$.

So the full expansion is valid if $|x| < \frac{1}{6}$.

Q2 a) $\dfrac{60x^2 + 5x + 7}{(4 - 3x)(1 + 4x)^2} \equiv$

$\qquad \dfrac{A}{(4 - 3x)} + \dfrac{B}{(1 + 4x)} + \dfrac{C}{(1 + 4x)^2}$

$60x^2 + 5x + 7 \equiv$

$\qquad A(1 + 4x)^2 + B(4 - 3x)(1 + 4x) + C(4 - 3x)$

Equating coefficients:
x^2 terms: $60 = 16A - 12B$
x terms: $5 = 8A + 13B - 3C$
constant terms: $7 = A + 4B + 4C$

Solving simultaneously gives:
$A = 3$, $B = -1$, $C = 2$.

Putting these values back into the expression gives:

$\dfrac{60x^2 + 5x + 7}{(4 - 3x)(1 + 4x)^2} \equiv$

$\qquad \dfrac{3}{(4 - 3x)} - \dfrac{1}{(1 + 4x)} + \dfrac{2}{(1 + 4x)^2}$

b) f(x) can also be expressed as:
$3(4 - 3x)^{-1} - (1 + 4x)^{-1} + 2(1 + 4x)^{-2}$
Expanding these three parts separately:
$(4 - 3x)^{-1} = 4^{-1}\left(1 - \frac{3}{4}x\right)^{-1}$

$\qquad = \frac{1}{4}\left(1 + \frac{3x}{4} + \frac{9x^2}{16} + \dots\right)$

$\qquad = \frac{1}{4} + \frac{3x}{16} + \frac{9x^2}{64} + \dots$

$(1 + 4x)^{-1} = 1 - 4x + 16x^2 + \dots$

$(1 + 4x)^{-2} = 1 - 8x + 48x^2 + \dots$

So $f(x) \approx 3\left(\frac{1}{4} + \frac{3x}{16} + \frac{9x^2}{64}\right) - (1 - 4x + 16x^2)$

$\qquad\qquad\qquad\qquad + 2(1 - 8x + 48x^2)$

$= \frac{3}{4} + \frac{9x}{16} + \frac{27x^2}{64} - 1 + 4x - 16x^2 + 2 - 16x + 96x^2$

$= \frac{7}{4} - \frac{183x}{16} + \frac{5147x^2}{64}$

c) $f(0.01) = \dfrac{60(0.01^2) + 5(0.01) + 7}{(4 - 3(0.01))(1 + 4(0.01))^2} = 1.64324\dots$

From the expansion:

$f(0.01) \approx \dfrac{7}{4} - \dfrac{183(0.01)}{16} + \dfrac{5147(0.01^2)}{64}$

$\qquad\quad = 1.64367$ (to 5 d.p.)

So the % error is:

$\left|\dfrac{1.64324 - 1.64367}{1.64324}\right| \times 100 = 0.026\%$ (to 2 s.f.)

Q3 a) $6x^3 + 11x^2 + 4x = x(3x + 4)(2x + 1)$

b) $\dfrac{22x^2 + 40x + 12}{6x^3 + 11x^2 + 4x} \equiv \dfrac{22x^2 + 40x + 12}{x(3x + 4)(2x + 1)}$

$\qquad\qquad \equiv \dfrac{A}{x} + \dfrac{B}{(3x + 4)} + \dfrac{C}{(2x + 1)}$

$22x^2 + 40x + 12 \equiv A(3x + 4)(2x + 1) + Bx(2x + 1)$
$\qquad\qquad\qquad\qquad\qquad + Cx(3x + 4)$

Equating coefficients:
constant terms: $12 = 4A \Rightarrow A = 3$
x^2 terms: $22 = 18 + 2B + 3C \Rightarrow 4 = 2B + 3C$
x terms: $40 = 33 + B + 4C \Rightarrow 7 = B + 4C$
Solving simultaneously gives: $B = -1$ and $C = 2$.

So $\dfrac{22x^2 + 40x + 12}{6x^3 + 11x^2 + 4x} \equiv \dfrac{3}{x} - \dfrac{1}{(3x + 4)} + \dfrac{2}{(2x + 1)}$

c) $(3x + 4)^{-1} = (4 + 3x)^{-1} = \frac{1}{4} - \frac{3x}{16} + \frac{9x^2}{64} + \dots$
This expansion has been done in question 1.
$(2x + 1)^{-1} = (1 + 2x)^{-1} = 1 - 2x + 4x^2 + \dots$

$\dfrac{22x^2 + 40x + 12}{6x^3 + 11x^2 + 4x} \equiv \dfrac{3}{x} - (3x + 4)^{-1} + 2(2x + 1)^{-1}$

$\approx \dfrac{3}{x} - \left(\dfrac{1}{4} - \dfrac{3x}{16} + \dfrac{9x^2}{64}\right) + 2(1 - 2x + 4x^2)$

$= \dfrac{3}{x} - \dfrac{1}{4} + \dfrac{3x}{16} - \dfrac{9x^2}{64} + 2 - 4x + 8x^2$

$= \dfrac{3}{x} + \dfrac{7}{4} - \dfrac{61x}{16} + \dfrac{503x^2}{64}$

d) $(3x + 4)^{-1}$ is valid if $|x| < \frac{4}{3}$.

$(2x + 1)^{-1}$ is valid if $|x| < \frac{1}{2}$.

$\dfrac{3}{x}$ is valid for $x \neq 0$.

So the full expansion is valid if $|x| < \frac{1}{2}$ and $x \neq 0$.
Make sure you don't get caught out here — the brackets are in the form $(qx + p)^n$, not $(p + qx)^n$.

Q4 a) $\dfrac{12x^2 - 27x - 33}{(3x + 1)(2x - 5)} = \dfrac{12x^2 - 27x - 33}{6x^2 - 13x - 5}$

Dividing gives:

$\qquad\qquad\qquad\quad 2$
$6x^2 - 13x - 5\overline{\smash{\big)}12x^2 - 27x - 33}$
$\qquad\qquad\quad\underline{-(12x^2 - 26x - 10)}$
$\qquad\qquad\qquad\qquad\quad -x - 23$

i.e. $2 + \dfrac{-x - 23}{6x^2 - 13x - 5}$ or $2 + \dfrac{-x - 23}{(3x + 1)(2x - 5)}$

So $A = 2$.
Splitting the rest into partial fractions and multiplying out the denominator gives:
$-x - 23 \equiv B(2x - 5) + C(3x + 1)$

Equating coefficients:
constant terms: $-23 = C - 5B$
x terms: $-1 = 2B + 3C$
Solving simultaneously gives: $B = 4$ and $C = -3$.
Putting these values into the partial fractions:

$$f(x) = 2 + \left(\frac{B}{(3x + 1)} + \frac{C}{(2x - 5)}\right)$$

$$= 2 + \frac{4}{(3x + 1)} - \frac{3}{(2x - 5)}$$

b) $(3x + 1)^{-1} = 1 - 3x + 9x^2 + \dots$

$$(2x - 5)^{-1} = -\frac{1}{5}\left(1 - \frac{2}{5}x\right)^{-1}$$

$$= -\frac{1}{5}\left(1 + \frac{2x}{5} + \frac{4x^2}{25} + \dots\right)$$

$$= -\frac{1}{5} - \frac{2x}{25} - \frac{4x^2}{125} - \dots$$

$$f(x) = 2 + 4(3x + 1)^{-1} - 3(2x - 5)^{-1}$$

$$\approx 2 + 4(1 - 3x + 9x^2) - 3\left(-\frac{1}{5} - \frac{2x}{25} - \frac{4x^2}{125}\right)$$

$$= 2 + 4 - 12x + 36x^2 + \frac{3}{5} + \frac{6x}{25} + \frac{12x^2}{125}$$

$$= \frac{33}{5} - \frac{294x}{25} + \frac{4512x^2}{125}$$

Review Exercise — Chapter 4

Q1 a) $(1 + 2x)^3$

$$= 1 + 3(2x) + \frac{3 \times 2}{1 \times 2}(2x)^2 + \frac{3 \times 2 \times 1}{1 \times 2 \times 3}(2x)^3$$

$$= 1 + 6x + 12x^2 + 8x^3$$

b) $(1 - x)^5 = 1 + 5(-x) + \frac{5 \times 4}{1 \times 2}(-x)^2 + \frac{5 \times 4 \times 3}{1 \times 2 \times 3}(-x)^3$

$$+ \frac{5 \times 4 \times 3 \times 2}{1 \times 2 \times 3 \times 4}(-x)^4 + \frac{5 \times 4 \times 3 \times 2 \times 1}{1 \times 2 \times 3 \times 4 \times 5}(-x)^5$$

$$= 1 - 5x + 10x^2 - 10x^3 + 5x^4 - x^5$$

c) $(1 - 4x)^4 = 1 + 4(-4x) + \frac{4 \times 3}{1 \times 2}(-4x)^2$

$$+ \frac{4 \times 3 \times 2}{1 \times 2 \times 3}(-4x)^3 + \frac{4 \times 3 \times 2 \times 1}{1 \times 2 \times 3 \times 4}(-4x)^4$$

$$= 1 - 16x + 96x^2 - 256x^3 + 256x^4$$

Be careful with terms like $(-4x)^2$ — remember to square everything in the brackets (the x, the 4 and the minus).

Q2 Positive integer values (and zero).

Q3 a) The x^2 term for $(1 + ax)^7$ is:

$$\left(\frac{7 \times 6}{1 \times 2}\right)(ax)^2 = 21a^2x^2$$

So $21a^2 = 189 \Rightarrow a^2 = 9 \Rightarrow a = 3$.
You're told that a is a positive integer, so take the positive root.

b) The x^4 term for $(1 - ax)^6$ is:

$$\left(\frac{6 \times 5 \times 4 \times 3}{1 \times 2 \times 3 \times 4}\right)(-ax)^4 = 15a^4x^4$$

So $15a^4 = 240 \Rightarrow a^4 = 16 \Rightarrow a = 2$.
Again, you're told that a is positive, so take the positive root.

Q4 $\left|\frac{dx}{c}\right| < 1$ (or $|x| < \left|\frac{c}{d}\right|$)

Q5 a) $(1 + x)^{-5} = 1 + (-5)x + \frac{-5 \times -6}{1 \times 2}x^2$

$$+ \frac{-5 \times -6 \times -7}{1 \times 2 \times 3}x^3 + \dots$$

$$= 1 - 5x + 15x^2 - 35x^3 + \dots$$

b) $(1 - 3x)^{-3} = 1 + (-3)(-3x) + \frac{-3 \times -4}{1 \times 2}(-3x)^2$

$$+ \frac{-3 \times -4 \times -5}{1 \times 2 \times 3}(-3x)^3 + \dots$$

$$= 1 + 9x + 54x^2 + 270x^3 + \dots$$

c) $(1 - 5x)^{\frac{1}{2}} = 1 + \frac{1}{2}(-5x) + \frac{\frac{1}{2} \times -\frac{1}{2}}{1 \times 2}(-5x)^2$

$$+ \frac{\frac{1}{2} \times -\frac{1}{2} \times -\frac{3}{2}}{1 \times 2 \times 3}(-5x)^3 + \dots$$

$$= 1 - \frac{5x}{2} - \frac{25x^2}{8} - \frac{125x^3}{16} + \dots$$

Q6 Q5 a): expansion valid for $|x| < 1$.

Q5 b): expansion valid for $|-3x| < 1 \Rightarrow |x| < \frac{1}{3}$

Q5 c): expansion valid for $|-5x| < 1 \Rightarrow |x| < \frac{1}{5}$

Q7 a) (i) $(3 + 2x)^{-2} = \left(3\left(1 + \frac{2}{3}x\right)\right)^{-2} = \frac{1}{9}\left(1 + \frac{2}{3}x\right)^{-2}$

$$\approx \frac{1}{9}\left(1 + (-2)\left(\frac{2}{3}x\right) + \frac{-2 \times -3}{1 \times 2}\left(\frac{2}{3}x\right)^2\right)$$

$$= \frac{1}{9}\left(1 - \frac{4}{3}x + \frac{4}{3}x^2\right)$$

$$= \frac{1}{9} - \frac{4}{27}x + \frac{4}{27}x^2$$

This expansion is valid for $\left|\frac{2x}{3}\right| < 1 \Rightarrow |x| < \frac{3}{2}$.

(ii) $(8 - x)^{\frac{1}{3}} = \left(8\left(1 - \frac{1}{8}x\right)\right)^{\frac{1}{3}} = 2\left(1 - \frac{1}{8}x\right)^{\frac{1}{3}}$

$$\approx 2\left(1 + \frac{1}{3}\left(-\frac{1}{8}x\right) + \frac{\frac{1}{3} \times -\frac{2}{3}}{1 \times 2}\left(-\frac{1}{8}x\right)^2\right)$$

$$= 2\left(1 - \frac{1}{24}x - \frac{1}{576}x^2\right)$$

$$= 2 - \frac{1}{12}x - \frac{1}{288}x^2$$

This expansion is valid for $\left|\frac{-x}{8}\right| < 1 \Rightarrow |x| < 8$.

b) $\frac{\sqrt[3]{8 - x}}{(3 + 2x)^2} = (8 - x)^{\frac{1}{3}}(3 + 2x)^{-2}$

$$\approx \left(2 - \frac{1}{12}x - \frac{1}{288}x^2\right)\left(\frac{1}{9} - \frac{4}{27}x + \frac{4}{27}x^2\right)$$

$$= 2\left(\frac{1}{9} - \frac{4}{27}x + \frac{4}{27}x^2\right) -$$

$$\frac{1}{12}x\left(\frac{1}{9} - \frac{4}{27}x\right) - \frac{1}{288}x^2\left(\frac{1}{9}\right)$$

$$= \frac{2}{9} - \frac{8x}{27} + \frac{8x^2}{27} - \frac{x}{108} + \frac{x^2}{81} - \frac{x^2}{2592}$$

$$= \frac{2}{9} - \frac{11x}{36} + \frac{799x^2}{2592}$$

The combined expansion is valid for the smaller of the individual valid ranges, i.e. $|x| < \frac{3}{2}$.

c) (i) $\sqrt[3]{8 - x} \approx 2 - \frac{1}{12}x - \frac{1}{288}x^2$

To find an approximation to $\sqrt[3]{7}$ use $x = 1$.
The validity for this expansion is $|x| < 8$ so you're fine to use $x = 1$.

$$\sqrt[3]{7} \approx 2 - \frac{1}{12} - \frac{1}{288} = \frac{551}{288}$$

(ii) The % error is:

$$\left|\frac{\sqrt[3]{7} - \frac{551}{288}}{\sqrt[3]{7}}\right| \times 100 = 0.014\% \text{ (to 2 s.f.)}$$

Q8 a) Write as an identity:

$$\frac{5 - 10x}{(1 + 2x)(2 - x)} \equiv \frac{A}{(1 + 2x)} + \frac{B}{(2 - x)}$$

So $5 - 10x \equiv A(2 - x) + B(1 + 2x)$

Let $x = 2$, then $5 - 20 = 5B \Rightarrow B = -3$

Let $x = -0.5$, then $5 + 5 = 2.5A \Rightarrow A = 4$

So $\dfrac{5 - 10x}{(1 + 2x)(2 - x)} \equiv \dfrac{4}{(1 + 2x)} - \dfrac{3}{(2 - x)}$

b) $(1 + 2x)^{-1} \approx 1 - 2x + 4x^2$

$(2 - x)^{-1} = 2^{-1}\left(1 - \frac{1}{2}x\right)^{-1} = \frac{1}{2}\left(1 - \frac{1}{2}x\right)^{-1}$

$\approx \frac{1}{2}\left(1 + \frac{1}{2}x + \frac{1}{4}x^2\right)$

$= \frac{1}{2} + \frac{x}{4} + \frac{x^2}{8}$

Using the result from a), this means that:

$\dfrac{5 - 10x}{(1 + 2x)(2 - x)} \approx 4(1 - 2x + 4x^2) - 3\left(\frac{1}{2} + \frac{x}{4} + \frac{x^2}{8}\right)$

$\approx 4 - 8x + 16x^2 - \frac{3}{2} - \frac{3x}{4} - \frac{3x^2}{8}$

$\approx \frac{5}{2} - \frac{35x}{4} + \frac{125x^2}{8}$

c) First, check that $x = 0.1$ is valid for the expansion.

$(1 + 2x)^{-1}$ is valid when $|x| < \frac{1}{2}$.

$(2 - x)^{-1}$ is valid when $|x| < 2$.

$x = 0.1$ is within both of these ranges so it is valid for the combined expansion.

Putting $x = 0.1$ into both sides of the expansion gives:

$\dfrac{5 - 10(0.1)}{(1 + 2(0.1))(2 - (0.1))} \approx \dfrac{5}{2} - \dfrac{35(0.1)}{4} + \dfrac{125(0.01)}{8}$

$\dfrac{5 - 1}{(1 + 0.2)(2 - 0.1)} \approx \dfrac{5}{2} - \dfrac{3.5}{4} + \dfrac{1.25}{8}$

$\dfrac{4}{1.2 \times 1.9} \approx 2.5 - 0.875 + 0.15625$

≈ 1.78125

So the % error when using this approximation is:

$$\left| \frac{\left(\frac{4}{1.2 \times 1.9}\right) - 1.78125}{\left(\frac{4}{1.2 \times 1.9}\right)} \right| \times 100 = 1.5\% \text{ (to 2 s.f.)}$$

Exam-Style Questions — Chapter 4

Q1 a) $f(x) = (9 - 4x)^{-\frac{1}{2}} = (9)^{-\frac{1}{2}}\left(1 - \frac{4}{9}x\right)^{-\frac{1}{2}} = \frac{1}{3}\left(1 - \frac{4}{9}x\right)^{-\frac{1}{2}}$

$\left(1 - \frac{4}{9}x\right)^{-\frac{1}{2}} = 1 + \left(-\frac{1}{2}\right)\left(-\frac{4}{9}x\right)$

$+ \left(\dfrac{-\frac{1}{2} \times -\frac{3}{2}}{1 \times 2}\right)\left(-\frac{4}{9}x\right)^2$

$+ \left(\dfrac{-\frac{1}{2} \times -\frac{3}{2} \times -\frac{5}{2}}{1 \times 2 \times 3}\right)\left(-\frac{4}{9}x\right)^3 + \dots$

$= 1 + \frac{2x}{9} + \left(\frac{3}{8}\right)\left(\frac{16}{81}x^2\right)$

$+ \left(-\frac{5}{16}\right)\left(-\frac{64}{729}x^3\right) + \dots$

$= 1 + \frac{2x}{9} + \frac{2x^2}{27} + \frac{20x^3}{729} + \dots$

So $f(x) = \frac{1}{3}\left(1 - \frac{4}{9}x\right)^{-\frac{1}{2}}$

$= \frac{1}{3}\left(1 + \frac{2x}{9} + \frac{2x^2}{27} + \frac{20x^3}{729} + \dots\right)$

$= \frac{1}{3} + \frac{2x}{27} + \frac{2x^2}{81} + \frac{20x^3}{2187} + \dots$

[5 marks available in total:

- *1 mark for factorising out $(9)^{-\frac{1}{2}}$ or $\frac{1}{3}$*
- *1 mark for expansion of an expression of the form $(1 + ax)^{-\frac{1}{2}}$*
- *2 marks for the penultimate line of working — 1 for the first two terms in brackets correct, 1 for the 3rd and 4th terms in brackets correct.*
- *1 mark for the final answer correct]*

Multiplying out those coefficients can be pretty tricky. Don't try to do things all in one go — you won't be penalised for writing an extra line of working, but you probably will lose marks if your final answer's wrong.

b) $\dfrac{2 - x}{\sqrt{(9 - 4x)}} = (2 - x)\left(\frac{1}{3} + \frac{2x}{27} + \frac{2x^2}{81} + \frac{20x^3}{2187} + \dots\right)$

You only need the first three terms of the expansion, so just write the terms up to x^2 when you multiply out the brackets:

$\dfrac{2 - x}{\sqrt{(9 - 4x)}} \approx 2\left(\frac{1}{3} + \frac{2x}{27} + \frac{2x^2}{81}\right) - x\left(\frac{1}{3} + \frac{2x}{27}\right)$

$= \frac{2}{3} + \frac{4x}{27} + \frac{4x^2}{81} - \frac{x}{3} - \frac{2x^2}{27}$

$= \frac{2}{3} - \frac{5x}{27} - \frac{2x^2}{81}$

[4 marks available in total:

- *1 mark for multiplying your answer to part (a) by $(2 - x)$*
- *1 mark for multiplying out brackets to find constant term, two x-terms and two x^2-terms*
- *1 mark for correct constant and x-terms in final answer*
- *1 mark for correct x^2-term in final answer]*

Q2 a) $36x^2 + 3x - 10 \equiv$

$A(1 - 3x)^2 + B(4 + 3x)(1 - 3x) + C(4 + 3x)$ *[1 mark]*

Let $x = \frac{1}{3}$, then:

$4 + 1 - 10 = 5C \Rightarrow -5 = 5C \Rightarrow C = -1$ *[1 mark]*

Let $x = -\frac{4}{3}$, then:

$64 - 4 - 10 = 25A \Rightarrow 50 = 25A \Rightarrow A = 2$ *[1 mark]*

Equating the coefficients of the x^2 terms:

$36 = 9A - 9B = 18 - 9B \Rightarrow -18 = 9B \Rightarrow B = -2$

[1 mark]

b) $f(x) = \dfrac{2}{(4 + 3x)} - \dfrac{2}{(1 - 3x)} - \dfrac{1}{(1 - 3x)^2}$

$= 2(4 + 3x)^{-1} - 2(1 - 3x)^{-1} - (1 - 3x)^{-2}$

Expand each bracket separately:

$(4 + 3x)^{-1} = 4^{-1}\left(1 + \frac{3}{4}x\right)^{-1} = \frac{1}{4}\left(1 + \frac{3}{4}x\right)^{-1}$

$= \frac{1}{4}\left(1 + (-1)\left(\frac{3}{4}x\right) + \frac{-1 \times -2}{1 \times 2}\left(\frac{3}{4}x\right)^2 + \dots\right)$

$= \frac{1}{4}\left(1 - \frac{3}{4}x + \frac{9}{16}x^2 + \dots\right) = \frac{1}{4} - \frac{3x}{16} + \frac{9x^2}{64} + \dots$

$(1 - 3x)^{-1} = 1 + (-1)(-3x) + \dfrac{-1 \times -2}{1 \times 2}(-3x)^2 + ...$

$\qquad\qquad = 1 + 3x + 9x^2 + ...$

$(1 - 3x)^{-2} = 1 + (-2)(-3x) + \dfrac{-2 \times -3}{1 \times 2}(-3x)^2 + ...$

$\qquad\qquad = 1 + 6x + 27x^2 + ...$

Putting it all together gives:

$f(x) \approx 2\left(\dfrac{1}{4} - \dfrac{3x}{16} + \dfrac{9x^2}{64}\right) - 2(1 + 3x + 9x^2)$
$\qquad\qquad\qquad\qquad\qquad - (1 + 6x + 27x^2)$

$f(x) \approx \dfrac{1}{2} - \dfrac{3x}{8} + \dfrac{9x^2}{32} - 2 - 6x - 18x^2 - 1 - 6x - 27x^2$

$\qquad = -\dfrac{5}{2} - \dfrac{99x}{8} - \dfrac{1431x^2}{32}$

[6 marks available in total:
- *1 mark for rewriting f(x) in the form*
  A(4 + 3x)$^{-1}$ + B(1 − 3x)$^{-1}$ + C(1 − 3x)$^{-2}$
- *1 mark for correct expansion of (4 + 3x)$^{-1}$*
- *1 mark for correct expansion of (1 − 3x)$^{-1}$*
- *1 mark for correct expansion of (1 − 3x)$^{-2}$*
- *1 mark for correct constant and x-terms*
  in final answer
- *1 mark for correct x^2-term in final answer]*

c) Expansion of $(4 + 3x)^{-1}$ is valid for

$\left|\dfrac{3x}{4}\right| < 1 \Rightarrow \dfrac{3|x|}{4} < 1 \Rightarrow |x| < \dfrac{4}{3}$

Expansions of $(1 - 3x)^{-1}$ and $(1 - 3x)^{-2}$ are valid for

$\left|\dfrac{-3x}{1}\right| < 1 \Rightarrow \dfrac{|-3||x|}{1} < 1 \Rightarrow |x| < \dfrac{1}{3}$

The combined expansion is valid for the narrower of these two ranges.

So the expansion of f(x) is valid for $|x| < \dfrac{1}{3}$.

[2 marks available in total:
- *1 mark for identifying the valid range of the*
  expansion of f(x) as being the narrower of the
  two valid ranges shown
- *1 mark for correct answer]*

Q3 a) $(16 + 3x)^{\frac{1}{4}} = 16^{\frac{1}{4}}\left(1 + \dfrac{3}{16}x\right)^{\frac{1}{4}} = 2\left(1 + \dfrac{3}{16}x\right)^{\frac{1}{4}}$

$\approx 2\left[1 + \left(\dfrac{1}{4}\right)\left(\dfrac{3}{16}x\right) + \dfrac{\frac{1}{4} \times -\frac{3}{4}}{1 \times 2}\left(\dfrac{3}{16}x\right)^2\right]$

$= 2\left[1 + \left(\dfrac{1}{4}\right)\left(\dfrac{3}{16}x\right) + \left(-\dfrac{3}{32}\right)\left(\dfrac{9}{256}x^2\right)\right]$

$= 2\left(1 + \dfrac{3x}{64} - \dfrac{27x^2}{8192}\right)$

$= 2 + \dfrac{3x}{32} - \dfrac{27x^2}{4096}$

[5 marks available in total:
- *1 mark for factorising out 16$^{\frac{1}{4}}$ or 2*
- *1 mark for expansion of an expression of the*
  form (1 + ax)$^{\frac{1}{4}}$
- *2 marks for the penultimate line of working —*
  1 for the first two terms in brackets correct,
  1 for the 3rd term in brackets correct.
- *1 mark for the final answer correct]*

b) (i) $16 + 3x = 12.4 \Rightarrow x = -1.2$

This lies within $|x| < \dfrac{16}{3}$, so it's a valid approximation.

So $(12.4)^{\frac{1}{4}} \approx 2 + \dfrac{3}{32}(-1.2) - \dfrac{27}{4096}(-1.2)^2$

$= 2 - 0.1125 - 0.0094921875$

$= 1.878008$ (to 6 d.p.)

[2 marks available in total:
- *1 mark for substituting x = −1.2 into*
  the expansion from part (a)
- *1 mark for correct answer]*

(ii) Percentage error

$= \left|\dfrac{\text{real value} - \text{estimate}}{\text{real value}}\right| \times 100$

$= \left|\dfrac{\sqrt[4]{12.4} - 1.878008}{\sqrt[4]{12.4}}\right| \times 100$ *[1 mark]*

$= \dfrac{|1.876529... - 1.878008|}{1.876529...} \times 100$

$= 0.0788\%$ (to 3 s.f.)   *[1 mark]*

Q4 a) $\left(1 - \dfrac{4}{3}x\right)^{-\frac{1}{2}}$

$\approx 1 + \left(-\dfrac{1}{2}\right)\left(-\dfrac{4}{3}x\right) + \dfrac{-\frac{1}{2} \times -\frac{3}{2}}{1 \times 2}\left(-\dfrac{4}{3}x\right)^2$

$\qquad\qquad + \dfrac{-\frac{1}{2} \times -\frac{3}{2} \times -\frac{5}{2}}{1 \times 2 \times 3}\left(-\dfrac{4}{3}x\right)^3$

$= 1 + \dfrac{2x}{3} + \dfrac{3}{8}\left(\dfrac{16}{9}x^2\right) + \left(-\dfrac{15}{48}\right)\left(-\dfrac{64}{27}x^3\right)$

$= 1 + \dfrac{2x}{3} + \dfrac{2x^2}{3} + \dfrac{20x^3}{27}$

[4 marks available in total:
- *1 mark for writing out binomial expansion*
  formula with n = $-\dfrac{1}{2}$
- *1 mark for writing out binomial expansion*
  formula substituting $-\dfrac{4}{3}x$ for x
- *1 mark for correct constant and x-terms in*
  final answer
- *1 mark for correct x^2- and x^3-terms in*
  final answer]

b) $\sqrt{\dfrac{27}{(3 - 4x)}} = \sqrt{\dfrac{27}{3\left(1 - \frac{4}{3}x\right)}} = \sqrt{\dfrac{9}{\left(1 - \frac{4}{3}x\right)}}$

$= \dfrac{3}{\sqrt{\left(1 - \frac{4}{3}x\right)}}$

$= 3\left(1 - \dfrac{4}{3}x\right)^{-\frac{1}{2}}$

$\approx 3\left(1 + \dfrac{2}{3}x + \dfrac{2}{3}x^2\right)$

$= 3 + 2x + 2x^2$

So $a = 3$, $b = 2$, $c = 2$.

Expansion is valid for:

$\left|-\dfrac{4}{3}x\right| < 1 \Rightarrow \left|-\dfrac{4}{3}\right||x| < 1 \Rightarrow |x| < \dfrac{3}{4}$

[3 marks available in total:
- *1 mark for showing expression is equal to $3\left(1 - \frac{4}{3}x\right)^{-\frac{1}{2}}$*
- *1 mark for using expansion from part (b) to find the correct values of a, b and c.*
- *1 mark for correct valid range]*

Q5 a) (i) $\sqrt{\dfrac{1 + 2x}{1 - 3x}} = \dfrac{\sqrt{1 + 2x}}{\sqrt{1 - 3x}}$

$$= (1 + 2x)^{\frac{1}{2}}(1 - 3x)^{-\frac{1}{2}} \quad \textit{[1 mark]}$$

$$(1 + 2x)^{\frac{1}{2}} \approx 1 + \frac{1}{2}(2x) + \frac{\frac{1}{2} \times -\frac{1}{2}}{1 \times 2}(2x)^2$$

$$= 1 + x - \frac{x^2}{2} \quad \textit{[1 mark]}$$

$$(1 - 3x)^{-\frac{1}{2}}$$

$$\approx 1 + \left(-\frac{1}{2}\right)(-3x) + \frac{-\frac{1}{2} \times -\frac{3}{2}}{1 \times 2}(-3x)^2$$

$$= 1 + \frac{3x}{2} + \frac{27x^2}{8} \quad \textit{[1 mark]}$$

$$\sqrt{\frac{1 + 2x}{1 - 3x}} \approx \left(1 + x - \frac{x^2}{2}\right)\left(1 + \frac{3x}{2} + \frac{27x^2}{8}\right)$$
[1 mark]

$$\approx 1 + \frac{3x}{2} + \frac{27x^2}{8} + x + \frac{3x^2}{2} - \frac{x^2}{2}$$
(ignoring any terms in x^3 or above)

$$= 1 + \frac{5x}{2} + \frac{35x^2}{8} \quad \textit{[1 mark]}$$

(ii) Expansion of $(1 + 2x)^{\frac{1}{2}}$ is valid for:

$$|2x| < 1 \Rightarrow |x| < \frac{1}{2}.$$

Expansion of $(1 - 3x)^{-\frac{1}{2}}$ is valid for:

$$|-3x| < 1 \Rightarrow |-3||x| < 1 \Rightarrow |x| < \frac{1}{3}.$$

The combined expansion is valid for the narrower of these two ranges.

So the expansion of $\sqrt{\dfrac{1 + 2x}{1 - 3x}}$ is valid for:

$$|x| < \frac{1}{3}.$$

[2 marks available in total:
- *1 mark for identifying the valid range of the expansion as being the narrower of the two valid ranges shown*
- *1 mark for correct answer]*

b) $x = \dfrac{2}{15} \Rightarrow$

$$\sqrt{\frac{1 + 2x}{1 - 3x}} = \sqrt{\frac{1 + \frac{4}{15}}{1 - \frac{6}{15}}}$$

$$= \sqrt{\frac{\left(\frac{19}{15}\right)}{\left(\frac{9}{15}\right)}} = \sqrt{\frac{19}{9}} = \frac{1}{3}\sqrt{19} \quad \textit{[1 mark]}$$

$$\sqrt{19} \approx 3\left(1 + \frac{5}{2}\left(\frac{2}{15}\right) + \frac{35}{8}\left(\frac{2}{15}\right)^2\right)$$

$$= 3\left(1 + \frac{1}{3} + \frac{7}{90}\right)$$

$$= 3\left(\frac{127}{90}\right)$$

$$= \frac{127}{30} \quad \textit{[1 mark]}$$

Q6 a) $13x - 17 \equiv A(2x - 1) + B(5 - 3x)$ *[1 mark]*

Let $x = \frac{1}{2}$, then:

$$\frac{13}{2} - 17 = B\left(5 - \frac{3}{2}\right) \Rightarrow -\frac{21}{2} = \frac{7}{2}B \Rightarrow B = -3$$
[1 mark]

Let $x = \frac{5}{3}$, then:

$$\frac{65}{3} - 17 = A\left(\frac{10}{3} - 1\right) \Rightarrow \frac{14}{3} = \frac{7}{3}A \Rightarrow A = 2$$
[1 mark]

b) (i) $(2x - 1)^{-1} = -(1 - 2x)^{-1}$ *[1 mark]*

$$\approx -\left(1 + (-1)(-2x) + \frac{-1 \times -2}{1 \times 2}(-2x)^2\right)$$

$$= -(1 + 2x + 4x^2)$$

$$= -1 - 2x - 4x^2 \quad \textit{[1 mark]}$$

(ii) $(5 - 3x)^{-1} = 5^{-1}\left(1 - \frac{3}{5}x\right)^{-1} = \frac{1}{5}\left(1 - \frac{3}{5}x\right)^{-1}$

$$\approx \frac{1}{5}\left(1 + (-1)\left(-\frac{3}{5}x\right) + \frac{-1 \times -2}{1 \times 2}\left(-\frac{3}{5}x\right)^2\right)$$

$$= \frac{1}{5}\left(1 + \frac{3}{5}x + \frac{9}{25}x^2\right)$$

$$= \frac{1}{5} + \frac{3x}{25} + \frac{9x^2}{125}$$

[5 marks available in total:
- *1 mark for factorising out 5^{-1} or $\frac{1}{5}$*
- *1 mark for expansion of an expression of the form $(1 + ax)^{-1}$*
- *2 marks for the penultimate line of working — 1 mark for the first two terms in brackets correct, 1 mark for the 3rd term in brackets correct.*
- *1 mark for the final answer correct]*

c) $\dfrac{13x - 17}{(5 - 3x)(2x - 1)} = \dfrac{2}{(5 - 3x)} - \dfrac{3}{(2x - 1)}$

$$= 2(5 - 3x)^{-1} - 3(2x - 1)^{-1} \quad \textit{[1 mark]}$$

$$\approx 2\left(\frac{1}{5} + \frac{3}{25}x + \frac{9}{125}x^2\right) - 3(-1 - 2x - 4x^2)$$

$$= \frac{2}{5} + \frac{6x}{25} + \frac{18x^2}{125} + 3 + 6x + 12x^2$$

$$= \frac{17}{5} + \frac{156x}{25} + \frac{1518x^2}{125} \quad \textit{[1 mark]}$$

Chapter 5: Differentiation and Integration

1. Differentiation with Parametric Equations

Exercise 1.1 — Differentiating parametric equations

Q1 a) $\dfrac{dx}{dt} = 2t$, $\dfrac{dy}{dt} = 3t^2 - 1$.

Using the chain rule, $\dfrac{dy}{dx} = \dfrac{dy}{dt} \div \dfrac{dx}{dt}$

so $\dfrac{dy}{dx} = \dfrac{3t^2 - 1}{2t}$

  b) $\dfrac{dx}{dt} = 3t^2 + 1$, $\dfrac{dy}{dt} = 4t$, so $\dfrac{dy}{dx} = \dfrac{4t}{3t^2 + 1}$

  c) $\dfrac{dx}{dt} = 4t^3$, $\dfrac{dy}{dt} = 3t^2 - 2t$,

so $\dfrac{dy}{dx} = \dfrac{3t^2 - 2t}{4t^3} = \dfrac{3t - 2}{4t^2}$

  d) $\dfrac{dx}{dt} = -\sin t$, $\dfrac{dy}{dt} = 4 - 2t$, so $\dfrac{dy}{dx} = \dfrac{2t - 4}{\sin t}$

Q2 a) $\dfrac{dx}{dt} = 2t$, $\dfrac{dy}{dt} = 2e^{2t}$, so $\dfrac{dy}{dx} = \dfrac{e^{2t}}{t}$

  b) When $t = 1$, $\dfrac{dy}{dx} = e^2$.

Q3 a) $\dfrac{dy}{dt} = 12t^2 - 4t$, $\dfrac{dx}{dt} = 3e^{3t}$, so $\dfrac{dy}{dx} = \dfrac{12t^2 - 4t}{3e^{3t}}$

  b) When $t = 0$, $\dfrac{dy}{dx} = 0$.

Q4 a) $\dfrac{dx}{dt} = 3t^2$, $\dfrac{dy}{dt} = 2t \cos t - t^2 \sin t$,

so $\dfrac{dy}{dx} = \dfrac{2t\cos t - t^2 \sin t}{3t^2} = \dfrac{2\cos t - t\sin t}{3t}$

  b) When $t = \pi$, $\dfrac{dy}{dx} = -\dfrac{2}{3\pi}$

Q5 a) $\dfrac{dx}{dt} = 2t \sin t + t^2 \cos t$,

$\dfrac{dy}{dt} = t^3 \cos t + 3t^2 \sin t - \sin t$,

so $\dfrac{dy}{dx} = \dfrac{t^3 \cos t + (3t^2 - 1)\sin t}{2t\sin t + t^2 \cos t}$

  b) When $t = \pi$, $\dfrac{dy}{dx} = \pi$.

Q6 a) $\dfrac{dx}{dt} = \dfrac{1}{t}$, $\dfrac{dy}{dt} = 6t - 3t^2$, so $\dfrac{dy}{dx} = 6t^2 - 3t^3$

  b) When $t = -1$, $\dfrac{dy}{dx} = 9$.

  c) At the stationary points $6t^2 - 3t^3 = 3t^2(2 - t) = 0$, so the stationary points occur at $t = 0$ and $t = 2$.
At $t = 0$, x is not defined.
At $t = 2$, the coordinates are ($\ln 2$, 4).

Exercise 1.2 — Finding tangents and normals

Q1 $\dfrac{dx}{dt} = 2t$, $\dfrac{dy}{dt} = 3t^2 - 6$.

Using the chain rule, $\dfrac{dy}{dx} = \dfrac{dy}{dt} \div \dfrac{dx}{dt}$,

so $\dfrac{dy}{dx} = \dfrac{3t^2 - 6}{2t}$.

When $t = 3$:

$\dfrac{dy}{dx} = \dfrac{21}{6} = \dfrac{7}{2}$, $x = 3^2 = 9$ and $y = 3^3 - 6(3) = 9$.

Putting this into $y = mx + c$ gives:

$9 = \dfrac{7}{2}(9) + c \Rightarrow c = -\dfrac{45}{2}$

So the equation of the tangent is:

$y = \dfrac{7}{2}x - \dfrac{45}{2} \Rightarrow 7x - 2y - 45 = 0$.

Q2 $\dfrac{dy}{dx} = \dfrac{3t^2 - 2t + 5}{3t^2 - 4t}$

When $t = -1$:

$\dfrac{dy}{dx} = \dfrac{10}{7}$, $x = -3$ and $y = -7$.

Putting this into $y = mx + c$ gives:

$-7 = \dfrac{10}{7}(-3) + c \Rightarrow c = -\dfrac{19}{7}$

So the equation of the tangent is $10x - 7y - 19 = 0$.

Q3 $\dfrac{dy}{dx} = \dfrac{3\cos t - t\sin t}{2\cos 2t}$

When $t = \pi$:

$\dfrac{dy}{dx} = -\dfrac{3}{2}$, $x = 0$ and $y = -\pi$.

The gradient of the normal is $\dfrac{2}{3}$.

Putting this into $y = mx + c$ gives:

$-\pi = \dfrac{2}{3}(0) + c \Rightarrow c = -\pi$

So the equation of the normal is $y = \dfrac{2}{3}x - \pi$.

Q4 $\dfrac{dy}{dx} = \dfrac{3t^2 - 2t}{1 + \ln t}$

When $t = 1$:

$\dfrac{dy}{dx} = \dfrac{3 - 2}{1 + 0} = 1$, $x = 0$ and $y = 3$.

Putting this into $y = mx + c$ gives:

$3 = 0 + c \Rightarrow c = 3$

So the equation of the tangent is: $y = x + 3$

Q5 $\dfrac{dy}{dx} = \dfrac{2\theta + \cos\theta - \theta\sin\theta}{\sin 2\theta + 2\theta\cos 2\theta}$

When $\theta = \dfrac{\pi}{2}$:

$\dfrac{dy}{dx} = -\dfrac{1}{2}$, $x = 0$ and $y = \dfrac{\pi^2}{4}$.

The gradient of the normal is 2.

Putting this into $y = mx + c$ gives:

$\dfrac{\pi^2}{4} = 2(0) + c \Rightarrow c = \dfrac{\pi^2}{4}$

So the equation of the normal is $y = 2x + \dfrac{\pi^2}{4}$.

Q6 a) $\dfrac{dy}{dx} = \dfrac{3 - 3t^2}{2t - 1}$

When $t = 2$:

$\dfrac{dy}{dx} = -3$, $x = 2$ and $y = -2$.

Putting this into $y = mx + c$ gives:

$-2 = -3(2) + c \Rightarrow c = 4$

So the equation of the tangent is $y = 4 - 3x$.

b) The gradient of the normal at $t = 2$ is $\dfrac{1}{3}$.

Putting this into $y = mx + c$ gives:

$-2 = \dfrac{1}{3}(2) + c \Rightarrow c = -\dfrac{8}{3}$

So the equation of the normal is $3y = x - 8$.

This crosses the x-axis at $y = 0$, so

$0 = x - 8 \Rightarrow x = 8$

and so the coordinates are $(8, 0)$.

Q7 a) $\dfrac{dy}{dx} = \dfrac{\theta \cos \theta + \sin \theta}{2 \cos 2\theta - 2 \sin \theta}$

b) When $\theta = \dfrac{\pi}{2}$: $\dfrac{dy}{dx} = -\dfrac{1}{4}$, $x = 0$ and $y = \dfrac{\pi}{2}$.

Putting this into $y = mx + c$ gives:

$\dfrac{\pi}{2} = -\dfrac{1}{4}(0) + c \Rightarrow c = \dfrac{\pi}{2}$

So the equation of the tangent is $y = \dfrac{\pi}{2} - \dfrac{1}{4}x$.

The gradient of the normal is 4. The normal also goes through the point $\left(0, \dfrac{\pi}{2}\right)$, so again $c = \dfrac{\pi}{2}$.
So the equation of the normal is $y = 4x + \dfrac{\pi}{2}$.

Q8 a) The path cuts the y-axis when $x = 0$, so $s^3 \ln s = 0$.

Since $\ln 0$ is undefined, $s = 0$ cannot be a solution, so the only solution is $s = 1$ (i.e. when $\ln s = 0$).

b) $\dfrac{dy}{dx} = \dfrac{3s^2 - s - 2s \ln s}{s^2 + 3s^2 \ln s} = \dfrac{3s - 1 - 2 \ln s}{s + 3s \ln s}$.

From a), when $x = 0$, $s = 1$.

When $s = 1$: $\dfrac{dy}{dx} = 2$, $x = 0$ and $y = 1$.

Putting this into $y = mx + c$ gives:

$1 = 2(0) + c \Rightarrow c = 1$.

So the equation of the tangent is $y = 2x + 1$.

Q9 a) $\dfrac{dy}{d\theta} = \dfrac{-\theta^3 \sin \theta - 3\theta^2 \cos \theta}{\theta^6} = \dfrac{-\theta \sin \theta - 3 \cos \theta}{\theta^4}$

$\dfrac{dx}{d\theta} = \theta^2 \cos \theta + 2\theta \sin \theta$

hence $\dfrac{dy}{dx} = \dfrac{-\theta \sin \theta - 3 \cos \theta}{\theta^6 \cos \theta + 2\theta^5 \sin \theta}$

This looks a bit complicated but leave it as it is
— you'll find the cos and sin terms usually disappear
when you substitute.

When $\theta = \pi$, $\dfrac{dy}{dx} = \dfrac{-\pi(0) - 3(-1)}{\pi^6(-1) + 2\pi^5(0)} = -\dfrac{3}{\pi^6}$.

b) The gradient of the normal when $\theta = \pi$ is $\dfrac{\pi^6}{3}$,

and $y = -\dfrac{1}{\pi^3}$, $x = 0$.

Putting this into $y = mx + c$ gives:

$-\dfrac{1}{\pi^3} = \dfrac{\pi^6}{3}(0) + c \Rightarrow c = -\dfrac{1}{\pi^3}$

So the equation of the normal is $y = \dfrac{\pi^6}{3}x - \dfrac{1}{\pi^3}$.

2. Implicit Differentiation
Exercise 2.1 — Implicit differentiation

Q1 a) $\dfrac{d}{dx}(y) + \dfrac{d}{dx}(y^3) = \dfrac{d}{dx}(x^2) + \dfrac{d}{dx}(4)$

$\dfrac{dy}{dx} + 3y^2 \dfrac{dy}{dx} = 2x + 0$

$(1 + 3y^2)\dfrac{dy}{dx} = 2x$

$\dfrac{dy}{dx} = \dfrac{2x}{1 + 3y^2}$

b) $2x + 2y\dfrac{dy}{dx} = 2 + 2\dfrac{dy}{dx}$

$(2y - 2)\dfrac{dy}{dx} = 2 - 2x$

$\dfrac{dy}{dx} = \dfrac{2 - 2x}{2y - 2} = \dfrac{1 - x}{y - 1}$

c) $9x^2 - 4\dfrac{dy}{dx} = 2y\dfrac{dy}{dx} + 1$

$9x^2 - 1 = (2y + 4)\dfrac{dy}{dx}$

$\dfrac{dy}{dx} = \dfrac{9x^2 - 1}{2y + 4}$

d) $5 - 2y\dfrac{dy}{dx} = 5x^4 - 6\dfrac{dy}{dx}$

$5 - 5x^4 = (2y - 6)\dfrac{dy}{dx}$

$\dfrac{dy}{dx} = \dfrac{5 - 5x^4}{2y - 6}$

e) $-\sin x + \cos y\dfrac{dy}{dx} = 2x + 3y^2\dfrac{dy}{dx}$

$(\cos y - 3y^2)\dfrac{dy}{dx} = 2x + \sin x$

$\dfrac{dy}{dx} = \dfrac{2x + \sin x}{\cos y - 3y^2}$

f) $3x^2y^2 + 2x^3y\dfrac{dy}{dx} - \sin x = 4y + 4x\dfrac{dy}{dx}$

$(2x^3y - 4x)\dfrac{dy}{dx} = 4y - 3x^2y^2 + \sin x$

$\dfrac{dy}{dx} = \dfrac{4y - 3x^2y^2 + \sin x}{2x^3y - 4x}$

g) $e^x + e^y\dfrac{dy}{dx} = 3x^2 - \dfrac{dy}{dx}$

$(e^y + 1)\dfrac{dy}{dx} = 3x^2 - e^x$

$\dfrac{dy}{dx} = \dfrac{3x^2 - e^x}{e^y + 1}$

h) $3y^2 + 6xy\dfrac{dy}{dx} + 4xy + 2x^2\dfrac{dy}{dx} = 3x^2 + 4$

$(6xy + 2x^2)\dfrac{dy}{dx} = 3x^2 + 4 - 3y^2 - 4xy$

$\dfrac{dy}{dx} = \dfrac{3x^2 + 4 - 3y^2 - 4xy}{6xy + 2x^2}$

Q2 a) $3x^2 + 2y + 2x\dfrac{dy}{dx} = 4y^3\dfrac{dy}{dx}$

$(4y^3 - 2x)\dfrac{dy}{dx} = 3x^2 + 2y$

$\dfrac{dy}{dx} = \dfrac{3x^2 + 2y}{4y^3 - 2x}$

b) $2xy + x^2\dfrac{dy}{dx} + 2y\dfrac{dy}{dx} = 3x^2$

$(x^2 + 2y)\dfrac{dy}{dx} = 3x^2 - 2xy$

$\dfrac{dy}{dx} = \dfrac{3x^2 - 2xy}{x^2 + 2y}$

c) $y^3 + 3xy^2\dfrac{dy}{dx} + \dfrac{dy}{dx} = \cos x$

$(3xy^2 + 1)\dfrac{dy}{dx} = \cos x - y^3$

$\dfrac{dy}{dx} = \dfrac{\cos x - y^3}{3xy^2 + 1}$

d) $-y\sin x + \cos x\dfrac{dy}{dx} + \sin y + x\cos y\dfrac{dy}{dx} = y + x\dfrac{dy}{dx}$

$(\cos x + x\cos y - x)\dfrac{dy}{dx} = y + y\sin x - \sin y$

$\dfrac{dy}{dx} = \dfrac{y + y\sin x - \sin y}{\cos x + x\cos y - x}$

e) $e^x + e^y\dfrac{dy}{dx} = y + x\dfrac{dy}{dx}$

$(e^y - x)\dfrac{dy}{dx} = y - e^x$

$\dfrac{dy}{dx} = \dfrac{y - e^x}{e^y - x}$

f) $\dfrac{1}{x} + 2x = 3y^2\dfrac{dy}{dx} + \dfrac{dy}{dx}$

$(3y^2 + 1)\dfrac{dy}{dx} = \dfrac{1}{x} + 2x$

$\dfrac{dy}{dx} = \dfrac{\frac{1}{x} + 2x}{3y^2 + 1} = \dfrac{1 + 2x^2}{3xy^2 + x}$

g) $2e^{2x} + 3e^{3y}\dfrac{dy}{dx} = 6xy^2 + 6x^2y\dfrac{dy}{dx}$

$(3e^{3y} - 6x^2y)\dfrac{dy}{dx} = 6xy^2 - 2e^{2x}$

$\dfrac{dy}{dx} = \dfrac{6xy^2 - 2e^{2x}}{3e^{3y} - 6x^2y}$

h) $\ln x + 1 + \dfrac{y}{x} + \ln x\dfrac{dy}{dx} = 5x^4 + 3y^2\dfrac{dy}{dx}$

$(\ln x - 3y^2)\dfrac{dy}{dx} = 5x^4 - \ln x - 1 - \dfrac{y}{x}$

$\dfrac{dy}{dx} = \dfrac{5x^4 - \ln x - 1 - \frac{y}{x}}{\ln x - 3y^2} = \dfrac{5x^5 - x\ln x - x - y}{x\ln x - 3xy^2}$

Q3 a) At $(0, 1)$: LHS: $e^0 + 2\ln 1 = 1$
RHS: $1^3 = 1$
So $(0, 1)$ is a point on the curve.

b) $e^x + \dfrac{2}{y}\dfrac{dy}{dx} = 3y^2\dfrac{dy}{dx}$

$\dfrac{dy}{dx} = \dfrac{e^x}{3y^2 - \frac{2}{y}} = \dfrac{ye^x}{3y^3 - 2}$.

At $(0, 1)$ the gradient is $\dfrac{1e^0}{3(1^3) - 2} = 1$

Q4 a) $3x^2 + 2y\dfrac{dy}{dx} - 2y - 2x\dfrac{dy}{dx} = 0$

$\dfrac{dy}{dx} = \dfrac{2y - 3x^2}{2y - 2x}$

b) Putting $x = -2$ into the equation gives:
$-8 + y^2 + 4y = 0$

Complete the square to solve...
$(y + 2)^2 - 4 - 8 = 0$
$y + 2 = \pm\sqrt{12} = \pm 2\sqrt{3}$
so $y = -2 \pm 2\sqrt{3}$

c) At $(-2, -2 + 2\sqrt{3})$:

$\dfrac{dy}{dx} = \dfrac{(-4 + 4\sqrt{3}) - 3(-2)^2}{(-4 + 4\sqrt{3}) - 2(-2)} = \dfrac{-16 + 4\sqrt{3}}{4\sqrt{3}}$

$= \dfrac{\sqrt{3} - 4}{\sqrt{3}}$

Rationalise the denominator: $= \dfrac{3 - 4\sqrt{3}}{3}$

$= 1 - \dfrac{4}{3}\sqrt{3}$

Q5 a) Putting $x = 1$ into the equation gives:
$1 - y = 2y^2 \Rightarrow 2y^2 + y - 1 = 0$
$\Rightarrow (2y - 1)(y + 1) = 0$
So $y = -1$ (given as the other point) and $y = \dfrac{1}{2}$.

So $a = \dfrac{1}{2}$.

b) $3x^2 - y - x\dfrac{dy}{dx} = 4y\dfrac{dy}{dx}$

$\dfrac{dy}{dx} = \dfrac{3x^2 - y}{4y + x}$

At $(1, -1)$, $\dfrac{dy}{dx} = \dfrac{3(1^2) - (-1)}{4(-1) + 1} = -\dfrac{4}{3}$

At $(1, \dfrac{1}{2})$, $\dfrac{dy}{dx} = \dfrac{3(1^2) - \left(\frac{1}{2}\right)}{4\left(\frac{1}{2}\right) + 1} = \dfrac{5}{6}$

Q6 a) Putting $x = 1$ into the equation gives:
$y + y^2 - y - 4 = 0 \Rightarrow y^2 - 4 = 0$
so it cuts the curve at $y = 2$ and $y = -2$.

b) $2xy + x^2\dfrac{dy}{dx} + y^2 + 2xy\dfrac{dy}{dx} = y + x\dfrac{dy}{dx} + 0$

$(x^2 + 2xy - x)\dfrac{dy}{dx} = y - 2xy - y^2$

$\dfrac{dy}{dx} = \dfrac{y - 2xy - y^2}{x^2 + 2xy - x}$

At $(1, 2)$, $\dfrac{dy}{dx} = \dfrac{2 - 2(1)(2) - 2^2}{1^2 + 2(1)(2) - 1} = -\dfrac{3}{2}$

At $(1, -2)$, $\dfrac{dy}{dx} = \dfrac{(-2) - 2(1)(-2) - (-2)^2}{1^2 + 2(1)(-2) - 1} = \dfrac{1}{2}$

Exercise 2.2 — Applications of implicit differentiation

Q1 a) Differentiating:
$2x + 2 + 3\dfrac{dy}{dx} - 2y\dfrac{dy}{dx} = 0 \Rightarrow \dfrac{dy}{dx} = \dfrac{2x + 2}{2y - 3}$.

At the stationary points, $\dfrac{dy}{dx} = 0$, so:
$2x + 2 = 0 \Rightarrow x = -1$

When $x = -1$, $y^2 - 3y + 1 = 0 \Rightarrow y = \dfrac{3 \pm \sqrt{5}}{2}$
$= 2.62$ or 0.38 (to 2 d.p.)

So there are 2 stationary points with coordinates $(-1, 2.62)$ and $(-1, 0.38)$.

b) Putting $x = 0$ into the equation gives:
$3y - y^2 = 0 \Rightarrow y(3 - y) = 0$
$\Rightarrow y = 0$ and $y = 3$

At $(0, 0)$, $\frac{dy}{dx} = \frac{2(0) + 2}{2(0) - 3} = -\frac{2}{3}$

The y-intercept is 0 (as it goes through $(0, 0)$).

So the equation of the tangent is $y = -\frac{2}{3}x$ or $3y = -2x$.

At $(0, 3)$, $\frac{dy}{dx} = \frac{2(0) + 2}{2(3) - 3} = \frac{2}{3}$

The y-intercept is 3 (as it goes through $(0, 3)$).

Putting this into $y = mx + c$ gives: $y = \frac{2}{3}x + 3$.

So the equation of the tangent is $3y = 2x + 9$.

You could have left your answers in $y = mx + c$ form, but this looks neater.

Q2 a) Differentiating:

$3x^2 + 2x + \frac{dy}{dx} = 2y\frac{dy}{dx}$

$\Rightarrow \frac{dy}{dx} = \frac{3x^2 + 2x}{2y - 1}$.

At the stationary points, $\frac{dy}{dx} = 0$, so:

$3x^2 + 2x = 0$

$\Rightarrow x(3x + 2) = 0$

$\Rightarrow x = 0$ or $x = -\frac{2}{3}$

When $x = 0$, $y = y^2 \Rightarrow y(y - 1) = 0$

$\Rightarrow y = 0$ or $y = 1$.

When $x = -\frac{2}{3}$, $-\frac{8}{27} + \frac{4}{9} + y = y^2$

$\Rightarrow \frac{4}{27} + y = y^2 \Rightarrow 27y^2 - 27y - 4 = 0$

This has solutions $y = 1.13$ and -0.13, to 2 d.p.

So there are 4 stationary points with coordinates $(0, 0)$, $(0, 1)$, $\left(-\frac{2}{3}, 1.13\right)$ and $\left(-\frac{2}{3}, -0.13\right)$.

b) Putting $x = 2$ into the equation gives:

$8 + 4 + y = y^2 \Rightarrow y^2 - y - 12 = 0$

$\Rightarrow (y - 4)(y + 3) = 0$

$\Rightarrow y = 4$ and $y = -3$

At $(2, 4)$, $\frac{dy}{dx} = \frac{3(2^2) + 2(2)}{2(4) - 1} = \frac{16}{7}$

Putting this into $y = mx + c$ gives:

$4 = \frac{16}{7}(2) + c \Rightarrow c = -\frac{4}{7}$

So the equation of the tangent is $7y = 16x - 4$.

At $(2, -3)$, $\frac{dy}{dx} = \frac{3(2^2) + 2(2)}{2(-3) - 1} = -\frac{16}{7}$

Putting this into $y = mx + c$ gives:

$-3 = -\frac{16}{7}(2) + c \Rightarrow c = \frac{11}{7}$

So the equation of the tangent is $7y = 11 - 16x$.

Q3 a) Putting $y = 1$ into the equation gives:

$x^2 + 1 = x + 7 \Rightarrow x^2 - x - 6 = 0$

$(x - 3)(x + 2) = 0 \Rightarrow x = 3$ and $x = -2$.

Differentiating:

$2xy + x^2\frac{dy}{dx} + 3y^2\frac{dy}{dx} = 1$

$\frac{dy}{dx} = \frac{1 - 2xy}{x^2 + 3y^2}$

At $(-2, 1)$, $\frac{dy}{dx} = \frac{1 - 2(-2)(1)}{(-2)^2 + 3(1^2)} = \frac{5}{7}$

so the gradient of the normal is $-\frac{7}{5}$.

Putting this into $y = mx + c$ gives:

$1 = -\frac{7}{5}(-2) + c \Rightarrow c = -\frac{9}{5}$

and so the equation of the normal is $5y = -7x - 9$.

At $(3, 1)$, $\frac{dy}{dx} = \frac{1 - 2(3)(1)}{(3)^2 + 3(1^2)} = -\frac{5}{12}$

so the gradient of the normal is $\frac{12}{5}$.

Putting this into $y = mx + c$ gives:

$1 = \frac{12}{5}(3) + c \Rightarrow c = -\frac{31}{5}$

so the equation of the normal is $5y = 12x - 31$.

b) The normals intersect when:

$-7x - 9 = 12x - 31$

$22 = 19x \Rightarrow x = \frac{22}{19}$

And so $5y = \frac{264}{19} - 31 = -\frac{325}{19} \Rightarrow y = -\frac{65}{19}$

So they intersect at $\left(\frac{22}{19}, -\frac{65}{19}\right)$.

Q4 a) Putting $x = 0$ into the equation gives:

$1 + y^2 = 5 - 3y \Rightarrow y^2 + 3y - 4 = 0$

$(y + 4)(y - 1) = 0 \Rightarrow y = -4$ or $y = 1$.

So $a = -4$ and $b = 1$ ($a < b$).

Differentiating:

$e^x + 2y\frac{dy}{dx} - y - x\frac{dy}{dx} = -3\frac{dy}{dx}$

$\frac{dy}{dx} = \frac{y - e^x}{2y - x + 3}$

At $(0, 1)$, $\frac{dy}{dx} = \frac{1 - e^0}{2(1) - 0 + 3} = 0$

so this is a stationary point.

b) At $(0, -4)$, $\frac{dy}{dx} = \frac{(-4) - e^0}{2(-4) - 0 + 3} = 1$.

So the gradient of the tangent is 1 and the gradient of the normal is -1.

$-4 = 0 + c$ (so $c = -4$) for both, since $x = 0$, so the equation of the tangent is $y = x - 4$ and the equation of the normal is $y = -x - 4$.

Q5 a) When $x = 1$:

$0 + y^2 = y + 6 \Rightarrow y^2 - y - 6 = 0$

$(y - 3)(y + 2) = 0 \Rightarrow y = 3$ or $y = -2$.

So the curve passes through $(1, 3)$ and $(1, -2)$.

b) Differentiating:

$\frac{1}{x} + 2y\frac{dy}{dx} = 2xy + x^2\frac{dy}{dx}$

$\frac{dy}{dx} = \frac{2xy - \frac{1}{x}}{2y - x^2} = \frac{2x^2y - 1}{2xy - x^3}$

At $(1, 3)$, $\frac{dy}{dx} = \frac{2(1^2)(3) - 1}{2(1)(3) - (1)^3} = 1$

so the gradient of the normal is -1.

Putting this into $y = mx + c$ gives:

$3 = -1(1) + c \Rightarrow c = 4$

so the equation of the normal is $y = 4 - x$.

At $(1, -2)$, $\frac{dy}{dx} = \frac{2(1^2)(-2) - 1}{2(1)(-2) - (1)^3} = 1$,

so the gradient of the normal is also -1.

$-2 = -1(1) + c \Rightarrow c = -1$

so the equation of the normal is $y = -x - 1$.

Because the gradients are the same these lines are parallel and can never intersect.

Q6 When $y = 0$:

$1 + x^2 = 0 + 4x \Rightarrow x^2 - 4x + 1 = 0$

Complete the square to solve...

$(x - 2)^2 - 4 + 1 = 0 \Rightarrow x - 2 = \pm\sqrt{3} \Rightarrow x = 2 \pm \sqrt{3}$

So $a = 2 + \sqrt{3}$ and $b = 2 - \sqrt{3}$.

Differentiating:

$e^y \dfrac{dy}{dx} + 2x = 3y^2 \dfrac{dy}{dx} + 4 \Rightarrow \dfrac{dy}{dx} = \dfrac{2x - 4}{3y^2 - e^y}$

At $(2 + \sqrt{3}, 0)$, $\dfrac{dy}{dx} = \dfrac{4 + 2\sqrt{3} - 4}{3(0) - e^0} = -2\sqrt{3}$

$0 = -2\sqrt{3}(2 + \sqrt{3}) + c \Rightarrow c = 4\sqrt{3} + 6$

So the tangent at this point is $y = 4\sqrt{3} + 6 - 2\sqrt{3}x$.

At $(2 - \sqrt{3}, 0)$, $\dfrac{dy}{dx} = \dfrac{4 - 2\sqrt{3} - 4}{3(0) - e^0} = 2\sqrt{3}$

$0 = 2\sqrt{3}(2 - \sqrt{3}) + c \Rightarrow c = 6 - 4\sqrt{3}$

So the tangent at this point is $y = 2\sqrt{3}x + 6 - 4\sqrt{3}$.

Q7 Differentiating:

$\ln x \dfrac{dy}{dx} + \dfrac{y}{x} + 2x = 2y \dfrac{dy}{dx} - \dfrac{dy}{dx}$

$\dfrac{dy}{dx} = \dfrac{\frac{y}{x} + 2x}{2y - \ln x - 1} = \dfrac{y + 2x^2}{2xy - x\ln x - x}$

$y + 2x^2 = 0 \Rightarrow \dfrac{dy}{dx} = \dfrac{y + 2x^2}{2xy - x\ln x - x} = 0$

So if a point on the curve satisfies $y + 2x^2 = 0$, then it's a stationary point.

Q8 **a)** Differentiating:

$2e^{2y} \dfrac{dy}{dx} + e^x = 2x \dfrac{dy}{dx} + 2y$

$\dfrac{dy}{dx} = \dfrac{2y - e^x}{2e^{2y} - 2x}$

When $y = 0$:

$1 + e^x - e^4 = 1$

$\Rightarrow e^x = e^4 \Rightarrow x = 4$

$\dfrac{dy}{dx} = \dfrac{2(0) - e^4}{2e^0 - 2(4)} = \dfrac{e^4}{6}$ (gradient of the tangent)

$0 = \dfrac{e^4}{6}(4) + c \Rightarrow c = -\dfrac{2e^4}{3}$.

So the equation of the tangent is $y = \dfrac{e^4}{6}(x - 4)$.

b) The gradient of the normal is $-6e^{-4}$.

$0 = -6e^{-4}(4) + c \Rightarrow c = 24e^{-4}$

So the normal is $y = 6e^{-4}(4 - x)$.

c) The lines intersect when

$\dfrac{e^4}{6}(x - 4) = 6e^{-4}(4 - x)$

$\Rightarrow e^8(x - 4) = 36(4 - x)$

$\Rightarrow e^8 x + 36x = 4e^8 + 144$

$\Rightarrow x(e^8 + 36) = 4e^8 + 144$

$\Rightarrow x = \dfrac{4e^8 + 144}{e^8 + 36}$

Q9 When $x = 2$:

$2y^2 + 4y - 24 = 4 + 2$

$\Rightarrow 2y^2 + 4y - 30 = 0$

$\Rightarrow y^2 + 2y - 15 = 0$

$\Rightarrow (y + 5)(y - 3) = 0 \Rightarrow y = -5$ and $y = 3$.

Differentiating:

$y^2 + 2yx \dfrac{dy}{dx} + 2y + 2x \dfrac{dy}{dx} - 9x^2 = 2x$

$\dfrac{dy}{dx} = \dfrac{2x - y^2 - 2y + 9x^2}{2yx + 2x}$

At $(2, -5)$, $\dfrac{dy}{dx} = \dfrac{4 - 25 + 10 + 36}{-20 + 4} = -\dfrac{25}{16}$

This is the gradient of the tangent at $(2, -5)$, so:

$-5 = -\dfrac{25}{16}(2) + c \Rightarrow c = -\dfrac{15}{8}$

So the equation of the tangent at $(2, -5)$ is:

$y = -\dfrac{25}{16}x - \dfrac{15}{8}$ or $16y = -25x - 30$

At $(2, 3)$, $\dfrac{dy}{dx} = \dfrac{4 - 9 - 6 + 36}{12 + 4} = \dfrac{25}{16}$

This is the gradient of the tangent at $(2, 3)$, so:

$3 = \dfrac{25}{16}(2) + c \Rightarrow c = -\dfrac{1}{8}$

So the equation of the tangent at $(2, 3)$ is:

$y = \dfrac{25}{16}x - \dfrac{1}{8}$ or $16y = 25x - 2$

The two tangents intersect when:

$-25x - 30 = 25x - 2 \Rightarrow 50x = -28$

$\Rightarrow x = -\dfrac{14}{25}$

And $16y = 25\left(-\dfrac{14}{25}\right) - 2 \Rightarrow 16y = -16 \Rightarrow y = -1$.

So they intersect at $\left(-\dfrac{14}{25}, -1\right)$.

Q10 **a)** When $x = \dfrac{\pi}{2}$:

$\cos y \cos \dfrac{\pi}{2} + \cos y \sin \dfrac{\pi}{2} = \dfrac{1}{2}$,

$0 + \cos y = \dfrac{1}{2} \Rightarrow y = \dfrac{\pi}{3}$

This is the only solution for y in the given interval.

When $x = \pi$:

$\cos y \cos \pi + \cos y \sin \pi = \dfrac{1}{2}$,

$-\cos y + 0 = \dfrac{1}{2} \Rightarrow y = \dfrac{2\pi}{3}$

You can use the CAST diagram or the graph of cos x to find this solution.

b) Differentiating:

$-\cos y \sin x - \sin y \cos x \dfrac{dy}{dx} +$
$\qquad \cos y \cos x - \sin y \sin x \dfrac{dy}{dx} = 0$

$\dfrac{dy}{dx} = \dfrac{\cos y \cos x - \cos y \sin x}{\sin y \cos x + \sin y \sin x}$

At $\left(\dfrac{\pi}{2}, \dfrac{\pi}{3}\right)$, $\dfrac{dy}{dx} = \dfrac{\cos \frac{\pi}{3} \cos \frac{\pi}{2} - \cos \frac{\pi}{3} \sin \frac{\pi}{2}}{\sin \frac{\pi}{3} \cos \frac{\pi}{2} + \sin \frac{\pi}{3} \sin \frac{\pi}{2}}$

$= \dfrac{0 - \frac{1}{2}}{0 + \frac{\sqrt{3}}{2}} = -\dfrac{1}{\sqrt{3}}$

This is the gradient of the tangent, so:

$\dfrac{\pi}{3} = -\dfrac{1}{\sqrt{3}}\left(\dfrac{\pi}{2}\right) + c \Rightarrow c = \dfrac{(2 + \sqrt{3})\pi}{6}$

So the equation of the tangent at $\left(\dfrac{\pi}{2}, \dfrac{\pi}{3}\right)$ is

$y = -\dfrac{1}{\sqrt{3}}x + \dfrac{(2 + \sqrt{3})\pi}{6}$.

At $\left(\pi, \frac{2\pi}{3}\right)$, $\dfrac{dy}{dx} = \dfrac{\cos\frac{2\pi}{3}\cos\pi - \cos\frac{2\pi}{3}\sin\pi}{\sin\frac{2\pi}{3}\cos\pi + \sin\frac{2\pi}{3}\sin\pi}$

$$= \dfrac{\frac{1}{2} - 0}{-\frac{\sqrt{3}}{2} + 0} = -\dfrac{1}{\sqrt{3}}$$

This is the gradient of the tangent, so:

$$\frac{2\pi}{3} = -\frac{1}{\sqrt{3}}(\pi) + c \Rightarrow c = \frac{(2+\sqrt{3})\pi}{3}$$

So the equation of the tangent at $\left(\pi, \frac{2\pi}{3}\right)$ is

$$y = -\frac{1}{\sqrt{3}}x + \frac{(2+\sqrt{3})\pi}{3}.$$

3. Integration Using Partial Fractions

Exercise 3.1 — Use of partial fractions

Q1 **a)** First write the function as partial fractions. Factorise the denominator and write as an identity:

$$\frac{24(x-1)}{9-4x^2} = \frac{24(x-1)}{(3-2x)(3+2x)} \equiv \frac{A}{(3-2x)} + \frac{B}{(3+2x)}$$

Add the fractions and cancel denominators:

$$\frac{24(x-1)}{(3-2x)(3+2x)} \equiv \frac{A(3+2x)+B(3-2x)}{(3-2x)(3+2x)}$$

$$\Rightarrow 24(x-1) \equiv A(3+2x) + B(3-2x)$$

Substituting $x = -\frac{3}{2}$ gives: $-60 = 6B \Rightarrow B = -10$.

Substituting $x = \frac{3}{2}$ gives: $12 = 6A \Rightarrow A = 2$.

So $\dfrac{24(x-1)}{9-4x^2} \equiv \dfrac{2}{(3-2x)} - \dfrac{10}{(3+2x)}$.

So the integral can be expressed:

$$\int \frac{24(x-1)}{9-4x^2}\,dx = \int \frac{2}{(3-2x)} - \frac{10}{(3+2x)}\,dx$$

$$= \frac{2}{-2}\ln|3-2x| - \frac{10}{2}\ln|3+2x| + C$$

$$= -\ln|3-2x| - 5\ln|3+2x| + C$$

b) $\dfrac{-4x^2-21x+82}{(5x+2)(x-3)(x-4)} \equiv \dfrac{A}{5x+2} + \dfrac{B}{x-3} + \dfrac{C}{x-4}$

$$\frac{-4x^2-21x+82}{(5x+2)(x-3)(x-4)} \equiv$$

$$\frac{A(x-3)(x-4)+B(5x+2)(x-4)+C(5x+2)(x-3)}{(5x+2)(x-3)(x-4)}$$

$$-4x^2-21x+82 \equiv$$

$$A(x-3)(x-4)+B(5x+2)(x-4)+C(5x+2)(x-3)$$

Substituting $x = 3$ gives: $-17 = -17B \Rightarrow B = 1$

Substituting $x = 4$ gives: $-66 = 22C \Rightarrow C = -3$

Equating coefficients of x^2 gives
$A + 5B + 5C = -4 \Rightarrow A + 5 + -15 = -4 \Rightarrow A = 6$

So $\dfrac{-4x^2-21x+82}{(5x+2)(x-3)(x-4)} \equiv \dfrac{6}{5x+2} + \dfrac{1}{x-3} - \dfrac{3}{x-4}$

So the integral can be expressed as:

$$\int \frac{-4x^2-21x+82}{(5x+2)(x-3)(x-4)}\,dx$$

$$= \int \frac{6}{5x+2} + \frac{1}{x-3} - \frac{3}{x-4}\,dx$$

$$= \frac{6}{5}\ln|5x+2| + \ln|x-3| - 3\ln|x-4| + C$$

c) In this case there is a repeated factor in the denominator so it'll need to feature in two of the denominators of the partial fractions (once on its own and once squared).

$$\frac{7x+4}{(x+2)^2(x-3)} \equiv \frac{A}{(x+2)^2} + \frac{B}{(x+2)} + \frac{C}{(x-3)}$$

Add the fractions and cancel denominators:

$$\frac{7x+4}{(x+2)^2(x-3)}$$

$$\equiv \frac{A(x-3)+B(x+2)(x-3)+C(x+2)^2}{(x+2)^2(x-3)}$$

$$7x+4 \equiv A(x-3)+B(x+2)(x-3)+C(x+2)^2$$

Substituting $x = 3$ gives: $25 = 25C \Rightarrow C = 1$

Substituting $x = -2$ gives: $-10 = -5A \Rightarrow A = 2$

No value can be substituted to get B on its own, so equate coefficients:

Equating coefficients of x^2 we get:
$B + C = 0 \Rightarrow B + 1 = 0 \Rightarrow B = -1$

So

$$\frac{7x+4}{(x+2)^2(x-3)} \equiv \frac{2}{(x+2)^2} - \frac{1}{(x+2)} + \frac{1}{(x-3)}$$

So the integral can be expressed:

$$\int \frac{7x+4}{(x+2)^2(x-3)}\,dx$$

$$= \int \frac{2}{(x+2)^2} - \frac{1}{(x+2)} + \frac{1}{(x-3)}\,dx$$

$$= -\frac{2}{x+2} - \ln|x+2| + \ln|x-3| + C$$

$$= \ln\left|\frac{x-3}{x+2}\right| - \frac{2}{x+2} + C$$

Q2 First write the function as partial fractions:

$$\frac{x}{(x-2)(x-3)} \equiv \frac{A}{x-2} + \frac{B}{x-3}$$

$$\Rightarrow \frac{x}{(x-2)(x-3)} \equiv \frac{A(x-3)+B(x-2)}{(x-2)(x-3)}$$

$$\Rightarrow x \equiv A(x-3) + B(x-2)$$

Substituting $x = 3$: $B = 3$

Substituting $x = 2$: $-A = 2 \Rightarrow A = -2$

So $\dfrac{x}{(x-2)(x-3)} \equiv \dfrac{-2}{x-2} + \dfrac{3}{x-3}$

$$\equiv \frac{3}{x-3} - \frac{2}{x-2}$$

$$\Rightarrow \int_0^1 \frac{x}{(x-2)(x-3)}\,dx = \int_0^1 \frac{3}{x-3} - \frac{2}{x-2}\,dx$$

$$= [3\ln|x-3| - 2\ln|x-2|]_0^1$$

$$= [3\ln|1-3| - 2\ln|1-2|]$$

$$\quad - [3\ln|0-3| - 2\ln|0-2|]$$

$$= 3\ln 2 - 2\ln 1 - 3\ln 3 + 2\ln 2$$

$$= 0 + 5\ln 2 - 3\ln 3$$

$$= \ln 2^5 - \ln 3^3 = \ln\frac{32}{27}$$

Note that the modulus is important in this question, for example $|1 - 2| = |-1| = 1$.

Q3 a) First factorise the denominator and then express as an identity.

$$\frac{6}{2x^2 - 5x + 2} = \frac{6}{(2x - 1)(x - 2)}$$

$$\equiv \frac{A}{2x - 1} + \frac{B}{x - 2}$$

$$\Rightarrow 6 \equiv A(x - 2) + B(2x - 1)$$

Substituting $x = 2$ gives $6 = 3B$ so $B = 2$.

Substituting $x = \frac{1}{2}$ gives $6 = -\frac{3}{2}A$ so $A = -4$.

So $\dfrac{6}{2x^2 - 5x + 2} \equiv -\dfrac{4}{2x - 1} + \dfrac{2}{x - 2}$

$$= \frac{2}{x - 2} - \frac{4}{2x - 1}$$

b) Using part a)

$$\int \frac{6}{2x^2 - 5x + 2}\,dx = \int \frac{2}{x - 2} - \frac{4}{2x - 1}\,dx$$

$$= 2\ln|x - 2| - \frac{4}{2}\ln|2x - 1| + C$$

$$= 2\ln|x - 2| - 2\ln|2x - 1| + C$$

$x > 2$ so $x - 2 > 0$ and $2x - 1 > 3$ so the modulus signs can be removed. So:

$$\int \frac{6}{2x^2 - 5x + 2}\,dx$$

$$= 2\ln(x - 2) - 2\ln(2x - 1) + C$$

$$= 2\ln\left(\frac{x - 2}{2x - 1}\right) + C = \ln\left[\left(\frac{x - 2}{2x - 1}\right)^2\right] + C$$

c) Using part b)

$$\int_3^5 \frac{6}{2x^2 - 5x + 2}\,dx = \left[\ln\left[\left(\frac{x - 2}{2x - 1}\right)^2\right]\right]_3^5$$

$$= \ln\left[\left(\frac{5 - 2}{10 - 1}\right)^2\right] - \ln\left[\left(\frac{3 - 2}{6 - 1}\right)^2\right]$$

$$= \ln\frac{1}{9} - \ln\frac{1}{25} = \ln\frac{25}{9}$$

Q4 First express the fraction as an identity:

$$\frac{3y + 5}{y(y + 10)} \equiv \frac{A}{y} + \frac{B}{y + 10}$$

$$\Rightarrow 3y + 5 \equiv A(y + 10) + By$$

Now use the equating coefficients method:

Equating constant terms: $10A = 5$ so $A = \frac{1}{2}$.

Equating y coefficients: $A + B = 3 \Rightarrow \frac{1}{2} + B = 3$

$$\Rightarrow B = \frac{5}{2}.$$

So $\dfrac{3y + 5}{y(y + 10)} \equiv \dfrac{1}{2y} + \dfrac{5}{2(y + 10)}$

Now the integration can be expressed:

$$\int_1^2 \frac{3y + 5}{y(y + 10)}\,dy = \int_1^2 \frac{1}{2y} + \frac{5}{2(y + 10)}\,dy$$

$$= \left[\frac{1}{2}\ln|y| + \frac{5}{2}\ln|y + 10|\right]_1^2$$

$$= \left[\frac{1}{2}\ln|2| + \frac{5}{2}\ln|2 + 10|\right] - \left[\frac{1}{2}\ln|1| + \frac{5}{2}\ln|1 + 10|\right]$$

$$= \left[\frac{1}{2}\ln 2 + \frac{5}{2}\ln 12\right] - \left[0 + \frac{5}{2}\ln 11\right]$$

$$= \frac{1}{2}\ln 2 + \frac{5}{2}\ln 12 - \frac{5}{2}\ln 11 = \frac{1}{2}\left(\ln 2 + 5\ln\frac{12}{11}\right)$$

$$= \frac{1}{2}\left(\ln 2 + \ln\left(\frac{12}{11}\right)^5\right) = 0.564 \ (3\,d.p.)$$

Q5 First express $\dfrac{f(x)}{g(x)} = \dfrac{3x^2 + 17x - 32}{(x - 4)(x - 1)(x + 3)}$ as partial fractions. Write it out as an identity:

$$\frac{3x^2 + 17x - 32}{(x - 4)(x - 1)(x + 3)} \equiv \frac{A}{(x - 4)} + \frac{B}{(x - 1)} + \frac{C}{(x + 3)}$$

$$3x^2 + 17x - 32 \equiv A(x - 1)(x + 3)$$
$$+ B(x - 4)(x + 3)$$
$$+ C(x - 4)(x - 1)$$

Substituting $x = 1$ gives: $-12 = -12B \Rightarrow B = 1$

Substituting $x = -3$ gives: $-56 = 28C \Rightarrow C = -2$

Substituting $x = 4$ gives: $84 = 21A \Rightarrow A = 4$

So

$$\frac{3x^2 + 17x - 32}{(x - 4)(x - 1)(x + 3)} \equiv \frac{4}{(x - 4)} + \frac{1}{(x - 1)} - \frac{2}{(x + 3)}$$

Now the integral can be expressed:

$$\int_b^a \frac{f(x)}{g(x)}\,dx = \int_b^a \frac{3x^2 + 17x - 32}{(x - 4)(x - 1)(x + 3)}\,dx$$

$$= \int_b^a \frac{4}{(x - 4)} + \frac{1}{(x - 1)} - \frac{2}{(x + 3)}\,dx$$

$$= \left[4\ln|x - 4| + \ln|x - 1| - 2\ln|x + 3|\right]_b^a$$

Notice that $x > 4$, so $x - 4 > 0$, $x - 1 > 3$ and $x + 3 > 7$ so the modulus signs can be removed. You have:

$$\int_b^a \frac{f(x)}{g(x)}\,dx = \left[4\ln(x - 4) + \ln(x - 1) - 2\ln(x + 3)\right]_b^a$$

$$= \left[\ln(x - 4)^4 + \ln(x - 1) - \ln(x + 3)^2\right]_b^a$$

$$= \left[\ln\left(\frac{(x - 4)^4(x - 1)}{(x + 3)^2}\right)\right]_b^a$$

$$= \ln\left(\frac{(a - 4)^4(a - 1)(b + 3)^2}{(b - 4)^4(b - 1)(a + 3)^2}\right)$$

Q6 Again, begin by writing the function as partial fractions.

$$\frac{-(t + 3)}{(3t + 2)(t + 1)} \equiv \frac{A}{(3t + 2)} + \frac{B}{(t + 1)}$$

$$\Rightarrow -(t + 3) \equiv A(t + 1) + B(3t + 2)$$

Substituting $t = -1$ gives: $-2 = -B$ so $B = 2$

Equating coefficients of t gives

$A + 3B = -1 \Rightarrow A + 6 = -1 \Rightarrow A = -7$

So $\dfrac{-(t + 3)}{(3t + 2)(t + 1)} \equiv \dfrac{2}{(t + 1)} - \dfrac{7}{(3t + 2)}$

The integral can be expressed:

$$\int_0^{\frac{2}{3}} \frac{-(t + 3)}{(3t + 2)(t + 1)}\,dx = \int_0^{\frac{2}{3}} \frac{2}{(t + 1)} - \frac{7}{(3t + 2)}\,dx$$

$$= \left[2\ln|t + 1| - \frac{7}{3}\ln|3t + 2|\right]_0^{\frac{2}{3}}$$

$$= \left[2\ln\left|\frac{5}{3}\right| - \frac{7}{3}\ln|4|\right] - \left[2\ln|1| - \frac{7}{3}\ln|2|\right]$$

$$= \left[2\ln\left(\frac{5}{3}\right) - \frac{7}{3}\ln(4)\right] - \left[0 - \frac{7}{3}\ln(2)\right]$$

$$= 2\ln\left(\frac{5}{3}\right) - \frac{7}{3}\ln(4) + \frac{7}{3}\ln(2)$$

$$= 2\ln\left(\frac{5}{3}\right) - \frac{7}{3}(\ln(4) - \ln(2))$$

$$= 2\ln\left(\frac{5}{3}\right) - \frac{7}{3}\ln\left(\frac{4}{2}\right) = 2\ln\left(\frac{5}{3}\right) - \frac{7}{3}\ln 2$$

Q7 a) $\dfrac{18x^2 + 3x - 8}{(2x + 1)(3x - 1)} \equiv \dfrac{18x^2 + 3x - 8}{6x^2 + x - 1}$

$$6x^2 + x - 1 \overline{\smash{\big)}\ 18x^2 + 3x - 8}$$
$$\underline{-(18x^2 + 3x - 3)}$$
$$-5$$

So $\dfrac{18x^2 + 3x - 8}{(2x + 1)(3x - 1)} \equiv 3 - \dfrac{5}{6x^2 + x - 1}$

$$\equiv 3 - \dfrac{5}{(2x + 1)(3x - 1)}$$

So $A = 3$ and $\dfrac{-5}{(2x + 1)(3x - 1)} \equiv \dfrac{B}{2x + 1} + \dfrac{C}{3x - 1}$

Solve this as you would with normal partial fractions:

$\Rightarrow -5 \equiv B(3x - 1) + C(2x + 1)$

Equating coefficients:
$-5 = -B + C$
$0 = 3B + 2C$

Solving simultaneously: $C = -3$ and $B = 2$

Your other option with questions like this is to just multiply through by the denominator of the original fraction, then use the substitution and equating coefficients methods to find A, B and C from there.

b) From a) you have:

$\dfrac{18x^2 + 3x - 8}{(2x + 1)(3x - 1)} \equiv 3 + \dfrac{2}{(2x + 1)} - \dfrac{3}{(3x - 1)}$

So the integral can be expressed:

$\displaystyle\int_2^5 \dfrac{18x^2 + 3x - 8}{(2x + 1)(3x - 1)}\,dx$

$= \displaystyle\int_2^5 3 + \dfrac{2}{(2x + 1)} - \dfrac{3}{(3x - 1)}\,dx$

$= \left[3x + \ln|2x + 1| - \ln|3x - 1|\right]_2^5$

$= \left[15 + \ln|11| - \ln|14|\right] - \left[6 + \ln|5| - \ln|5|\right]$

$= 15 + \ln 11 - \ln 14 - 6 = 9 + \ln\!\left(\dfrac{11}{14}\right)$

So $p = 9$ and $q = \dfrac{11}{14}$.

4. Using Trigonometric Identities in Integration

Exercise 4.1 — Integrating using the double angle formulas

Q1 a) Using the cos double angle formula:

$\cos^2 x = \dfrac{1}{2}(\cos 2x + 1)$

So the integral is:

$\displaystyle\int \cos^2 x\,dx = \int \dfrac{1}{2}(\cos 2x + 1)\,dx$

$= \dfrac{1}{2}\!\left(\dfrac{1}{2}\sin 2x + x\right) + C$

$= \dfrac{1}{4}\sin 2x + \dfrac{1}{2}x + C$

b) $6\sin x \cos x = 3(2\sin x \cos x) = 3\sin 2x$

So the integral is:

$\displaystyle\int 6\sin x \cos x\,dx = \int 3\sin 2x\,dx = -\dfrac{3}{2}\cos 2x + C$

c) $\sin^2 6x = \dfrac{1}{2}(1 - \cos(2 \times 6x)) = \dfrac{1}{2}(1 - \cos 12x)$

So the integral is:

$\displaystyle\int \sin^2 6x\,dx = \int \dfrac{1}{2}(1 - \cos 12x)\,dx$

$= \dfrac{1}{2}\!\left(x - \dfrac{1}{12}\sin 12x\right) + C$

$= \dfrac{1}{2}x - \dfrac{1}{24}\sin 12x + C$

d) Using the tan double angle formula:

$\dfrac{2\tan 2x}{1 - \tan^2 2x} = \tan 4x$

So the integral is:

$\displaystyle\int \dfrac{2\tan 2x}{1 - \tan^2 2x}\,dx = \int \tan 4x\,dx$

$= -\dfrac{1}{4}\ln|\cos 4x| + C$

$\left(\text{or} = \dfrac{1}{4}\ln|\sec 4x| + C\right)$

e) $2\sin 4x \cos 4x = \sin 8x$

So the integral is:

$\displaystyle\int 2\sin 4x \cos 4x\,dx = \int \sin 8x\,dx = -\dfrac{1}{8}\cos 8x + C$

f) $2\cos^2 4x = 2\!\left(\dfrac{1}{2}(\cos 8x + 1)\right) = \cos 8x + 1$

So the integral is:

$\displaystyle\int 2\cos^2 4x\,dx = \int \cos 8x + 1\,dx$

$= \dfrac{1}{8}\sin 8x + x + C$

g) $\cos x \sin x = \dfrac{1}{2}(2\cos x \sin x) = \dfrac{1}{2}\sin 2x$

So the integral is:

$\displaystyle\int \cos x \sin x\,dx = \int \dfrac{1}{2}\sin 2x\,dx$

$= \dfrac{1}{2}\!\left(-\dfrac{1}{2}\cos 2x\right) + C$

$= -\dfrac{1}{4}\cos 2x + C$

h) $\sin 3x \cos 3x = \dfrac{1}{2}(2\sin 3x \cos 3x) = \dfrac{1}{2}\sin 6x$

So the integral is:

$\displaystyle\int \sin 3x \cos 3x\,dx = \int \dfrac{1}{2}\sin 6x\,dx$

$= \dfrac{1}{2}\!\left(-\dfrac{1}{6}\cos 6x\right) + C$

$= -\dfrac{1}{12}\cos 6x + C$

i) $\dfrac{6\tan 3x}{1 - \tan^2 3x} = 3\!\left(\dfrac{2\tan 3x}{1 - \tan^2 3x}\right) = 3\tan 6x$

So the integral is:

$\displaystyle\int \dfrac{6\tan 3x}{1 - \tan^2 3x}\,dx = \int 3\tan 6x\,dx$

$= 3\!\left(-\dfrac{1}{6}\ln|\cos 6x|\right) + C$

$= -\dfrac{1}{2}\ln|\cos 6x| + C$

$\left(\text{or} = \dfrac{1}{2}\ln|\sec 6x| + C\right)$

j) $5\sin 2x\cos 2x = \frac{5}{2}(2\sin 2x\cos 2x) = \frac{5}{2}\sin 4x$

So the integral is:

$$\int 5\sin 2x\cos 2x\,dx = \int \frac{5}{2}\sin 4x\,dx$$
$$= \frac{5}{2}\left(-\frac{1}{4}\cos 4x\right) + C$$
$$= -\frac{5}{8}\cos 4x + C$$

k) $(\sin x + \cos x)^2$
$$= \sin^2 x + 2\sin x\cos x + \cos^2 x$$
$$= \sin^2 x + \cos^2 x + 2\sin x\cos x$$
$$= 1 + 2\sin x\cos x$$
$$= 1 + \sin 2x$$

$\sin^2 x + \cos^2 x \equiv 1$ has been used to simplify here.

So the integral is:

$$\int (\sin x + \cos x)^2\,dx = \int 1 + \sin 2x\,dx$$
$$= x - \frac{1}{2}\cos 2x + C$$

l) $4\sin x\cos x\cos 2x = 2(2\sin x\cos x)\cos 2x$
$$= 2\sin 2x\cos 2x$$
$$= \sin 4x$$

So the integral is:

$$\int 4\sin x\cos x\cos 2x\,dx = \int \sin 4x\,dx$$
$$= -\frac{1}{4}\cos 4x + C$$

m) $(\cos x + \sin x)(\cos x - \sin x)$
$$= \cos^2 x - \cos x\sin x + \sin x\cos x - \sin^2 x$$
$$= \cos^2 - \sin^2 x$$
$$= \cos 2x$$

So the integral is:

$$\int (\cos x + \sin x)(\cos x - \sin x)\,dx = \int \cos 2x\,dx$$
$$= \frac{1}{2}\sin 2x + C$$

n) $\sin^2 x\cot x = \sin^2 x\frac{1}{\tan x} = \sin^2 x\frac{\cos x}{\sin x}$
$$= \sin x\cos x = \frac{1}{2}\sin 2x$$

So the integral is:

$$\int \sin^2 x\cot x\,dx = \int \frac{1}{2}\sin 2x\,dx$$
$$= \frac{1}{2}\left(-\frac{1}{2}\cos 2x\right) + C$$
$$= -\frac{1}{4}\cos 2x + C$$

Q2 a) $\sin^2 x = \frac{1}{2}(1 - \cos 2x)$

So the integral is:

$$\int_0^{\frac{\pi}{4}} \sin^2 x\,dx = \int_0^{\frac{\pi}{4}} \frac{1}{2}(1 - \cos 2x)\,dx$$
$$= \frac{1}{2}\left[\left(x - \frac{1}{2}\sin 2x\right)\right]_0^{\frac{\pi}{4}}$$
$$= \frac{1}{2}\left(\left(\frac{\pi}{4} - \frac{1}{2}\sin\frac{\pi}{2}\right) - \left(-\frac{1}{2}\sin 0\right)\right)$$
$$= \frac{1}{2}\left(\left(\frac{\pi}{4} - \left(\frac{1}{2} \times 1\right)\right) - \left(-\frac{1}{2} \times 0\right)\right)$$
$$= \frac{1}{2}\left(\frac{\pi}{4} - \frac{1}{2}\right) = \frac{\pi}{8} - \frac{1}{4}$$

b) $\cos^2 2x = \frac{1}{2}(\cos 4x + 1)$

So the integral is:

$$\int_0^\pi \frac{1}{2}(\cos 4x + 1)\,dx = \left[\frac{1}{2}\left(\frac{1}{4}\sin 4x + x\right)\right]_0^\pi$$
$$= \left[\left(\frac{1}{8}\sin 4x + \frac{x}{2}\right)\right]_0^\pi$$
$$= \left(\frac{1}{8}\sin 4\pi + \frac{\pi}{2}\right) - \left(\frac{1}{8}\sin 0 + \frac{0}{2}\right)$$
$$= \left(\frac{1}{8} \times 0 + \frac{\pi}{2}\right) - (0 + 0) = \frac{\pi}{2}$$

c) $\sin\frac{x}{2}\cos\frac{x}{2} = \frac{1}{2}\left(2\sin\frac{x}{2}\cos\frac{x}{2}\right) = \frac{1}{2}\sin x$

So the integral is:

$$\int_0^\pi \sin\frac{x}{2}\cos\frac{x}{2}\,dx = \int_0^\pi \frac{1}{2}\sin x\,dx$$
$$= -\frac{1}{2}[\cos x]_0^\pi$$
$$= -\frac{1}{2}(\cos \pi - \cos 0)$$
$$= -\frac{1}{2}(-1 - 1) = 1$$

d) $\sin^2 2x = \frac{1}{2}(1 - \cos 4x)$

So the integral is:

$$\int_{\frac{\pi}{4}}^{\frac{\pi}{2}} \sin^2 2x\,dx = \int_{\frac{\pi}{4}}^{\frac{\pi}{2}} \frac{1}{2}(1 - \cos 4x)\,dx$$
$$= \frac{1}{2}\left[x - \frac{1}{4}\sin 4x\right]_{\frac{\pi}{4}}^{\frac{\pi}{2}}$$
$$= \frac{1}{2}\left(\left[\frac{\pi}{2} - \frac{1}{4}\sin 2\pi\right] - \left[\frac{\pi}{4} - \frac{1}{4}\sin \pi\right]\right)$$
$$= \frac{1}{2}\left(\left[\frac{\pi}{2} - 0\right] - \left[\frac{\pi}{4} - 0\right]\right) = \frac{\pi}{8}$$

e) $\cos 2x\sin 2x = \frac{1}{2}(2\sin 2x\cos 2x) = \frac{1}{2}\sin 4x$

So the integral is:

$$\int_0^{\frac{\pi}{4}} \cos 2x\sin 2x\,dx = \int_0^{\frac{\pi}{4}} \frac{1}{2}\sin 4x\,dx$$
$$= \frac{1}{2}\left[\left(-\frac{1}{4}\cos 4x\right)\right]_0^{\frac{\pi}{4}}$$
$$= -\frac{1}{8}[\cos 4x]_0^{\frac{\pi}{4}}$$
$$= -\frac{1}{8}(\cos \pi - \cos 0)$$
$$= -\frac{1}{8}(-1 - 1) = \frac{1}{4}$$

f) $\sin^2 x - \cos^2 x = -(\cos^2 x - \sin^2 x)$
$$= -\cos 2x$$

So the integral is:

$$\int_{\frac{\pi}{4}}^{\frac{\pi}{2}} \sin^2 x - \cos^2 x\,dx = \int_{\frac{\pi}{4}}^{\frac{\pi}{2}} -\cos 2x\,dx$$
$$= -\frac{1}{2}[\sin 2x]_{\frac{\pi}{4}}^{\frac{\pi}{2}}$$
$$= -\frac{1}{2}\left(\sin \pi - \sin\frac{\pi}{2}\right)$$
$$= -\frac{1}{2}(0 - 1) = \frac{1}{2}$$

Exercise 4.2 — Integrating using other trigonometric identities

Q1 **a)** $\cot^2x - 4 = (\csc^2x - 1) - 4$
$$= \csc^2x - 5$$

So the integral is:
$$\int \cot^2x - 4 \, dx = \int \csc^2x - 5 \, dx$$
$$= -\cot x - 5x + C$$

b) $\tan^2x = \sec^2x - 1$

So the integral is:
$$\int \tan^2x \, dx = \int \sec^2x - 1 \, dx$$
$$= \tan x - x + C$$

c) $3\cot^2x = 3(\csc^2x - 1) = 3\csc^2x - 3$

So the integral is:
$$\int 3\cot^2x \, dx = \int 3\csc^2x - 3 \, dx$$
$$= -3\cot x - 3x + C$$

d) $\tan^2 4x = \sec^2 4x - 1$

So the integral is:
$$\int \tan^2 4x \, dx = \int \sec^2 4x - 1 \, dx$$
$$= \frac{1}{4}\tan 4x - x + C$$

Q2 $\tan^2x + \cos^2x - \sin^2x = (\sec^2x - 1) + \cos 2x$

So the integral is:
$$\int_0^{\frac{\pi}{4}} \tan^2x + \cos^2x - \sin^2x \, dx$$
$$= \int_0^{\frac{\pi}{4}} \sec^2x - 1 + \cos 2x \, dx$$
$$= \left[\tan x - x + \frac{1}{2}\sin 2x\right]_0^{\frac{\pi}{4}}$$
$$= \left[\tan\frac{\pi}{4} - \frac{\pi}{4} + \frac{1}{2}\sin\frac{2\pi}{4}\right] - \left[\tan 0 - 0 + \frac{1}{2}\sin 0\right]$$
$$= \left[1 - \frac{\pi}{4} + \frac{1}{2}\right] - [0 - 0 + 0]$$
$$= \frac{3}{2} - \frac{\pi}{4}$$

Q3 **a)** $\tan^3x + \tan^5x = \tan^3x(1 + \tan^2x)$
$$= \tan^3x\sec^2x$$
$$= \sec^2x\tan^3x$$

This is a product containing $\tan x$ to a power, and its derivative $\sec^2 x$.

Using the formula with $f(x) = \tan x$, $f'(x) = \sec^2 x$, $n = 3$ and $n + 1 = 4$ gives:
$$\int 4\sec^2x\tan^3x \, dx = \tan^4x + C$$
So the integral is:
$$\int \tan^3x + \tan^5x \, dx = \int \sec^2x\tan^3x \, dx$$
$$= \frac{1}{4}\int 4\sec^2x\tan^3x \, dx$$
$$= \frac{1}{4}\tan^4x + C$$

b) $\cot^5x + \cot^3x = \cot^3x(\cot^2x + 1) = \cot^3x\csc^2x$

Again, this is a product of a function to a power and its derivative so use the formula with $f(x) = \cot x$, $f'(x) = -\csc^2x$, $n = 3$ and $n + 1 = 4$.
$$\int -4\csc^2x\cot^3x \, dx = \cot^4x + C$$
So the integral is:
$$\int \cot^5x + \cot^3x \, dx = \int \csc^2x\cot^3x \, dx$$
$$= -\frac{1}{4}\int -4\csc^2x\cot^3x \, dx$$
$$= -\frac{1}{4}\cot^4x + C$$

c) $\sin^3x = \sin x\sin^2x$
$$= \sin x(1 - \cos^2x)$$
$$= \sin x - \sin x\cos^2x$$

The second term of this function is a product of a function to a power and its derivative. Using the result with $f(x) = \cos x$, $f'(x) = -\sin x$, $n = 2$ and $n + 1 = 3$ gives:
$$\int -3\sin x\cos^2x \, dx = \cos^3x + c$$
So the integral is:
$$\int \sin^3x \, dx = \int \sin x - \sin x\cos^2x \, dx$$
$$= \int \sin x \, dx + \int -\sin x\cos^2x \, dx$$
$$= -\cos x + \frac{1}{3}\cos^3x + C$$

Q4 $4 + \cot^2 3x = 4 + (\csc^2 3x - 1) = 3 + \csc^2 3x$

So the integral is:
$$\int 4 + \cot^2 3x \, dx = \int 3 + \csc^2 3x \, dx$$
$$= 3x - \frac{1}{3}\cot 3x + C$$

Q5 **a)** Let $A = 5x$ and $B = 3x$, then
$$\sin 5x + \sin 3x \equiv 2\sin\left(\frac{5x + 3x}{2}\right)\cos\left(\frac{5x - 3x}{2}\right)$$
$$\equiv 2\sin 4x\cos x$$

b) $\int 2\sin 4x\cos x \, dx = \int \sin 5x + \sin 3x \, dx$
$$= -\frac{1}{5}\cos 5x - \frac{1}{3}\cos 3x + C$$

Q6 $(\sec x + \tan x)^2 = \sec^2x + 2\tan x\sec x + \tan^2x$
$$= \sec^2x + 2\tan x\sec x + (\sec^2x - 1)$$
$$= 2\sec^2x + 2\tan x\sec x - 1$$

So the integral is:
$$\int (\sec x + \tan x)^2 \, dx = \int 2\sec^2x + 2\tan x\sec x - 1 \, dx$$
$$= 2\tan x + 2\sec x - x + C$$

Q7 $(\cot x + \csc x)^2 = \cot^2x + 2\cot x\csc x + \csc^2x$
$$= (\csc^2x - 1) + 2\cot x\csc x + \csc^2x$$
$$= 2\csc^2x + 2\cot x\csc x - 1$$

Just keep using the identities that you know until you get to something that you know how to integrate.

So the integral is:
$$\int (\cot x + \csc x)^2 \, dx$$
$$= \int 2\csc^2x + 2\cot x\csc x - 1 \, dx$$
$$= -2\cot x - 2\csc x - x + C$$

5. Differential Equations

Exercise 5.1 — Differential equations

Q1 The rate of change of N with respect to t is $\dfrac{dN}{dt}$.

So $\dfrac{dN}{dt} \propto N \Rightarrow \dfrac{dN}{dt} = kN$, for some $k > 0$.

Q2 The rate of change of x with respect to t is $\dfrac{dx}{dt}$.

So $\dfrac{dx}{dt} \propto \dfrac{1}{x^2} \Rightarrow \dfrac{dx}{dt} = \dfrac{k}{x^2}$, for some $k > 0$.

Q3 Let the variable t represent time.

Then the rate of change of A with respect to t is $\dfrac{dA}{dt}$.

So $\dfrac{dA}{dt} \propto \sqrt{A} \Rightarrow \dfrac{dA}{dt} = -k\sqrt{A}$, for some $k > 0$.

Don't forget to include a minus sign when the situation involves a rate of decrease.

Q4 Let the variable t represent time.

Then the rate of change of y with respect to t is $\dfrac{dy}{dt}$.

So $\dfrac{dy}{dt} \propto (y - \lambda) \Rightarrow \dfrac{dy}{dt} = -k(y - \lambda)$, for some $k > 0$.

Q5 Let the variable t represent time.
V is the volume in the container and it is equal to $V_{in} - V_{out}$. Then the rate of change of V with respect to t is $\dfrac{dV}{dt} = \dfrac{dV_{in}}{dt} - \dfrac{dV_{out}}{dt}$.

$\dfrac{dV_{in}}{dt}$ is directly proportional to V so $\dfrac{dV_{in}}{dt} = kV$ for some constant k, $k > 0$ and $\dfrac{dV_{out}}{dt} = 20$.

So the overall rate of change of V is $\dfrac{dV}{dt} = kV - 20$, for some $k > 0$.

Exercise 5.2 — Solving differential equations

Q1 a) $\dfrac{dy}{dx} = 8x^3 \Rightarrow dy = 8x^3\,dx$

$\Rightarrow \int 1\,dy = \int 8x^3\,dx$

$\Rightarrow y = 2x^4 + C$

b) $\dfrac{dy}{dx} = 5y \Rightarrow \dfrac{1}{y}dy = 5\,dx$

$\Rightarrow \int \dfrac{1}{y}\,dy = \int 5\,dx$

$\Rightarrow \ln|y| = 5x + \ln k$

$\Rightarrow y = e^{5x + \ln k} = ke^{5x}$

c) $\dfrac{dy}{dx} = 6x^2y \Rightarrow \dfrac{1}{y}dy = 6x^2 dx$

$\Rightarrow \int \dfrac{1}{y}\,dy = \int 6x^2\,dx$

$\Rightarrow \ln|y| = 2x^3 + \ln k$

$\Rightarrow y = e^{2x^3 + \ln k} = ke^{2x^3}$

d) $\dfrac{dy}{dx} = \dfrac{y}{x} \Rightarrow \dfrac{1}{y}dy = \dfrac{1}{x}dx$

$\Rightarrow \int \dfrac{1}{y}\,dy = \int \dfrac{1}{x}\,dx$

$\Rightarrow \ln|y| = \ln|x| + \ln k = \ln|kx|$

$\Rightarrow y = kx$

e) $\dfrac{dy}{dx} = (y + 1)\cos x \Rightarrow \dfrac{1}{y+1}dy = \cos x\,dx$

$\Rightarrow \int \dfrac{1}{y+1}\,dy = \int \cos x\,dx$

$\Rightarrow \ln|y + 1| = \sin x + \ln k$

$\Rightarrow y + 1 = e^{\sin x + \ln k}$

$\Rightarrow y = ke^{\sin x} - 1$

f) $\dfrac{dy}{dx} = \dfrac{(3x - 6)y}{(x - 4)(2x - 5)}$

$\Rightarrow \dfrac{1}{y}dy = \dfrac{(3x - 6)}{(x - 4)(2x - 5)}\,dx$

$\Rightarrow \int \dfrac{1}{y}\,dy = \int \dfrac{(3x - 6)}{(x - 4)(2x - 5)}\,dx$

The integration on the right hand side needs to be split into partial fractions before you can integrate.

$\dfrac{(3x - 6)}{(x - 4)(2x - 5)} \equiv \dfrac{A}{(x - 4)} + \dfrac{B}{(2x - 5)}$

$\Rightarrow (3x - 6) \equiv A(2x - 5) + B(x - 4)$

Substitution:

$x = 4$: $6 = 3A \Rightarrow A = 2$

$x = \dfrac{5}{2}$: $\dfrac{3}{2} = -\dfrac{3}{2}B \Rightarrow B = -1$

So

$\int \dfrac{(3x - 6)}{(x - 4)(2x - 5)}\,dx \equiv \int \dfrac{2}{(x - 4)} - \dfrac{1}{(2x - 5)}\,dx$

So $\int \dfrac{1}{y}\,dy = \int \dfrac{2}{(x - 4)} - \dfrac{1}{(2x - 5)}\,dx$

$\Rightarrow \ln|y| = 2\ln|x - 4| - \dfrac{1}{2}\ln|2x - 5| + \ln k$

$\Rightarrow \ln|y| = \ln|(x - 4)^2| - \ln|\sqrt{2x - 5}| + \ln k$

$\Rightarrow \ln|y| = \ln\left|\dfrac{k(x - 4)^2}{\sqrt{2x - 5}}\right|$

$\Rightarrow y = \dfrac{k(x - 4)^2}{\sqrt{2x - 5}}$

Q2 a) $\dfrac{dy}{dx} = -\dfrac{x}{y} \Rightarrow y\,dy = -x\,dx$

$\Rightarrow \int y\,dy = \int -x\,dx$

$\Rightarrow \dfrac{1}{2}y^2 = -\dfrac{1}{2}x^2 + c$

$\Rightarrow y^2 = -x^2 + C$

So when $x = 0$ and $y = 2$, $C = 4 \Rightarrow y^2 + x^2 = 4$

b) $\dfrac{dx}{dt} = \dfrac{2}{\sqrt{x}} \Rightarrow \sqrt{x}\,dx = 2\,dt$

$\Rightarrow \int x^{\frac{1}{2}}\,dx = \int 2\,dt$

$\Rightarrow \dfrac{2}{3}x^{\frac{3}{2}} = 2t + C$

So when $t = 5$ and $x = 9$,

$\dfrac{2}{3}(27) = 10 + C \Rightarrow 18 = 10 + C \Rightarrow C = 8$

$\Rightarrow \dfrac{2}{3}x^{\frac{3}{2}} = 2t + 8$

$\Rightarrow x^{\frac{3}{2}} = 3t + 12$

$\Rightarrow x^3 = (3t + 12)^2$

You could have left out the last couple of steps here, as the question didn't specify the form of the answer.

c) $\frac{dV}{dt} = 3(V-1) \Rightarrow \frac{1}{V-1}dV = 3\,dt$

$\qquad\qquad \Rightarrow \int \frac{1}{V-1}dV = \int 3\,dt$

$\qquad\qquad \Rightarrow \ln|V-1| = 3t + \ln k$

$\qquad\qquad \Rightarrow V = ke^{3t} + 1$

So when $t = 0$ and $V = 5$,
$5 = k + 1 \Rightarrow k = 4$
$\qquad\qquad \Rightarrow V = 4e^{3t} + 1$

d) $\frac{dy}{dx} = \frac{\tan y}{x} \Rightarrow \frac{1}{\tan y}dy = \frac{1}{x}dx$

$\qquad\qquad \Rightarrow \int \cot y\,dy = \int \frac{1}{x}dx$

$\qquad\qquad \Rightarrow \ln|\sin y| = \ln|x| + \ln k$

$\qquad\qquad \Rightarrow \sin y = kx$

So when $x = 2$ and $y = \frac{\pi}{2}$,
$1 = 2k \Rightarrow k = \frac{1}{2} \Rightarrow \sin y = \frac{x}{2}$

e) $\frac{dx}{dt} = 10x(x+1) \Rightarrow \frac{1}{x(x+1)}dx = 10\,dt$

Using partial fractions, $\frac{1}{x(x+1)} \equiv \frac{1}{x} - \frac{1}{x+1}$,

so $\int \frac{1}{x} - \frac{1}{x+1}dx = \int 10\,dt$

$\Rightarrow \ln|x| - \ln|x+1| = 10t + \ln k$

$\Rightarrow \ln\left|\frac{x}{x+1}\right| = 10t + \ln k$

$\Rightarrow \frac{x}{x+1} = ke^{10t}$

So when $t = 0$ and $x = 1$, $\frac{1}{2} = k$

$\Rightarrow \frac{x}{x+1} = \frac{1}{2}e^{10t}$

Q3 a) $\frac{dV}{dt} = a - bV \Rightarrow \frac{1}{a-bV}dV = dt$

$\qquad\qquad \Rightarrow \int \frac{1}{a-bV}dV = \int 1\,dt$

$\qquad\qquad \Rightarrow -\frac{1}{b}\ln|a-bV| = t + C$

$\qquad\qquad \Rightarrow \ln|a-bV| = -bt - bC$

b and C are both constants, so let $-bC = \ln k$:

$\qquad\qquad \Rightarrow \ln|a-bV| = -bt + \ln k$

$\qquad\qquad \Rightarrow a - bV = ke^{-bt}$

$\qquad\qquad \Rightarrow bV = a - ke^{-bt}$

$\qquad\qquad \Rightarrow V = \frac{a}{b} - Ae^{-bt} \text{ (letting } A = k \div b)$

b) When $t = 0$ and $V = \frac{a}{4b}$,

$\frac{a}{4b} = \frac{a}{b} - A \Rightarrow A = \frac{a}{b} - \frac{a}{4b} = \frac{4a-a}{4b} = \frac{3a}{4b}$

c) As t gets very large, e^{-bt} gets very close to zero, so V approaches $\frac{a}{b}$.

Q4 a) $\frac{dx}{dt} = (x+2)(2x+3)\tan t$

$\qquad \Rightarrow \frac{1}{(x+2)(2x+3)}dx = \tan t\,dt$

Using partial fractions,

$\frac{1}{(x+2)(2x+3)} \equiv \frac{2}{2x+3} - \frac{1}{x+2}$,

so $\int \frac{2}{2x+3} - \frac{1}{x+2}dx = \int \tan t\,dt$

$\Rightarrow \ln(2x+3) - \ln(x+2) = \ln(\sec t) + \ln k$

$\Rightarrow \ln\frac{2x+3}{x+2} = \ln(k\sec t)$

$\Rightarrow \frac{2x+3}{x+2} = k\sec t = \frac{k}{\cos t}$

So when $t = 0$ and $x = 0$, $\frac{3}{2} = k$

$\Rightarrow \frac{2x+3}{x+2} = \frac{3}{2\cos t}$

b) $t = \frac{\pi}{3} \Rightarrow \frac{2x+3}{x+2} = \frac{3}{2\cos\frac{\pi}{3}} = 3$

$\Rightarrow 2x+3 = 3x+6 \Rightarrow x = -3$

Exercise 5.3 — Applying differential equations to real-life problems

Q1 a) $\frac{dN}{dt} = kN \Rightarrow \frac{1}{N}dN = k\,dt$

$\qquad\qquad \Rightarrow \int \frac{1}{N}dN = \int k\,dt$

$\qquad\qquad \Rightarrow \ln N = kt + \ln A$

$\qquad\qquad \Rightarrow N = e^{kt + \ln A} = Ae^{kt}$

Note that you don't need to put modulus signs in $\ln N$ here, as N can't be negative — you can't have a negative number of germs in your body. The same principle will apply to a lot of real-life differential equations questions.

b) $t = 0, N = 200 \Rightarrow 200 = Ae^0 = A$

$\qquad\qquad \Rightarrow N = 200e^{kt}$

$t = 8, N = 400 \Rightarrow 400 = 200e^{8k}$

$\qquad\qquad \Rightarrow \ln 2 = 8k$

$\qquad\qquad \Rightarrow k = \frac{1}{8}\ln 2$

$\qquad\qquad \Rightarrow N = 200e^{\frac{t}{8}\ln 2}$

So $t = 24 \Rightarrow N = 200e^{3\ln 2} = 1600$

Q2 a) $\frac{dV}{dt} \propto V \Rightarrow \frac{dV}{dt} = -kV, \text{ for some } k > 0$

$\qquad\qquad \Rightarrow \frac{1}{V}dV = -k\,dt$

$\qquad\qquad \Rightarrow \int \frac{1}{V}dV = \int -k\,dt$

$\qquad\qquad \Rightarrow \ln V = -kt + \ln A$

$\qquad\qquad \Rightarrow V = Ae^{-kt}$

$t = 0, V = V_0 \Rightarrow V_0 = Ae^0 = A$

$\qquad\qquad \Rightarrow V = V_0 e^{-kt}$

b) $t = 1, V = \frac{1}{2}V_0 \Rightarrow \frac{1}{2}V_0 = V_0 e^{-k}$

$\qquad\qquad \Rightarrow \frac{1}{2} = e^{-k}$

$\qquad\qquad \Rightarrow \ln\frac{1}{2} = -k$

$\qquad\qquad \Rightarrow k = \ln 2$

$\qquad\qquad \Rightarrow V = V_0 e^{-t\ln 2}$

So $V = 0.05V_0 \Rightarrow 0.05V_0 = V_0 e^{-t\ln 2}$

$\qquad\qquad \Rightarrow 0.05 = e^{-t\ln 2}$

$\qquad\qquad \Rightarrow \ln 0.05 = -t\ln 2$

$\qquad\qquad \Rightarrow t = \ln 0.05 \div -\ln 2 = 4.322 \text{ years}$

$\qquad\qquad \Rightarrow t = 4 \text{ years, 4 months}$
$\qquad\qquad\qquad \text{(or 52 months)}$

You could have used months as the units of time instead, and started with $t = 12$. You'd get the same answer.

Q3 a) $\dfrac{\mathrm{d}N}{\mathrm{d}t} \propto N \;\Rightarrow\; \dfrac{\mathrm{d}N}{\mathrm{d}t} = kN$

b) $\dfrac{\mathrm{d}N}{\mathrm{d}t} = kN \;\Rightarrow\; \displaystyle\int \dfrac{1}{N}\,\mathrm{d}N = \int k\,\mathrm{d}t$

$\Rightarrow\; \ln N = kt + \ln A$

$\Rightarrow\; N = \mathrm{e}^{kt + \ln A} = A\mathrm{e}^{kt}$

$N = 20$ at $t = 0 \;\Rightarrow\; 20 = A\mathrm{e}^0 = A \;\Rightarrow\; N = 20\mathrm{e}^{kt}$

$N = 30$ at $t = 4 \;\Rightarrow\; 30 = 20\mathrm{e}^{4k}$

$\Rightarrow\; k = 0.25\ln 1.5$

$\Rightarrow\; N = 20\mathrm{e}^{0.25t\ln 1.5}$

So $N = 1000 \;\Rightarrow\; 1000 = 20\mathrm{e}^{0.25t\ln 1.5}$

$\Rightarrow\; \ln 50 = 0.25t\ln 1.5$

$\Rightarrow\; t = 4\ln 50 \div \ln 1.5 = 38.59$

So the field will be over-run in 39 weeks.

c) $\dfrac{\mathrm{d}N}{\mathrm{d}t} \propto \sqrt{N} \;\Rightarrow\; \dfrac{\mathrm{d}N}{\mathrm{d}t} = k\sqrt{N}$

$\Rightarrow\; \displaystyle\int \dfrac{1}{\sqrt{N}}\,\mathrm{d}N = \int k\,\mathrm{d}t$

$\Rightarrow\; 2\sqrt{N} = kt + C$

$N = 20$ at $t = 0 \;\Rightarrow\; 2\sqrt{20} = 4\sqrt{5} = C$

$\Rightarrow\; 2\sqrt{N} = kt + 4\sqrt{5}$

$N = 30$ at $t = 4 \;\Rightarrow\; 2\sqrt{30} = 4k + 4\sqrt{5}$

$\Rightarrow\; k = \dfrac{\sqrt{30} - 2\sqrt{5}}{2}$

$\Rightarrow\; 2\sqrt{N} = \dfrac{\sqrt{30} - 2\sqrt{5}}{2}t + 4\sqrt{5}$

So $N = 1000 \;\Rightarrow\; 2\sqrt{1000} = \dfrac{\sqrt{30} - 2\sqrt{5}}{2}t + 4\sqrt{5}$

$\Rightarrow\; t = \dfrac{4\sqrt{1000} - 8\sqrt{5}}{\sqrt{30} - 2\sqrt{5}} = 108.05$

So the field will be over-run in 108 weeks.

Be careful with all these square roots knocking about — it's easy to make a mistake.

Q4 a) $\dfrac{\mathrm{d}x}{\mathrm{d}t} = \dfrac{1}{x^2(t + 1)}$

$V = x^3 \;\Rightarrow\; \dfrac{\mathrm{d}V}{\mathrm{d}x} = 3x^2$

So $\dfrac{\mathrm{d}V}{\mathrm{d}t} = \dfrac{\mathrm{d}V}{\mathrm{d}x} \times \dfrac{\mathrm{d}x}{\mathrm{d}t} = \dfrac{3x^2}{x^2(t + 1)} = \dfrac{3}{t + 1}$

b) $\dfrac{\mathrm{d}V}{\mathrm{d}t} = \dfrac{3}{t + 1} \;\Rightarrow\; \displaystyle\int 1\,\mathrm{d}V = \int \dfrac{3}{t + 1}\,\mathrm{d}t$

$\Rightarrow\; V = 3\ln(t + 1) + C$

$V = 15$ at $t = 0 \;\Rightarrow\; 15 = 3\ln(1) + C \;\Rightarrow\; C = 15$

$\Rightarrow\; V = 3\ln(t + 1) + 15$

So $V = 19 \;\Rightarrow\; 19 = 3\ln(t + 1) + 15$

$\Rightarrow\; \dfrac{4}{3} = \ln(t + 1)$

$\Rightarrow\; t = \mathrm{e}^{\frac{4}{3}} - 1 = 2.79$ seconds (3 s.f.)

Q5 a) $\dfrac{\mathrm{d}y}{\mathrm{d}t} = k(p - y) \;\Rightarrow\; \displaystyle\int \dfrac{1}{p - y}\,\mathrm{d}y = \int k\,\mathrm{d}t$

$\Rightarrow\; -\ln(p - y) = kt + \ln a$

$\Rightarrow\; \ln(p - y) = -kt - \ln a$

$\Rightarrow\; p - y = \mathrm{e}^{-kt - \ln a} = \mathrm{e}^{-kt}\mathrm{e}^{-\ln a}$

$\mathrm{e}^{-kt}\mathrm{e}^{\ln\frac{1}{a}} = \dfrac{1}{a}\mathrm{e}^{-kt} = A\mathrm{e}^{-kt}$

$\Rightarrow\; y = p - A\mathrm{e}^{-kt}$

b) If $p = 30\,000$ and $y = 10\,000$ at $t = 0$, then

$10\,000 = 30\,000 - A\mathrm{e}^0 = 30\,000 - A$

$\Rightarrow\; A = 20\,000$

$\Rightarrow\; y = 30\,000 - 20\,000\mathrm{e}^{-kt}$

$t = 5, \; y = 12\,000$

$\Rightarrow\; 12\,000 = 30\,000 - 20\,000\mathrm{e}^{-5k}$

$\Rightarrow\; \mathrm{e}^{-5k} = 18\,000 \div 20\,000 = 0.9$

$\Rightarrow\; -5k = \ln 0.9$

$\Rightarrow\; k = -0.2\ln 0.9$

$\Rightarrow\; y = 30\,000 - 20\,000\mathrm{e}^{0.2t\ln 0.9}$

So $y = 25\,000 \;\Rightarrow\; 20\,000\mathrm{e}^{0.2t\ln 0.9} = 5000$

$\Rightarrow\; \mathrm{e}^{0.2t\ln 0.9} = 0.25$

$\Rightarrow\; 0.2t\ln 0.9 = \ln 0.25$

$\Rightarrow\; t = 5\ln 0.25 \div \ln 0.9$

$= 65.79 = 66$ days

c)

$y = 30\,000 - 20\,000\mathrm{e}^{0.2\ln 0.9t}$

Remember that 0.2ln0.9t is negative when sketching the graph.

d) $t = 92 \;\Rightarrow\; y = 30\,000 - 20\,000\mathrm{e}^{18.4\ln 0.9}$

$= 30\,000 - 20\,000\mathrm{e}^{-1.939}$

$= 30\,000 - 20\,000(0.1439)$

$= 27122$ members

So no, the target will not be achieved.

Don't forget, you'll often need to relate your answer back to the question when you've finished calculating.

Review Exercise — Chapter 5

Q1 a) $\dfrac{\mathrm{d}x}{\mathrm{d}t} = 2t, \; \dfrac{\mathrm{d}y}{\mathrm{d}t} = 9t^2 - 4$, so

$\dfrac{\mathrm{d}y}{\mathrm{d}x} = \dfrac{\mathrm{d}y}{\mathrm{d}t} \div \dfrac{\mathrm{d}x}{\mathrm{d}t} = \dfrac{9t^2 - 4}{2t}$

b) The stationary points are when $\dfrac{9t^2 - 4}{2t} = 0$

$\Rightarrow\; 9t^2 = 4 \;\Rightarrow\; t = \pm\dfrac{2}{3}$

When $t = \dfrac{2}{3}$: $x = \left(\dfrac{2}{3}\right)^2 = \dfrac{4}{9}$,

$y = 3\left(\dfrac{2}{3}\right)^3 - 4\left(\dfrac{2}{3}\right) = \dfrac{8}{9} - \dfrac{8}{3} = -\dfrac{16}{9}$

When $t = -\dfrac{2}{3}$: $x = \left(-\dfrac{2}{3}\right)^2 = \dfrac{4}{9}$,

$y = 3\left(-\dfrac{2}{3}\right)^3 - 4\left(-\dfrac{2}{3}\right) = -\dfrac{8}{9} + \dfrac{8}{3} = \dfrac{16}{9}$

So the stationary points are $\left(\dfrac{4}{9}, -\dfrac{16}{9}\right)$ and $\left(\dfrac{4}{9}, \dfrac{16}{9}\right)$.

Q2 a) $\dfrac{\mathrm{d}y}{\mathrm{d}x} = \dfrac{3t^2 + 6t - 9}{3t^2 - 2t}$.

At the turning point $\dfrac{\mathrm{d}y}{\mathrm{d}x} = 0$, so:

$3t^2 + 6t - 9 = 0$

$\Rightarrow\; 3(t^2 + 2t - 3) = 0$

$\Rightarrow\; 3(t - 1)(t + 3) = 0 \;\Rightarrow\; t = 1 \text{ or } t = -3$

When $t = 1$, $x = 0$, $y = -5$.

When $t = -3$, $x = -36$, $y = 27$.

So the coordinates of the turning points are $(0, -5)$ and $(-36, 27)$.

b) C cuts the x-axis when $y = 0$,

$\Rightarrow t^3 + 3t^2 - 9t = 0 \Rightarrow t(t^2 + 3t - 9) = 0$

$\Rightarrow t = 0$ or $t = \dfrac{-3 \pm 3\sqrt{5}}{2}$.

When $t = 0$, $x = 0$ and $y = 0$, so C passes through the origin.

Use the quadratic formula to find the other values of t.

c) When $t = 2$, $\dfrac{dy}{dx} = \dfrac{3(2)^2 + 6(2) - 9}{3(2)^2 - 2(2)} = \dfrac{15}{8}$,

$x = 2^3 - 2^2 = 4$, and $y = 2^3 + 3(2)^2 - 9(2) = 2$.

Putting this into $y = mx + c$ gives:

$2 = \dfrac{15}{8}(4) + c \Rightarrow c = -\dfrac{11}{2}$

The equation of the tangent is $y = \dfrac{15}{8}x - \dfrac{11}{2}$

or $8y = 15x - 44$.

Q3 a) $\dfrac{dy}{dx} = \dfrac{2e^{2s} + 2se^{2s} + e^{2s}}{3se^s + 3e^s}$

$= \dfrac{e^{2s}(3 + 2s)}{3e^s(s + 1)} = \dfrac{e^s(3 + 2s)}{3(s + 1)}$

When $s = 0$, $\dfrac{dy}{dx} = 1$, $x = 0$, $y = 1$,

so the equation of the tangent is $y = x + 1$.

When $s = 2$, $\dfrac{dy}{dx} = \dfrac{7e^2}{9}$, $y = 3e^4$, $x = 6e^2$.

Putting this into $y = mx + c$ gives:

$3e^4 = \left(\dfrac{7e^2}{9}\right)6e^2 + c \Rightarrow c = \dfrac{27e^4 - 42e^4}{9} = -\dfrac{15e^4}{9}$

so the equation of the tangent is $y = \left(\dfrac{7e^2}{9}\right)x - \dfrac{15e^4}{9}$

or $9y = 7e^2 x - 15e^4$.

b) The lines intersect when:

$9x + 9 = 7e^2x - 15e^4$

$(7e^2 - 9)x = 9 + 15e^4$

$x = \dfrac{9 + 15e^4}{7e^2 - 9}$, $y = \dfrac{9 + 15e^4}{7e^2 - 9} + 1$

Q4 a) The gradient $\dfrac{dy}{dx} = \dfrac{t - 6}{3t^2 + 2t}$.

b) The turning point is when $t - 6 = 0$, so $t = 6$, because the denominator cannot be 0.

When $t = 6$, $x = 252$ and $y = -18$, so the coordinates of the turning point are $(252, -18)$.

c) When $y = 0$:

$\dfrac{1}{2}t^2 - 6t = 0 \Rightarrow t^2 - 12t = 0 \Rightarrow t(t - 12) = 0$

$\Rightarrow t = 0$ or $t = 12$

When $t = 0$, the gradient is undefined.

When $t = 12$, $\dfrac{dy}{dx} = \dfrac{1}{76}$ and $x = 1872$.

Putting this into $y = mx + c$ gives:

$0 = \dfrac{1}{76}(1872) + c \Rightarrow c = -\dfrac{468}{19}$

So the equation of the tangent is

$y = \dfrac{1}{76}x - \dfrac{468}{19}$

Q5 a) Differentiate each term separately with respect to x:

$\dfrac{d}{dx}4x^2 - \dfrac{d}{dx}2y^2 = \dfrac{d}{dx}7x^2y$

Differentiate $4x^2$ first:

$\Rightarrow 8x - \dfrac{d}{dx}2y^2 = \dfrac{d}{dx}7x^2y$

Differentiate $2y^2$ using chain rule:

$\Rightarrow 8x - \dfrac{d}{dy}2y^2\dfrac{dy}{dx} = \dfrac{d}{dx}7x^2y$

$\Rightarrow 8x - 4y\dfrac{dy}{dx} = \dfrac{d}{dx}7x^2y$

Differentiate $7x^2y$ using product rule:

$\Rightarrow 8x - 4y\dfrac{dy}{dx} = 7x^2\dfrac{d}{dx}y + y\dfrac{d}{dx}7x^2$

$\Rightarrow 8x - 4y\dfrac{dy}{dx} = 7x^2\dfrac{dy}{dx} + 14xy$

Rearrange to make $\dfrac{dy}{dx}$ the subject:

$\Rightarrow (4y + 7x^2)\dfrac{dy}{dx} = 8x - 14xy$

$\Rightarrow \dfrac{dy}{dx} = \dfrac{8x - 14xy}{4y + 7x^2}$

b) Differentiate each term separately with respect to x:

$\dfrac{d}{dx}3x^4 - \dfrac{d}{dx}2xy^2 = \dfrac{d}{dx}y$

$\Rightarrow 12x^3 - 2y^2 - 4xy\dfrac{dy}{dx} = \dfrac{dy}{dx}$

Rearrange to make $\dfrac{dy}{dx}$ the subject:

$\Rightarrow (1 + 4xy)\dfrac{dy}{dx} = 12x^3 - 2y^2$

$\Rightarrow \dfrac{dy}{dx} = \dfrac{12x^3 - 2y^2}{1 + 4xy}$

c) Differentiate each term separately with respect to x:

$\dfrac{d}{dx}\cos x \sin y = \dfrac{d}{dx}xy$

$\Rightarrow (\cos x \cos y)\dfrac{dy}{dx} - \sin y \sin x = x\dfrac{dy}{dx} + y$

Rearrange to make $\dfrac{dy}{dx}$ the subject:

$\Rightarrow (\cos x \cos y - x)\dfrac{dy}{dx} = y + \sin x \sin y$

$\Rightarrow \dfrac{dy}{dx} = \dfrac{\sin x \sin y + y}{\cos x \cos y - x}$

Q6 a) At $(1, -4)$, $\dfrac{dy}{dx} = \dfrac{8x - 14xy}{4y + 7x^2}$

$= \dfrac{8(1) - 14(1)(-4)}{4(-4) + 7(1)^2} = \dfrac{8 + 56}{-16 + 7} = -\dfrac{64}{9}$

b) At $(1, 1)$, $\dfrac{dy}{dx} = \dfrac{12x^3 - 2y^2}{1 + 4xy}$

$= \dfrac{12(1)^3 - 2(1)^2}{1 + 4(1)(1)} = \dfrac{12 - 2}{1 + 4} = \dfrac{10}{5} = 2$

So the gradient of the normal is $-\dfrac{1}{2}$.

Q7 a) $\cos x - x \sin x + y \cos x + \sin x \dfrac{dy}{dx} = 3y^2\dfrac{dy}{dx}$

$\dfrac{dy}{dx} = \dfrac{\cos x - x \sin x + y \cos x}{3y^2 - \sin x}$

b) At the stationary points, $\dfrac{dy}{dx} = 0$, hence

$\cos x - x \sin x + y \cos x = 0$

$y \cos x = x \sin x - \cos x$,

so $y = \dfrac{x \sin x}{\cos x} - \dfrac{\cos x}{\cos x} = x \tan x - 1$, as required.

Use the identity tan x ≡ sin x / cos x for the last part.

c) When $x = \frac{\pi}{2}$, $\frac{\pi}{2}(0) + y = y^3$, hence $y^3 - y = 0$
$\Rightarrow y(y + 1)(y - 1) = 0$, giving $y = 0$, $y = 1$ and
$y = -1$, so the three points on the curve have
coordinates $(\frac{\pi}{2}, 0)$, $(\frac{\pi}{2}, 1)$ and $(\frac{\pi}{2}, -1)$.

d) $(\frac{\pi}{2}, 0)$: $\frac{dy}{dx} = \frac{0 - \frac{\pi}{2} + 0}{0 - 1} = \frac{\pi}{2}$

$0 = \frac{\pi^2}{4} + c$, so the equation of the tangent is
$y = \frac{\pi}{2}x - \frac{\pi^2}{4}$

$(\frac{\pi}{2}, 1)$: $\frac{dy}{dx} = \frac{0 - \frac{\pi}{2} + 0}{3 - 1} = -\frac{\pi}{4}$

$1 = -\frac{\pi^2}{8} + c$, so the equation of the tangent is
$y = (1 + \frac{\pi^2}{8}) - \frac{\pi}{4}x$

$(\frac{\pi}{2}, -1)$: $\frac{dy}{dx} = \frac{0 - \frac{\pi}{2} + 0}{3 - 1} = -\frac{\pi}{4}$

$-1 = -\frac{\pi^2}{8} + c$, so the equation of the tangent is
$y = (\frac{\pi^2}{8} - 1) - \frac{\pi}{4}x$

The last two tangents both have gradient $-\frac{\pi}{4}$, so
they are parallel and will never intersect.

Q8 a) When $x = 1$, $y = y^2 - 6$, so $y^2 - y - 6 = 0$
$\Rightarrow (y - 3)(y + 2) = 0 \Rightarrow y = 3$, $y = -2$,
so $a = 3$, $b = -2$.

b) $\ln x + 1 + 2xy + x^2\frac{dy}{dx} = y^2 + 2yx\frac{dy}{dx} - 6$

$\frac{dy}{dx} = \frac{\ln x + 2xy - y^2 + 7}{2xy - x^2}$

At $(1, 3)$: $\frac{dy}{dx} = \frac{0 + 6 - 9 + 7}{6 - 1} = \frac{4}{5}$

Gradient of normal is $-\frac{5}{4}$

$3 = -\frac{5}{4} + c \Rightarrow c = \frac{17}{4}$

Hence the equation of the normal is $4y = 17 - 5x$

At $(1, -2)$: $\frac{dy}{dx} = \frac{0 - 4 - 4 + 7}{-4 - 1} = \frac{-1}{-5} = \frac{1}{5}$

Gradient of normal is -5

$-2 = -5 + c \Rightarrow c = 3$

Hence the equation of the normal is $y = 3 - 5x$

c) The normals intersect where $\frac{17}{4} - \frac{5}{4}x = 3 - 5x$

$\frac{15}{4}x = -\frac{5}{4} \Rightarrow x = -\frac{1}{3}$, so $y = 3 + \frac{5}{3} = \frac{14}{3}$,

so the point of intersection is at $(-\frac{1}{3}, \frac{14}{3})$.

Q9 $\frac{3x + 10}{(2x + 3)(x - 4)} \equiv \frac{A}{2x + 3} + \frac{B}{x - 4}$

$\Rightarrow 3x + 10 \equiv A(x - 4) + B(2x + 3)$

Use the substitution method to get A and B.

Substituting $x = 4$ gives: $22 = 11B \Rightarrow B = 2$.

Substituting $x = -\frac{3}{2}$ gives: $\frac{11}{2} = -\frac{11}{2}A \Rightarrow A = -1$.

So writing the function as partial fractions:

$\frac{3x + 10}{(2x + 3)(x - 4)} \equiv -\frac{1}{2x + 3} + \frac{2}{x - 4}$

So the integral can be expressed:

$\int \frac{3x + 10}{(2x + 3)(x - 4)}\,dx$

$= \int -\frac{1}{2x + 3} + \frac{2}{x - 4}\,dx$

$= -\frac{1}{2}\ln|2x + 3| + 2\ln|x - 4| + C$

Q10 Writing $f(x)$ as partial fractions:

$\frac{-2x^2 + 12x + 31}{(x - 3)^2(2x + 1)} \equiv \frac{A}{(x - 3)^2} + \frac{B}{(x - 3)} + \frac{C}{(2x + 1)}$

$\Rightarrow \frac{-2x^2 + 12x + 31}{(x - 3)^2(2x + 1)}$

$= \frac{A(2x + 1) + B(x - 3)(2x + 1) + C(x - 3)^2}{(x - 3)^2(2x + 1)}$

$\Rightarrow -2x^2 + 12x + 31$

$= A(2x + 1) + B(x - 3)(2x + 1) + C(x - 3)^2$

Use the substitution method to work out some of the
constants:

Substituting $x = 3$ gives: $49 = 7A \Rightarrow A = 7$.

Substituting $x = -\frac{1}{2}$ gives: $\frac{49}{2} = \frac{49}{4}C \Rightarrow C = 2$.

Now equating coefficients of x^2 gives: $2B + C = -2$
$\Rightarrow 2B + 2 = -2 \Rightarrow 2B = -4 \Rightarrow B = -2$.

So writing $f(x)$ as partial fractions:

$\frac{-2x^2 + 12x + 31}{(x - 3)^2(2x + 1)} = \frac{7}{(x - 3)^2} - \frac{2}{(x - 3)} + \frac{2}{(2x + 1)}$

So the integral can be expressed:

$\int_4^9 f(x)\,dx$

$= \int_4^9 \frac{-2x^2 + 12x + 31}{(x - 3)^2(2x + 1)}\,dx$

$= \int_4^9 \frac{7}{(x - 3)^2} - \frac{2}{(x - 3)} + \frac{2}{(2x + 1)}\,dx$

$= \int_4^9 7(x - 3)^{-2} - \frac{2}{(x - 3)} + \frac{2}{(2x + 1)}\,dx$

$= \left[\frac{1}{-1}(7(x - 3)^{-1}) - 2\ln|x - 3| + \ln|2x + 1|\right]_4^9$

$= \left[-\frac{7}{(x - 3)} - 2\ln|x - 3| + \ln|2x + 1|\right]_4^9$

$= \left[-\frac{7}{6} - 2\ln|6| + \ln|19|\right] - \left[-\frac{7}{1} - 2\ln|1| + \ln|9|\right]$

$= -\frac{7}{6} - 2\ln|6| + \ln|19| + 7 + 0 - \ln|9|$ (as $\ln 1 = 0$)

$= -\frac{7}{6} - \ln 36 + \ln 19 + 7 - \ln 9$

$= \frac{35}{6} + \ln\left(\frac{19}{36 \times 9}\right) = \frac{35}{6} + \ln\left(\frac{19}{324}\right)$

Q11 $\frac{2\tan 3x}{1 - \tan^2 3x} = \tan(2(3x)) = \tan 6x$

So $\int \frac{2\tan 3x}{1 - \tan^2 3x}\,dx = \int \tan 6x\,dx$

$= \frac{1}{6}(-\ln|\cos 6x|) + C$

$= -\frac{1}{6}\ln|\cos 6x| + C$

$(\text{or} = \frac{1}{6}\ln|\sec 6x| + C)$

Q12 $\cos^2 4x + \cot^2 4x = \frac{1}{2}(\cos 8x + 1) + (\operatorname{cosec}^2 4x - 1)$

$\qquad\qquad\qquad\qquad = \frac{1}{2}\cos 8x + \operatorname{cosec}^2 4x - \frac{1}{2}$

So the integral is:

$\int \cos^2 4x + \cot^2 4x \, dx = \int \frac{1}{2}\cos 8x + \operatorname{cosec}^2 4x - \frac{1}{2} \, dx$

$\qquad\qquad\qquad = \frac{1}{2}\left(\frac{1}{8}\sin 8x\right) - \frac{1}{4}\cot 4x - \frac{1}{2}x + C$

$\qquad\qquad\qquad = \frac{1}{16}\sin 8x - \frac{1}{4}\cot 4x - \frac{1}{2}x + C$

Q13 a) $\dfrac{dx}{dy} \propto x^2 \quad\Rightarrow\quad \dfrac{dx}{dy} = kx^2$, for some $k > 0$

b) $\dfrac{dV}{dt} \propto \dfrac{1}{\sqrt{V}} \quad\Rightarrow\quad \dfrac{dV}{dt} = -\dfrac{k}{\sqrt{V}}$, for some $k > 0$

c) $\dfrac{ds}{dt} \propto (s_0 - s) \quad\Rightarrow\quad \dfrac{ds}{dt} = -k(s_0 - s)$, for some $k > 0$

Q14 $\dfrac{dy}{dx} = \dfrac{1}{y}\cos x \Rightarrow y\,dy = \cos x\,dx$

so $\int y\,dy = \int \cos x\,dx \Rightarrow \dfrac{y^2}{2} = \sin x + C_0$

$\Rightarrow y^2 = 2\sin x + C_1 \,(\text{where } C_1 = 2C_0)$

Q15 $\dfrac{dx}{dt} = kte^t \Rightarrow dx = kte^t\,dt$

$\qquad\qquad \Rightarrow \int 1\,dx = \int kte^t\,dt$

$\qquad\qquad \Rightarrow x = k(te^t - e^t) + C$

$\qquad\qquad\qquad$ (using integration by parts)

$x = 0, t = 1 \quad\Rightarrow\quad 0 = k(e - e) + C \Rightarrow C = 0$

$x = -3, t = 0 \quad\Rightarrow\quad -3 = k(0 - e^0) = -k \Rightarrow k = 3$

So $x = 3(te^t - e^t) = 3e^t(t - 1)$

Q16 a) $\dfrac{dx}{d\theta} = \cos^2 x\cot\theta \quad\Rightarrow\quad \int \sec^2 x\,dx = \int \cot\theta\,d\theta$

$\qquad\qquad\qquad\qquad \Rightarrow \tan x = \ln|\sin\theta| + C$

b) $x = \dfrac{\pi}{4}, \theta = \dfrac{\pi}{2} \quad\Rightarrow\quad \tan\dfrac{\pi}{4} = \ln\left|\sin\dfrac{\pi}{2}\right| + C$

$\qquad\qquad\qquad\qquad \Rightarrow 1 = \ln 1 + C$

$\qquad\qquad\qquad\qquad \Rightarrow C = 1$

$\qquad\qquad\qquad\qquad \Rightarrow \tan x = \ln|\sin\theta| + 1$

c) $\theta = \dfrac{\pi}{6} \Rightarrow \tan x = \ln\left|\sin\dfrac{\pi}{6}\right| + 1$

$\qquad\qquad\qquad = \ln\dfrac{1}{2} + 1 = 0.306...$

$\qquad\qquad \Rightarrow \quad x = 0.298 \text{ to 3 d.p.}$

Q17 a) $\dfrac{dS}{dt} = kS$

b) $\dfrac{dS}{dt} = kS \quad\Rightarrow\quad \int \dfrac{1}{S}dS = \int k\,dt$

$\qquad\qquad\qquad \Rightarrow \ln|S| = kt + \ln A$

$\qquad\qquad\qquad \Rightarrow S = Ae^{kt}$

At $t = 0$, $S = 30 \Rightarrow 30 = Ae^0$

$\qquad\qquad\qquad\qquad \Rightarrow A = 30$

$\qquad\qquad\qquad\qquad \Rightarrow S = 30e^{kt}$

When $t = 0$, $\dfrac{dS}{dt} = 6$ and $S = 30$

$\Rightarrow \dfrac{dS}{dt} = kS \Rightarrow 6 = k \times 30 \Rightarrow k = \dfrac{6}{30} = 0.2$

So $S = 30e^{0.2t}$.

So $S = 150 \Rightarrow 150 = 30e^{0.2t}$

$\qquad\qquad\quad \Rightarrow \ln 5 = 0.2t$

$\qquad\qquad\quad \Rightarrow t = 5\ln 5 = 8.047$

It will take the squirrels 8 weeks to take over the forest.

Q18 a) $\dfrac{dT}{dt} = -k(T - 21) \quad\Rightarrow\quad \int \dfrac{1}{T - 21}dT = \int -k\,dt$

$\qquad\qquad\qquad\qquad \Rightarrow \ln(T - 21) = -kt + \ln A$

$\qquad\qquad\qquad\qquad \Rightarrow T = Ae^{-kt} + 21$

$T = 90$ at $t = 0 \qquad \Rightarrow 90 = Ae^0 + 21$

$\qquad\qquad\qquad\qquad \Rightarrow A = 90 - 21 = 69$

$\qquad\qquad\qquad\qquad \Rightarrow T = 69e^{-kt} + 21$

So $T = 80$ at $t = 5 \Rightarrow 80 = 69e^{-5k} + 21$

$\qquad\qquad\qquad\qquad \Rightarrow e^{-5k} = \dfrac{59}{69}$

$\qquad\qquad\qquad\qquad \Rightarrow k = -\dfrac{1}{5}\ln\dfrac{59}{69} = 0.0313$

$\qquad\qquad\qquad\qquad \Rightarrow T = 69e^{-0.0313t} + 21$

b) (i) $t = 15 \Rightarrow T = 69e^{-0.470} + 21 = 64.1\ ^\circ\text{C}$

(ii) $T = 40 \Rightarrow 40 = 69e^{-0.0313t} + 21$

$\qquad\qquad\quad \Rightarrow e^{-0.0313t} = \dfrac{19}{69}$

$\qquad\qquad\quad \Rightarrow t = 41.2 \text{ mins}$

c)

If you struggled sketching this graph look back at your C3 notes for sketching exponential graphs.

Exam-Style Questions — Chapter 5

Q1 a) Start by differentiating x and y with respect to θ:

$\dfrac{dy}{d\theta} = 2\cos\theta$ *[1 mark]*

$\dfrac{dx}{d\theta} = 3 + 3\sin 3\theta$ *[1 mark]*

$\dfrac{dy}{dx} = \dfrac{dy}{d\theta} \div \dfrac{dx}{d\theta} = \dfrac{2\cos\theta}{3 + 3\sin 3\theta}$ *[1 mark]*

b) (i) We need the value of θ at $(\pi + 1, \sqrt{3})$:

$y = 2\sin\theta = \sqrt{3}$, for $-\pi \le \theta \le \pi$

$\Rightarrow \theta = \dfrac{\pi}{3}$ or $\dfrac{2\pi}{3}$ *[1 mark]*

If $\theta = \dfrac{\pi}{3}$, then

$x = 3\theta - \cos 3\theta = \pi - \cos\pi = \pi + 1$.

If $\theta = \dfrac{2\pi}{3}$, then

$x = 3\theta - \cos 3\theta = 2\pi - \cos 2\pi = 2\pi - 1$.

So at $(\pi + 1, \sqrt{3})$, $\theta = \dfrac{\pi}{3}$ *[1 mark]*

$\theta = \dfrac{\pi}{3}$

$\Rightarrow \dfrac{dy}{dx} = \dfrac{2\cos\dfrac{\pi}{3}}{3 + 3\sin\pi} = \dfrac{2\left(\dfrac{1}{2}\right)}{3 + 0} = \dfrac{1}{3}$ *[1 mark]*

(ii) $\theta = \dfrac{\pi}{6} \Rightarrow x = \dfrac{\pi}{2} - \cos\dfrac{\pi}{2} = \dfrac{\pi}{2} - 0 = \dfrac{\pi}{2}$

$\theta = \dfrac{\pi}{6} \Rightarrow y = 2\sin\dfrac{\pi}{6} = 2 \times \dfrac{1}{2} = 1$

So $\theta = \dfrac{\pi}{6}$ at the point $\left(\dfrac{\pi}{2}, 1\right)$ *[1 mark]*

$$\theta = \frac{\pi}{6} \Rightarrow \frac{dy}{dx} = \frac{2\cos\frac{\pi}{6}}{3 + 3\sin\frac{\pi}{2}}$$

$$= \frac{2\left(\frac{\sqrt{3}}{2}\right)}{3 + 3(1)} = \frac{\sqrt{3}}{6} \ \text{[1 mark]}$$

Gradient of normal =

$$-\frac{1}{\left(\frac{dy}{dx}\right)} = -\frac{6}{\sqrt{3}} = -\frac{6\sqrt{3}}{3} = -2\sqrt{3} \ \text{[1 mark]}$$

So the normal is $y = -2\sqrt{3}\,x + c$ for some c.

$$\Rightarrow 1 = -2\sqrt{3} \times \frac{\pi}{2} + c = -\pi\sqrt{3} + c$$

$$\Rightarrow c = 1 + \pi\sqrt{3}$$

The equation of the normal is
$$y = -2\sqrt{3}\,x + 1 + \pi\sqrt{3} \ \text{[1 mark]}$$

Q2 a) Begin by factorising the denominator of f(x):

$$f(x) = \frac{11x^2 + 42x + 36}{3x^3 + 16x^2 + 28x + 16}$$

$$\equiv \frac{11x^2 + 42x + 36}{(x+2)^2(3x+4)}$$

Now express it as partial fractions:

$$\frac{11x^2 + 42x + 36}{(x+2)^2(3x+4)} = \frac{A}{(x+2)^2} + \frac{B}{x+2} + \frac{C}{3x+4}$$

$$\Rightarrow 11x^2 + 42x + 36$$
$$\equiv A(3x+4) + B(x+2)(3x+4) + C(x+2)^2 \ \text{[1 mark]}$$

Use the substitution method to find A and C:

Substituting $x = -2$ gives: $-4 = -2A \Rightarrow A = 2$.

Substituting $x = -\frac{4}{3}$ gives: $-\frac{4}{9} = \frac{4}{9}C \Rightarrow C = -1$.

[1 mark for finding A and C]

Use the equating coefficients method to find B:

Equating coefficients of x^2 gives: $3B + C = 11$
$\Rightarrow 3B - 1 = 11 \Rightarrow 3B = 12 \Rightarrow B = 4$ *[1 mark]*.

So $f(x) = \frac{2}{(x+2)^2} + \frac{4}{x+2} - \frac{1}{3x+4}$ *[1 mark]*.

b) $\int f(x)\,dx$

$$= \int \frac{2}{(x+2)^2} + \frac{4}{x+2} - \frac{1}{3x+4}\,dx$$

$$= \int 2(x+2)^{-2} + \frac{4}{x+2} - \frac{1}{3x+4}\,dx$$

$$= -2(x+2)^{-1} + 4\ln|x+2| - \frac{1}{3}\ln|3x+4| + C$$

$$= -\frac{2}{x+2} + 4\ln|x+2| - \frac{1}{3}\ln|3x+4| + C$$

[1 mark for each of the first three terms, lose 1 mark if +C is missing]

Q3 Use the identity $\sec^2 x \equiv 1 + \tan^2 x$ to write $2\tan^2 3x + 2$ as $2\sec^2 3x$ *[1 mark]*. The integral becomes:

$$\int 2\tan^2 3x + 2\,dx = \int 2\sec^2 3x\,dx = \frac{2}{3}\tan 3x + C$$

[1 mark for 2/3, 1 mark for tan 3x]

Q4 a) $x^2y + y^2x - 2y^2 - xy^3 = 0$

$$\Rightarrow \frac{d}{dx}x^2y + \frac{d}{dx}y^2x - \frac{d}{dx}2y^2 - \frac{d}{dx}xy^3 = 0$$

$$\Rightarrow \frac{d}{dx}x^2y + \frac{d}{dx}y^2x - \frac{d}{dx}2y^2 - \frac{d}{dx}xy^3 = 0$$

$$\Rightarrow 2xy + x^2\frac{dy}{dx} + y^2 + 2yx\frac{dy}{dx}$$
$$- 4y\frac{dy}{dx} - y^3 - 3xy^2\frac{dy}{dx} = 0 \ \text{[1 mark]}$$

$$\Rightarrow x^2\frac{dy}{dx} + 2yx\frac{dy}{dx} - 4y\frac{dy}{dx} - 3xy^2\frac{dy}{dx}$$
$$= y^3 - y^2 - 2xy \ \text{[1 mark]}$$

$$\frac{dy}{dx} = \frac{2xy + y^2 - y^3}{3xy^2 - x^2 - 2xy + 4y} \ \text{[1 mark]}$$

b) At stationary points, $\frac{dy}{dx} = 0$,

so $2xy + y^2 - y^3 = 0$ *[1 mark]*
$\Rightarrow 2xy = y^3 - y^2$

$$\Rightarrow x = \frac{y^3 - y^2}{2y}$$

and hence $x = \frac{y^2 - y}{2}$ as required. *[1 mark]*

c) When $x = 2$, $4y + 2y^2 - 2y^2 - 2y^3 = 0$ *[1 mark]*
$\Rightarrow 4y - 2y^3 = 0 \Rightarrow 2y(2 - y^2) = 0$,
giving $y = 0$, $y = \pm\sqrt{2}$ as required. *[1 mark]*

d) $\frac{dy}{dx} = \frac{4\sqrt{2} + 2 - 2\sqrt{2}}{12 - 4 - 4\sqrt{2} + 4\sqrt{2}}$

$$= \frac{2\sqrt{2} + 2}{8} = \frac{\sqrt{2} + 1}{4} \ \text{[1 mark]}$$

The equation of the tangent is the equation of the curve *[1 mark]*

$$\sqrt{2} = \frac{\sqrt{2}}{2} + \frac{1}{2} + c, \text{ hence } c = \frac{\sqrt{2} - 1}{2} \ \text{[1 mark]}$$

and the equation of the tangent is:

$$y = \left(\frac{\sqrt{2} + 1}{4}\right)x + \frac{\sqrt{2} - 1}{2} \ \text{[1 mark]}$$

Q5 a) (i) Using implicit differentiation:

$$3e^x + 6y = 2x^2y \Rightarrow \frac{d}{dx}3e^x + \frac{d}{dx}6y = \frac{d}{dx}2x^2y$$

$$\Rightarrow 3e^x + 6\frac{dy}{dx} = 2x^2\frac{dy}{dx} + y\frac{d}{dx}2x^2$$

$$\Rightarrow 3e^x + 6\frac{dy}{dx} = 2x^2\frac{dy}{dx} + 4xy \ \text{[1 mark]}$$

$$\Rightarrow (2x^2 - 6)\frac{dy}{dx} = 3e^x - 4xy \ \text{[1 mark]}$$

$$\Rightarrow \frac{dy}{dx} = \frac{3e^x - 4xy}{2x^2 - 6} \ \text{[1 mark]}$$

(ii) At the stationary points of C, $\frac{dy}{dx} = 0$

$$\Rightarrow \frac{3e^x - 4xy}{2x^2 - 6} = 0 \ \text{[1 mark]}$$

$$\Rightarrow 3e^x - 4xy = 0$$

$$\Rightarrow y = \frac{3e^x}{4x} \ \text{[1 mark]}$$

b) Substitute $y = \frac{3e^x}{4x}$ into the original equation of curve C:

$$3e^x + 6y = 2x^2y \Rightarrow 3e^x + 6\frac{3e^x}{4x} = 2x^2\frac{3e^x}{4x} \ \text{[1 mark]}$$

$$\Rightarrow 3e^x\left(1 + \frac{3}{2x} - \frac{x}{2}\right) = 0$$

$3e^x = 0$ has no solutions, so $\left(1 + \frac{3}{2x} - \frac{x}{2}\right) = 0$
[1 mark]

$$\Rightarrow x^2 - 2x - 3 = 0$$

$$\Rightarrow (x+1)(x-3) = 0$$

$$\Rightarrow x = -1 \text{ and } x = 3$$

$$x = -1 \Rightarrow y = \frac{3e^{-1}}{4(-1)} = -\frac{3}{4e}$$

$$x = 3 \Rightarrow y = \frac{3e^3}{4(3)} = \frac{1}{4}e^3$$

So the stationary points of C are $(-1, -\frac{3}{4e})$ and $(3, \frac{1}{4}e^3)$

[2 marks — 1 mark for each correct pair of coordinates]

Don't forget — if the question asks you for an exact answer, that usually means leaving it in terms of something like π or ln or, in this case, e.

Q6 a) First find the value of t when $y = -6$:
$y = 2 - t^3 = -6 \Rightarrow t^3 = 8 \Rightarrow t = 2$ *[1 mark]*
$\Rightarrow x = 2^2 + 2(2) - 3 = 5$
Now find the gradient of the curve:
$\frac{dy}{dt} = -3t^2, \quad \frac{dx}{dt} = 2t + 2$
So $\frac{dy}{dx} = \frac{dy}{dt} \div \frac{dx}{dt} = \frac{-3t^2}{2t+2}$ *[1 mark]*
So when $t = 2$, $\frac{dy}{dx} = \frac{-3(2)^2}{2(2)+2} = \frac{-12}{6} = -2$
[1 mark]

So the tangent at $y = -6$ is
$y = -2x + c \Rightarrow -6 = -2(5) + c \Rightarrow c = 4$
The equation of L is $y = -2x + 4$ *[1 mark]*

b) (i) Substitute $y = 2 - t^3$ and $x = t^2 + 2t - 3$ into the equation of L:
$y = -2x + 4$
$\Rightarrow 2 - t^3 = -2(t^2 + 2t - 3) + 4$ *[1 mark]*
$\Rightarrow 2 - t^3 = -2t^2 - 4t + 10$
$\Rightarrow t^3 - 2t^2 - 4t + 8 = 0$
We know from part (a) that $t = 2$ is a root, so take out $(t - 2)$ as a factor:
$\Rightarrow (t - 2)(t^2 - 4) = 0$ *[1 mark]*
$\Rightarrow (t - 2)(t + 2)(t - 2) = 0$
$\Rightarrow t = 2$ or $t = -2$ *[1 mark]*
So t must be -2 at P.
$t = -2 \Rightarrow x = (-2)^2 + 2(-2) - 3 = -3$,
$y = 2 - (-2)^3 = 10$.
The coordinates of P are $(-3, 10)$ *[1 mark]*

(ii) At P, $t = -2$,
so $\frac{dy}{dx} = \frac{-3(-2)^2}{2(-2)+2} = \frac{-12}{-2} = 6$ *[1 mark]*
So the gradient of the normal at P is
$-\frac{1}{\left(\frac{dy}{dx}\right)} = -\frac{1}{6}$ *[1 mark]*
The equation of the normal at P is
$y = -\frac{1}{6}x + c \Rightarrow 10 = -\frac{(-3)}{6} + c \Rightarrow c = \frac{19}{2}$
So the normal to the curve at point P is
$y = -\frac{1}{6}x + \frac{19}{2}$ *[1 mark]*

Q7 a) $\frac{dy}{dx} = \frac{\cos x \cos^2 y}{\sin x} \Rightarrow \frac{1}{\cos^2 y} dy = \frac{\cos x}{\sin x} dx$
$\Rightarrow \int \sec^2 y \, dy = \int \frac{\cos x}{\sin x} dx$
$\Rightarrow \tan y = \ln|\sin x| + C$
[4 marks available — 1 mark for separating the variables into functions of x and y, 1 mark for correct integration of RHS, 1 mark for correct integration of LHS, 1 mark for general solution]

b) If $y = \pi$ when $x = \frac{\pi}{6}$, that means that
$\tan \pi = \ln\left|\sin \frac{\pi}{6}\right| + C \Rightarrow 0 = \ln\left|\frac{1}{2}\right| + C$ *[1 mark]*
So $C = -\ln \frac{1}{2} = \ln 2$
So $\tan y = \ln|\sin x| + \ln 2$
or $\tan y = \ln |2 \sin x|$ *[1 mark]*
This is the particular solution — you found the general solution in part a).

Q8 a) c is the value of y when $x = 2$. If $x = 2$, then
$6x^2y - 7 = 5x - 4y^2 - x^2$
$\Rightarrow 6(2)^2y - 7 = 5(2) - 4y^2 - (2)^2$
$\Rightarrow 24y - 7 = 6 - 4y^2$
$\Rightarrow 4y^2 + 24y - 13 = 0$
$\Rightarrow (2y + 13)(2y - 1) = 0$
$\Rightarrow y = -6.5$ or $y = 0.5$ *[1 mark]*
$c > 0$, so $c = 0.5$ *[1 mark]*

b) (i) Q is another point on C where $y = 0.5$.
If $y = 0.5$, then $6x^2y - 7 = 5x - 4y^2 - x^2$
$\Rightarrow 6x^2(0.5) - 7 = 5x - 4(0.5)^2 - x^2$ *[1 mark]*
$\Rightarrow 3x^2 - 7 = 5x - 1 - x^2$
$\Rightarrow 4x^2 - 5x - 6 = 0$
$\Rightarrow (x - 2)(4x + 3)$
$\Rightarrow x = 2$ or $x = -0.75$
$x \neq 2$, as $x = 2$ at the other point where T crosses C. So the coordinates of Q are $(-0.75, 0.5)$. *[1 mark]*

(ii) To find the gradient of C, use implicit differentiation.
Differentiate each term separately with respect to x:
$\frac{d}{dx}6x^2y - \frac{d}{dx}7 = \frac{d}{dx}5x - \frac{d}{dx}4y^2 - \frac{d}{dx}x^2$
[1 mark]
Differentiate x-terms and constant terms:
$\Rightarrow \frac{d}{dx}6x^2y - 0 = 5 - \frac{d}{dx}4y^2 - 2x$
[1 mark]
Differentiate y-terms using chain rule:
$\Rightarrow \frac{d}{dx}6x^2y = 5 - \frac{d}{dy}4y^2\frac{dy}{dx} - 2x$
$\Rightarrow \frac{d}{dx}6x^2y = 5 - 8y\frac{dy}{dx} - 2x$ *[1 mark]*
Differentiate xy-terms using product rule:
$\Rightarrow 6x^2\frac{dy}{dx} + y\frac{d}{dx}6x^2 = 5 - 8y\frac{dy}{dx} - 2x$
$\Rightarrow 6x^2\frac{dy}{dx} + 12xy = 5 - 8y\frac{dy}{dx} - 2x$
[1 mark]
Rearrange to make $\frac{dy}{dx}$ the subject:
$\Rightarrow 6x^2\frac{dy}{dx} + 8y\frac{dy}{dx} = 5 - 2x - 12xy$
$\Rightarrow \frac{dy}{dx} = \frac{5 - 2x - 12xy}{6x^2 + 8y}$ *[1 mark]*
So at $Q = (-0.75, 0.5)$,
$\frac{dy}{dx} = \frac{5 - 2(-0.75) - 12(-0.75)(0.5)}{6(-0.75)^2 + 8(0.5)}$
$= \frac{11}{7.375} = 1.49$ to 3 s.f. *[1 mark]*

Q9 Use the identity $\csc^2 x \equiv 1 + \cot^2 x$ to write $2\cot^2 x$ as $2\csc^2 x - 2$ *[1 mark]*. The integral becomes:

$$\int 2\csc^2 x - 2\,dx = -2\cot x - 2x + C$$

[1 mark for −2cot x, 1 mark for −2x + C]

Q10 a) First solve the differential equation to find S:

$$\frac{dS}{dt} = k\sqrt{S} \Rightarrow \frac{1}{\sqrt{S}}\,dS = k\,dt$$

$$\Rightarrow \int S^{-\frac{1}{2}}\,dS = \int k\,dt \quad \textit{[1 mark]}$$

$$\Rightarrow 2S^{\frac{1}{2}} = kt + C$$

$$\Rightarrow S = \left(\tfrac{1}{2}(kt + C)\right)^2 = \tfrac{1}{4}(kt + C)^2 \quad \textit{[1 mark]}$$

At the start of the campaign, $t = 0$.
Putting $t = 0$ and $S = 81$ into the equation gives:
$81 = \frac{1}{4}(0 + C)^2 \Rightarrow 324 = C^2 \Rightarrow C = 18$
(C must be positive, otherwise the sales would be decreasing). *[1 mark]*.

This gives the equation $S = \frac{1}{4}(kt + 18)^2$ *[1 mark]*.

b) When $t = 0$, $S = 81$ and $\frac{dS}{dt} = 18$.
Substituting this into $\frac{dS}{dt} = k\sqrt{S}$ gives $k = 2$.
Using $S = \frac{1}{4}(kt + 18)^2$ with $t = 5$ and $k = 2$ gives
$\frac{1}{4}((5 \times 2) + 18)^2 = 196$ kg sold.
[3 marks available — 1 mark for finding the value of k, 1 mark for substituting correct values of t and k and 1 mark for answer]

c) To find the value of t when $S = 225$, solve the equation $225 = \frac{1}{4}(2t + 18)^2$ *[1 mark]*:

$$225 = \tfrac{1}{4}(2t + 18)^2 \Rightarrow 900 = (2t + 18)^2$$

$$\Rightarrow 30 = 2t + 18 \Rightarrow 12 = 2t \Rightarrow 6 = t$$

So it will be 6 days *[1 mark]* before 225 kg of cheese is sold.

Chapter 6: Vectors

1. Vectors

Exercise 1.1 — Introducing vectors

Q1 a) vector **b)** scalar **c)** vector

Q2 a)

b)

c) $\mathbf{a} + \mathbf{b}$

d) $\mathbf{a} - \mathbf{b}$

Q3 a) $\overrightarrow{AC}$ **b)** $\overrightarrow{BA}$ **c)** $\overrightarrow{DB}$

Q4 a) $\overrightarrow{XY} = -\mathbf{q}$

b) $\overrightarrow{YZ} = \overrightarrow{YX} + \overrightarrow{XZ} = \mathbf{q} + \mathbf{p}$

c) $\overrightarrow{ZY} = \overrightarrow{ZX} + \overrightarrow{XY} = -\mathbf{p} - \mathbf{q}$
   or $\overrightarrow{ZY} = -\overrightarrow{YZ} = -\mathbf{q} - \mathbf{p}$

Q5 $4\mathbf{b} + 8\mathbf{a} = 4(2\mathbf{a} + \mathbf{b}) = -4(-\mathbf{b} - 2\mathbf{a})$,
so $4\mathbf{b} + 8\mathbf{a}$, $2\mathbf{a} + \mathbf{b}$ and $-\mathbf{b} - 2\mathbf{a}$ are parallel.

$2\mathbf{p} + \mathbf{q} = 2(\frac{1}{2}\mathbf{q} + \mathbf{p})$, so $2\mathbf{p} + \mathbf{q}$ and $\frac{1}{2}\mathbf{q} + \mathbf{p}$ are parallel.

$5(2\mathbf{a} - \mathbf{b}) = 5(2\mathbf{a} - \mathbf{b})$,
so $5(2\mathbf{a} - \mathbf{b})$ and $2\mathbf{a} - \mathbf{b}$ are parallel.

Q6 a) $\overrightarrow{DF} = \frac{2}{3}\overrightarrow{DC}$. $\overrightarrow{DC}$ is parallel to $\overrightarrow{AB}$ and the same length because ABCD is a rectangle, so $\overrightarrow{DC} = \overrightarrow{AB} = \mathbf{b}$. So $\overrightarrow{DF} = \frac{2}{3}\mathbf{b}$.

b) $\overrightarrow{BE} = \overrightarrow{BA} + \overrightarrow{AE} = -\overrightarrow{AB} + \frac{1}{2}\overrightarrow{AD} = -\mathbf{b} + \frac{1}{2}\mathbf{d}$

c) $\overrightarrow{EF} = \overrightarrow{ED} + \overrightarrow{DF} = \frac{1}{2}\overrightarrow{AD} + \overrightarrow{DF} = \frac{1}{2}\mathbf{d} + \frac{2}{3}\mathbf{b}$

Q7 $\overrightarrow{AB} = \overrightarrow{OB} - \overrightarrow{OA} = \mathbf{b} - \mathbf{a}$
$\overrightarrow{BC} = \overrightarrow{OC} - \overrightarrow{OB} = (5\mathbf{a} - 4\mathbf{b}) - \mathbf{b} = 5(\mathbf{a} - \mathbf{b})$
So $\overrightarrow{BC} = -5\overrightarrow{AB}$, so A, B & C, lie on the same straight line i.e. they are collinear.

Q8 a) $\overrightarrow{JL} = \overrightarrow{JD} + \overrightarrow{DL}$, now: $\overrightarrow{JD} = \frac{1}{2}\overrightarrow{ED} = \frac{1}{2}\mathbf{d}$ and
$\overrightarrow{DL} = \frac{1}{2}\overrightarrow{DF} = \frac{1}{2}(-\overrightarrow{ED} + \overrightarrow{EF}) = \frac{1}{2}(-\mathbf{d} + \mathbf{f})$
So $\overrightarrow{JL} = \overrightarrow{JD} + \overrightarrow{DL} = \frac{1}{2}\mathbf{d} + \frac{1}{2}(-\mathbf{d} + \mathbf{f})$
$= \frac{1}{2}(\mathbf{d} - \mathbf{d} + \mathbf{f}) = \frac{1}{2}\mathbf{f}$

b) JL is parallel to EF and has half the length of EF.

Exercise 1.2 — Position vectors and Three-dimensional vectors

Q1 $\overrightarrow{OA} = \begin{pmatrix} 2 \\ 3 \end{pmatrix}$ $\quad \overrightarrow{OB} = \begin{pmatrix} 4 \\ -5 \end{pmatrix}$

Q2 $\overrightarrow{OR} = 4\mathbf{i} - 5\mathbf{j} + \mathbf{k}$ $\qquad \overrightarrow{OS} = -3\mathbf{i} - \mathbf{k}$

There's no $\mathbf{j}$ component written for $\overrightarrow{OS}$ because its $\mathbf{j}$ component is zero (you don't write $-3\mathbf{i} + 0\mathbf{j} - \mathbf{k}$).

Q3 a) C $(-1, 2)$, D $(4, -3)$

b) $\overrightarrow{CD} = \overrightarrow{OD} - \overrightarrow{OC} = (4\mathbf{i} - 3\mathbf{j}) - (-\mathbf{i} + 2\mathbf{j}) = 5\mathbf{i} - 5\mathbf{j}$
$\overrightarrow{DC} = -\overrightarrow{CD} = -(5\mathbf{i} - 5\mathbf{j}) = -5\mathbf{i} + 5\mathbf{j}$

Q4 $\overrightarrow{GH} = \overrightarrow{OH} - \overrightarrow{OG} = \begin{pmatrix} -1 \\ 4 \\ 9 \end{pmatrix} - \begin{pmatrix} 2 \\ -3 \\ 4 \end{pmatrix} = \begin{pmatrix} -3 \\ 7 \\ 5 \end{pmatrix}$

$\overrightarrow{HG} = -\overrightarrow{GH} = -\begin{pmatrix} -3 \\ 7 \\ 5 \end{pmatrix} = \begin{pmatrix} 3 \\ -7 \\ -5 \end{pmatrix}$

Q5 $\overrightarrow{PM} = \overrightarrow{MQ}$ because M is the midpoint of PQ.
This is because the lines are the same length and point in the same direction.

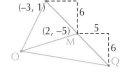

$\overrightarrow{MQ} = \overrightarrow{PM} = \overrightarrow{OM} - \overrightarrow{OP} = 2\mathbf{i} - 5\mathbf{j} - (-3\mathbf{i} + \mathbf{j}) = 5\mathbf{i} - 6\mathbf{j}$
So $\overrightarrow{OQ} = \overrightarrow{OM} + \overrightarrow{MQ} = 2\mathbf{i} - 5\mathbf{j} + (5\mathbf{i} - 6\mathbf{j}) = 7\mathbf{i} - 11\mathbf{j}$

Q6 $\overrightarrow{OA} = \begin{pmatrix} 2 \\ 4 \end{pmatrix}$, $\overrightarrow{OB} = \begin{pmatrix} 0 \\ 1 \end{pmatrix}$, $\overrightarrow{OC} = \begin{pmatrix} -1 \\ 3 \end{pmatrix}$

You could use unit form instead of column vectors to answer this question if you prefer.

$\overrightarrow{AB} = \overrightarrow{OB} - \overrightarrow{OA} = \begin{pmatrix} 0 \\ 1 \end{pmatrix} - \begin{pmatrix} 2 \\ 4 \end{pmatrix} = \begin{pmatrix} -2 \\ -3 \end{pmatrix}$

$\overrightarrow{BC} = \overrightarrow{OC} - \overrightarrow{OB} = \begin{pmatrix} -1 \\ 3 \end{pmatrix} - \begin{pmatrix} 0 \\ 1 \end{pmatrix} = \begin{pmatrix} -1 \\ 2 \end{pmatrix}$

$\overrightarrow{CA} = \overrightarrow{OA} - \overrightarrow{OC} = \begin{pmatrix} 2 \\ 4 \end{pmatrix} - \begin{pmatrix} -1 \\ 3 \end{pmatrix} = \begin{pmatrix} 3 \\ 1 \end{pmatrix}$

Q7 a) $\overrightarrow{DE} = 4\mathbf{i} + \mathbf{j}$, $\overrightarrow{EF} = 2\mathbf{i} + 6\mathbf{j}$,
$\overrightarrow{FG} = -2\mathbf{i} + 5\mathbf{j}$, $\overrightarrow{GD} = -4\mathbf{i} - 12\mathbf{j}$
Column vectors would also be fine for this question.

b) DEFG is a trapezium. $\overrightarrow{GD} = -2\overrightarrow{EF}$ so GD is parallel to EF – but DE is not parallel to FG

You can use unit form or column vectors for Q8.

Q8 $\overrightarrow{JK} = \overrightarrow{OK} - \overrightarrow{OJ} = -\mathbf{i} + 3\mathbf{j} - (4\mathbf{i} - 3\mathbf{k}) = -5\mathbf{i} + 3\mathbf{j} + 3\mathbf{k}$
$\overrightarrow{KL} = \overrightarrow{OL} - \overrightarrow{OK} = 2\mathbf{i} + 2\mathbf{j} + 7\mathbf{k} - (-\mathbf{i} + 3\mathbf{j}) = 3\mathbf{i} - \mathbf{j} + 7\mathbf{k}$
$\overrightarrow{LJ} = \overrightarrow{OJ} - \overrightarrow{OL} = 4\mathbf{i} - 3\mathbf{k} - (2\mathbf{i} + 2\mathbf{j} + 7\mathbf{k}) = 2\mathbf{i} - 2\mathbf{j} - 10\mathbf{k}$
Don't get put off by the three dimensional coordinates of this triangle's vertices — the triangle is in three dimensions but you work out the answers in exactly the same way you would with a two-dimensional triangle.

2. Magnitude of Vectors

Exercise 2.1 — Magnitude of two-dimensional vectors

Q1 a) $\sqrt{6^2 + 8^2} = \sqrt{36 + 64} = \sqrt{100} = 10$
b) $\sqrt{12^2 + (-5)^2} = 13$
c) $\sqrt{2^2 + 4^2} = \sqrt{20} = 2\sqrt{5}$
d) $\sqrt{(-3)^2 + (-1)^2} = \sqrt{10}$
e) $\sqrt{(24)^2 + (-7)^2} = 25$
f) $\sqrt{(-\sqrt{13})^2 + 6^2} = \sqrt{13 + 36} = \sqrt{49} = 7$
g) $\sqrt{3^2 + (\sqrt{7})^2} = 4$
h) $\sqrt{0^2 + (-7)^2} = 7$

Q2 $|\overrightarrow{OS}| = \sqrt{10^2 + 5^2} = \sqrt{100 + 25} = \sqrt{125} = 5\sqrt{5}$

Q3 a) $\mathbf{a} + \mathbf{b} = (2\mathbf{i} + \mathbf{j}) + (2\mathbf{i} - 4\mathbf{j}) = 4\mathbf{i} - 3\mathbf{j}$
The magnitude of the resultant is $\sqrt{4^2 + (-3)^2} = 5$
b) $\mathbf{u} + \mathbf{v} = 4\mathbf{i} - 4\mathbf{j}$, $|4\mathbf{i} - 4\mathbf{j}| = \sqrt{4^2 + 4^2} = \sqrt{32}$
$= 4\sqrt{2}$
c) $\mathbf{f} + \mathbf{g} = \begin{pmatrix} 24 \\ -10 \end{pmatrix}$, $\left| \begin{pmatrix} 24 \\ -10 \end{pmatrix} \right| = \sqrt{24^2 + (-10)^2} = 26$
d) $\mathbf{d} + \mathbf{e} = \begin{pmatrix} 3 \\ -6 \end{pmatrix}$, $\left| \begin{pmatrix} 3 \\ -6 \end{pmatrix} \right| = \sqrt{3^2 + (-6)^2} = \sqrt{45} = 3\sqrt{5}$

Q4 $\overrightarrow{AC} = 4\mathbf{i} + 3\mathbf{j}$, $|\overrightarrow{AC}| = \sqrt{4^2 + 3^2} = 5$

Q5 $|\mathbf{b} - \mathbf{a}| = |9\mathbf{i} - 12\mathbf{j}| = \sqrt{9^2 + (-12)^2} = 15$

Q6 $\overrightarrow{MN} = -11\mathbf{i} + 60\mathbf{j}$, $|\overrightarrow{MN}| = \sqrt{(-11)^2 + 60^2} = 61$

Q7 $\left| \begin{pmatrix} 16 \\ -12 \end{pmatrix} \right| = \sqrt{16^2 + (-12)^2} = 20$
The unit vector is $\frac{1}{20}\begin{pmatrix} 16 \\ -12 \end{pmatrix} = \begin{pmatrix} \frac{16}{20} \\ -\frac{12}{20} \end{pmatrix} = \begin{pmatrix} 0.8 \\ -0.6 \end{pmatrix}$

Q8 $\overrightarrow{TU} = -8\mathbf{i} + 6\mathbf{j}$, $|\overrightarrow{TU}| = \sqrt{(-8)^2 + 6^2} = 10$
The unit vector is $\frac{1}{10}(-8\mathbf{i} + 6\mathbf{j}) = -0.8\mathbf{i} + 0.6\mathbf{j}$

Q9 $\overrightarrow{FG} = \overrightarrow{OG} - \overrightarrow{OF} = \begin{pmatrix} a \\ -5 \end{pmatrix} - \begin{pmatrix} 4 \\ 7 \end{pmatrix} = \begin{pmatrix} a - 4 \\ -12 \end{pmatrix}$
$|\overrightarrow{FG}| = \sqrt{(a - 4)^2 + (-12)^2} = \sqrt{a^2 - 8a + 160}$
$|\overrightarrow{FG}| = 13$, so: $a^2 - 8a + 160 = 13^2 = 169$
$a^2 - 8a - 9 = 0$
$(a + 1)(a - 9) = 0$
So $a = -1$ or $a = 9$

Exercise 2.2 — Magnitude of three-dimensional vectors

Q1 a) $\sqrt{1^2 + 4^2 + 8^2} = \sqrt{1 + 16 + 64} = \sqrt{81} = 9$
b) $\sqrt{4^2 + 2^2 + 4^2} = \sqrt{36} = 6$
c) $\sqrt{(-4)^2 + (-5)^2 + 20^2} = \sqrt{441} = 21$
d) $\sqrt{7^2 + 1^2 + (-7)^2} = \sqrt{99} = 3\sqrt{11}$
e) $\sqrt{(-2)^2 + 4^2 + (-6)^2} = \sqrt{56} = \sqrt{4}\sqrt{14} = 2\sqrt{14}$

Q2 a) The resultant is:
$(\mathbf{i} + \mathbf{j} + 2\mathbf{k}) + (\mathbf{i} + 2\mathbf{j} + 4\mathbf{k}) = 2\mathbf{i} + 3\mathbf{j} + 6\mathbf{k}$
Its magnitude is: $\sqrt{2^2 + 3^2 + 6^2} = \sqrt{49} = 7$
b) resultant: $2\mathbf{i} + 14\mathbf{j} + 23\mathbf{k}$
magnitude: $\sqrt{2^2 + 14^2 + 23^2} = \sqrt{729} = 27$

c) resultant: $\begin{pmatrix} 2 \\ 6 \\ 9 \end{pmatrix}$, magnitude: $\sqrt{2^2 + 6^2 + 9^2} = 11$

d) resultant: $\begin{pmatrix} 2 \\ 5 \\ 14 \end{pmatrix}$, magnitude: $\sqrt{2^2 + 5^2 + 14^2} = 15$

e) resultant: $\begin{pmatrix} 10 \\ 2 \\ 14 \end{pmatrix}$

magnitude: $\sqrt{10^2 + 2^2 + 14^2} = 10\sqrt{3}$

Q3 a) $\sqrt{(5-3)^2 + (6-4)^2 + (6-5)^2}$
$= \sqrt{2^2 + 2^2 + 1^2} = \sqrt{4+4+1} = \sqrt{9} = 3$

b) $\sqrt{(-11-7)^2 + (1-2)^2 + (15-9)^2}$
$= \sqrt{324 + 1 + 36} = \sqrt{361} = 19$

c) $\sqrt{(6-10)^2 + (10-(-2))^2 + (-4-(-1))^2}$
$= \sqrt{16 + 144 + 9} = \sqrt{169} = 13$

d) $\sqrt{(7-0)^2 + (0-(-4))^2 + (14-10)^2}$
$= \sqrt{49 + 16 + 16} = \sqrt{81} = 9$

e) $\sqrt{(2-(-4))^2 + (4-7)^2 + (-12-10)^2}$
$= \sqrt{36 + 9 + 484} = \sqrt{529} = 23$

f) $\sqrt{(30-7)^2 + (9-(-1))^2 + (-6-4)^2}$
$= \sqrt{529 + 100 + 100} = \sqrt{729} = 27$

Q4 $|2\mathbf{m} - \mathbf{n}| = |-6\mathbf{i} - 5\mathbf{j} + 10\mathbf{k}|$
$= \sqrt{(-6)^2 + (-5)^2 + 10^2} = 12.68857... = 12.69$ to 4 s.f.

Q5 $|\overrightarrow{AO}| = |\overrightarrow{OA}| = \sqrt{1^2 + (-4)^2 + 3^2} = \sqrt{26}$
$|\overrightarrow{BO}| = |\overrightarrow{OB}| = \sqrt{(-1)^2 + (-3)^2 + 5^2} = \sqrt{35}$
It's pretty clear that the magnitude of $\overrightarrow{AO}$ is going to be the same as $\overrightarrow{OA}$ so there's no need to find $\overrightarrow{AO}$.

$\overrightarrow{BA} = \overrightarrow{OA} - \overrightarrow{OB} = (\mathbf{i} - 4\mathbf{j} + 3\mathbf{k}) - (-\mathbf{i} - 3\mathbf{j} + 5\mathbf{k})$
$= 2\mathbf{i} - \mathbf{j} - 2\mathbf{k}$
$|\overrightarrow{BA}| = \sqrt{2^2 + (-1)^2 + (-2)^2} = 3$
Triangle AOB is right-angled because:
$|\overrightarrow{AO}|^2 + |\overrightarrow{BA}|^2 = (\sqrt{26})^2 + 3^2 = 26 + 9$
$= 35 = (\sqrt{35})^2 = |\overrightarrow{BO}|^2$

Q6 $|\mathbf{v}| = \sqrt{4^2 + (-4)^2 + (-7)^2} = 9$

so the unit vector is $\frac{1}{9}\mathbf{v} = \begin{pmatrix} \frac{4}{9} \\ -\frac{4}{9} \\ -\frac{7}{9} \end{pmatrix}$

Q7 $|\overrightarrow{PQ}| = \sqrt{(q-4)^2 + 6^2 + (2q-3)^2}$
So: $\sqrt{(q-4)^2 + 6^2 + (2q-3)^2} = 11$
$q^2 - 8q + 16 + 36 + 4q^2 - 12q + 9 = 121$
$5q^2 - 20q - 60 = 0$
$q^2 - 4q - 12 = 0$
$(q-6)(q+2) = 0$
Either $q = 6$, then Q is (4, 5, 13),
or $q = -2$, then Q is (-4, 5, -3).

3. Vector Equations of Lines
Exercise 3.1 —
Vector equations of lines in 2D

Q1 a) The gradient is $\frac{3}{1} = 3$
The y-intercept has position vector $\begin{pmatrix} 0 \\ 2 \end{pmatrix}$,
which gives it coordinates (0, 2).

b) $m = \frac{2}{1} = 2$
The y-intercept has coordinates (0, –5).

c) $m = \frac{15}{3} = 5$
The y-intercept has coordinates (0, 0).

For questions where you're asked to find the vector equation of a line there will always be alternative answers because the equation isn't unique. The answers given are the ones you'll get most easily from the information in the question.

Q2 a) E.g.
From the Cartesian equation $m = 1 = \frac{1}{1}$ and $c = 2$
So $\begin{pmatrix} 1 \\ 1 \end{pmatrix}$ is a vector in the direction of the line and
$\begin{pmatrix} 0 \\ 2 \end{pmatrix}$ is a point on the line.
That gives the equation: $\mathbf{r} = \begin{pmatrix} 0 \\ 2 \end{pmatrix} + t\begin{pmatrix} 1 \\ 1 \end{pmatrix}$

b) From the Cartesian equation y is constant, so the line is horizontal, so the direction vector must be horizontal (have a zero $\mathbf{j}$ component) e.g. $\begin{pmatrix} 1 \\ 0 \end{pmatrix}$.
$c = 7$, so $\begin{pmatrix} 0 \\ 7 \end{pmatrix}$ is a point on the line.
So an equation is e.g. $\mathbf{r} = \begin{pmatrix} 0 \\ 7 \end{pmatrix} + t\begin{pmatrix} 1 \\ 0 \end{pmatrix}$

c) $m = -4 = \frac{-4}{1}$ and $c = 0$
So $\begin{pmatrix} 1 \\ -4 \end{pmatrix}$ is a vector in the direction of the line and $\begin{pmatrix} 0 \\ 0 \end{pmatrix}$ is a point on the line.
That gives the equation, e.g. $\mathbf{r} = \begin{pmatrix} 0 \\ 0 \end{pmatrix} + t\begin{pmatrix} 1 \\ -4 \end{pmatrix}$

d) $m = -3 = \frac{-3}{1}$ and $c = 5$
So $\begin{pmatrix} 1 \\ -3 \end{pmatrix}$ is a vector in the direction of the line and $\begin{pmatrix} 0 \\ 5 \end{pmatrix}$ is a point on the line.
That gives the equation, e.g. $\mathbf{r} = \begin{pmatrix} 0 \\ 5 \end{pmatrix} + t\begin{pmatrix} 1 \\ -3 \end{pmatrix}$

Q3 a) E.g. $m = -3 = \frac{-3}{1}$, so $\begin{pmatrix} 1 \\ -3 \end{pmatrix}$ is a vector in the direction of the line and $\begin{pmatrix} 2 \\ 6 \end{pmatrix}$ lies on the line.
This gives the vector equation $\mathbf{r} = \begin{pmatrix} 2 \\ 6 \end{pmatrix} + t\begin{pmatrix} 1 \\ -3 \end{pmatrix}$

b) E.g. $m = \frac{1}{2}$, so $\begin{pmatrix} 2 \\ 1 \end{pmatrix}$ is in the direction of the line and $\begin{pmatrix} 2 \\ 2 \end{pmatrix}$ lies on the line, this gives $\mathbf{r} = \begin{pmatrix} 2 \\ 2 \end{pmatrix} + t\begin{pmatrix} 2 \\ 1 \end{pmatrix}$.

c) $m = 0$ so the Cartesian form of the line equation is $y = c$, i.e. the vertical coordinate stays constant along the line and the line is horizontal. So the direction vector must be horizontal (that is have a zero $\mathbf{j}$ component) e.g. $\begin{pmatrix} 1 \\ 0 \end{pmatrix}$, this gives equation e.g. $\mathbf{r} = \begin{pmatrix} 1 \\ -5 \end{pmatrix} + t\begin{pmatrix} 1 \\ 0 \end{pmatrix}$

Q4 a) $\binom{0}{0}$ lies on the line, so the y-intercept is $c = 0$.

The direction of the line is $\binom{1}{1}$, so the gradient is $\frac{1}{1} = 1 = m$.

This gives the equation $y = x$.

b) $\binom{0}{-4}$ lies on the line so $c = -4$.

The direction of the line is $\binom{-1}{2}$, so $m = \frac{2}{-1} = -2$.

This gives the equation $y = -2x - 4$

c) The gradient m is $\frac{1}{2}$, so $y = \frac{1}{2}x + c$

We want to find c. We know $\binom{6}{0}$ is a point on the line, so when $x = 6$, $y = 0$. Putting this into the equation $y = \frac{1}{2}x + c$ gives that $c = -3$.

So the answer is $y = \frac{1}{2}x - 3$

d) The direction vector $\binom{3}{0}$ tells us that as you move along the line there is a vertical displacement of zero for every horizontal displacement of 3, so the line is horizontal which means that y is constant.

We know $\binom{1}{2}$ is a point on the line, so when $x = 1$, $y = 2$. But y is constant so it's always 2, so the answer is $y = 2$

e) The gradient m is $\frac{5}{2}$, so $y = \frac{5}{2}x + c$

We want to find c. We know $\binom{-2}{3}$ is a point on the line, so when $x = -2$, $y = 3$. Putting this into the equation $y = \frac{5}{2}x + c$ gives that $c = 8$.

So the answer is $y = \frac{5}{2}x + 8$.

f) The direction vector $\binom{0}{1}$ tells us that as you move along the line there is a horizontal displacement of zero for every vertical displacement of 1, so the line is vertical which means that x is constant.

We know $\binom{5}{0}$ is a point on the line, so when $y = 0$, $x = 5$. But x is constant so it's always 5, so the answer is $x = 5$.

Q5 a) The position vector of point A on the line is $\binom{2}{5}$.

$\mathbf{b} = \binom{-1}{2}$ is a vector with the same direction as the line, so a vector equation of the line is

e.g. $\mathbf{r} = \binom{2}{5} + t\binom{-1}{2}$ so $\mathbf{r} = 2\mathbf{i} + 5\mathbf{j} + t(2\mathbf{j} - \mathbf{i})$.

You can always rearrange your answers so that they're in the form $r = ai + bj$. Here $r = i(2 - t) + j(5 + 2t)$.

b) The position vector of point A on the line is $\binom{-1}{0}$.

$\mathbf{b} = \binom{3}{4}$ is a vector with the same direction as the line so an equation is e.g. $\mathbf{r} = \binom{-1}{0} + t\binom{3}{4}$ so $\mathbf{r} = -\mathbf{i} + t(3\mathbf{i} + 4\mathbf{j})$.

c) The position vector of point A on the line is $\binom{-3}{-1}$.

$\mathbf{b} = \binom{6}{-1}$ is a vector with the same direction as the line so an equation is e.g. $\mathbf{r} = \binom{-3}{-1} + t\binom{6}{-1}$ so $\mathbf{r} = -3\mathbf{i} - \mathbf{j} + t(6\mathbf{i} - \mathbf{j})$.

d) The position vector of point A on the line is $\binom{0}{4}$.

$\mathbf{b} = \binom{-3}{-5}$ $\left(\text{or } \binom{3}{5}\right)$ is a vector with the same direction as the line so an equation is e.g.

$\mathbf{r} = \binom{0}{4} + t\binom{-3}{-5}$ or $\binom{0}{4} + t\binom{3}{5}$

so $\mathbf{r} = 4\mathbf{j} + t(-3\mathbf{i} - 5\mathbf{j})$ or $4\mathbf{j} + t(3\mathbf{i} + 5\mathbf{j})$.

Q6 a) Plugging the vectors $\mathbf{p} = \mathbf{i} = \binom{1}{0}$ and

$\mathbf{q} = 2\mathbf{i} + \mathbf{j} = \binom{2}{1}$ into the formula $\mathbf{r} = \mathbf{c} + t(\mathbf{d} - \mathbf{c})$ gives the equation: $\mathbf{r} = \mathbf{p} + t(\mathbf{q} - \mathbf{p}) = \binom{1}{0} + t\binom{1}{1}$

so $\mathbf{r} = \mathbf{i} + t(\mathbf{i} + \mathbf{j})$.

There are three other combinations you could have to give you a different equation, e.g. $r = q + t(p - q)$.

Parts b) and c) are answered in the same way as a)

b) E.g. $\mathbf{r} = \mathbf{f} + t(\mathbf{g} - \mathbf{f}) = \binom{3}{-4} + t\binom{-1}{9}$

so $\mathbf{r} = 3\mathbf{i} - 4\mathbf{j} + t(9\mathbf{j} - \mathbf{i})$.

c) E.g. $\mathbf{r} = \mathbf{n} + t(\mathbf{m} - \mathbf{n}) = \binom{-1}{3} + t\binom{-4}{-\frac{9}{2}}$

$= \binom{-1}{3} + t\binom{8}{9}$ so $\mathbf{r} = -\mathbf{i} + 3\mathbf{j} + t(8\mathbf{i} + 9\mathbf{j})$.

You can multiply the direction vector by −2 to get (positive) whole numbers because any parallel vector will do, but the question doesn't ask you to do this so you don't have to.

Exercise 3.2 — Vector equations of lines in 3D

For questions where you're asked to find the vector equation of a line there will always be alternative answers because the equation isn't unique. The answers given are the ones you'll get most easily from the information in the question.

Q1 a) $\overrightarrow{OX} = \mathbf{a} + \mathbf{b} = \begin{pmatrix} 4 \\ -3 \\ -2 \end{pmatrix} + \begin{pmatrix} 1 \\ 2 \\ 3 \end{pmatrix} = \begin{pmatrix} 4+1 \\ -3+2 \\ -2+3 \end{pmatrix} = \begin{pmatrix} 5 \\ -1 \\ 1 \end{pmatrix}$

$\overrightarrow{OY} = \mathbf{a} + 2\mathbf{b} = \begin{pmatrix} 4 \\ -3 \\ -2 \end{pmatrix} + 2\begin{pmatrix} 1 \\ 2 \\ 3 \end{pmatrix} = \begin{pmatrix} 6 \\ 1 \\ 4 \end{pmatrix}$

$\overrightarrow{OZ} = \begin{pmatrix} 7 \\ 3 \\ 7 \end{pmatrix}$, $\overrightarrow{OQ} = \begin{pmatrix} 3 \\ -5 \\ -5 \end{pmatrix}$

b) E.g. $\mathbf{r} = \begin{pmatrix} 4 \\ -3 \\ -2 \end{pmatrix} + \lambda\begin{pmatrix} 1 \\ 2 \\ 3 \end{pmatrix}$

Q2 Point C corresponds to $\lambda = 0$, so it has position vector

$\mathbf{r} = \begin{pmatrix} 2 \\ 1 \\ 3 \end{pmatrix} + 0 \times \begin{pmatrix} 1 \\ -1 \\ 4 \end{pmatrix} = \begin{pmatrix} 2 \\ 1 \\ 3 \end{pmatrix}$ and coordinates (2, 1, 3).

D has position vector $\mathbf{r} = \begin{pmatrix} 2 \\ 1 \\ 3 \end{pmatrix} + 1 \times \begin{pmatrix} 1 \\ -1 \\ 4 \end{pmatrix} = \begin{pmatrix} 3 \\ 0 \\ 7 \end{pmatrix}$ and coordinates (3, 0, 7).

E has position vector $\mathbf{r} = \begin{pmatrix} 2 \\ 1 \\ 3 \end{pmatrix} + 4 \times \begin{pmatrix} 1 \\ -1 \\ 4 \end{pmatrix} = \begin{pmatrix} 6 \\ -3 \\ 19 \end{pmatrix}$ and coordinates (6, –3, 19).

F has position vector $\mathbf{r} = \begin{pmatrix} 2 \\ 1 \\ 3 \end{pmatrix} + (-2) \times \begin{pmatrix} 1 \\ -1 \\ 4 \end{pmatrix} = \begin{pmatrix} 0 \\ 3 \\ -5 \end{pmatrix}$ and coordinates (0, 3, –5).

Q3 By choosing $t = 1$ you get the position vector
$\mathbf{r} = 3\mathbf{j} - 4\mathbf{k} + (-\mathbf{i} + 2\mathbf{j}) = -\mathbf{i} + 5\mathbf{j} - 4\mathbf{k}$. The coordinates of the point with this position vector are (–1, 5, –4) Other points are (0, 3, –4) and (–2, 7, –4).
These are just example points, you can have any points found by choosing a value for t in the equation.

Q4 a) You know two points on the line:
S and the origin O.
S has coordinates (–1, 4, 5), so position vector
$\mathbf{s} = \begin{pmatrix} -1 \\ 4 \\ 5 \end{pmatrix}$. O has position vector $\mathbf{o} = \begin{pmatrix} 0 \\ 0 \\ 0 \end{pmatrix}$.

Plugging these into the formula $\mathbf{r} = \mathbf{c} + \lambda(\mathbf{d} - \mathbf{c})$ gives, e.g.

$$\mathbf{r} = \lambda \begin{pmatrix} -1 \\ 4 \\ 5 \end{pmatrix} \underline{\text{or}} \ \mathbf{r} = \begin{pmatrix} -1 \\ 4 \\ 5 \end{pmatrix} + \lambda \begin{pmatrix} 1 \\ -4 \\ -5 \end{pmatrix}$$

b) The coordinates of 2 more points can be found by substituting 2 values in for the parameter λ.

E.g. When $\lambda = 2$, $\mathbf{r} = 2 \begin{pmatrix} -1 \\ 4 \\ 5 \end{pmatrix} = \begin{pmatrix} -2 \\ 8 \\ 10 \end{pmatrix}$

which gives the point (–2, 8, 10) and

when $\lambda = -1$, $\mathbf{r} = -1 \begin{pmatrix} -1 \\ 4 \\ 5 \end{pmatrix} = \begin{pmatrix} 1 \\ -4 \\ -5 \end{pmatrix}$ which

gives the point (1, –4, –5).

Q5 a) (i) Using the formula $\mathbf{r} = \mathbf{a} + t\mathbf{b}$ for the vector equation of a line through the point with position vector $\mathbf{a}$ and parallel to $\mathbf{b}$ gives:

$$\mathbf{r} = \begin{pmatrix} 4 \\ 2 \\ -1 \end{pmatrix} + t \begin{pmatrix} -2 \\ 0 \\ 3 \end{pmatrix}$$

Parts (ii) and (iii) are answered in the same way

(ii) E.g. $\mathbf{r} = \begin{pmatrix} 0 \\ 0 \\ 1 \end{pmatrix} + t \begin{pmatrix} 1 \\ -1 \\ 0 \end{pmatrix}$

(iii) E.g. $\mathbf{r} = (2\mathbf{i} + \mathbf{j}) + t(5\mathbf{i} - \mathbf{k})$

b) First check if P lies on line **(i)**. If P lies on **(i)** there's some t that solves

$$\begin{pmatrix} -2 \\ 2 \\ 1 \end{pmatrix} = \begin{pmatrix} 4 \\ 2 \\ -1 \end{pmatrix} + t \begin{pmatrix} -2 \\ 0 \\ 3 \end{pmatrix} \Rightarrow \begin{pmatrix} -2 \\ 2 \\ 1 \end{pmatrix} = \begin{pmatrix} 4 - 2t \\ 2 \\ -1 + 3t \end{pmatrix}$$

$\Rightarrow -2 = 4 - 2t$ and $1 = -1 + 3t \Rightarrow t = 3$ and $t = \frac{2}{3}$

So P doesn't lie on **(i)**, now check if it lies on **(ii)**:

$$\begin{pmatrix} -2 \\ 2 \\ 1 \end{pmatrix} = \begin{pmatrix} 0 \\ 0 \\ 1 \end{pmatrix} + t \begin{pmatrix} 1 \\ -1 \\ 0 \end{pmatrix} \Rightarrow \begin{pmatrix} -2 \\ 2 \\ 1 \end{pmatrix} = \begin{pmatrix} t \\ -t \\ 1 \end{pmatrix}$$

$\Rightarrow -2 = t$ and $2 = -t \Rightarrow t = -2$
So P lies on **(ii)** and corresponds to $t = -2$
You find which line the remaining points lie on in the same way.
Now check if Q lies on line **(i)**. If Q lies on **(i)** there's some t that solves

$$\begin{pmatrix} 2 \\ 2 \\ 2 \end{pmatrix} = \begin{pmatrix} 4 \\ 2 \\ -1 \end{pmatrix} + t \begin{pmatrix} -2 \\ 0 \\ 3 \end{pmatrix} \Rightarrow \begin{pmatrix} 2 \\ 2 \\ 2 \end{pmatrix} = \begin{pmatrix} 4 - 2t \\ 2 \\ -1 + 3t \end{pmatrix}$$

$\Rightarrow 2 = 4 - 2t$ and $2 = -1 + 3t \Rightarrow t = 1$ and $t = 1$
Both equations are solved by the same value of t, so Q lies on line **(i)** and corresponds to $t = 1$.
R must lie on line **(iii)**, so solve:

$$\begin{pmatrix} -3 \\ 1 \\ 1 \end{pmatrix} = \begin{pmatrix} 2 \\ 1 \\ 0 \end{pmatrix} + t \begin{pmatrix} 5 \\ 0 \\ -1 \end{pmatrix} \Rightarrow \begin{pmatrix} -3 \\ 1 \\ 1 \end{pmatrix} = \begin{pmatrix} 2 + 5t \\ 1 \\ -t \end{pmatrix}$$

$\Rightarrow -3 = 2 + 5t$ and $1 = -t \Rightarrow t = -1$ and $t = -1$
R lies on **(iii)** and corresponds to $t = -1$.

Q6 Line L has equation $\mathbf{r} = -6\mathbf{i} - \mathbf{j} + \mathbf{k} + t(\mathbf{i} - 3\mathbf{k})$, so the vector it's parallel to is $(\mathbf{i} - 3\mathbf{k})$. The line that's parallel to L is also parallel to $(\mathbf{i} - 3\mathbf{k})$, so the direction vector of this new line is $(\mathbf{i} - 3\mathbf{k})$. The line passes through the point with position vector $(5\mathbf{i} - \mathbf{j} + 3\mathbf{k})$, so the equation is: $\mathbf{r} = (5\mathbf{i} - \mathbf{j} + 3\mathbf{k}) + t(\mathbf{i} - 3\mathbf{k})$.

Q7 For P, $\begin{pmatrix} -4 \\ a \\ 10 \end{pmatrix} = \begin{pmatrix} -2 \\ 5 \\ 4 \end{pmatrix} + s \begin{pmatrix} 1 \\ 2 \\ -3 \end{pmatrix} = \begin{pmatrix} -2 + s \\ 5 + 2s \\ 4 - 3s \end{pmatrix}$, so:

$-4 = -2 + s \Rightarrow s = -2$, then $5 + 2s = a$, so $a = 1$
b and c are found using the same method.

For Q, $\begin{pmatrix} b \\ c \\ -11 \end{pmatrix} = \begin{pmatrix} -2 \\ 5 \\ 4 \end{pmatrix} + s \begin{pmatrix} 1 \\ 2 \\ -3 \end{pmatrix} = \begin{pmatrix} -2 + s \\ 5 + 2s \\ 4 - 3s \end{pmatrix}$

$4 - 3s = -11 \Rightarrow s = 5$, then $-2 + s = b$, so $b = 3$,
also $5 + 2s = c$, so $c = 15$.

Q8 a) Any vector parallel to $\begin{pmatrix} 3 \\ 2 \\ -1 \end{pmatrix}$ will do,

so any scalar multiple, e.g. $\mathbf{r} = \begin{pmatrix} -4 \\ 0 \\ 1 \end{pmatrix} + s \begin{pmatrix} 6 \\ 4 \\ -2 \end{pmatrix}$.

b) Any other point on the line will do, so find a point by choosing a value for s in the original equation,

e.g. $s = 1$ gives: $\mathbf{r} = \begin{pmatrix} -4 \\ 0 \\ 1 \end{pmatrix} + \begin{pmatrix} 3 \\ 2 \\ -1 \end{pmatrix} = \begin{pmatrix} -1 \\ 2 \\ 0 \end{pmatrix}$ as the

position vector of a new point on the line.

So the new equation is $\mathbf{r} = \begin{pmatrix} -1 \\ 2 \\ 0 \end{pmatrix} + s \begin{pmatrix} 3 \\ 2 \\ -1 \end{pmatrix}$.

Q9 a) We have position vectors $\mathbf{c} = \begin{pmatrix} 7 \\ 0 \\ -3 \end{pmatrix}$ and $\mathbf{d} = \begin{pmatrix} -1 \\ 1 \\ -3 \end{pmatrix}$,

put these into $\mathbf{r} = \mathbf{c} + t(\mathbf{d} - \mathbf{c})$:

$$\mathbf{r} = \begin{pmatrix} 7 \\ 0 \\ -3 \end{pmatrix} + t \begin{pmatrix} -8 \\ 1 \\ 0 \end{pmatrix}$$

b) We have position vectors $\mathbf{c} = \begin{pmatrix} -1 \\ 1 \\ 4 \end{pmatrix}$ and $\mathbf{d} = \begin{pmatrix} -4 \\ 1 \\ 0 \end{pmatrix}$, put these into $\mathbf{r} = \mathbf{c} + t(\mathbf{d} - \mathbf{c})$:

$$\mathbf{r} = \begin{pmatrix} -1 \\ 1 \\ 4 \end{pmatrix} + t\begin{pmatrix} -3 \\ 0 \\ -4 \end{pmatrix}$$

c) We have position vectors $\mathbf{c} = \begin{pmatrix} 2 \\ 5 \\ 0 \end{pmatrix}$ and $\mathbf{d} = \begin{pmatrix} -2 \\ -1 \\ 2 \end{pmatrix}$, put these into $\mathbf{r} = \mathbf{c} + t(\mathbf{d} - \mathbf{c})$:

$$\mathbf{r} = \begin{pmatrix} 2 \\ 5 \\ 0 \end{pmatrix} + t\begin{pmatrix} -4 \\ -6 \\ 2 \end{pmatrix}$$

Exercise 3.3 —
Intersecting, parallel and skew lines

For questions where you're asked to find the vector equation of a line there will always be alternative answers because the equation isn't unique. The answers given are the ones you'll get most easily from the information in the question.

Q1 a) $\begin{pmatrix} 0 \\ 7 \\ 0 \end{pmatrix} = -\frac{7}{2}\begin{pmatrix} 0 \\ -2 \\ 0 \end{pmatrix}$ which means the direction vectors of the lines are parallel, so the lines are parallel.

b) Not parallel as the direction vectors ($\mathbf{j} + \mathbf{k}$) and ($2\mathbf{i} + 2\mathbf{k}$) aren't parallel (the first vector has a zero $\mathbf{i}$ component and the second doesn't so they can't be parallel).

Q2 a) $\begin{pmatrix} a \\ 0 \\ -1 \end{pmatrix}$ and $\begin{pmatrix} 10 \\ b \\ -5 \end{pmatrix}$ are parallel, so $\begin{pmatrix} a \\ 0 \\ -1 \end{pmatrix} = \lambda\begin{pmatrix} 10 \\ b \\ -5 \end{pmatrix}$

for some λ,

$-1 = -5\lambda$ so $\lambda = \frac{1}{5}$

$\Rightarrow a = \frac{1}{5} \times 10 = 2$ and $0 = \frac{1}{5}b \Rightarrow b = 0$

b) $\begin{pmatrix} 2 \\ c \\ -4 \end{pmatrix}$ and $\begin{pmatrix} d \\ 3 \\ 2 \end{pmatrix}$ are parallel, so $\begin{pmatrix} 2 \\ c \\ -4 \end{pmatrix} = s\begin{pmatrix} d \\ 3 \\ 2 \end{pmatrix}$

for some s,

$-4 = 2s$ so $s = -2$

and $c = (-2) \times 3 \Rightarrow c = -6$ and

$2 = -2d \Rightarrow d = -1$

$c = -6$, $d = -1$

Q3 a) Lines intersect when $\begin{pmatrix} 2 \\ 1 \\ 0 \end{pmatrix} + \lambda\begin{pmatrix} 1 \\ -2 \\ 1 \end{pmatrix} = \begin{pmatrix} -3 \\ 0 \\ -1 \end{pmatrix} + \mu\begin{pmatrix} 4 \\ 3 \\ 0 \end{pmatrix}$

This gives us the equations:

$2 + \lambda = -3 + 4\mu$

$1 - 2\lambda = 3\mu$

$\lambda = -1$

Plug $\lambda = -1$ from the third row into the other rows: $\quad 2 - 1 = -3 + 4\mu \Rightarrow 4\mu = 4 \Rightarrow \mu = 1$

$\quad\quad 1 + 2 = 3\mu \Rightarrow 3 = 3\mu \Rightarrow \mu = 1$

There is a consistent solution so the lines intersect at the point with position vector:

$$\begin{pmatrix} 2 \\ 1 \\ 0 \end{pmatrix} - \begin{pmatrix} 1 \\ -2 \\ 1 \end{pmatrix} = \begin{pmatrix} -3 \\ 0 \\ -1 \end{pmatrix} + \begin{pmatrix} 4 \\ 3 \\ 0 \end{pmatrix} = \begin{pmatrix} 1 \\ 3 \\ -1 \end{pmatrix}$$

So the coordinates are (1, 3, −1)

Don't forget to give your answer as coordinates instead of leaving it as a vector.

b) Lines intersect when $\begin{pmatrix} -1 \\ 7 \\ 1 \end{pmatrix} + \lambda\begin{pmatrix} 2 \\ -2 \\ 1 \end{pmatrix} = \begin{pmatrix} 1 \\ 3 \\ 2 \end{pmatrix} + \mu\begin{pmatrix} 2 \\ -1 \\ 1 \end{pmatrix}$

This gives us the equations:

$-1 + 2\lambda = 1 + 2\mu$

$7 - 2\lambda = 3 - \mu$

$1 + \lambda = 2 + \mu$

Solve simultaneously:

(eqn 2) + (eqn 3): $\quad 8 - \lambda = 5 \Rightarrow \lambda = 3$

Plugging this back into (eqn 2) gives:

$7 - (2 \times 3) = 3 - \mu \Rightarrow \mu = 2$

Plug this into the first equation to check the solution is consistent:

$-1 + 2\lambda = 1 + 2\mu \Rightarrow -1 + (2 \times 3) = 1 + (2 \times 2)$

$\Rightarrow 5 = 5$

This is true so there's a consistent solution and the lines intersect at the point with position vector:

$$\begin{pmatrix} -1 \\ 7 \\ 1 \end{pmatrix} + 3\begin{pmatrix} 2 \\ -2 \\ 1 \end{pmatrix} = \begin{pmatrix} 1 \\ 3 \\ 2 \end{pmatrix} + 2\begin{pmatrix} 2 \\ -1 \\ 1 \end{pmatrix} = \begin{pmatrix} 5 \\ 1 \\ 4 \end{pmatrix}$$

So the coordinates are (5, 1, 4)

c) Lines intersect when

$$\begin{pmatrix} 5 \\ 7 \\ -3 \end{pmatrix} + s\begin{pmatrix} 1 \\ 3 \\ -2 \end{pmatrix} = \begin{pmatrix} -4 \\ 15 \\ -10 \end{pmatrix} + t\begin{pmatrix} 1 \\ -4 \\ 3 \end{pmatrix}$$

This gives us the equations:

$5 + s = -4 + t$

$7 + 3s = 15 + -4t$

$-3 + -2s = -10 + 3t$

Solve simultaneously:

(eqn 2) − 3(eqn 1): $-8 = 27 - 7t \Rightarrow t = 5$

Putting this back into (eqn 1) gives:

$5 + s = -4 + 5 \Rightarrow s = -4$

Plug this into the third equation to check the solution is consistent: $\quad -3 + -2s = -10 + 3t$

$\Rightarrow -3 + (-2 \times (-4)) = -10 + (3 \times 5) \Rightarrow 5 = 5$

This is true so there's a consistent solution and the lines intersect at the point with position vector:

$$\begin{pmatrix} 5 \\ 7 \\ -3 \end{pmatrix} + -4\begin{pmatrix} 1 \\ 3 \\ -2 \end{pmatrix} = \begin{pmatrix} -4 \\ 15 \\ -10 \end{pmatrix} + 5\begin{pmatrix} 1 \\ -4 \\ 3 \end{pmatrix} = \begin{pmatrix} 1 \\ -5 \\ 5 \end{pmatrix}$$

So the coordinates are (1, −5, 5)

Q4 $\begin{pmatrix} 1 \\ 0 \\ a \end{pmatrix} + \lambda\begin{pmatrix} -1 \\ b \\ 2 \end{pmatrix} = \begin{pmatrix} 2 \\ -3 \\ 2 \end{pmatrix} = \begin{pmatrix} 0 \\ c \\ 3 \end{pmatrix} + \mu\begin{pmatrix} 2 \\ 1 \\ d \end{pmatrix}$

Solving along the top row:

$1 - \lambda = 2 \Rightarrow \lambda = -1$, $2 = 2\mu \Rightarrow \mu = 1$

Now plug the values for λ and μ back into each line equation and solve each separately:

$$\begin{pmatrix} 1 \\ 0 \\ a \end{pmatrix} - \begin{pmatrix} -1 \\ b \\ 2 \end{pmatrix} = \begin{pmatrix} 2 \\ -b \\ a-2 \end{pmatrix} = \begin{pmatrix} 2 \\ -3 \\ 2 \end{pmatrix} \Rightarrow b = 3, a = 4$$

$$\begin{pmatrix} 0 \\ c \\ 3 \end{pmatrix} + \begin{pmatrix} 2 \\ 1 \\ d \end{pmatrix} = \begin{pmatrix} 2 \\ c+1 \\ 3+d \end{pmatrix} = \begin{pmatrix} 2 \\ -3 \\ 2 \end{pmatrix} \Rightarrow c = -4, d = -1$$

Q5 a) If the lines are intersecting there will be a solution

to: $\begin{pmatrix} 4 \\ 0 \\ 1 \end{pmatrix} + \lambda \begin{pmatrix} 1 \\ 2 \\ 1 \end{pmatrix} = \begin{pmatrix} -1 \\ 3 \\ 2 \end{pmatrix} + \mu \begin{pmatrix} -1 \\ 1 \\ 0 \end{pmatrix}$

This gives equations: $4 + \lambda = -1 - \mu$
$2\lambda = 3 + \mu$
$1 + \lambda = 2$

The third row gives that $\lambda = 1$, plugging this into
the other rows gives: $4 + 1 = -1 - \mu \Rightarrow \mu = -6$
$2 = 3 + \mu \Rightarrow \mu = -1$

There's no consistent solution so the lines don't
intersect. Their direction vectors are also not
scalar multiples of one another as one has a zero
coefficient and the other doesn't.
This means the lines are not parallel.
Therefore the lines are neither parallel nor
intersecting, so they must be skew.

b) If the lines are intersecting there will be a solution

to: $\begin{pmatrix} 1 \\ 1 \\ -1 \end{pmatrix} + \lambda \begin{pmatrix} -1 \\ 2 \\ 3 \end{pmatrix} = \begin{pmatrix} -2 \\ 4 \\ 1 \end{pmatrix} + \mu \begin{pmatrix} 1 \\ -1 \\ 3 \end{pmatrix}$

This gives equations: $1 - \lambda = -2 + \mu$
$1 + 2\lambda = 4 - \mu$
$-1 + 3\lambda = 1 + 3\mu$

Solving simultaneously:
(eqn 1) + (eqn 2): $2 + \lambda = 2 \Rightarrow \lambda = 0$
Plugging this back into equation 1 gives:
$1 - 0 = -2 + \mu \Rightarrow \mu = 3$
Plugging these values into equation 3 gives:
$-1 + 3\lambda = 1 + 3\mu \Rightarrow -1 + 0 = 1 + 9$
$\Rightarrow -1 = 10$

This isn't true which means there's no consistent
solution so the lines don't intersect.
Their direction vectors are also not scalar

multiples of one another, otherwise $\frac{-1}{1} = \frac{2}{-1} = \frac{3}{3}$
would hold.
This means the lines are not parallel.
Therefore the lines are neither parallel nor
intersecting, so they must be skew.

c) If the lines are intersecting there will be a solution

to: $\begin{pmatrix} 3 \\ 1 \\ 1 \end{pmatrix} + s \begin{pmatrix} -1 \\ 2 \\ 1 \end{pmatrix} = \begin{pmatrix} 2 \\ -2 \\ 0 \end{pmatrix} + t \begin{pmatrix} 1 \\ 1 \\ -3 \end{pmatrix}$

This gives equations: $3 - s = 2 + t$
$1 + 2s = -2 + t$
$1 + s = -3t$

Solving simultaneously:
(eqn 1) – (eqn 2): $2 - 3s = 4 \Rightarrow 3s = -2 \Rightarrow s = -\frac{2}{3}$
Plugging this back into equation 1 gives:
$\frac{11}{3} = 2 + t \Rightarrow t = \frac{5}{3}$
Plugging these values into equation 3 gives:
$1 + s = -3t \Rightarrow \frac{1}{3} = -3 \times \frac{5}{3} \Rightarrow \frac{1}{3} = -5$
This isn't true which means there's no consistent
solution so the lines don't intersect.
Their direction vectors are also not scalar
multiples of one another, since if they were you'd
have $\frac{-1}{1} = \frac{2}{1} = \frac{1}{-3}$, which doesn't hold.

This means the lines are not parallel.
Therefore the lines are neither parallel nor
intersecting, so they must be skew.

Q6 If the lines are the same then all of their points are the
same so there will be solutions to:

$\begin{pmatrix} 3 - \lambda \\ 4 + \lambda \\ -\lambda \end{pmatrix} = \begin{pmatrix} -6 - \mu \\ -8 + \mu \\ -\mu \end{pmatrix}$

Solving each line gives: $\lambda = \mu + 9$, $\lambda = \mu - 12$, $\lambda = \mu$.
There's no consistent solution so the lines aren't the
same, they're just parallel.

Q7 a) If the lines are intersecting there will be a solution

to: $\begin{pmatrix} 4 \\ -5 \\ 1 \end{pmatrix} + p \begin{pmatrix} 2 \\ 4 \\ 3 \end{pmatrix} = \begin{pmatrix} 2 \\ -1 \\ 0 \end{pmatrix} + q \begin{pmatrix} 1 \\ 3 \\ 2 \end{pmatrix}$

This gives equations: $4 + 2p = 2 + q$ (eqn 1)
$-5 + 4p = -1 + 3q$ (eqn 2)
$1 + 3p = 2q$ (eqn 3)

Taking $2 \times$ (eqn 1) – (eqn 3) gives:
$7 + p = 4 \Rightarrow p = -3$
Plugging this back into (eqn 1) gives: $q = -4$
Check this in (eqn 2): $-5 + 4(-3) = -1 + 3(-4)$
$-17 = -13$

This doesn't hold so the lines don't intersect, so
they must be skew.

b) If the lines are intersecting there will be a solution

to: $\begin{pmatrix} 1 \\ -1 \\ 4 \end{pmatrix} + \lambda \begin{pmatrix} 1 \\ -1 \\ 1 \end{pmatrix} = \begin{pmatrix} 2 \\ 4 \\ 7 \end{pmatrix} + \mu \begin{pmatrix} 2 \\ 1 \\ 3 \end{pmatrix}$

This gives equations: $1 + \lambda = 2 + 2\mu$ (eqn 1)
$-1 - \lambda = 4 + \mu$ (eqn 2)
$4 + \lambda = 7 + 3\mu$ (eqn 3)

(eqn 1) + (eqn 2) gives: $0 = 6 + 3\mu \Rightarrow \mu = -2$
Plugging this back into (eqn 2) gives:
$-1 - \lambda = 4 + \mu \Rightarrow -1 - \lambda = 2 \Rightarrow \lambda = -3$
Check this in (eqn 3): $4 + \lambda = 7 + 3\mu$
$\Rightarrow 4 - 3 = 7 + 3(-2)$
$\Rightarrow 1 = 1$

This is true so $\lambda = -3$ and $\mu = -2$ solve all of the
equations and the lines intersect. Plugging either
of these values back into the appropriate equation
gives the intersection position vector as: $\begin{pmatrix} -2 \\ 2 \\ 1 \end{pmatrix}$

Q8 a) $\overrightarrow{AC} = \overrightarrow{OC} - \overrightarrow{OA} = \begin{pmatrix} 1 \\ 4 \\ 2 \end{pmatrix} - \begin{pmatrix} 2 \\ 1 \\ 1 \end{pmatrix} = \begin{pmatrix} -1 \\ 3 \\ 1 \end{pmatrix}$

This is a direction vector for the line containing
AC.

A, with position vector $\begin{pmatrix} 2 \\ 1 \\ 1 \end{pmatrix}$ lies on the line
containing AC.
So an equation for the line containing AC is:

$$\mathbf{r} = \begin{pmatrix} 2 \\ 1 \\ 1 \end{pmatrix} + s \begin{pmatrix} -1 \\ 3 \\ 1 \end{pmatrix}$$

$\overrightarrow{BD} = \overrightarrow{OD} - \overrightarrow{OB} = \begin{pmatrix} -1 \\ 3 \\ -3 \end{pmatrix} - \begin{pmatrix} 3 \\ -1 \\ 1 \end{pmatrix} = \begin{pmatrix} -4 \\ 4 \\ -4 \end{pmatrix}$

This is a direction vector for the line containing
BD.

B, with position vector $\begin{pmatrix} 3 \\ -1 \\ 1 \end{pmatrix}$ lies on the line containing BD.

So an equation for the line containing BD is:

$$\mathbf{r} = \begin{pmatrix} 3 \\ -1 \\ 1 \end{pmatrix} + t\begin{pmatrix} -4 \\ 4 \\ -4 \end{pmatrix} = \begin{pmatrix} 3 \\ -1 \\ 1 \end{pmatrix} + t\begin{pmatrix} -1 \\ 1 \\ -1 \end{pmatrix}$$

You could have used point C rather than A or point D rather than B. You can, and probably should, simplify the direction vector like has been done above by cancelling the scalar multiple of 4.

b) The lines containing the diagonals intersect when

$$\begin{pmatrix} 2 \\ 1 \\ 1 \end{pmatrix} + s\begin{pmatrix} -1 \\ 3 \\ 1 \end{pmatrix} = \begin{pmatrix} 3 \\ -1 \\ 1 \end{pmatrix} + t\begin{pmatrix} -1 \\ 1 \\ -1 \end{pmatrix}$$

This gives equations:
$\quad 2 - s = 3 - t \quad$ (eqn 1)
$\quad 1 + 3s = -1 + t \quad$ (eqn 2)
$\quad 1 + s = 1 - t \quad$ (eqn 3)

(eqn 1) + (eqn 2) gives: $3 + 2s = 2 \Rightarrow s = -\frac{1}{2}$

Plugging this back into (eqn 1) gives:

$2 - s = 3 - t \Rightarrow 2 + \frac{1}{2} = 3 - t \Rightarrow t = \frac{1}{2}$

Check this in (eqn 3):
$$1 + s = 1 - t$$
$$\Rightarrow 1 - \frac{1}{2} = 1 - \frac{1}{2}$$
$$\Rightarrow \frac{1}{2} = \frac{1}{2}$$

This is true so $s = -\frac{1}{2}$ and $t = \frac{1}{2}$ solve all of the equations and the lines intersect. Plugging either of these values back into the appropriate equation gives the coordinates of the point of intersection as $\left(\frac{5}{2}, -\frac{1}{2}, \frac{1}{2}\right)$.

So the coordinates of E are $\left(\frac{5}{2}, -\frac{1}{2}, \frac{1}{2}\right)$

4. Scalar Product
Exercise 4.1 — The scalar product

Q1 a) We use the formula $\mathbf{a}.\mathbf{b} = |\mathbf{a}||\mathbf{b}|\cos\theta$.
We have $|\mathbf{a}| = 4$, $|\mathbf{b}| = 6$ and $\theta = 60°$, so:
$\mathbf{a}.\mathbf{b} = 4 \times 6 \times \cos(60°) = 4 \times 6 \times 0.5 = 12$

b) If you draw both vectors away from the same point, then the angle between them is 30°.

$|\mathbf{a}| = 5$, $|\mathbf{b}| = 10$, $\theta = 30°$, $\mathbf{a}.\mathbf{b} = 5 \times 10 \times \frac{\sqrt{3}}{2}$
$= 25\sqrt{3}$

c) $\mathbf{a}.\mathbf{b} = 0$, as the vectors are perpendicular.

d) $|\mathbf{a}| = 8$, $|\mathbf{b}| = 11$, $\theta = 180° - 60° = 120°$ as both vectors must be pointing away from θ,
$\mathbf{a}.\mathbf{b} = 8 \times 11 \times \left(-\frac{1}{2}\right) = -44$

Q2 a) $\mathbf{i}.3\mathbf{j} = 0$, because $\mathbf{i}$ and $\mathbf{j}$ are perpendicular

b) $2\mathbf{j}.-\mathbf{j} = -|2| \times |1| = -2$, because the vectors are parallel but in opposite directions.

c) $4\mathbf{k}.-\mathbf{i} = 0$, because $\mathbf{i}$ and $\mathbf{k}$ are perpendicular.

d) $\mathbf{k}.6\mathbf{k} = |1| \times |6| = 6$, because $\mathbf{k}$ and $6\mathbf{k}$ are parallel.

Q3 a) We use the formula $\mathbf{a}.\mathbf{b} = |\mathbf{a}||\mathbf{b}|\cos\theta$.
We have $|\mathbf{a}| = 2$, $|\mathbf{b}| = 5$ and $\mathbf{a}.\mathbf{b} = 3$, so:
$3 = 2 \times 5 \times \cos\theta = 10\cos\theta$
$$\Rightarrow \cos\theta = \frac{3}{10} \Rightarrow \theta = 72.54...°$$
So θ is 73° to the nearest degree.

b) $|\mathbf{a}| = 1.2$, $|\mathbf{b}| = 5.6$ and $\mathbf{a}.\mathbf{b} = 3$,
call the angle between the two vectors ϕ, so:
$3 = 1.2 \times 5.6 \times \cos\phi = 6.72\cos\phi$
$$\Rightarrow \cos\phi = \frac{3}{6.72} \Rightarrow \phi = 63.48...°$$
$\theta = 180° - \phi$, so $\theta = 180° - 63.48...° = 117°$
to the nearest degree

Exercise 4.2 —
Scalar product from vector components

Q1 a) $\mathbf{a} = \begin{pmatrix} 1 \\ 4 \end{pmatrix}$, $\mathbf{b} = \begin{pmatrix} -2 \\ 1 \end{pmatrix}$,
$\mathbf{a}.\mathbf{b} = a_1 b_1 + a_2 b_2 = (1 \times (-2)) + (4 \times 1) = 2$

b) $\mathbf{a}.\mathbf{b} = (2 \times 1) + ((-1) \times 3) = 2 - 3 = -1$

c) $\mathbf{a}.\mathbf{b} = ((-2) \times (-1)) + ((-6) \times 2) + (1 \times 9)$
$= 2 - 12 + 9 = -1$

d) $\mathbf{a}.\mathbf{b} = (3 \times 2) + (1 \times 3) + ((-4) \times 1) = 6 + 3 - 4 = 5$

e) $\mathbf{a}.\mathbf{b} = (0 \times 6) + (5 \times 0) + ((-6) \times 5) = 0 + 0 - 30 = -30$

Q2 a) $8 = \begin{pmatrix} 4 \\ e \end{pmatrix}.\begin{pmatrix} -2 \\ 4 \end{pmatrix} = -8 + 4e \Rightarrow 4e = 16 \Rightarrow e = 4$

b) $8 = -14 - f + 15 \Rightarrow f = -7$

c) $8 = -2g - 10 + 12 \Rightarrow g = -3$

Q3 a) Scalar product $= 40 + 40 = 80$
Perpendicular vectors have a scalar product of 0, so the vectors are not perpendicular.

b) Scalar product $= 0 + 0 + 0 = 0$, perpendicular.

c) Scalar product $= -6 + 24 - 10 = 8$,
not perpendicular.

d) Scalar product $= -2 - 2 + 4 = 0$, perpendicular.

e) Scalar product $= 0 + 50 + 0 = 50$,
not perpendicular.

Q4 a) $4\mathbf{i} + a\mathbf{j}$ and $5\mathbf{i} - 10\mathbf{j}$ are perpendicular, so their scalar product is 0.
$0 = (4\mathbf{i} + a\mathbf{j}).(5\mathbf{i} - 10\mathbf{j}) = 20 - 10a \Rightarrow 10a = 20$
$\Rightarrow a = 2$

b) $0 = 10b + 6 - 36 \Rightarrow b = 3$

c) $0 = -2 + 3 + c \Rightarrow c = -1$

d) $0 = -3d + 27 - 48 \Rightarrow d = -7$

Q5 Let $\mathbf{a} = \begin{pmatrix} 4 \\ -1 \\ 3 \end{pmatrix}$ and $\mathbf{b} = \begin{pmatrix} -12 \\ 3 \\ -9 \end{pmatrix}$.

$\mathbf{a}.\mathbf{b} = -48 - 3 - 27 = -78$
$|\mathbf{a}| = \sqrt{4^2 + (-1)^2 + 3^2} = \sqrt{26}$
$|\mathbf{b}| = \sqrt{(-12)^2 + 3^2 + (-9)^2} = \sqrt{234}$
$|\mathbf{a}||\mathbf{b}| = \sqrt{26}\sqrt{234} = \sqrt{26}\sqrt{3}\sqrt{78} = \sqrt{78}\sqrt{78} = 78$
$|\mathbf{a}||\mathbf{b}| = -\mathbf{a}.\mathbf{b}$ so $\mathbf{a}$ and $\mathbf{b}$ are parallel.

Q6 We need to find vectors $(\alpha\mathbf{i} + \beta\mathbf{j} + \gamma\mathbf{k})$ so that:

$(3\mathbf{i} - \mathbf{j} - 2\mathbf{k}).(\alpha\mathbf{i} + \beta\mathbf{j} + \gamma\mathbf{k}) = 3\alpha - \beta - 2\gamma = 0$

So pick any α, β and γ so that this holds, e.g.

fix $\alpha = 1$ and $\beta = 1 \Rightarrow 3 - 1 - 2\gamma = 0 \Rightarrow \gamma = 1$

So $\mathbf{i} + \mathbf{j} + \mathbf{k}$ is perpendicular to $3\mathbf{i} - \mathbf{j} - 2\mathbf{k}$

You can find other perpendicular vectors by fixing any two of the coefficients as other values.
To make sure they're not parallel to the first vector you find, you could keep $\alpha = 1$ and just vary β.

Exercise 4.3 —
Finding angles between vectors

Q1 **a)** $|\mathbf{p}| = \sqrt{4^2 + 3^2} = 5$, $|\mathbf{q}| = \sqrt{12^2 + 5^2} = 13$

$\mathbf{p}.\mathbf{q} = (4 \times 12) + (3 \times 5) = 63$

Using the formula $\cos\theta = \dfrac{\mathbf{p}.\mathbf{q}}{|\mathbf{p}\|\mathbf{q}|}$,

we get $\cos\theta = \dfrac{63}{5 \times 13} \Rightarrow \theta = 14.3°$ to 1 d.p.

b) $|\mathbf{r}| = \sqrt{2^2 + (-1)^2} = \sqrt{5}$, $|\mathbf{s}| = \sqrt{(-6)^2 + 3^2} = \sqrt{45}$

$\mathbf{r}.\mathbf{s} = -12 - 3 = -15$

$\cos\theta = \dfrac{-15}{\sqrt{5}\sqrt{45}} \Rightarrow \theta = 180.0°$ to 1 d.p.

c) $|\mathbf{a}| = \sqrt{(-2)^2 + (-4)^2} = 2\sqrt{5}$,

$|\mathbf{b}| = \sqrt{3^2 + (-1)^2} = \sqrt{10}$

$\mathbf{a}.\mathbf{b} = -6 + 4 = -2$

$\cos\theta = \dfrac{-2}{2\sqrt{5}\sqrt{10}} \Rightarrow \theta = 98.1°$ to 1 d.p.

Q2 **a)** $|\mathbf{a}| = 3$, $|\mathbf{b}| = 7$, $\mathbf{a}.\mathbf{b} = 8$,

so $\cos\theta = \dfrac{8}{3 \times 7} \Rightarrow \theta = 67.6°$ to 1 d.p.

b) $\cos\theta = \dfrac{38}{9 \times 11} \Rightarrow \theta = 67.4°$ to 1 d.p.

c) $\cos\theta = \dfrac{49}{11 \times 9} \Rightarrow \theta = 60.3°$ to 1 d.p.

d) $\cos\theta = \dfrac{-5}{19\sqrt{51}} \Rightarrow \theta = 92.1°$ to 1 d.p.

e) $\cos\theta = \dfrac{126}{27 \times 6} \Rightarrow \theta = 38.9°$ to 1 d.p.

Q3 **a)** $\overrightarrow{AB} = \overrightarrow{OB} - \overrightarrow{OA} = \begin{pmatrix}-1\\3\end{pmatrix} - \begin{pmatrix}-4\\-1\end{pmatrix} = \begin{pmatrix}3\\4\end{pmatrix}$

$\overrightarrow{AC} = \overrightarrow{OC} - \overrightarrow{OA} = \begin{pmatrix}4\\5\end{pmatrix} - \begin{pmatrix}-4\\-1\end{pmatrix} = \begin{pmatrix}8\\6\end{pmatrix}$

b) $|\overrightarrow{AB}| = \sqrt{3^2 + 4^2} = 5$, $|\overrightarrow{AC}| = \sqrt{8^2 + 6^2} = 10$

c) $(\overrightarrow{AB}).(\overrightarrow{AC}) = 24 + 24 = 48$

d) $\cos\theta = \dfrac{48}{5 \times 10} \Rightarrow \theta = 16.260...°$,

so angle BAC is 16° to the nearest degree.

Q4 **a)** $\overrightarrow{PQ} = \mathbf{q} - \mathbf{p} = 2\mathbf{i} + 9\mathbf{j} + 14\mathbf{k}$

$\overrightarrow{PR} = \mathbf{r} - \mathbf{p} = 2\mathbf{i} + 6\mathbf{j} - 2\mathbf{k}$

b) $|\overrightarrow{PQ}| = \sqrt{281}$, $|\overrightarrow{PR}| = \sqrt{44}$

c) $(\overrightarrow{PQ}).(\overrightarrow{PR}) = 4 + 54 - 28 = 30$

d) $\cos(QPR) = \dfrac{30}{\sqrt{281} \times \sqrt{44}}$

$\Rightarrow$ Angle QPR = 74.3° to 3 significant figures.

Q5 **a)** $\overrightarrow{TS} = -\mathbf{t} + \mathbf{s} = \begin{pmatrix}-2\\-2\\3\end{pmatrix}$ and $\overrightarrow{RS} = -\mathbf{r} + \mathbf{s} = \begin{pmatrix}4\\-1\\2\end{pmatrix}$

$(\overrightarrow{TS}).(\overrightarrow{RS}) = \begin{pmatrix}-2\\-2\\3\end{pmatrix}.\begin{pmatrix}4\\-1\\2\end{pmatrix} = -8 + 2 + 6 = 0$

b) TS is perpendicular to RS because their scalar product is zero. So TS is a line of symmetry of triangle TRU since TRU is isosceles with TR = TU. So S is the midpoint of RU.

c) $\overrightarrow{OU} = \overrightarrow{OS} + \overrightarrow{SU}$ and S is the midpoint of RU, therefore $\overrightarrow{SU} = \overrightarrow{RS}$.

So $\overrightarrow{OU} = \overrightarrow{OS} + \overrightarrow{RS} = \begin{pmatrix}1\\-1\\3\end{pmatrix} + \begin{pmatrix}4\\-1\\2\end{pmatrix} = \begin{pmatrix}5\\-2\\5\end{pmatrix}$

So U is (5, −2, 5).

Q6 **a)** $\overrightarrow{OD} = \overrightarrow{OA} + \overrightarrow{AD} = \overrightarrow{OA} + \overrightarrow{BC}$ since ABCD is a parallelogram, so AD and BC are parallel and the same length.

$\overrightarrow{OD} = \overrightarrow{OA} + \overrightarrow{BC} = \overrightarrow{OA} + \overrightarrow{OC} - \overrightarrow{OB}$

$= \mathbf{i}(-4 + 6 - 0) + \mathbf{j}(5 + 13 - 4) + \mathbf{k}(-6 + 0 - 2)$

$= 2\mathbf{i} + 14\mathbf{j} - 8\mathbf{k}$

b) $\overrightarrow{AB} = \mathbf{b} - \mathbf{a} = \mathbf{i}(0 - -4) + \mathbf{j}(4 - 5) + \mathbf{k}(2 - -6)$

$= 4\mathbf{i} - \mathbf{j} + 8\mathbf{k}$,

$\overrightarrow{AD} = \mathbf{d} - \mathbf{a} = \mathbf{i}(2 - -4) + \mathbf{j}(14 - 5) + \mathbf{k}(-8 - -6)$

$= 6\mathbf{i} + 9\mathbf{j} - 2\mathbf{k}$

c) $|\overrightarrow{AB}| = 9, |\overrightarrow{AD}| = 11$

d) $\overrightarrow{AB} \cdot \overrightarrow{AD} = (4 \times 6) + (-1 \times 9) + (8 \times -2) = -1$

$\cos(\angle BAD) = \dfrac{-1}{9 \times 11} \Rightarrow \angle BAD = 90.58°$ (to 4 s.f.)

Q7 **a)** O is the midpoint of AB, so $\overrightarrow{AO} = \overrightarrow{OB} = \mathbf{p}$, then:

$\overrightarrow{AC} = \overrightarrow{AO} + \overrightarrow{OC} = \mathbf{p} + \mathbf{q}$, $\overrightarrow{CB} = \overrightarrow{OB} - \overrightarrow{OC} = \mathbf{p} - \mathbf{q}$

b) Apply the commutative and distributive laws:

*Remember that the commutative law says that it doesn't matter which way round you multiply the vectors **p.q** or **q.p** and the distributive law says that you can multiply out the brackets.*

$(\overrightarrow{AC}).(\overrightarrow{CB}) = (\mathbf{p} + \mathbf{q}).(\mathbf{p} - \mathbf{q}) = \mathbf{p}.(\mathbf{p} - \mathbf{q}) + \mathbf{q}.(\mathbf{p} - \mathbf{q})$

$= \mathbf{p}.\mathbf{p} + \mathbf{p}.(-\mathbf{q}) + \mathbf{q}.\mathbf{p} + \mathbf{q}.(-\mathbf{q})$

$= \mathbf{p}.\mathbf{p} - \mathbf{p}.\mathbf{q} + \mathbf{q}.\mathbf{p} - \mathbf{q}.\mathbf{q} = \mathbf{p}.\mathbf{p} - \mathbf{q}.\mathbf{q}$

c) $\mathbf{p}.\mathbf{p} = |\mathbf{p}||\mathbf{p}|\cos 0 = |\mathbf{p}||\mathbf{p}| \times 1 = |\mathbf{p}|^2 = r^2$ because the length of **p** is the radius r of the circle.

The angle between a vector and itself is 0° because that's how much you have to rotate a vector by so that it's pointing in the same direction as itself.

Also $\mathbf{q}.\mathbf{q} = |\mathbf{q}||\mathbf{q}|\cos 0 = |\mathbf{q}||\mathbf{q}| \times 1 = |\mathbf{q}|^2 = r^2$

Then $(\overrightarrow{AC}).(\overrightarrow{CB}) = \mathbf{p}.\mathbf{p} - \mathbf{q}.\mathbf{q} = r^2 - r^2 = 0$

So AC is perpendicular to CB, i.e. angle ACB = 90°.

Exercise 4.4 —
Finding the angle between two lines

Q1 a) The direction vectors of the lines are:

$$2\mathbf{i} - 4\mathbf{j} - 6\mathbf{k} = \begin{pmatrix} 2 \\ -4 \\ -6 \end{pmatrix} \text{ and } -\mathbf{i} + 2\mathbf{j} + 3\mathbf{k} = \begin{pmatrix} -1 \\ 2 \\ 3 \end{pmatrix}.$$

Because $\begin{pmatrix} 2 \\ -4 \\ -6 \end{pmatrix} = -2\begin{pmatrix} -1 \\ 2 \\ 3 \end{pmatrix}$ the vectors are parallel,

so the lines are parallel.

b) The direction vectors of the lines are:

$$\begin{pmatrix} 4 \\ -1 \\ 1 \end{pmatrix} \text{ and } \begin{pmatrix} 1 \\ -4 \\ 0 \end{pmatrix}$$

The lines are not parallel as one direction vector has zero **k** component and the other doesn't.
Scalar product = 4 + 4 + 0 = 8, so they're not perpendicular.
The lines are neither parallel nor perpendicular.

c) The direction vectors of the lines are:

$$2\mathbf{j} - 7\mathbf{k} = \begin{pmatrix} 0 \\ 2 \\ -7 \end{pmatrix} \text{ and } 2\mathbf{i} - 7\mathbf{k} = \begin{pmatrix} 2 \\ 0 \\ -7 \end{pmatrix}$$

The lines are not parallel as one direction vector has zero **i** component and the other doesn't.
Scalar product = 0 + 0 + 49 = 49,
so they're not perpendicular.
The lines are neither parallel nor perpendicular.

d) The direction vectors of the lines are:

$$\mathbf{i} + \mathbf{j} = \begin{pmatrix} 1 \\ 1 \\ 0 \end{pmatrix} \text{ and } \mathbf{i} - \mathbf{j} + 2\mathbf{k} = \begin{pmatrix} 1 \\ -1 \\ 2 \end{pmatrix}$$

Scalar product = 1 − 1 + 0 = 0
The vectors are perpendicular, so the lines are perpendicular.

e) The direction vectors of the lines are: $\begin{pmatrix} 0 \\ 0 \\ 4 \end{pmatrix}$ and $\begin{pmatrix} -4 \\ 8 \\ 0 \end{pmatrix}$
Scalar product = 0 + 0 + 0 = 0.
The lines are perpendicular.

Q2 a) $\mathbf{b}_1 = \begin{pmatrix} 2 \\ 2 \\ 1 \end{pmatrix}, \mathbf{b}_2 = \begin{pmatrix} 2 \\ 3 \\ 6 \end{pmatrix}$

$|\mathbf{b}_1| = 3, |\mathbf{b}_2| = 7, (\mathbf{b}_1).(\mathbf{b}_2) = 16$

$\cos\theta = \dfrac{16}{3 \times 7} \Rightarrow \theta = 40.4°$ to 1 d.p.

b) $\mathbf{b}_1 = 4\mathbf{i} + 4\mathbf{j} - 7\mathbf{k} = \begin{pmatrix} 4 \\ 4 \\ -7 \end{pmatrix}, \mathbf{b}_2 = 8\mathbf{i} + \mathbf{j} - 4\mathbf{k} = \begin{pmatrix} 8 \\ 1 \\ -4 \end{pmatrix}$

$\cos\theta = \dfrac{64}{9 \times 9} \Rightarrow \theta = 37.8°$ to 1 d.p.

c) $\mathbf{b}_1 = \begin{pmatrix} 6 \\ -7 \\ 5 \end{pmatrix}, \mathbf{b}_2 = \begin{pmatrix} 2 \\ 1 \\ -1 \end{pmatrix}$

$(\mathbf{b}_1).(\mathbf{b}_2) = 12 - 7 - 5 = 0 \Rightarrow \theta = 90°$

d) $\mathbf{b}_1 = 7\mathbf{i} - 6\mathbf{j} + 6\mathbf{k} = \begin{pmatrix} 7 \\ -6 \\ 6 \end{pmatrix}, \mathbf{b}_2 = -4\mathbf{i} + 2\mathbf{j} - 2\mathbf{k} = \begin{pmatrix} -4 \\ 2 \\ -2 \end{pmatrix}$

$\cos\theta = \dfrac{-52}{11 \times 2\sqrt{6}} \Rightarrow \theta = 164.8°$ to 1 d.p.
Acute angle: 180 − θ = 15.2°

e) $\mathbf{b}_1 = -3\mathbf{i} - 5\mathbf{j} + 2\mathbf{k} = \begin{pmatrix} -3 \\ -5 \\ 2 \end{pmatrix}, \mathbf{b}_2 = 2\mathbf{i} + \mathbf{k} = \begin{pmatrix} 2 \\ 0 \\ 1 \end{pmatrix}$

$\cos\theta = \dfrac{-4}{\sqrt{38}\sqrt{5}} \Rightarrow \theta = 106.9°$ to 1 d.p.
Acute angle: 180 − θ = 73.1°

Q3 The lines are perpendicular so:

$$0 = \begin{pmatrix} 4 \\ 6 \\ -1 \end{pmatrix}.\begin{pmatrix} 5 \\ -2 \\ z \end{pmatrix} = 20 - 12 - z \Rightarrow z = 8$$

Q4 a) Line containing AB:
E.g. $\mathbf{r} = \overrightarrow{OA} + \lambda\overrightarrow{AB}$

$$= \begin{pmatrix} -1 \\ -2 \\ 6 \end{pmatrix} + \lambda\left(\begin{pmatrix} p \\ -1 \\ 3 \end{pmatrix} - \begin{pmatrix} -1 \\ -2 \\ 6 \end{pmatrix}\right)$$

$$\mathbf{r} = \begin{pmatrix} -1 \\ -2 \\ 6 \end{pmatrix} + \lambda\begin{pmatrix} p+1 \\ 1 \\ -3 \end{pmatrix}$$

Line containing BC: E.g. $\mathbf{r} = \begin{pmatrix} -1 \\ 0 \\ 2 \end{pmatrix} + \mu\begin{pmatrix} p+1 \\ -1 \\ 1 \end{pmatrix}$

b) The angle ABC is 90° so the lines are perpendicular.
Taking the scalar product of the direction vectors:

$$0 = \begin{pmatrix} p+1 \\ 1 \\ -3 \end{pmatrix}.\begin{pmatrix} p+1 \\ -1 \\ 1 \end{pmatrix} = (p+1)^2 - 1 - 3 = p^2 + 2p - 3$$

$p^2 + 2p - 3 = 0 \Rightarrow (p+3)(p-1) = 0$
So $p = -3$ or $p = 1$

Q5 a) $\overrightarrow{OC} = \dfrac{3}{2}\overrightarrow{OA} = \dfrac{3}{2}\begin{pmatrix} 4 \\ 2 \\ -2 \end{pmatrix} = \begin{pmatrix} 6 \\ 3 \\ -3 \end{pmatrix}$

$\overrightarrow{OD} = 2\overrightarrow{OB} = 2\begin{pmatrix} -1 \\ 3 \\ 1 \end{pmatrix} = \begin{pmatrix} -2 \\ 6 \\ 2 \end{pmatrix}$

b) L_1: E.g.

$$\mathbf{r} = \begin{pmatrix} 4 \\ 2 \\ -2 \end{pmatrix} + \lambda\left(\begin{pmatrix} -2 \\ 6 \\ 2 \end{pmatrix} - \begin{pmatrix} 4 \\ 2 \\ -2 \end{pmatrix}\right) = \begin{pmatrix} 4 \\ 2 \\ -2 \end{pmatrix} + \lambda\begin{pmatrix} -6 \\ 4 \\ 4 \end{pmatrix}$$

L_2: E.g.

$$\mathbf{r} = \begin{pmatrix} -1 \\ 3 \\ 1 \end{pmatrix} + \mu\left(\begin{pmatrix} 6 \\ 3 \\ -3 \end{pmatrix} - \begin{pmatrix} -1 \\ 3 \\ 1 \end{pmatrix}\right) = \begin{pmatrix} -1 \\ 3 \\ 1 \end{pmatrix} + \mu\begin{pmatrix} 7 \\ 0 \\ -4 \end{pmatrix}$$

c) If the lines are intersecting they intersect when
$$\begin{pmatrix} 4 \\ 2 \\ -2 \end{pmatrix} + \lambda \begin{pmatrix} -6 \\ 4 \\ 4 \end{pmatrix} = \begin{pmatrix} -1 \\ 3 \\ 1 \end{pmatrix} + \mu \begin{pmatrix} 7 \\ 0 \\ -4 \end{pmatrix}$$
This gives the equations:
$$4 - 6\lambda = -1 + 7\mu$$
$$2 + 4\lambda = 3$$
$$-2 + 4\lambda = 1 - 4\mu$$
The second equation gives $\lambda = \frac{1}{4}$,
putting this into the first equation gives $\mu = \frac{1}{2}$.
Subbing these values into the third equation
gives: $-2 + 4\left(\frac{1}{4}\right) = 1 - 4\left(\frac{1}{2}\right) \Rightarrow -1 = -1$
This is true so all of the equations are solved by
the same values and the lines intersect.

d) $\cos\theta = \dfrac{-58}{\sqrt{68}\sqrt{65}} \Rightarrow \theta = 150.7°$ to 1 d.p.
Acute angle: $180 - 150.7 = 29.3°$

Q6 a) A has position vector $\begin{pmatrix} 3 \\ 8 \\ -5 \end{pmatrix}$ and B has
position vector $\begin{pmatrix} 8 \\ -2 \\ 0 \end{pmatrix}$.
L: E.g.
$$\mathbf{r} = \begin{pmatrix} 3 \\ 8 \\ -5 \end{pmatrix} + \lambda\left(\begin{pmatrix} 8 \\ -2 \\ 0 \end{pmatrix} - \begin{pmatrix} 3 \\ 8 \\ -5 \end{pmatrix}\right) = \begin{pmatrix} 3 \\ 8 \\ -5 \end{pmatrix} + \lambda\begin{pmatrix} 5 \\ -10 \\ 5 \end{pmatrix}$$

b) P lies on L so P has position vector:
$$\begin{pmatrix} 3 \\ 8 \\ -5 \end{pmatrix} + \lambda\begin{pmatrix} 5 \\ -10 \\ 5 \end{pmatrix} = \begin{pmatrix} 3+5\lambda \\ 8-10\lambda \\ -5+5\lambda \end{pmatrix}$$ for some λ.
OP is perpendicular to L so the scalar product of
$\overrightarrow{OP}$ and the direction vector of L must be zero:
$$0 = \begin{pmatrix} 5 \\ -10 \\ 5 \end{pmatrix}.\begin{pmatrix} 3+5\lambda \\ 8-10\lambda \\ -5+5\lambda \end{pmatrix}$$
$$= 5(3+5\lambda) - 10(8-10\lambda) + 5(-5+5\lambda)$$
$$\Rightarrow 150\lambda = 90 \Rightarrow \lambda = \frac{3}{5}$$
So $\overrightarrow{OP} = \begin{pmatrix} 3+5\lambda \\ 8-10\lambda \\ -5+5\lambda \end{pmatrix} = \begin{pmatrix} 3+3 \\ 8-6 \\ -5+3 \end{pmatrix} = \begin{pmatrix} 6 \\ 2 \\ -2 \end{pmatrix}$,
and the coordinates of P are $(6, 2, -2)$.

c) The distance of P from O is:
$$|\overrightarrow{OP}| = \sqrt{6^2 + 2^2 + (-2)^2} = \sqrt{44} = \sqrt{4}\sqrt{11} = 2\sqrt{11}$$

Q7 a) Vector equation of l is:
$$\mathbf{r} = (-3\mathbf{i} + 2\mathbf{j} + 4\mathbf{k}) + t((5\mathbf{i} - \mathbf{j} - \mathbf{k}) - (-3\mathbf{i} + 2\mathbf{j} + 4\mathbf{k}))$$
$$\Rightarrow \mathbf{r} = (-3\mathbf{i} + 2\mathbf{j} + 4\mathbf{k}) + t(8\mathbf{i} - 3\mathbf{j} - 5\mathbf{k})$$

b) $\overrightarrow{BA} = 7\mathbf{i} - 8\mathbf{j} - 2\mathbf{k}$, $|\overrightarrow{BA}| = \sqrt{117}$, $|\overrightarrow{BC}| = \sqrt{98}$
$(\overrightarrow{BA}).(\overrightarrow{BC}) = 90$, $\cos\theta = \dfrac{90}{\sqrt{117}\sqrt{98}}$
$\theta = 32.8°$ to 1 d.p.

c)

The shortest distance from A to l is the length of
the line segment AP where P lies on l and AP is
perpendicular to l.
Find the length of AP using trig:
First, $|\overrightarrow{AB}| = \sqrt{117}$ from part b).
Now AP is the opposite side to angle ABP so:
Opposite = $\sin\theta \times$ Hypotenuse
AP = $\sin(32.8) \times \sqrt{117} = 5.86$ to 2 d.p.

Review Exercise — Chapter 6

Q1 *Any multiples of the vectors will do:*
a) e.g. $\mathbf{a}$ and $4\mathbf{a}$
b) e.g. $6\mathbf{i} + 8\mathbf{j} - 4\mathbf{k}$ and $9\mathbf{i} + 12\mathbf{j} - 6\mathbf{k}$
c) e.g. $\begin{pmatrix} 2 \\ 4 \\ -2 \end{pmatrix}$ and $\begin{pmatrix} 4 \\ 8 \\ -4 \end{pmatrix}$

Q2 a) $\overrightarrow{AB} = \overrightarrow{AO} + \overrightarrow{OB} = -\overrightarrow{OA} + \overrightarrow{OB} = \mathbf{b} - \mathbf{a}$
Parts b) − d) are answered using the same method as a)
b) $\overrightarrow{BA} = -\overrightarrow{OB} + \overrightarrow{OA} = \mathbf{a} - \mathbf{b}$
or $\overrightarrow{BA} = -\overrightarrow{AB} = -(\mathbf{b} - \mathbf{a}) = \mathbf{a} - \mathbf{b}$
c) $\overrightarrow{CB} = -\overrightarrow{OC} + \overrightarrow{OB} = \mathbf{b} - \mathbf{c}$
d) $\overrightarrow{AC} = -\overrightarrow{OA} + \overrightarrow{OC} = \mathbf{c} - \mathbf{a}$

Q3 a) $\overrightarrow{HO}$ is parallel to $\overrightarrow{OE}$ and has the same length
(as the hexagon is regular), so $\overrightarrow{HO} = \overrightarrow{OE} = \mathbf{e}$ and
$\overrightarrow{HE} = \overrightarrow{HO} + \overrightarrow{OE} = \mathbf{e} + \mathbf{e} = 2\mathbf{e}$
b) $\overrightarrow{OG}$ is parallel to $\overrightarrow{DO}$ and has the same length so
$\overrightarrow{DG} = \overrightarrow{DO} + \overrightarrow{OG} = -\mathbf{d} + (-\mathbf{d}) = -2\mathbf{d}$
c) $\overrightarrow{ED} = \overrightarrow{EO} + \overrightarrow{OD} = -\mathbf{e} + \mathbf{d} = \mathbf{d} - \mathbf{e}$
d) $\overrightarrow{CO}$ is parallel to $\overrightarrow{DE}$ and has the same length so
$\overrightarrow{CE} = \overrightarrow{CO} + \overrightarrow{OE} = \overrightarrow{DE} + \overrightarrow{OE}$
$\quad = -\overrightarrow{ED} + \overrightarrow{OE} = -(\mathbf{d} - \mathbf{e}) + \mathbf{e} = 2\mathbf{e} - \mathbf{d}$
e) $\overrightarrow{EF}$ is parallel to $\overrightarrow{DO}$ and has the same length so
$\overrightarrow{DF} = \overrightarrow{DE} + \overrightarrow{EF} = \overrightarrow{DE} + \overrightarrow{DO}$
$\quad = -\overrightarrow{ED} - \overrightarrow{OD} = -(\mathbf{d} - \mathbf{e}) - \mathbf{d} = \mathbf{e} - 2\mathbf{d}$

Q4 $2\mathbf{i} - 4\mathbf{j} + 5\mathbf{k}$

Q5 $\overrightarrow{XO} = -\overrightarrow{OX} = -(6\mathbf{i} - \mathbf{j}) = -6\mathbf{i} + \mathbf{j} = \begin{pmatrix} -6 \\ 1 \\ 0 \end{pmatrix}$
$\overrightarrow{YO} = -\overrightarrow{OY} = -(4\mathbf{i} - 4\mathbf{j} + 7\mathbf{k}) = -4\mathbf{i} + 4\mathbf{j} - 7\mathbf{k} = \begin{pmatrix} -4 \\ 4 \\ -7 \end{pmatrix}$

Q6 $\overrightarrow{RS} = \overrightarrow{OS} - \overrightarrow{OR} = \begin{pmatrix} -5 \\ -7 \end{pmatrix} - \begin{pmatrix} 3 \\ -1 \end{pmatrix} = \begin{pmatrix} -8 \\ -6 \end{pmatrix}$
$|\overrightarrow{RS}| = \sqrt{(-8)^2 + (-6)^2} = \sqrt{64 + 36} = \sqrt{100} = 10$
*Another way to answer this question is to put the
coordinates of R and S straight into the formula for the
distance between two points:* $\sqrt{(x_2 - x_1)^2 + (y_2 - y_1)^2}$.

Q7 a) $\sqrt{3^2 + 4^2 + (-2)^2} = \sqrt{29}$
b) $\sqrt{1^2 + 2^2 + (-1)^2} = \sqrt{6}$

Q8 a) $\sqrt{1^2 + 2^2 + 3^2} = \sqrt{14}$
b) $\sqrt{3^2 + (-1)^2 + (-2)^2} = \sqrt{14}$
c) $|\overrightarrow{AB}|$ is the distance between A and B, which is
given by the formula:
$$\sqrt{(3-1)^2 + (-1-2)^2 + (-2-3)^2} = \sqrt{38}$$

Q9 $\begin{pmatrix} \frac{2}{3} \\ \frac{2}{3} \\ -\frac{1}{3} \end{pmatrix}$ is the unit vector in the direction of $\overrightarrow{XY}$,

so you know that $\overrightarrow{XY} = |\overrightarrow{XY}| \begin{pmatrix} \frac{2}{3} \\ \frac{2}{3} \\ -\frac{1}{3} \end{pmatrix} = 6 \begin{pmatrix} \frac{2}{3} \\ \frac{2}{3} \\ -\frac{1}{3} \end{pmatrix} = \begin{pmatrix} 4 \\ 4 \\ -2 \end{pmatrix}$

Then $\overrightarrow{OY} = \overrightarrow{OX} + \overrightarrow{XY} = \begin{pmatrix} -2 \\ 1 \\ 0 \end{pmatrix} + \begin{pmatrix} 4 \\ 4 \\ -2 \end{pmatrix} = \begin{pmatrix} 2 \\ 5 \\ -2 \end{pmatrix}$,

and the coordinates of Y are (2, 5, −2).

Q10 a) $\mathbf{r} = (4\mathbf{i} + \mathbf{j} + 2\mathbf{k}) + t(3\mathbf{i} + \mathbf{j} - \mathbf{k})$ or $\mathbf{r} = \begin{pmatrix} 4 \\ 1 \\ 2 \end{pmatrix} + t \begin{pmatrix} 3 \\ 1 \\ -1 \end{pmatrix}$

b) $\mathbf{r} = (2\mathbf{i} - \mathbf{j} + \mathbf{k}) + t((2\mathbf{j} + 3\mathbf{k}) - (2\mathbf{i} - \mathbf{j} + \mathbf{k}))$
$\Rightarrow \mathbf{r} = (2\mathbf{i} - \mathbf{j} + \mathbf{k}) + t(-2\mathbf{i} + 3\mathbf{j} + 2\mathbf{k})$

or $\mathbf{r} = \begin{pmatrix} 2 \\ -1 \\ 1 \end{pmatrix} + t \begin{pmatrix} -2 \\ 3 \\ 2 \end{pmatrix}$

In Q10 you're just plugging the vectors you're given into the formula for a vector line equation: $\mathbf{r} = \mathbf{a} + t\mathbf{b}$.

Q11 *All of the points are found by choosing a value for t, any points found in this way will do.*
The coordinates of the points given by $\mathbf{r}$ are:
$(3 + t(-1), 2 + t(3), 4 + t(0))$
E.g. If $t = 1$ the coordinates of the point given by $\mathbf{r}$ are: $(3 + 1(-1), 2 + 1(3), 4 + 1(0)) = (2, 5, 4)$
If $t = 2$ the coordinates of the point given by $\mathbf{r}$ are: $(3 + 2(-1), 2 + 2(3), 4 + 2(0)) = (1, 8, 4)$
If $t = -1$ the coordinates of the point given by $\mathbf{r}$ are: $(3 + -1(-1), 2 + -1(3), 4 + -1(0)) = (4, -1, 4)$

Q12 a)

b) $\overrightarrow{OB} = \frac{1}{2}\overrightarrow{OA} = \frac{1}{2}(2\mathbf{i} + 8\mathbf{j} - 4\mathbf{k}) = \mathbf{i} + 4\mathbf{j} - 2\mathbf{k}$
$\overrightarrow{OC} = 2\overrightarrow{OA} = 2(2\mathbf{i} + 8\mathbf{j} - 4\mathbf{k}) = 4\mathbf{i} + 16\mathbf{j} - 8\mathbf{k}$
$\overrightarrow{OD} = -\overrightarrow{OA} = -(2\mathbf{i} + 8\mathbf{j} - 4\mathbf{k}) = -2\mathbf{i} - 8\mathbf{j} + 4\mathbf{k}$

c) Line L passes through the origin so an equation is:
$\mathbf{r} = t(2\mathbf{i} + 8\mathbf{j} - 4\mathbf{k})$.

Q13 a) $\overrightarrow{PQ} = \begin{pmatrix} 5 \\ -2 \\ -1 \end{pmatrix} - \begin{pmatrix} 3 \\ -5 \\ 2 \end{pmatrix} = \begin{pmatrix} 2 \\ 3 \\ -3 \end{pmatrix}$

b) The line passes through P and is parallel to $\overrightarrow{PQ}$ so an equation is,
e.g: $\mathbf{r} = \overrightarrow{OP} + t\overrightarrow{PQ} = \begin{pmatrix} 3 \\ -5 \\ 2 \end{pmatrix} + t \begin{pmatrix} 2 \\ 3 \\ -3 \end{pmatrix}$

Q14 a) E.g. an equation for line m is $\mathbf{r} = \begin{pmatrix} 1 \\ 1 \\ 3 \end{pmatrix} + \lambda \begin{pmatrix} 3 \\ -1 \\ 4 \end{pmatrix}$,

an equation for line n is $\mathbf{r} = \begin{pmatrix} 9 \\ -3 \\ 9 \end{pmatrix} + \mu \begin{pmatrix} -1 \\ 1 \\ 1 \end{pmatrix}$

The lines aren't parallel as their direction vectors aren't scalar multiples of one another.

The lines intersect when $\begin{pmatrix} 1+3\lambda \\ 1-\lambda \\ 3+4\lambda \end{pmatrix} = \begin{pmatrix} 9-\mu \\ -3+\mu \\ 9+\mu \end{pmatrix}$

So solving these equations:
$1 - \lambda = -3 + \mu \Rightarrow \mu = 4 - \lambda$
$1 + 3\lambda = 9 - \mu \Rightarrow 1 + 3\lambda = 9 - (4 - \lambda) = 5 + \lambda$
$\Rightarrow 2\lambda = 4 \Rightarrow \lambda = 2$
Plugging this value back into the first equation gives:
$1 + (3 \times 2) = 9 - \mu \Rightarrow \mu = 2$
Plugging the λ and μ values into the third equation gives:
$3 + (4 \times 2) = 9 + 2 \Rightarrow 11 = 11$
This is true so $\lambda = 2$, $\mu = 2$ solve all the equations.
So the point of intersection has position vector:
$\begin{pmatrix} 1+(3\times 2) \\ 1-2 \\ 3+(4\times 2) \end{pmatrix} = \begin{pmatrix} 9-2 \\ -3+2 \\ 9+2 \end{pmatrix} = \begin{pmatrix} 7 \\ -1 \\ 11 \end{pmatrix}$,
and coordinates (7, −1, 11).

b) Using the formula for the distance between two points:
$AC^2 = (7 - 1)^2 + (-1 - 1)^2 + (11 - 3)^2$
$= 36 + 4 + 64 = 104$
$CB^2 = (9 - 7)^2 + (-3 - (-1))^2 + (9 - 11)^2$
$= 4 + 4 + 4 = 12$
$BA^2 = (1 - 9)^2 + (1 - (-3))^2 + (3 - 9)^2$
$= 64 + 16 + 36 = 116$
So $BA^2 = 116 = 104 + 12 = AC^2 + CB^2$
Therefore triangle ABC is right-angled.

Q15 a) $(3\mathbf{i} + 4\mathbf{j}) \cdot (\mathbf{i} - 2\mathbf{j} + 3\mathbf{k}) = (3 \times 1) + (4 \times (-2)) + (0 \times 3)$
$= 3 - 8 + 0 = -5$

b) $\begin{pmatrix} 4 \\ 2 \\ 1 \end{pmatrix} \cdot \begin{pmatrix} 3 \\ -4 \\ -3 \end{pmatrix} = (4 \times 3) + (2 \times -4) + (1 \times -3) = 1$

Q16 a) $\overrightarrow{PQ} = -\mathbf{a} + \mathbf{b} = \mathbf{b} - \mathbf{a}$

b) Using the commutative and distributive laws and the definition of scalar product:
$(\mathbf{b} - \mathbf{a}) \cdot (\mathbf{b} - \mathbf{a}) = \mathbf{b}.\mathbf{b} + \mathbf{b}.(-\mathbf{a}) + (-\mathbf{a}).\mathbf{b} + (-\mathbf{a}).(-\mathbf{a})$
$= \mathbf{b}.\mathbf{b} - \mathbf{a}.\mathbf{b} - \mathbf{a}.\mathbf{b} + \mathbf{a}.\mathbf{a}$
$= |\mathbf{b}|^2(\cos 0) - 2|\mathbf{a}||\mathbf{b}|\cos\theta + |\mathbf{a}|^2(\cos 0)$
$= |\mathbf{b}|^2 - 2|\mathbf{a}||\mathbf{b}|\cos\theta + |\mathbf{a}|^2$
$= b^2 - 2ab\cos\theta + a^2$

c) $c^2 = |\overrightarrow{PQ}|^2$, and
$(\mathbf{b} - \mathbf{a}) \cdot (\mathbf{b} - \mathbf{a}) = \overrightarrow{PQ}.\overrightarrow{PQ} = |\overrightarrow{PQ}|^2 (\cos 0) = |\overrightarrow{PQ}|^2$,
so $c^2 = (\mathbf{b} - \mathbf{a}) \cdot (\mathbf{b} - \mathbf{a}) = b^2 - 2ab\cos\theta + a^2$
$= a^2 + b^2 - 2ab\cos\theta$

Q17 a) $\begin{pmatrix} 2 \\ -1 \\ 2 \end{pmatrix} + t\begin{pmatrix} -4 \\ 6 \\ -2 \end{pmatrix} = \begin{pmatrix} 3 \\ 2 \\ 4 \end{pmatrix} + u\begin{pmatrix} -1 \\ 3 \\ 0 \end{pmatrix}$

Where the lines intersect, these 3 equations are
true: $\qquad 2 - 4t = 3 - u$
$\qquad\qquad -1 + 6t = 2 + 3u$
$\qquad\qquad 2 - 2t = 4$

Solve the third equation to give $t = -1$.
Substituting $t = -1$ into the top equation gives
$2 - 4(-1) = 3 - u \Rightarrow 6 = 3 - u \Rightarrow u = -3$.
Now check $t = -1$ and $u = -3$ in the 2nd equation.
$-1 + 6t = -1 + 6(-1) = -7$ and
$2 + 3u = 2 + 3(-3) = -7$ so these values also work
in the 2nd equation, so the lines intersect.

Substituting $t = -1$ in the first vector line equation
(or $u = -3$ into the second vector line equation)
gives the position vector of the intersection point:

$\begin{pmatrix} 6 \\ -7 \\ 4 \end{pmatrix}$

b) To find the angle between the lines, consider the
direction components of the vector equations.
Find their scalar product:
$\begin{pmatrix} -4 \\ 6 \\ -2 \end{pmatrix} \cdot \begin{pmatrix} -1 \\ 3 \\ 0 \end{pmatrix} = 4 + 18 + 0 = 22$

Find the magnitude of the 1st vector:
$\sqrt{(-4)^2 + 6^2 + (-2)^2} = \sqrt{56}$
and the magnitude of the 2nd vector:
$\sqrt{(-1)^2 + 3^2 + (0)^2} = \sqrt{10}$

Plugging these into the formula $\cos\theta = \dfrac{\mathbf{b_1.b_2}}{|\mathbf{b_1}\|\mathbf{b_2}|}$
gives:
$\cos\theta = \dfrac{22}{\sqrt{56}\sqrt{10}} \Rightarrow \theta = 21.6°$ to 1 d.p.

Q18 Find values for a, b and c that give a scalar product of
0 when the two vectors are multiplied together.
So a, b and c that solve:
$\qquad (3\mathbf{i} + 4\mathbf{j} - 2\mathbf{k}) . (a\mathbf{i} + b\mathbf{j} + c\mathbf{k}) = 3a + 4b - 2c = 0$
E.g. $a = 2$, $b = 1$ and $c = 5$ give the perpendicular
vector $2\mathbf{i} + \mathbf{j} + 5\mathbf{k}$
*There are lots of possible answers here — to find one just
pick values for a and b, then see what value of c is needed to
make the scalar product zero.*

Q19 a) The lines intersect when $\begin{pmatrix} x + 2\lambda \\ 1 + 2\lambda \\ 5 + 3\lambda \end{pmatrix} = \begin{pmatrix} -1 + 3\mu \\ -2 - \mu \\ 3 - 2\mu \end{pmatrix}$

Solving the bottom two equations simultaneously
by taking two lots of the second equation from
the third equation gives: $\lambda = -4$ and $\mu = 5$. Now
plug these values into the top equation to find x:
$x + 2\lambda = -1 + 3\mu \Rightarrow x + (2 \times (-4)) = -1 + (3 \times 5)$
$\qquad\qquad\qquad\qquad\qquad \Rightarrow x = 22$

b) Plugging the value for μ into the second
vector line equation gives the position vector $\begin{pmatrix} 14 \\ -7 \\ -7 \end{pmatrix}$,
so the coordinates of the point of
intersection are (14, −7, −7).

c) To find the angle between the lines, consider the
direction components of the vector equations.
Find their scalar product:
$\begin{pmatrix} 2 \\ 2 \\ 3 \end{pmatrix} \cdot \begin{pmatrix} 3 \\ -1 \\ -2 \end{pmatrix} = 6 - 2 - 6 = -2$

Find the magnitude of the 1st vector:
$\sqrt{2^2 + 2^2 + 3^2} = \sqrt{17}$
and the magnitude of the 2nd vector:
$\sqrt{3^2 + (-1)^2 + (-2)^2} = \sqrt{14}$

Plugging these into the formula $\cos\theta = \dfrac{\mathbf{b_1.b_2}}{|\mathbf{b_1}\|\mathbf{b_2}|}$
gives:
$\cos\theta = \dfrac{-2}{\sqrt{17}\sqrt{14}} \Rightarrow \theta = 97.4°$ to 1 d.p.
Acute angle is $180 - 97.4° = 82.6°$

Exam-Style Questions — Chapter 6

Q1 a) $\overrightarrow{AB} = \mathbf{b} - \mathbf{a} = \begin{pmatrix} 3 \\ 2 \\ 1 \end{pmatrix} - \begin{pmatrix} 1 \\ 5 \\ 9 \end{pmatrix} = \begin{pmatrix} 2 \\ -3 \\ -8 \end{pmatrix}$

*[2 marks available — 1 mark for attempting to
subtract position vector a from position vector b,
1 mark for correct answer.]*

b) l_1:

$\mathbf{r} = \mathbf{c} + \mu(\mathbf{d} - \mathbf{c}) = \begin{pmatrix} -2 \\ 4 \\ 3 \end{pmatrix} + \mu\left(\begin{pmatrix} 5 \\ -1 \\ -7 \end{pmatrix} - \begin{pmatrix} -2 \\ 4 \\ 3 \end{pmatrix}\right)$

$\qquad\qquad\qquad\qquad\qquad\qquad\qquad$ *[1 mark]*

$\mathbf{r} = \begin{pmatrix} -2 \\ 4 \\ 3 \end{pmatrix} + \mu\begin{pmatrix} 7 \\ -5 \\ -10 \end{pmatrix}$ *[1 mark]*

c) Equation of line through AB:

$\overrightarrow{AB}: \mathbf{r} = \mathbf{a} + t(\mathbf{b} - \mathbf{a}) = \begin{pmatrix} 1 \\ 5 \\ 9 \end{pmatrix} + t\begin{pmatrix} 2 \\ -3 \\ -8 \end{pmatrix}$ *[1 mark]*

At intersection of lines:
$\begin{pmatrix} 1 \\ 5 \\ 9 \end{pmatrix} + t\begin{pmatrix} 2 \\ -3 \\ -8 \end{pmatrix} = \begin{pmatrix} -2 \\ 4 \\ 3 \end{pmatrix} + \mu\begin{pmatrix} 7 \\ -5 \\ -10 \end{pmatrix}$ *[1 mark]*

Any two of: $1 + 2t = -2 + 7\mu$
$\qquad\qquad\quad 5 - 3t = 4 - 5\mu$
$\qquad\qquad\quad 9 - 8t = 3 - 10\mu$ *[1 mark]*
Solving any two equations simultaneously gives
$t = 2$ or $\mu = 1$ *[1 mark]*

Substituting $t = 2$ in the equation of the line
through AB (or $\mu = 1$ in the equation for l_1) gives:
(5, −1, −7) *[1 mark]*

d) (i) The vectors needed are $\begin{pmatrix} 2 \\ -3 \\ -8 \end{pmatrix}$ and $\begin{pmatrix} 7 \\ -5 \\ -10 \end{pmatrix}$
(direction vector of l_1).

$$\begin{pmatrix} 2 \\ -3 \\ -8 \end{pmatrix} \cdot \begin{pmatrix} 7 \\ -5 \\ -10 \end{pmatrix} = 14 + 15 + 80 = 109$$
[1 mark]

magnitude of 1st vector:
$$\sqrt{2^2 + (-3)^2 + (-8)^2} = \sqrt{77}$$
magnitude of 2nd vector:
$$\sqrt{7^2 + (-5)^2 + (-10)^2} = \sqrt{174}$$
[1 mark]

$\cos\theta = \dfrac{109}{\sqrt{77}\sqrt{174}}$ *[1 mark]*

$\Rightarrow\ \theta = 19.7°$ *[1 mark]*

(ii) Draw a diagram:

[1 mark for showing that the shortest distance is perpendicular to l_1]
X is the intersection point found in part **c)**,
with coordinates (5, −1, −7)
Distance from A to X =
$$\sqrt{(5-1)^2 + (-1-5)^2 + (-7-9)^2} = \sqrt{308}$$
[1 mark]
Now you've got a right-angled triangle, so just use trig to find the side you want:
Shortest distance from A to l_1
$$= \sqrt{308} \times \sin 19.7°\ \textit{[1 mark]}$$
$$= 5.9 \text{ units } \textit{[1 mark]}$$
The tricky thing here is figuring out how to go about it. Drawing a diagram definitely helps you see what you know and what you need to work out. Often, you'll be meant to use something you worked out in a previous question part.

Q2 a) $-3\begin{pmatrix} 1 \\ -4 \\ 2 \end{pmatrix} = \begin{pmatrix} -3 \\ 12 \\ -6 \end{pmatrix}$ *[1 mark]*

b) Horizontal component: $3 + (\mu \times 1) = 2$ gives
$\mu = -1$ *[1 mark]*
$$\mathbf{r} = \begin{pmatrix} 3 \\ -3 \\ -2 \end{pmatrix} - 1\begin{pmatrix} 1 \\ -4 \\ 2 \end{pmatrix} = \begin{pmatrix} 2 \\ 1 \\ -4 \end{pmatrix} \textit{[1 mark]}$$
This is the position vector of the point A(2, 1, −4)

c) B lies on l_2 so it has position vector
$$\mathbf{b} = \begin{pmatrix} 10 \\ -21 \\ 11 \end{pmatrix} + \lambda\begin{pmatrix} -3 \\ 12 \\ -6 \end{pmatrix} \textit{[1 mark]}$$
So $\overrightarrow{AB} = \mathbf{b} - \mathbf{a}$
$$= \begin{pmatrix} 10 \\ -21 \\ 11 \end{pmatrix} + \lambda\begin{pmatrix} -3 \\ 12 \\ -6 \end{pmatrix} - \begin{pmatrix} 2 \\ 1 \\ -4 \end{pmatrix} = \begin{pmatrix} 8 - 3\lambda \\ -22 + 12\lambda \\ 15 - 6\lambda \end{pmatrix} \textit{[1 mark]}$$

The scalar product of the direction vector of l_1 and $\overrightarrow{AB}$ must be zero as they're perpendicular:
$$\begin{pmatrix} 1 \\ -4 \\ 2 \end{pmatrix} \cdot \begin{pmatrix} 8 - 3\lambda \\ -22 + 12\lambda \\ 15 - 6\lambda \end{pmatrix} \textit{[1 mark]}$$
$$= (8 - 3\lambda) + (88 - 48\lambda) + (30 - 12\lambda)$$
$$= 126 - 63\lambda = 0$$
$$\Rightarrow\ \lambda = 2\ \textit{[1 mark]}$$
Substitute in $\lambda = 2$ to find the position vector **b**:
$$\mathbf{b} = \begin{pmatrix} 10 \\ -21 \\ 11 \end{pmatrix} + 2\begin{pmatrix} -3 \\ 12 \\ -6 \end{pmatrix} \textit{[1 mark]} = \begin{pmatrix} 4 \\ 3 \\ -1 \end{pmatrix}$$

Position vector of B $= \begin{pmatrix} 4 \\ 3 \\ -1 \end{pmatrix}$ *[1 mark]*

You could have found the product of $\overrightarrow{AB}$ and the direction bit of the l_2 vector equation, as $\overrightarrow{AB}$ is perpendicular to both l_1 and l_2. But the numbers for the l_1 vector are smaller, which makes your calculations easier.

d) $\overrightarrow{AB} = \mathbf{b} - \mathbf{a}$
$$= \begin{pmatrix} 4 \\ 3 \\ -1 \end{pmatrix} - \begin{pmatrix} 2 \\ 1 \\ -4 \end{pmatrix} = \begin{pmatrix} 2 \\ 2 \\ 3 \end{pmatrix} \textit{[1 mark]}$$
$|\overrightarrow{AB}| = \sqrt{2^2 + 2^2 + 3^2} = \sqrt{17} = 4.1$ *[1 mark]*

Q3 a) $(\overrightarrow{OA}) \cdot (\overrightarrow{OB})$ *[1 mark]*
$$= \begin{pmatrix} 3 \\ 2 \\ 1 \end{pmatrix} \cdot \begin{pmatrix} 3 \\ -4 \\ -1 \end{pmatrix} = 9 - 8 - 1 = 0 \textit{ [1 mark]}$$
Therefore, side OA is perpendicular to side OB, and the triangle has a right angle. *[1 mark]*
You could also have found the lengths $|OA|$, $|OB|$ and $|AB|$ and shown by Pythagoras that AOB is a right-angled triangle ($|AB|^2 = |OA|^2 + |OB|^2$).

b) $\overrightarrow{BA} = \mathbf{a} - \mathbf{b} = \begin{pmatrix} 3 \\ 2 \\ 1 \end{pmatrix} - \begin{pmatrix} 3 \\ -4 \\ -1 \end{pmatrix} = \begin{pmatrix} 0 \\ 6 \\ 2 \end{pmatrix}$ *[1 mark]*
$$\overrightarrow{BO} = \begin{pmatrix} -3 \\ 4 \\ 1 \end{pmatrix}$$
$\overrightarrow{BA} \cdot \overrightarrow{BO} = 24 + 2 = 26$ *[1 mark]*
$|\overrightarrow{BA}| = \sqrt{6^2 + 2^2} = \sqrt{40}$ and
$|\overrightarrow{BO}| = \sqrt{(-3)^2 + 4^2 + 1^2} = \sqrt{26}$ *[1 mark]*
$\cos \angle ABO = \dfrac{\overrightarrow{BA} \cdot \overrightarrow{BO}}{|\overrightarrow{BA}| \cdot |\overrightarrow{BO}|} = \dfrac{26}{\sqrt{40}\sqrt{26}}$ *[1 mark]*
$\angle ABO = 36.3°$ *[1 mark]*

c) (i) $\overrightarrow{AC} = \mathbf{c} - \mathbf{a} = \begin{pmatrix} 3 \\ -1 \\ 0 \end{pmatrix} - \begin{pmatrix} 3 \\ 2 \\ 1 \end{pmatrix} = \begin{pmatrix} 0 \\ -3 \\ -1 \end{pmatrix}$ *[1 mark]*

$|\overrightarrow{AC}| = \sqrt{(-3)^2 + (-1)^2} = \sqrt{10}$ and
$|\overrightarrow{OC}| = \sqrt{3^2 + (-1)^2} = \sqrt{10}$ *[1 mark]*
Sides AC and OC are the same length, so the triangle is isosceles. *[1 mark]*

(ii) You know the side lengths AC and OC from part **c) (i)**. Calculate length of OA:

$|\overrightarrow{OA}| = \sqrt{3^2 + 2^2 + 1^2} = \sqrt{14}$ *[1 mark]*

Now find the height of the triangle, x, using Pythagoras:

$x = \sqrt{(\sqrt{10})^2 - \left(\frac{\sqrt{14}}{2}\right)^2} = \sqrt{6.5}$ *[1 mark]*

Area $= \frac{1}{2}$(base × height)

$= \frac{1}{2}(\sqrt{14} \times \sqrt{6.5})$ *[1 mark]*

$= 4.77$ square units *[1 mark]*

d) (i) $\mathbf{r} = \mathbf{a} + t(\mathbf{b} - \mathbf{a})$

$\mathbf{r} = \begin{pmatrix} 3 \\ 2 \\ 1 \end{pmatrix} + t\left(\begin{pmatrix} 3 \\ -4 \\ -1 \end{pmatrix} - \begin{pmatrix} 3 \\ 2 \\ 1 \end{pmatrix}\right)$ *[1 mark]*

$\mathbf{r} = \begin{pmatrix} 3 \\ 2 \\ 1 \end{pmatrix} + t\begin{pmatrix} 0 \\ -6 \\ -2 \end{pmatrix}$ *[1 mark]*

(ii) Bottom row: $1 - 2t = 0$, $t = \frac{1}{2}$ *[1 mark]*

$\mathbf{r} = \begin{pmatrix} 3 \\ 2 \\ 1 \end{pmatrix} + \frac{1}{2}\begin{pmatrix} 0 \\ -6 \\ -2 \end{pmatrix} = \begin{pmatrix} 3 \\ -1 \\ 0 \end{pmatrix}$

$a = 3$ *[1 mark]*, $b = -1$ *[1 mark]*

Q4 a) $\overrightarrow{OC} = \overrightarrow{OD} + \overrightarrow{DC}$ *[1 mark]*

As ABCD is a parallelogram $\overrightarrow{DC} = \overrightarrow{AB}$:

so $\overrightarrow{DC} = \overrightarrow{AB} = \overrightarrow{OB} - \overrightarrow{OA} = \begin{pmatrix} -1 \\ 1 \\ 8 \end{pmatrix} - \begin{pmatrix} -5 \\ -4 \\ 6 \end{pmatrix} = \begin{pmatrix} 4 \\ 5 \\ 2 \end{pmatrix}$,

[1 mark for correctly finding $\overrightarrow{DC}$]

and $\overrightarrow{OD} = \begin{pmatrix} -7 \\ 0 \\ 5 \end{pmatrix}$,

so $\overrightarrow{OC} = \overrightarrow{OD} + \overrightarrow{DC} = \begin{pmatrix} -7 \\ 0 \\ 5 \end{pmatrix} + \begin{pmatrix} 4 \\ 5 \\ 2 \end{pmatrix} = \begin{pmatrix} -3 \\ 5 \\ 7 \end{pmatrix}$.

[1 mark for the correct answer]

b) $\overrightarrow{DC}$ is in the direction of L_1, and D lies on L_1, so an equation for L_1 is: $\mathbf{r} = \overrightarrow{OD} + t\overrightarrow{DC}$ *[1 mark]*

$= \begin{pmatrix} -7 \\ 0 \\ 5 \end{pmatrix} + t\begin{pmatrix} 4 \\ 5 \\ 2 \end{pmatrix}$ *[1 mark]*

You could have used point C instead and put the vector $\overrightarrow{OC}$ you found in part a) into the equation. The fact that the question describes L_1 as containing DC suggests that you should use $\overrightarrow{DC}$ as your direction vector.

c) A and C lie on L_2, so by plugging their position vectors into the formula for a vector line equation from two points: $\mathbf{r} = \mathbf{c} + s(\mathbf{d} - \mathbf{c})$, you get an equation for L_2: $\mathbf{r} = \overrightarrow{OA} + s(\overrightarrow{OC} - \overrightarrow{OA})$ *[1 mark]*

$= \begin{pmatrix} -5 \\ -4 \\ 6 \end{pmatrix} + s\left(\begin{pmatrix} -3 \\ 5 \\ 7 \end{pmatrix} - \begin{pmatrix} -5 \\ -4 \\ 6 \end{pmatrix}\right)$ *[1 mark]*

$= \begin{pmatrix} -5 \\ -4 \\ 6 \end{pmatrix} + s\begin{pmatrix} 2 \\ 9 \\ 1 \end{pmatrix}$ *[1 mark]*

Plugging in $\mathbf{c} = \overrightarrow{OC}$ and $\mathbf{d} = \overrightarrow{OA}$ is also fine.

d) Draw a diagram:

The shortest distance from L_1 to the origin is OP, where P lies on L_1 and OP is perpendicular to L_1.
[1 mark for showing that the shortest distance is perpendicular to L_1]

It doesn't matter if your diagram doesn't look exactly like this, as long as it shows that OP is perpendicular to L_1.

P lies on L_1, so $\overrightarrow{OP} = \begin{pmatrix} -7 + 4t \\ 5t \\ 5 + 2t \end{pmatrix}$ for some t.

The direction vector of L_1 is $\begin{pmatrix} 4 \\ 5 \\ 2 \end{pmatrix}$.

$\overrightarrow{OP}$ is perpendicular to L_1, so the scalar product of $\overrightarrow{OP}$ and the direction vector of L_1 is zero.
[1 mark for giving the two vectors and stating that their scalar product is zero]

i.e. $\begin{pmatrix} -7 + 4t \\ 5t \\ 5 + 2t \end{pmatrix} \cdot \begin{pmatrix} 4 \\ 5 \\ 2 \end{pmatrix} = 0$

$\Rightarrow -28 + 16t + 25t + 10 + 4t = 0$ *[1 mark]*

$\Rightarrow 45t = 18 \Rightarrow t = \frac{2}{5}$ *[1 mark]*

Plugging this back into $\overrightarrow{OP}$ gives: $\overrightarrow{OP} = \begin{pmatrix} -\frac{27}{5} \\ 2 \\ \frac{29}{5} \end{pmatrix}$,

[1 mark] so the distance from O to P is $|\overrightarrow{OP}| = \sqrt{\left(-\frac{27}{5}\right)^2 + 2^2 + \left(\frac{29}{5}\right)^2} = 8.17$ to 3 s.f.
[1 mark]

You could also have found the angle OCP using the scalar product formula and then used trigonometry to work out $|OP| = |OC|\sin\theta$.

Q5 a) l passes through J and K so by plugging $\overrightarrow{OJ}$ and $\overrightarrow{OK}$ into the equation $\mathbf{r} = \mathbf{c} + t(\mathbf{d} - \mathbf{c})$ you get an equation for l:

$\mathbf{r} = \overrightarrow{OJ} + t(\overrightarrow{OK} - \overrightarrow{OJ})$

$= \begin{pmatrix} 2 \\ -2 \\ 1 \end{pmatrix} + t\left(\begin{pmatrix} 3 \\ 1 \\ -1 \end{pmatrix} - \begin{pmatrix} 2 \\ -2 \\ 1 \end{pmatrix} \right)$ *[1 mark]*

$= \begin{pmatrix} 2 \\ -2 \\ 1 \end{pmatrix} + t\begin{pmatrix} 1 \\ 3 \\ -2 \end{pmatrix}$ *[1 mark]*

Letting $\mathbf{c} = \overrightarrow{OK}$ and $\mathbf{d} = \overrightarrow{OJ}$ is also fine.

b) To find the acute angle between l and OJ use the formula $\cos\theta = \dfrac{\mathbf{a}\cdot\mathbf{b}}{|\mathbf{a}||\mathbf{b}|}$, where $\mathbf{a}$ is $\begin{pmatrix} 1 \\ 3 \\ -2 \end{pmatrix}$, the direction vector of l, $\mathbf{b} = \overrightarrow{OJ} = \begin{pmatrix} 2 \\ -2 \\ 1 \end{pmatrix}$, and θ is the angle between l and OJ that $\mathbf{a}$ and $\mathbf{b}$ both point away from.

Then: $\mathbf{a}.\mathbf{b} = \begin{pmatrix} 1 \\ 3 \\ -2 \end{pmatrix} . \begin{pmatrix} 2 \\ -2 \\ 1 \end{pmatrix} = 2 - 6 - 2 = -6$ *[1 mark]*

$|\mathbf{a}| = \sqrt{1^2 + 3^2 + (-2)^2} = \sqrt{14}$

$|\mathbf{b}| = \sqrt{2^2 + (-2)^2 + 1^2} = \sqrt{9} = 3$

[1 mark for correctly finding both magnitudes]

So $\cos\theta = \dfrac{-6}{3\sqrt{14}} \Rightarrow \theta = 122°$, to the nearest degree. *[1 mark]* So the acute angle is $180 - \theta = 58°$ to the nearest degree. *[1 mark]*

c) J and K lie on l, so if J, K and G are collinear then G must lie on l too (as l is the only line that both J and K lie on and collinear points all lie on the same straight line).

If G lies on l then: $\begin{pmatrix} 1 \\ -5 \\ 3 \end{pmatrix} = \begin{pmatrix} 2+t \\ -2+3t \\ 1-2t \end{pmatrix}$ for some t. *[1 mark]*

Solving each line gives:

$1 = 2 + t \Rightarrow t = -1$

$-5 = -2 + 3t \Rightarrow -3 = 3t \Rightarrow t = -1$

$3 = 1 - 2t \Rightarrow t = -1$

There's a consistent solution ($t = -1$) so G lies on l (as do J and K) so J, K and G are collinear.
[1 mark for showing and stating that there is a consistent solution]

You could answer part c) by showing that the line segments JK and KG are parallel, but the method given is easier as you already know that J and K lie on l.

d) As with **c)** H must lie on l if J, K and H are collinear.

If H lies on l then: $\begin{pmatrix} 5 \\ 11 \\ -2 \end{pmatrix} = \begin{pmatrix} 2+t \\ -2+3t \\ 1-2t \end{pmatrix}$ for some t. *[1 mark]*

Solving each line gives:

$5 = 2 + t \Rightarrow t = 3$

$11 = -2 + 3t \Rightarrow 13 = 3t \Rightarrow t = \dfrac{13}{3}$

$-2 = 1 - 2t \Rightarrow t = \dfrac{3}{2}$

There's no consistent solution so G doesn't lie on l and J and K do — so J, K and G are not collinear.
[1 mark for showing and stating that there is no consistent solution]

Again, you could show that JK and KH aren't parallel, but the method given is easier.

Q6 a) At an intersection point:

$\begin{pmatrix} 3 \\ 0 \\ -2 \end{pmatrix} + \lambda\begin{pmatrix} 1 \\ 3 \\ -2 \end{pmatrix} = \begin{pmatrix} 0 \\ 2 \\ 1 \end{pmatrix} + \mu\begin{pmatrix} 2 \\ -5 \\ -3 \end{pmatrix}$ *[1 mark]*

This gives equations: $3 + \lambda = 2\mu$

$3\lambda = 2 - 5\mu$

$-2 - 2\lambda = 1 - 3\mu$ *[1 mark]*

Solving the first two simultaneously gives:
$\lambda = -1, \mu = 1$ *[1 mark]*
Substituting these values in the third gives:
$-2 - 2(-1) = 1 - 3(1) \Rightarrow 0 \neq -2$ *[1 mark]*
So the lines don't intersect.

You could have solved any two of the equations simultaneously, then substituted the results in the remaining equation to show that they don't work and there's no intersection point.

b) (i) At the intersection point of PQ and l_1:

$\begin{pmatrix} 3 \\ 0 \\ -2 \end{pmatrix} + \lambda\begin{pmatrix} 1 \\ 3 \\ -2 \end{pmatrix} = \begin{pmatrix} 5 \\ 4 \\ -9 \end{pmatrix} + t\begin{pmatrix} 0 \\ 2 \\ 3 \end{pmatrix}$ *[1 mark]*

This gives equations: $3 + \lambda = 5$

$3\lambda = 4 + 2t$

$-2 - 2\lambda = -9 + 3t$

[1 mark for any two equations]
Solving two of these gives: $\lambda = 2, t = 1$
[1 mark]

Intersection point has position vector

$\begin{pmatrix} 5 \\ 4 \\ -9 \end{pmatrix} + 1\begin{pmatrix} 0 \\ 2 \\ 3 \end{pmatrix} = \begin{pmatrix} 5 \\ 6 \\ -6 \end{pmatrix}$,

so coordinates (5, 6, –6) *[1 mark]*

(ii) If perpendicular, the scalar product of direction vectors of lines will equal 0:

$$\begin{pmatrix} 0 \\ 2 \\ 3 \end{pmatrix} \cdot \begin{pmatrix} 1 \\ 3 \\ -2 \end{pmatrix}$$ *[1 mark]*

$= (0 \times 1) + (2 \times 3) + (3 \times -2) = 0$ *[1 mark]*

(iii) Call intersection point X.

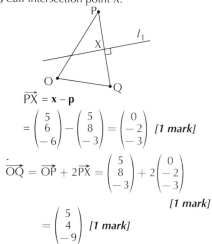

$\overrightarrow{PX} = \mathbf{x} - \mathbf{p}$

$$= \begin{pmatrix} 5 \\ 6 \\ -6 \end{pmatrix} - \begin{pmatrix} 5 \\ 8 \\ -3 \end{pmatrix} = \begin{pmatrix} 0 \\ -2 \\ -3 \end{pmatrix}$$ *[1 mark]*

$$\overrightarrow{OQ} = \overrightarrow{OP} + 2\overrightarrow{PX} = \begin{pmatrix} 5 \\ 8 \\ -3 \end{pmatrix} + 2\begin{pmatrix} 0 \\ -2 \\ -3 \end{pmatrix}$$

[1 mark]

$$= \begin{pmatrix} 5 \\ 4 \\ -9 \end{pmatrix}$$ *[1 mark]*

The trick with this one is to realise that point Q lies the same distance from the intersection point as P does — drawing a quick sketch will definitely help.

Glossary

A

Algebraic fraction
A fraction made up of algebraic expressions.

B

Binomial expansion
A method of expanding functions of the form $(a + bx)^n$. Can be used to give a finite expansion or to find an approximation of a value.

C

Cartesian equation
An equation relating the perpendicular axes x and y in 2D (or x, y and z in 3D). Cartesian coordinates are given in the form (x, y) in 2D (or (x, y, z) in 3D).

Chain rule
A method for **differentiating** a function of a function.

Coefficient
The constant multiplying the variable(s) in an algebraic term.

Collinear points
Three or more points are collinear if they all lie on the same straight line.

Column vector
A **vector** written in the form of a column of numbers inside brackets.

Constant of integration
A constant term coming from an **integration**, representing any number.

Cosec
The **reciprocal** of the sine function, sometimes written as cosecant.

Cot
The **reciprocal** of the tangent function, sometimes written as cotangent.

D

Definite integral
An **integral** which is evaluated over an interval given by two **limits**.

Degree
The highest power of x in a polynomial.

Derivative
The result you get when you **differentiate** something.

Differential equation
An equation connecting variables with their rates of change.

Differentiation
A method for finding the rate of change of a function with respect to a variable — the opposite of **integration**.

Divisor
The number or expression you're dividing by in a division.

E

Equating coefficients
Forming equations from the **coefficients** of equivalent terms on each side of an **identity** in order to calculate the value of unknowns in the identity.

Exponential function
A function of the form $y = a^x$. $y = e^x$ is known as 'the' exponential function.

F

Factor Theorem
An extension of the **Remainder Theorem** that helps you factorise a polynomial. If $f(a) = 0$ then $(x - a)$ is a **factor** of $f(x)$.

G

General solution
A solution to a **differential equation** that includes an unknown constant term.

I

i unit vector
The standard horizontal **unit vector** (i.e. along the x-axis).

Identity
An equation that is true for all values of a variable, usually denoted by the '$\equiv$' sign.

Implicit differentiation
A method of differentiating an **implicit relation**.

Implicit relation
An equation in x and y written in the form $f(x, y) = g(x, y)$, instead of $y = f(x)$.

Improper algebraic fraction
An **algebraic fraction** in which the **degree** of the numerator is greater than or equal to the degree of the denominator.

Indefinite integral
An **integral** which contains a constant of integration that comes from integrating without limits.

Integral
The result you get when you **integrate** something.

Integration
Process for finding the equation of a function, given its **derivative** — the opposite of **differentiation**.

J

j unit vector
The standard vertical **unit vector** (i.e. along the y-axis).

K

k unit vector
The standard **unit vector** used in 3D to represent movement along the z-axis.

L

Limits
The numbers between which you integrate to find a **definite integral**.

M

Magnitude
The size of a **vector**.

Modulus
The modulus of a number is its positive numerical value.
The modulus of a function, $f(x)$, makes every value of $f(x)$ positive by removing any minus signs.
The modulus of a **vector** is the same as its **magnitude**.

N

Normal
A straight line that crosses a curve at a given point and is perpendicular to the curve at that point.

P

Parameter
The variable linking a set of **parametric equations** (usually t or θ).

Parametric equations
A set of equations defining x and y in terms of another variable, called the **parameter**.

Partial fractions
A way of writing an **algebraic fraction** with several linear factors in its denominator as a sum of fractions with linear denominators.

Particular solution
A solution to a **differential equation** where known values have been used to find the constant term.

Percentage error
The difference between a value and its approximation, as a percentage of the real value.

Position vector
A **vector** that describes the position of a point in relation to the origin.

Product rule
A method for **differentiating** a product of two functions.

Q

Quotient
In algebraic division, the quotient is the expression you get when you divide by the **divisor**, not including the **remainder**.

Quotient rule
A method of **differentiating** one function divided by another.

R

Rational expression
A function that can be written as a fraction where the numerator and denominator are both polynomials.

Reciprocal
The reciprocal of a number or function is 1 divided by the number or function.

Remainder (algebraic division)
The expression left over following an algebraic division that has a **degree** lower than the **divisor**.

Remainder Theorem
A method used to work out the remainder from an **algebraic division**, but without actually having to do the division. The **remainder** when $f(x)$ is divided by $(x - a)$ is $f(a)$.

Resultant vector
The **vector** you get by adding two or more vectors together.

S

Scalar product
An operation on two **vectors** that produces a scalar result. Used for finding the angle between **vectors**.

Sec
The **reciprocal** of the cosine function, sometimes written as secant.

Separating variables
A method for solving **differential equations** by first rewriting in the form $\frac{1}{g(y)} \, dy = f(x) \, dx$ in order to integrate.

Skew lines
Lines in three dimensions that are neither parallel nor intersecting.

Stationary point
A point on a curve where the gradient is 0.

Substitution (identities)
Substituting in values of x to eliminate unknowns in order to calculate the value of other unknowns in an **identity**.

T

Tangent
A straight line which just touches a curve at a point, without going through it and that has the same gradient as the curve at that point.

Turning point
A **stationary point** that is a (local) maximum or minimum point on a curve.

U

Unit vector
A **vector** with a length or magnitude of 1 unit.

V

Vector
A quantity that has both size and direction.

Index

C4 Formula Sheet

The formulas below will be included in the formula book for your exams — make sure you know exactly **when you need them** and **how to use them**. These are the formulas relating specifically to the C4 module, but remember you might also need any formulas relevant to C1, C2 and C3 in C4.

Trigonometric Identities

$$\sin (A \pm B) \equiv \sin A \cos B \pm \cos A \sin B$$

$$\cos (A \pm B) \equiv \cos A \cos B \mp \sin A \sin B$$

$$\tan (A \pm B) \equiv \frac{\tan A \pm \tan B}{1 \mp \tan A \tan B} \qquad (A \pm B \neq (k + \tfrac{1}{2})\pi)$$

$$\sin A + \sin B \equiv 2\sin\frac{A + B}{2} \cos\frac{A - B}{2}$$

$$\sin A - \sin B \equiv 2\cos\frac{A + B}{2} \sin\frac{A - B}{2}$$

$$\cos A + \cos B \equiv 2\cos\frac{A + B}{2} \cos\frac{A - B}{2}$$

$$\cos A - \cos B \equiv -2\sin\frac{A + B}{2} \sin\frac{A - B}{2}$$

Binomial Series

$$(1 + x)^n = 1 + nx + \frac{n(n - 1)}{1 \times 2}x^2 + \dots + \frac{n(n - 1)\dots(n - r + 1)}{1 \times 2 \times \dots \times r}x^r + \dots \quad (|x| < 1, \, n \in \mathbb{R})$$

MAC4T61